Colour Vision

Colour Vision

Physiology and psychophysics

Edited by

J D Mollon
and
L T Sharpe

The Psychological Laboratory
University of Cambridge
Cambridge, England

1983

ACADEMIC PRESS
A Subsidiary of Harcourt Brace Jovanovich, Publishers

London   New York
Paris   San Diego   San Francisco
São Paulo   Sydney   Tokyo   Toronto

ACADEMIC PRESS INC. (LONDON) LTD.
24/28 Oval Road
London NW1

United States Edition published by
ACADEMIC PRESS INC.
111 Fifth Avenue
New York, New York 10003

British Library Cataloguing in Publication Data
Colour vision.
1. Color vision-Congresses
I. Mollon, J.D.
II. Sharpe, L.T.
612'.84   QP483

ISBN 0-12-504280-9

LCCCN 82-074570

Printed in Great Britain by
Galliard (Printers) Limited, Great Yarmouth

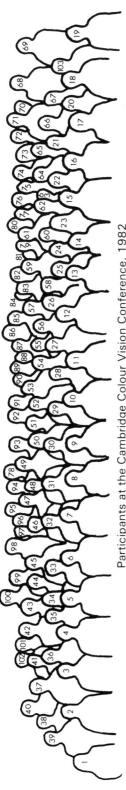

Participants at the Cambridge Colour Vision Conference, 1982

1 A. Gillett 2 J. Krauskopf 3 K. Sadza 4 Ch. M. M. de Weert 5 C. Guld 6 H. J. A. Dartnall 7 R. W. G. Hunt 8 F. W. Campbell 9 R. W. Ditchburn 10 L. Hurvich 11 D. Jameson 12 J. Krüger 13 D. I. A. MacLeod 14 L. Fallowfield 15 H. Kalmus 16 M. Alpern 17 B. Rogowitz 18 C. Stromeyer 19 H. Krastel 20 O. E. Favreau 21 A. Adams 22 O. Estévez 23 K. T. Mullen 24 Mrs. Yaguchi 25 M. Mitsuboshi 26 H. Heynen 27 M. Aguilar 28 M. Ikeda 29 G. Haegerstrom-Portnoy 30 S. M. Jaeckel 31 C. R. Cavonius 32 J. Bowmaker 33 H. Hemmendinger 34 C. Neumeyer 35 O. Da Pos 36 D. Williams 37 J. Thornton 38 J. D. Mollon 39 P. Gouras 40 R. W. Massof 41 J. Walraven 42 S. K. Shevell 43 G. Scheibner-Herzig 44 L. Hill 45 W. D. Wright 46 F. H. G. Pitt 47 P. K. Kaiser 48 H. M. Petry 49 J. D. Moreland 50 M. Wienrich 51 P. W. Trezona 52 J. J. Kulikowski 53 P. H. Silver 54 D. Teller 55 M. Boesten 56 B. Willkomm 57 C. P. Gibson 58 H. Yaguchi 59 K. K. De Valois 60 V. Smith 61 M. Richter 62 P. Cavanagh 63 F. Tanaka 64 J. L. Vola 65 D. H. Foster 66 M. A. Pak 67 E. Wolf 68 O. D. Creutzfeldt 69 A. Valberg 70 E. King-Smith 71 A. Derrington 72 M. Webster 73 S. Alvarez 74 J. McCann 75 B. B. Lee 76 H. C. Nothdurft 77 G. Jacobs 78 A. Reeves 79 C. Zrenner 80 A. Stockman 81 S. Braun 82 E. Zrenner 83 J. A. v. Esch 84 M. Krystek 85 R. L. De Valois 86 L. T. Sharpe 87 S. P. Taylor 88 P. Lennie 89 C. Ingling 90 H. B. Barlow 91 C. Michael 92 D. Hood 93 J. Larimer 94 R. W. Rodieck 95 B. van Dijk 96 G. Wyszecki 97 H. Terstiege 98 B. W. Tansley 99 H. Scheibner 100 V. O. Andersen 101 J. M. Valeton 102 B. Reese 103 A. Movshon.

Contributors

A. J. Adams   School of Optometry, University of California, Berkeley, Berkeley, California 94720, USA.

M. Alpern   Vision Research Laboratory, 5044 Kresge II, Box 56, University of Michigan, Ann Arbor, MI 48109, USA.

S. L. Alvarez   Department of Ophthalmic Optics, University of Manchester, Institute of Science and Technology, PO Box 88, Manchester M60 1QD, U.K.

V. O. Andersen   Institute of Neurophysiology, University of Copenhagen, Panum Institute, Blegdamsvej 3C, DK-2200 Copenhagen N., Denmark.

S. Anstis   Department of Psychology, York University, 4700 Keele St., Downsview, Ontario M3J 1P3, Canada.

M. Ayama   Department of Information Processing, Tokyo Institute of Technology Graduate School, Nagatsuta, Midori-ku, Yokohama, 227 Japan.

D. Baylor   Department of Neurobiology, Stanford University School of Medicine, Stanford, Calif. 94305, USA.

J. Bowmaker   School of Biology, Queen Mary College, Mile End Road, London E1 4NS, U.K.

R. Boynton   University of California, Department of Psychology, C-009, La Jolla, California 92093, USA.

S. Braun   Klinikum der Universität Heidelberg, Augenklinik Abteilung 5.1.1. Bergheimer Strasse 20, 6900 Heidelberg 1, Federal Republic of Germany.

F. W. Campbell   Department of Physiology, Downing Street, Cambridge CB2 3EG, U.K.

P. Cavanagh   Departement de Psychologie, Université de Montréal, Case postale 6128, Succursale 'A', Montréal, P.Q., H3C 3J7, Canada.

C. R. Cavonius   Inst. für Arbeitsphysiologie, Ardeystrasse 67, D-46 Dortmund, Federal Republic of Germany.

G. M. Chioran   University of Ohio, College of Optometry, 338 West 19th Avenue, Columbus, Ohio 43210, USA.

G. R. Cole   Division of Applied Sciences, Harvard University, Cambridge, MA 02138, USA.

R. J. Collier   Center for Visual Science, University of Rochester, Rochester, N.Y. 14505, USA.

B. A. Collins   Department of Zoology, The Ohio State University, Columbus, Ohio 43210, USA.

Wm. B. Cowan   Division of Physics, National Research Council of Canada, Ottawa, Ontario, K1A 0R6, Canada.

O. Creutzfeldt   Max-Planck-Institut für Biophysikalische Chemie, Am Fassberg, 3400 Goettingen-Nikolausberg, Federal Republic of Germany.

H. J. A. Dartnall   Laboratory of Experimental Psychology, University of Sussex, Falmer, Brighton BN1 9QG, Sussex, U.K.

A. M. Derrington Department of Psychology, University of Durham, South Rd., Durham, U.K.

K. K. De Valois Department of Psychology, University of California, Berkeley, Berkeley, California 94720, USA.

T. Dijkhuis Laboratorium voor Medische Fysica, Herengracht 196, 1016 BS Amsterdam, The Netherlands.

O. Estévez Laboratorium voor Medische Fysica, Herengracht 196, 1016 BS Amsterdam, The Netherlands.

M. A. Finkelstein Department of Psychology, University of South Florida, Tampa, Fla. 33620, USA.

B. Fischer Albert-Ludwigs-Universität, Abteilung Klinische Neurologie und Neurophysiologie, Hansastrasse 9, D-7800 Freiburg i.Br., Federal Republic of Germany.

D. Foster Department of Communication and Neuroscience, University of Keele, Keele, Staffordshire ST5 5BG, U.K.

P. Gouras Department of Ophthalmology, Columbia University, College of Physicians & Surgeons, 630 West 168 St., New York, N.Y. 10032, USA.

C. Guld Institute of Neurophysiology, University of Copenhagen, Panum Institute, Blegdamsvej 3C, Dk-2200 Copenhagen N., Denmark.

G. Haegerstrom-Portnoy, School of Optometry, University of California, Berkeley, Calif. 94720, USA.

J. P. Handte Department of Behavioural Sciences. The University of Chicago, 5848 S. University Avenue, Chicago, II 60637, USA.

D. Hood Department of Psychology, Schermerhorn Hall, Columbia University, New York, NY 10027, USA.

K. L. Houston Research Laboratories, Polaroid Corporation, Cambridge, Massachusetts 02139, USA.

R. W. G. Hunt 10 Kewferry Road, Northwood, Middlesex, HA6 2NY, U.K.

M. Ikeda Department of Information Processing, Tokyo Institute of Technology Graduate School, Nagatsuta, Midori-ku, Yokohama, 227 Japan.

C. R. Ingling Ohio State University, Institute for Research in Vision, 1314 Kinnear Road, Columbus, Ohio 43212, USA.

G. H. Jacobs Department of Psychology, University of California, Santa Barbara, California 93106, USA.

W. Jaeger Klinikum der Universität Heidelberg, Augenklinik Abteilung 5.1.1., Bergheimer Strasse 20, 6900 Heidelberg 1, Federal Republic of Germany.

H. Kalmus The Galton Laboratory, Department of Genetics and Biometry, University College London, Wolfson House, 4 Stephenson Way, London NW1 2HE, U.K.

E. King-Smith University of Ohio, College of Optometry, 338 West 19th Avenue, Columbus, Ohio 43210, USA.

J. J. Koenderink Department of Medical and Physiological Physics, State University of Utrecht, Princetonplein 5, 3584 CC Utrecht, The Netherlands.

H. Krastel Klinikum der Universität Heidelberg, Augenklinik Abteilung 5.1.1., Bergheimer Strasse 20, 6900 Heidelberg 1, Federal Republic of Germany.

J. Krauskopf 2C-546 Bell Labs, Murray Hill, N.J. 07974, USA.

R. E. Kronauer Division of Applied Sciences, Pierce Hall, Harvard University, Cambridge, Mass 02138, USA.

J. Krüger Albert-Ludwigs-Universität, Abteilung Klinische Neurologie und Neurophysiologie, Hansastrasse 9, D-7800 Freiburg i.Br., Federal Republic of Germany.

J. Larimer   Temple University, Department of Psychology, Broad Street and Montgomery Avenue, Philadelphia, PA 19122, USA.

B. B. Lee   Department of Neurobiology, Max Planck Institute for Biophysical Chemistry, D-3400 Goettingen-Nikolausberg, Federal Republic of Germany.

P. Lennie   Center for Visual Science, 274, Psychology Building, University of Rochester, Rochester, NY 14627, USA.

J. S. Levine   Laboratory of Sensory Physiology, Marine Biological Laboratory, Woods Hole, MA 02543, USA.

L. E. Lipetz   Laboratory of Sensory Physiology, Marine Biological Laboratory, Woods Hole, MA 02543, USA.

D. I. A. MacLeod   University of California, Department of Psychology, C009, La Jolla, California 92093, USA.

E. F. MacNichol   Marine Biological Laboratory, Woods Hole, MA 02543, USA.

J. J. McCann   Research Laboratories, Polaroid Corporation, Cambridge, MA 02139, USA.

M. E. McCourt   Department of Psychology, University of California, Santa Barbara, CA 93106, USA.

R. J. W. Mansfield   Departments of Neurology and Ophthalmology, Boston University School of Medicine, 80 East Concord St., Boston, MA 02118, USA.

E. Martinez   Institute of Biomedical Research, Apadado Postal 70228, Cuidad University, 04510, Mexico DF, Mexico.

J. Matheny   Sensory Sciences Center, University of Texas Health Science Center at Houston, PO Box 20708, Houston, Texas 77025, USA.

K. E. Maughan   Department of Psychology, Carleton University, Ottawa, Ontario, Canada, K1S 5B6.

L. Meharg   Sensory Sciences Center, University of Texas Health Science Center at Houston, PO Box 20708, Houston, Texas 77025, USA.

C. R. Michael   Yale University, School of Medicine, Department of Physiology, 333 Cedar Street, PO Box 3333, New Haven, Connecticut 06510, USA.

Muneo Mitsuboshi   Division of Psychology, Department of Behavioural Science, Hokkaido University, N-10, W-7, Kita-ku, Sapporo 060, Japan.

J. D. Mollon   Department of Experimental Psychology, Downing Street, Cambridge, CB2 3EB, U.K.

J. Neitz   Department of Psychology, University of California, Santa Barbara, California 93106, USA.

J. Nick   Department of Psychology, Temple University, Philadelphia, PA 19122, USA.

C. Noorlander   Department of Medical and Physiological Physics, State University of Utrecht, Princetonplein 5, 3584 CC Utrecht, The Netherlands.

B. Nunn   Department of Physiology, University of Cambridge, Downing Street, Cambridge, CB2 3EG, U.K.

J. Pokorny   Eye Research Laboratories, University of Chicago, 939 East 57th Street, Chicago, Ill. 60637, USA.

E. N. Pugh Jr   University of Pennsylvania, Department of Psychology, 3813-15 Walnut Street T3, Philadelphia 19104, USA.

A. Reeves   Department of Psychology, Northeastern University, Boston, MA 02115, USA.

A. W. Robertson   Department of Psychology, Carleton University Ottawa, Canada, K1S 5B6.

R. W. Rodieck   Department of Ophthalmology, RJ-10, University of Washington, Seattle, Washington 98195, USA.

K. J. Sadza   Heideparkseweg 138, 6532TB Nijmegen, The Netherlands.

H. Scheibner   Physiologisches Institut II, Universität Düsseldorf, Moorenstrasse 5, D-4000 Düsseldorf, Federal Republic of Germany.

K. L. Sellers   University of Ohio, College of Optometry, 338 West 19th Avenue, Columbus, Ohio 43210, USA.

L. T. Sharpe   Neurologische Universitätsklinik, 78 Freiburg i.Br., Hansastrasse 9, Federal Republic of Germany.

S. K. Shevell   The University of Chicago, Department of Behavioral Sciences, 5848 South University Avenue, Chicago, Ill. 60637, USA.

O. Sjö   Department of Ophthalmology, University Hospital, Blegdamsvej 9, DK-2100 Copenhagen, Denmark.

V. Smith   Eye Research Laboratories, University of Chicago, 939 East 57th Street, Chicago, Ill. 60637, USA.

R. Snelgar   Department of Communication and Neuroscience, University of Keele, Keele, Staffordshire, ST5 5BG, U.K.

H. Spekreijse   Laboratory of Medical Physics, Herengracht 196, 1016 BS Amsterdam, The Netherlands.

H. G. Sperling   Sensory Sciences Center, University of Texas Health Science Center at Houston, PO Box 20708, Houston, Texas 77025, USA.

C. F. Stromeyer   Division of Engineering and Applied Physics, Harvard University, Pierce Hall, Cambridge, MA 02138, USA.

E. Switkes   Department of Psychobiology, University of California, Santa Cruz, CA 95064, USA.

M. Tanaka   Max-Planck-Institut für Biophysikalische Chemie, Am Fassberg, 3400 Goettingen-Nikolausberg, Federal Republic of Germany.

B. W. Tansley   Department of Psychology, Carleton University, Ottawa, Canada, K1S 5B6.

D. Y. Teller   Department of Psychology, University of Washington, Seattle, Washington 98195, USA.

H. Terstiege   Bundesanstalt für Materialprüfung, Unter den Eichen 87, D-1000 Berlin 45, Federal Republic of Germany.

B. J. Thompson   Department of Engineering and Applied Science, University of Rochester, Rochester, NY 14505, USA.

J. Thornton   Polaroid Vision Research Laboratory, 2 Osborn Street, Cambridge, MA 02139, USA.

D. Tigwell   Max-Planck-Institut für Biophysikalische Chemie, Am Fassberg, 3400 Goettingen-Nikolausberg, Federal Republic of Germany.

A. Valberg   Institute of Physics, University of Oslo, PO Box 1048, Blindern, Oslo 3, Norway.

B. van Dijk   Laboratorium voor Medische Fysica, Universiteit van Amsterdam, Herengracht 196, 1016 B5, Amsterdam, The Netherlands.

J. A. van Esch   Department of Medical and Physiological Physics, State University of Utrecht, Princetonplein 5, 3584 CC Utrecht, The Netherlands.

T. Viancour   Sensory Sciences Center, University of Texas Health Science Center at Houston, PO Box 20708, Houston, Texas 77025, USA.

F. Viénot   Museum National D'Histoire Naturelle, Laboratoire de Physique appliquée aux Sciences Naturelles, 43 Rue Cuvier, 75231 PARIS Cedex 05, France.

V. Virsu   Department of Psychology, University of Helsinki, Ritarikatu 5, SF-00170 Helsinki 17, Finland.

M. Webster   Department of Psychology, University of California, Berkeley, Berkeley, CA 94720, USA.

C. M. M. de Weert   Psychologisch Laboratorium, Katholieke Universiteit, Postbus 9104, 6500 Nijmegen, The Netherlands.

M. Wienrich   Max-Planck-Institut für Physiologische & Klinische Forschung, W. G. Kerckhoff-Institut, Parkstrasse 1, D-6350 Bad Nauheim, Federal Republic of Germany.

D. Williams   Center for Visual Science, University of Rochester, Rochester, NY 14627, USA.

E. Wolf   Physiologisches Institut II der Universität Düsseldorf, Moorenstrasse 5, 4000 Düsseldorf 1, Federal Republic of Germany.

Hirohisa Yaguchi   Department of Information Processing, Tokyo Institute of Technology, Nagatsuta, Midori-ku, Yokohama 227, Japan.

Q. Zaidi   Eye Research Laboratories, University of Chicago, 939 East 57th Street, Chicago, Ill. 60637, USA.

E. Zrenner   Max-Planck-Institut für Physiologische & Klinische Forschung, Parkstrasse 1, D-6350 Bad Nauheim, Federal Republic of Germany.

Contents

SECTION V: ELECTROPHYSIOLOGY: cortex

**SECTION VI: PSYCHOPHYSICS – Opponent processes
in detection and colour appearance**

SECTION VII: PSYCHOPHYSICS – Chromatic discrimination

**SECTION VIII: PSYCHOPHYSICS – Spatial and temporal
interactions**

Preface

We live in a world that is increasingly colour-coded. Not only are colours used for differentiation in technical fields such as electronics, transport signalling and military identification, but also the general public are daily exposed to colour coding in drugs, road signs, maps of transport systems and of large buildings, commercial packaging, advertising logos, teaching materials, and teletext systems. Colour visual-display-units are about to come into widespread use. Thus there are today strong practical reasons why we should improve our understanding of what limits our capacity to differentiate wavelengths, of how the neural analysis of colour is related to that of other attributes of the visual stimulus, and of why some 8% of the male population are deficient in colour discrimination.

Colour vision has never been the private preserve of any single one of the conventional disciplines of science. Its subtle but lawful complexities have attracted physicists, experimental psychologists, physiologists, ophthalmologists and optometrists. To this day, colour scientists are scattered among many different types of institution and their publications are similarly distributed among a variety of journals. In August 1982 an international meeting was held at Cambridge with the explicit purposes of bringing together colour specialists from different disciplines and of preparing the present handbook. It was the organisers' intention that the book should cover all aspects of colour vision, from the retinal photopigments to sensation; that equal weight should be given to physiological and psychophysical results; and that tutorial material should be included in order to introduce specific research problems and techniques to the non-specialist. We have concentrated on man – and on his primate relatives, who, it now seems, provide close models for both normal and deficient human colour vision.

Those who study colour vision are conscious that it is a field with a past. Much can be deduced about colour vision by purely sensory experiments in which an observer is asked to say whether two physically different lights appear alike or different; and the results have lent themselves to elegant geometrical analyses. Consequently, in the last three centuries, the problems of colour vision have engaged the attention of some of the most distinguished of natural scientists. It was fitting therefore that the present meeting should be held at the University of Cambridge, the university of Newton, Thomas Young, Clerk

Maxwell and Lord Rayleigh. Indeed, for many at the meeting, the beginnings of modern colour science were betokened by a holograph notebook (lent for display by the Fitzwilliam Museum) in which Newton recorded his purchase in 1667 of three prisms for three shillings. In the present book we have included a short account of Cambridge contributions to colour science, which was given by F. W. Campbell as a Prologue to the scientific sessions; and a memoir by M. Alpern of the Cambridge physiologist W. A. H. Rushton, which is the text of an after-dinner talk given in Trinity College during the meeting.

Cambridge last saw an international meeting on colour vision in 1947. The proceedings of that meeting (*Documenta Ophthalmologica*, vol 3, 1949) still repay careful reading; but we now enjoy an agreed corpus of physiological knowledge that was not available thirty-five years ago. In 1947 the spectral sensitivities of the photoreceptors, and indeed the number of types of photo-receptor, were matters for wide disagreement. No electrophysiological record-ings were available from single cells in the primate visual system. Today, though they might make local qualifications, most colour scientists would agree on the following account of the early stages of colour analysis in the human visual system:

Our sensations of hue depend upon the relative rates of absorption of photons in three classes of retinal photoreceptor, which have peak sensitivities at wavelengths of approximately 560 nm, 530 nm and 420–430 nm. The short-wavelength receptors are rarer than the long- and middle-wavelength receptors. The spectral sensitivities (i.e. the curves that relate sensitivity to wavelength) of the different classes of receptor are broad and overlapping and the electrical signal of an individual receptor preserves no information about the wavelength of the light that is being absorbed. So, in order that the visual system should be able to separate changes in colour from changes in intensity, some post-receptoral neurons receive inputs of opposite sign from different classes of photoreceptor. Among retinal ganglion cells and among the cells of the parvo-cellular layers of the lateral geniculate nucleus, there are two main classes of these 'colour-opponent' neurons. The most common type receives an input of one sign (excitatory or inhibitory) from the long-wavelength receptors and an input of the opposite sign from the middle-wavelength receptors; this type of neuron is also spatially opponent in that the two inputs are drawn from spatially distinct regions of the receptor array, a disc-shaped central region and a concentric surround. A somewhat rarer type of colour-opponent neuron receives an input of one sign from the short-wavelength receptors and an input of opposite sign from the long- and middle-wavelength receptors; in this case the excitatory and inhibitory inputs are drawn from the same disc-shaped area of the receptor array. The reader will be able to add flesh to this skeleton by referring to Sections I and IV of the present book.

On one central issue the present book probably marks a turning point. Thirty-five years ago colour scientists were concerned to develop psychophysical techniques for isolating the responses of individual classes of receptor − by removing other classes of receptor from play by means of monochromatic adapting fields, or by choosing spatial and temporal parameters that favoured one class, or by choosing observers who lacked one or more class. About eight years ago interest began to shift to psychophysical techniques for isolating different types of post-receptoral channel. Thus it seemed that a liminal target was likely to be detected by 'chromatically opponent' channels if the target was of large area and long duration and if an achromatic adapting field was present. Under such conditions the spectral sensitivity of the eye has multiple peaks (one of which lies at a wavelength much longer than the wavelength of peak sensitivity of the long-wavelength receptors); and when targets, or adapting fields, of different wavelengths are combined, the effect of the combination may be less than predicted by simple additivity. On the other hand, if a target is small and brief and if a monochromatic adapting field is present, then it may seem that detection is mediated by a 'non-opponent' pathway: the spectral sensitivity of the eye has a single peak and additivity is often found to hold. The dichotomy between 'opponent' and 'non-opponent' channels has proved a very fruitful concept in recent research and the reader will find that it is discussed, in various forms, in several papers in the present volume. Equally, however, the reader will find an increasing realisation that the psychophysicist's dichotomy has never agreed with the physiological knowledge outlined in the preceding paragraph: the same retinal ganglion cell may apparently signal either local achromatic contrast or the presence of homogeneous colour. The psychophysicist's 'channels' may represent the same cells operating in different modes; and central mechanisms may have to consider the output of a population of cells in order to separate spatial and chromatic information. On this issue, see especially papers 17, 35 and 39.

Some other recurrent issues can be identified in the pages that follow. Are there variations between 'normal' observers in the spectral positions of their photopigments (see papers 2, 4, 5, 6 and 7)? Are the colour-specific neurons of the visual cortex grouped into 'columns' (papers 25 and 26)? Are there areas of prestriate cortex that are specialised for the analysis of colour (papers 26 and 27)? Why is our vision so odd when discrimination depends only on signals originating in the short-wave receptors (papers 40, 44−48)? What is the relation between, on the one hand, the opponent processes revealed by measurements of thresholds and, on the other, the phenomenological antagonism of particular pairs of hues (papers 33, 34, 35, 36 and 54)? How do we recognise the spectral reflectances of objects despite large changes in the spectral composition of the illuminant (papers 49 and 50)?

Very recently, colour vision research has found a new tool in the form of the computer-controlled colour television monitor. Raster displays of this type allow the generation of colour stimuli that vary elaborately in space, in time, and in chromaticity; but such displays have to be selected and used with care and we have therefore included two tutorial papers (11 and 12) that describe not only the versatility but also the limitations and pitfalls of computer-controlled displays. Specific uses of raster displays are illustrated in a number of other papers (13, 14, 21, 38, 40, 42, 49 and 51).

The papers included in this volume have been refereed. The editors and referees have deliberately not sought to impose a common theoretical approach on the papers selected for inclusion, but, in the brief time available, have tried merely to eliminate obvious non-sequiturs, internal inconsistencies, and obscurities of expression. We have not attempted to impose British spelling on our American colleagues. Since we hope that the book may provide bibliographic access to the scattered literature on colour vision, we have tried to minimise the number of errors in the references and have added a detailed index. A number of abbreviations that are used more than locally in the text are defined in the index. We thank all the contributors for their helpfulness during the editing process.

Acknowledgements

The meeting from which this book derives was primarily sponsored by the Human Factors Committee of the Scientific Affairs Division of NATO (Grant No: SA.9.3.03C(82/1)191-BAB). Additional support was given by The Royal Society; by the Wellcome Trust; and by the U.S. Army Research Institute for the Behavioral and Social Sciences through its European Science Coordination Office at the European Research Office of the U.S. Army, London.

Preparation of this book has been supported by the aforementioned office of the U.S. Army Research Institute; and by the U.S. Naval Air Systems Command through a grant monitored by the Office of Naval Research, Arlington, Virginia (Grant No: N00014-82-G-0111).

The editors and the contributors are grateful to the above bodies for making possible the meeting and the book. Statements of opinion in the text should not be construed as the opinions of the above bodies.

Throughout the planning of the meeting and the editing of this book we have been guided by an international committee consisting of Professor C. R. Cavonius (Dortmund), Dr. O. Estévez (Amsterdam) and Dr. J. Krauskopf (Murray Hill, NJ). We most sincerely thank these colleagues for their help. We have been indebted to Betty Clifton for secretarial assistance during the organisation of the meeting and the preparation of the book. We also wish to thank Professor N. J. Mackintosh and Professor R. D. Keynes for providing facilities for the meeting; Trinity College, Cambridge, for its hospitality to our delegates; and Mr. C. Hood for several kindnesses at the time of the meeting.

J. D. Mollon, L. T. Sharpe
Cambridge, January, 1983

Plate 1. Rainbow over Woolsthorpe Manor, Lincolnshire, 7th October, 1979. This photograph of Newton's birthplace is by Professor R. L. Bishop, of the Department of Physics, Acadia University, Novia Scotia, and is reproduced by his kind permission. An account of the happy circumstances in which this remarkable photograph was taken can be found in *Notes and Records of the Royal Society of London,* Volume 36, No. 1. Therein is also contained a reproduction of Newton's description and explanation of rainbow formation.

Prologue: Cambridge Colour Contributions

F. W. CAMPBELL

Newton (1642–1727) was born on Christmas Day in the same year Galileo Galilei (1564–1642) died. He spent his childhood on a farm called Woolsthorpe Manor, Lincolnshire, some 10 hours by horse from Cambridge (see Plate 1 by R. L. Bishop). This part of England has long sunny periods interrupted by heavy showers, so that rainbows would be a frequent occurrence. Did these inspire his intense interest in light, colour and physics (as did the apple falling to the ground) in 1665 when he left Trinity College to escape the ravages of the Great Plague to stay with his Mother?

I have examined many coloured displays of the spectrum in dozens of text-books of physics, photography and visual psychology including some very recent ones such as Hurvich (1981). Let us examine this real spectrum generated by a diffraction grating (to spread out more evenly the long-wave end). What you see is red, green, blue and dim-blue or violet. Where is orange, yellow and indigo shown by all the textbooks? The only illustrated spectrum I could find that was nearly correct was that of R. A. Houstoun (1923) a very experienced spectroscopist. He gives a very clear account of how Newton might have made this initial mistake which we have all copied for 300 years. What did Newton say in OPTICKS?

> ... I held the Paper so that the Spectrum might fall upon this delineated Figure, and agree with it exactly, whilst an *Assistant, whose Eyes for distinguishing Colours were more critical than mine,* ... note the Confines of the Colours, that is ... red ... orange ... yellow ... green ... blue ... indigo ... and ... violet ... . (My italics.)

As Houston (1923) explains, at the time of Newton the harmonic series of Pythagoras dominated mathematical thinking and it was even used to explain the number and motions of the 7 Planets. It was a short step to argue that the "Music of the Spheres"

(Kepler's "Harmonices Mundi") also applied to the Spectrum of Newton. If Newton's assistant had not been so eager to please his master our current textbooks would be different.

Thomas Young (1773–1829) of Emmanuel College did not have this misconception for he wrote (Young, 1802):

> ... Now, as it is almost impossible to conceive each sensitive point of the retina to contain an infinite number of particles, each capable of vibrating in perfect unison with every possible undulation, it becomes necessary to suppose the number limited; for instance to the three principal colours, red, yellow and blue ... and that each of the particles is capable of being put into motion less or more forcibly by undulations differing less or more from a perfect unison ... each sensitive filament of the nerve may consist of three portions, one for each principal colour (1802a).

Later (1802b) he added:

> *In consequence of Dr Wollaston's correction of the description of the prismatic spectrum ... it becomes necessary to modify the supposition that I advanced in the last Bakerian lecture, respecting the ... fibres of the retina; substituting red,* green *and violet for red,* yellow *and blue.* (My italics.)

William Hyde Wollaston (1766–1828) of Caius College (1782) was well acquainted with the appearance of the Spectrum. Isaac Asimov (1972) writes:

> ... Wollaston (1766–1828) of Caius College was one of the first to observe ultraviolet light, though the credit is usually given to the more thorough research of Ritter. More important; Wollaston in 1802 was the first to note that dark lines crossed the spectrum, an observation that Newton had unaccountably missed. To Wollaston, however, it seemed that they were merely the natural boundaries between the various colors of the spectrum and he let the matter rest, a classic example of a missed opportunity...

If Newton had noticed the Fraunhofer (1787–1826) lines, modern chemistry might have started a century earlier.

When I was at school we were forced to recite the order of all the seven colours. When I became a medical student and was told that Thomas Young just looked at a Spectrum and came up with three colours, I marvelled at his genius (which he had) and intuitive insight. In fact, he just wrote down what he saw!

It is difficult to photograph a spectrum for the dyes chosen have a narrower spectral sensitivity compared with the eye. To illustrate the "missing yellow", two projectors were placed on either side of a white screen to produce two linear ramps of light intensity. Red or green filters were placed in the projectors. No yellow is seen where they overlap. If the yellow region is isolated with black flanking paper a vivid yellow is produced. Plate 2 shows the effect. The reader can mask with his fingers.

James Clerk Maxwell (1831–1879) moved from Peterhouse (then St Peter's

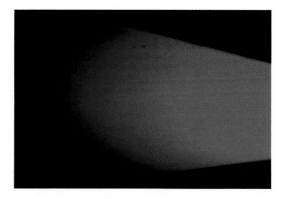

Plate 2(a). A linear ramp of red light.

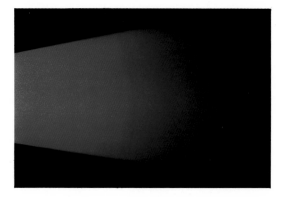

Plate 2(b). A linear ramp of green light.

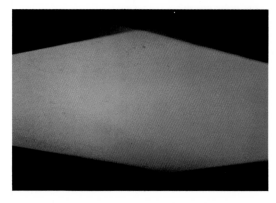

Plate 2(c). The two ramps combined. Notice the absence of a clear region of pure yellow. Owing to limitations of colour reproduction, the effects are not as vivid in this printed photograph as in the original demonstration.

Plate 3. Clerk Maxwell's colour-mixing top, as it was displayed during the Cambridge Colour Conference, August 1982. The top is in the possession of the Cavendish Laboratory, University of Cambridge. Shown with the top is a collection of discs that are preserved with it.

College) to Trinity because he was certain that William Thomson (Lord Kelvin) (1824–1907) would beat him to a Peterhouse Fellowship. His rooms in Great Court were facing North while Newton's faced South. He could not use the sun but this did not deter him from contributing to colour vision! Using the North Light so popular in artists' studios, he worked out the linear rules of *additive* colour vision using his spinning discs (Plate 3). Later he made the first trichromatic photograph. The subject was a piece of Maxwell's family tartan – a worthy subject for a true Scotsman isolated in England! Maxwell met William Nicol (1768–1851), the founder of polarimetry, in Edinburgh when Maxwell was still a boy of 16 years. This gave him a lasting interest in optics and vision.

Herman Ludwig Ferdinand von Helmholtz (1821–1894) was a close friend of Lord Kelvin in Glasgow and frequently "holidayed" with him on his steam yacht on the River Clyde (the Kelvin Compass for iron hulls was developed on board). As mentioned above, Maxwell and Kelvin were also close friends. Helmholtz played an important role in clearly distinguishing the difference between *additive* and *subtractive* colour mixing and publicising it in "Physiological Optics". The prior confusion was thus clarified. I was therefore very disappointed to find that Helmholtz's pull-out Spectrum in the First Edition had a large yellow section. Knowing that Herman never got anything wrong I searched for a verbal description. Here it is:

> ... A prismatic spectrum, short enough to be viewed in its entirety all at once, appears to consist of only four coloured sections, namely, red, green, blue and violet, the transition-colours disappearing almost entirely by contrast with these main colours. At best yellow may still be discerned in the green next to the red. This separation of colours is enhanced by the fact that three of the more prominent dark lines of the solar spectrum, namely *D*, *F* and *G*, happen to lie about on the boundary lines of the four intervals of the spectrum above mentioned. But even without being able to distinguish these lines, the same separation of colours is manifest. The transition-colours are indeed more easily seen in a longer spectrum, but yet the visual impression of them is always considerably modified by the proximity of such brilliant saturated colours as are seen in the spectrum, which *prevents the transition-colours from being seen in their own right.* To distinguish exactly the series of pure colours in the spectrum, they must be isolated. A way of doing this is to project a fairly pure spectrum on a screen with a small slit in it, which permits the light of some single region of the spectrum to pass through it and be received on another white screen beyond. By gradually moving the slit from one end of the spectrum to the other, the whole series of hues can be inspected separately one after the other. Then it will be found that there is nowhere any abrupt transition in the series, and that the hues merge continuously each into the next. The richness and intense saturation of the succession of colours and the delicate transition of hues make this experiment at the same time one of the most splendid spectacles that optics has to show.

Dr Eberhard Zrenner kindly checked recently the translation from the First Edition of Helmholtz and also discovered another quote (p. 270) as follows:

... and that finally borders between colours in the spectrum do not exist in reality, but are drawn arbitrarily by us out of our love of nomenclature.

Eberhart also verified that the Spectrum colours were done by hand and have a large yellow section. Apparently, Helmholtz had not checked the publisher's output.

We all share a sense of sadness that William Rushton is not giving this Prologue. Much of what I have told you I learned from William. Many of the Demonstrations were contrived by him with the masterly help and ingenuity of Clive Hood, here (spontaneous applause for Clive). William would not want us to be sad so let me remind you of one of his puckish stories. In Cambridge Colleges, Fellows must get permission to even nail a picture to the panelling in their rooms. William once said to the Trinity Bursar for Buildings, "If I drilled a small hole in my window shutter, what would you say?" The Bursar replied, "If your name was Isaac Newton, I would say nothing!"

William not only had a great sense of humour he was a scientific poet. Let me at least get him to give the Epilogue (from his Prentice Lecture, 1963).

Epilogue
We who investigate the workings of the human eye occupy a quite special place in the body of science, for our concern is both with the objective and the sub-jective. The eye is the window in that wall which separates the body from the mind and we may look both out and in. Never in history has the view been more exciting than it is today when new techniques on every side invite us to explore gardens that for centuries have been locked to all but speculation.

We need not be too dismayed at the great grasp of those giants that have preceded us. For by standing upon their shoulders we may reach what they could only envisage.

Twenty years later W. A. H. Rushton is now one of these giants. Let us not fail them and proceed to explore the gardens that lie before us.

Bibliography

Asimov's Biographical Encyclopedia of Science and Technology (1975). London, Pan Books.

Houston, R. A. (1923). *Light and Colour*. London, England, Longmans, Green and Co.

Hurvich, Leo, M. (1981). *Color Vision*. Sunderland, Massachusetts, USA, Sinauer Associates Inc.

Newton, Sir Isaac (1730). *Opticks: or a Treatise of the Reflections, Refractions, Inflections and Colours of Light*. Based on the Fourth Edition, London, Dover Publications Inc., 1952.

Rushton, W. A. H. (1964). Prentice Lecture: Colour Blindness and Cone Pigments. *Am. J. Optom. & Archives of Am. Academy of Optometry* **41**, 265–282.

Young, Thomas (1802a). On the Theory of Light and Colours. *Phil. Trans.* **1802**, 12–48.

Young, Thomas (1802b). An Account of some cases of the Production of Colours, not hitherto described. *Phil. Trans.* **1802**, 387–397.

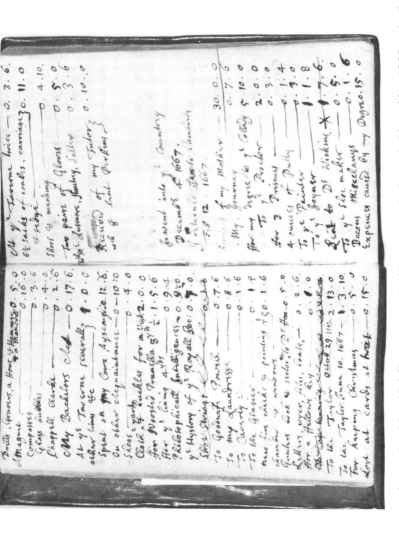

FIG. 1 Two pages of a notebook in which Newton recorded his expenses in the period from May 1665 to April 1669. Three-quarters of the way down the right-hand page is an entry: "ffor 3 Prismes 0.3.0". Other entries vividly illustrate Newton's domestic and experimental life: "Lost at cards at twist 0.15.0"; "At yᵉ Taverne twice 0.3.6"; "shoos 0.3.6"; "Drills, Gravers, a Hone & Hammer & a Mandrill". Returning to Cambridge in February 1667 he records "Received of my Mother 30.0.0". This notebook is in the possession of the Fitzwilliam Museum and was exhibited during the Cambridge Colour Vision meeting. (Reproduced by Permission of the Syndics of the Fitzwilliam Museum, Cambridge.)

Visual Transduction in Single Photoreceptors of the Monkey *Macaca fascicularis*

B. J. NUNN and D. A. BAYLOR

Introduction

Our present understanding of visual transduction in primate photoreceptors derives largely from psychophysical experiments and assumed parallels with the behavior of receptors in cold-blooded animals. Although useful information about mammalian receptors has been obtained from recordings of massed responses (e.g. Penn and Hagins, 1972; Baron and Boynton, 1975), it is desirable to examine the activity of one cell at a time. Here we give a brief account of experiments in which a suction electrode (Baylor, Lamb and Yau, 1979a) was used to study single receptors in the retina of the cynomolgus monkey, *Macaca fascicularis*. This animal makes Rayleigh color matches in the same way as human trichromats (DeValois, Morgan, Polson, Mead and Hull, 1974) and microspectrophotometry reveals spectral absorptions similar to those of human photoreceptors (Bowmaker, Dartnall and Mollon, 1980; Bowmaker and Dartnall, 1980). Up to now our work has concentrated on the properties of rods, but preliminary experiments suggest the feasibility of examining cones with the same methods.

Methods

Retinas were obtained from donor monkeys in heart-lung transplant experiments carried out in the Cardiovascular Surgery Department at Stanford. Enucleation was performed under deep ketamine-pentobarbital anesthesia

COLOUR VISION
ISBN 0 12 000000 0

while the eye was still circulated with oxygenated blood. Dark adaptation was aided by suturing the eyelids over a black plastic occluder 20–30 min before removal of the eye. Dim red light was used for cleaning and opening the globe, but retinal isolation and all subsequent steps were performed under infrared light, using infrared/visible image converters. Portions of the isolated retina were placed receptor-side up on the Sylgard bottom of a Petri dish containing Locke's solution and chopped into cubic pieces about 200 μm on a side with a razor blade. To remove sticky extracellular material the pieces were briefly exposed to collagenase. They were then transferred to the recording chamber on the stage of a compound inverted microscope. The solution was warmed to near 37°C, oxygenated, and stirred. In most experiments the Locke's solution in the chamber was buffered to pH 7.4 with HEPES, but in some experiments a flowing solution containing bicarbonate buffer at pH 7.4 was used with similar results. The suction electrode used for recording membrane current had an orifice about 2.0 μm in diameter. A rod outer segment projecting from near the edge of a piece of retina was usually chosen for study, care being taken that other outer segments were not in the path of the stimuli and that only one outer segment was drawn into the electrode. Figure 1 shows a photomicrograph of a suction electrode near some pieces of retina. The stimuli were plane polarized with the electric vector transverse to the cell axis and were applied diffusely at right-angles to the outer segment. Narrow spectral bands 10 nm in half-width were obtained with calibrated interference filters, while the stimulus intensity was controlled with a calibrated series of neutral density filters. At the end of each experimental day the source intensity was calibrated by placing the silicon photodiode probe of a United Detector Technology digital irradiance meter in the position of the experimental chamber. The irradiance measured with a given interference filter was converted into the equivalent quantal flux at the center wavelength of the filter's transmission curve.

Results and Discussion

Parameters of Flash Response of Rods

When a rod outer segment was drawn into the suction electrode, it showed a steady inward dark current (Hagins, Penn and Yoshikami, 1970; Baylor *et al.*, 1979a) up to 19 pA in amplitude. Brief flashes of visible light transiently suppressed the inward current in graded fashion. Figure 2 shows a family of responses to 10 msec flashes of increasing intensity, with the outward photocurrent (current in light minus the dark current) plotted upward. Apart from its shorter time scale, the general features of this family are similar to those of responses recorded in the same way from toad rods (Baylor *et al.*, 1979a).

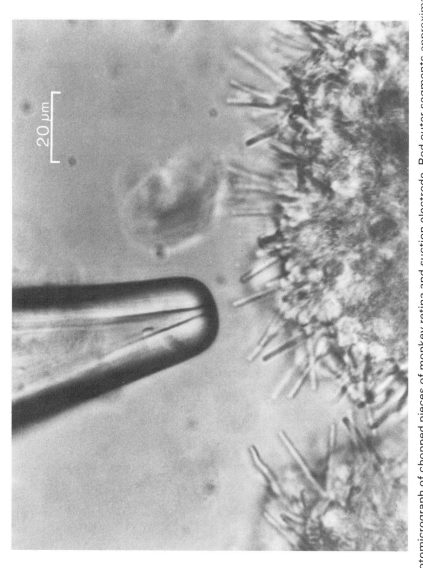

FIG. 1 Photomicrograph of chopped pieces of monkey retina and suction electrode. Rod outer segments approximately 2 μm in diameter project from pieces. For photography, 5% dextran was added to the Locke's solution in order to reduce motion of outer segments.

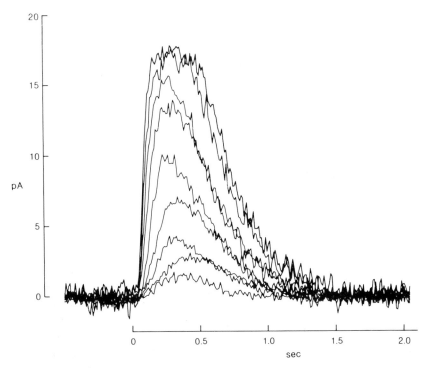

FIG. 2   Responses of a rod of *Macaca fascicularis* to brief flashes of increasing intensity. Superimposed traces plotting the outer segment current relative to its dark value as a function of time after the 10 msec flashes. Photon densities of the 501 nm stimuli were increased by factors of about 2 between 1.5 and 200 photons μm^{-2}. Lower traces averaged from up to 10 sweeps, uppermost trace a single sweep. Temperature 34.2°C. Low-pass filtered, bandwidth 0–50 Hz.

The response to a dim flash showed an s-shaped delay and was usually well fitted by an equation of the kind introduced by Fuortes and Hodgkin (1964), describing the impulse response of a chain of 5 or 6 buffered low pass filters with time constants of 50–60 msec. For responses less than about 1/5 the saturating amplitude the response scaled in proportion to flash strength, and the sensitivity (peak response amplitude/flash strength) was near 0.5 pA photon^{-1} μm^2 at 500 nm. Flashes near 15 photons μm^{-2} gave a half-saturating response; assuming an effective collecting area of 2 μm^2 for the outer segment, this flash strength would give 30 photoisomerizations. A flash causing more than about 200 isomerizations saturated the photocurrent, i.e., completely suppressed the inward dark current.

The relation between the peak response amplitude *r* and flash photon density i was described fairly well by (see Lamb, McNaughton and Yau, 1981)

$$r = r_{max} (1 - e^{-ki}) \tag{1}$$

where r_{max} is the saturating amplitude and k is a proportionality constant near $0.046 \, \mu m^2$ at 500 nm. The observed relation was consistently somewhat steeper than the rectangular hyperbola (Michaelis relation) that often fits photoreceptor responses.

Desensitization of Rods by Backgrounds

Flash on step experiments were performed to determine the effect of steady background lights in reducing rod sensitivity. The test flash was kept dim enough to elicit a flash in the linear response region, and responses to many flashes were averaged to reduce the effects of photon noise (next section). Desensitization came on abruptly as the steady response drove the transduction mechanism toward saturation; the steady intensity needed to reduce the flash sensitivity to half its dark-adapted value was in the region of 150 isomerizations sec^{-1}. In comparison Penn and Hagins (1972) found 350 isomerizations $rod^{-1} sec^{-1}$ in massed recordings from rat retina. Both values are of the same order of magnitude as the rate of isomerizations at which rod saturation begins in psychophysical increment threshold experiments on humans (Aguilar and Stiles, 1954; Hayhoe, MacLeod and Bruch, 1976), about 4×10^2 isomerizations $rod^{-1} sec^{-1}$. The electrical measurements thus support the notion that the psychophysical saturation of rods occurs within the outer segment itself. In contrast, the Weber-Fechner behavior seen psychophysically cannot depend on a sensitivity regulation within the outer segment. Thus, the human increment threshold is doubled by a background giving only one isomerization per rod per 100 seconds. Our experiments show no major change in outer segment sensitivity for backgrounds 10^4 times brighter.

Single Photon Effect

Responses to dim lights displayed prominent fluctuations consistent with a single photon effect about 0.5 pA in amplitude. This corresponds to about 3% of the dark current of the rod.

The traces in Fig. 3 illustrate such fluctuations in a rod's responses to long steps of dim light at three intensities. With increasing stimulus strength the mean response and the variance of the membrane current scaled up. Assuming that the response consists of the simple superposition of a series of randomly-occurring independent events of fixed size and shape, the size of the event is given approximately by the ratio of the variance increase to the mean response. A more refined estimate is obtained by scaling this figure by the "shape factor" characteristic of the event (Katz and Miledi, 1972). Analysis of the three

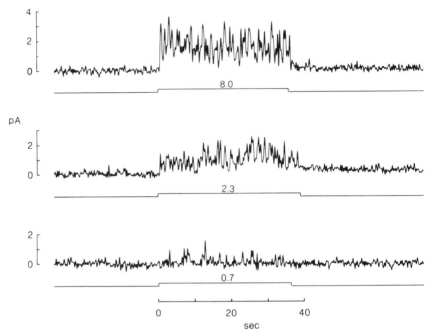

FIG. 3   Photon noise in the response of a rod to dim steady light at three inten-sities. Photocurrent plotted as a function of time, timing of light shown by stimulus monitor traces below. Numbers above monitor traces give step intensity in photons μm^{-2} sec^{-1} at 501 nm. Mean response and variance increase in each trial were (from below upwards): 0.162 pA and 0.059 pA^2; 0.938 pA and 0.278 pA^2; 1.68 pA and 0.494 pA^2. Estimated single photon event amplitudes were 0.51, 0.43 and 0.41 pA.

traces in Fig. 3 in this way, using the shape factor of 1.43 appropriate for the form of the average response to a dim flash, gave an average estimate of 0.45 pA for the peak amplitude of the event.

If each event is triggered by a single photoisomerization, then the mean frequency of occurrence in steady light should be given by the product of the light intensity and the effective collecting area (Baylor and Hodgkin, 1973) over which the outer segment captures photons and converts them to photo-isomerizations. As a check of the idea that an event is triggered by a single photoisomerization, the apparent collecting area calculated from mean response, event amplitude and mean duration, and applied light intensity, can be compared with that expected from the known pigment density and dimen-sions of the outer segment. The mean figure for apparent collecting area from the three traces in Fig. 3 was 2.2 μm^2. Now an outer segment 25 μm long and 2 μm in diameter, with a specific axial pigment density of 0.016 μm^{-1} (Harosi, 1975; Bowmaker, Dartnall and Mollon, 1980), and a quantum efficiency of excitation of 0.67 (Dartnall, 1972), should have a collecting area of 1.9 μm^2 when excited by light polarized transversely to the axis. The agreement between the collecting areas obtained in the two ways supports the assumption that the noise in the dim light response results from a single photon effect about 0.5 pA in size.

A similar analysis can be made using a very dim flash as the stimulus. In such experiments it was found that the response was "quantized", with an event amplitude of about 0.7 pA. The probability of occurrence of the unit events was given by the Poisson distribution with a mean appropriate for the applied flash intensity and a collecting area near 2 μm^2. Estimates of the unit response amplitude from flash experiments on 4 cells were between 0.5 and 0.9 pA.

Analysis of the photon noise of toad rods (Baylor, Lamb and Yau, 1979b) gave an event amplitude around 1 pA.

Spectral Sensitivity of Rods

Detailed measurements were made on the spectral sensitivity of 10 rods from three monkeys. The sensitivity was determined as the reciprocal of the flash photon density required to elicit a constant response, using the method of Naka and Rushton (1966). In order to prevent bias due to changes in the condition of the cell, the sensitivity at 501 nm was repeatedly determined and all sensitivities were expressed relative to average sensitivities at this reference wavelength.

Figure 4 shows the collected results. Data from different cells were positioned on the logarithmic ordinate so that the vertical differences were minimized. After this scaling the curves agree well with one another and show a peak in the blue-green.

In order to estimate the wavelength of maximal sensitivity, the Dartnall nomogram tabulated by Wyszecki and Stiles (1967) was fitted to the averaged log sensitivities plotted on a wavenumber scale. A satisfactory fit was obtained with the curve of a rhodopsin absorbing maximally at 491 nm. Shifting the nomogram curve by more than a few nm obviously worsened the fit to the results, and our best estimate of the peak is 491 ± 3 nm.

In microspectrophotometric measurements on rods from the same species, Bowmaker *et al.* (1980) found a peak at 500.1 ± 1.6 nm. The difference between these results and ours is unexplained. One possible explanation would be a difference in the sampling of the parent population, another an unforeseen experimental problem. It is perhaps significant that a difference between the electrical sensitivity and absorption measurements has also been reported for "red" rods of the toad *Bufo marinus*, where Harosi (1975) found the peak at 502 nm by measuring spectral absorption, Baylor *et al.* (1979a) 498 nm by recording membrane current. A genuine difference in spectral absorption and

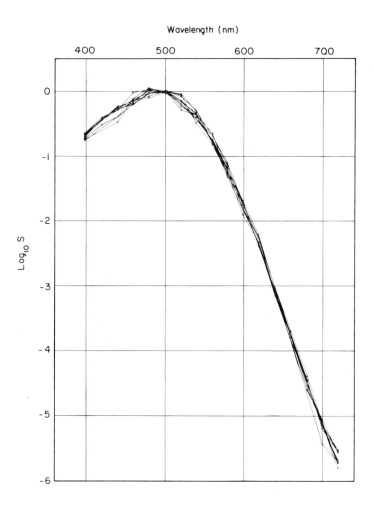

FIG. 4   Collected spectral sensitivities from ten *Macaca fascicularis* rods. Ordinate is $\log_{10}$ relative quantum sensitivity, abscissa wavelength. Five rods were from one monkey, four from another, and one from a third. Lines drawn to connect experimental points. Sensitivities determined as described in the text.

spectral sensitivity would be interesting and might have several explanations, including a wavelength dependence of the probability that a photon absorbed in rhodopsin generates an electrical excitation. Until proven otherwise, however, a more mundane explanation seems more likely.

How do the electrical measures of spectral sensitivity compare with psychophysical results on human scotopic sensitivity? Because the light in our experiments was applied transversely to the outer segment, the path length was very short and therefore self-screening of the rhodopsin negligible. Assuming a constant quantum efficiency of response production, the electrical measures should give directly the form of rhodopsin's molecular extinction coefficient as a function of wavelength. Psychophysical measures are complicated by 1) absorption of light in the lens and vitreous, and 2) self-screening of rhodopsin because of axial passage through the outer segment. These factors should be negligible, however, at wavelengths longer than about 620 nm. Over the region 640–720 nm the linear variation of log sensitivity with wavenumber in the monkey rod results agreed closely with the averaged psychophysical results of Crawford (1949), the linear regression slopes differing by only 1.5%. An iterative computer program was used to determine simultaneously the

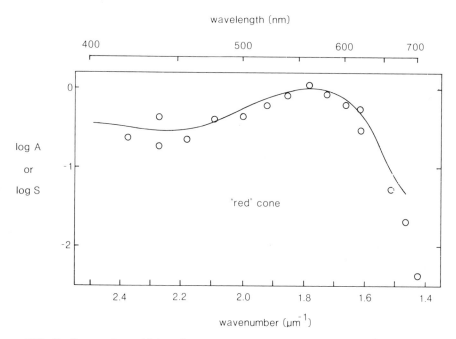

FIG. 5   Spectral sensitivity of a presumed red-sensitive cone. Relative quantum sensitivity plotted as a function of wavenumber (wavelength scale above). Smooth curve the average absorption of human red-sensitive cones from Bowmaker and Dartnall (1980).

scaling of the lens density spectrum tabulated by Wyszecki and Stiles (1967) and degree of self-screening required to correct the shorter wavelength portion of Crawford's curve to ours. When Crawford's results were corrected for a lens density of 1.62 at 400 nm and a peak axial pigment density of 0.36, they were in close agreement with the monkey sensitivities over the entire region 400–720 nm.

Cones

It would be useful to determine the sensitivity of the three cone mechanisms throughout the visible region in the same way as for the rods. The low density of cones in the peripheral retina makes them difficult to find, and location and chopping of the fovea also present problems. Recordings have nevertheless been obtained from a few cones, identified by their lower sensitivity and faster light responses. The spectral sensitivity of one cone is shown in Fig. 5. Its peak sensitivity appears to lie between 550 and 580 nm, and the form of the relation is similar to the averaged human red cone absorption measured by Bowmaker and Dartnall (1980) shown as the dotted curve.

Acknowledgements

We wish to thank Drs D. Modry and S. W. Jamieson and Messrs Jesse Gutierrez and Grant Hoyt of the Department of Cardiovascular Surgery, Stanford Medical School, for their kind cooperation. Gunther Kuhn gave invaluable technical assistance. Supported by grant EY 01543 from the National Eye Institute, USPHS.

References

Aguilar, M. and Stiles, W. S. (1954). Saturation of the rod mechanism of the retina at high levels of stimulation. *Optica Acta* **1**: 59–65.

Baron, W. S. and Boynton, R. M. (1975). Response of primate cones to sinusoidally flickering homochromatic stimuli. *J. Physiol.* **246**: 311–331.

Baylor, D. A. and Hodgkin, A. L. (1973). Detection and resolution of visual stimuli by turtle photoreceptors. *J. Physiol.* **234**: 163–198.

Baylor, D. A., Lamb, T. D. and Yau, K.-W. (1979a). The membrane current of single rod outer segments. *J. Physiol.* **288**: 589–611.

Baylor, D. A., Lamb, T. D. and Yau, K.-W. (1979b). Responses of retinal rods to single photons. *J. Physiol.* **288**: 613–634.

Bowmaker, J. K. and Dartnall, H. J. A. (1980). Visual pigments of rods and cones in a human retina. *J. Physiol.* **298**: 501–511.

Bowmaker, J. K., Dartnall, H. J. A. and Mollon, J. D. (1980). Microspectrophoto-metric demonstration of four classes of photoreceptor in an old world primate (*Macaca fascicularis*). *J. Physiol.* **298**: 131–143.

Crawford, B. H. (1949). The scotopic visibility function. *Proc. Phys. Soc.* **B62**: 321–334.

Dartnall, H. J. A. (1972). Photosensitivity. In *Photochemistry of Vision* (ed. Dartnall, H. J. A.), pp. 122–145. New York: Springer.

DeValois, R. L., Morgan, H. C., Polson, M. C., Mead, W. R., and Hull, E. M. (1974). Psychophysical studies of monkey vision. I. Macaque luminosity and color vision tests. *Vision Res.* **14**: 53–67.

Fuortes, M. G. F. and Hodgkin, A. L. (1964). Changes in time scale and sensitivity in the ommatidia of *Limulus*. *J. Physiol.* **172**: 239–263.

Hagins, W. A., Penn, R. D. and Yoshikami, S. (1970). Dark current and photocurrent in retinal rods. *Biophys. J.* **10**: 380–412.

Harosi, F. I. (1975). Absorption spectra and linear dichroism of some amphibian photoreceptors. *J. gen. Physiol.* **66**: 357–382.

Hayhoe, M. M., MacLeod, D. I. A. and Bruch, T. A. (1976). Rod-cone independence in dark adaptation. *Vision Res.* **16**: 591–600.

Katz, B. and Miledi, R. (1972). The statistical nature of the acetylcholine potential and its molecular components. *J. Physiol.* **224**: 665–699.

Lamb, T. D., McNaughton, P. A. and Yau, K.-W. (1981). Spatial spread of activation and background desensitization in toad rod outer segments. *J. Physiol.* **319**: 463–496.

Naka, K. I. and Rushton, W. A. H. (1966). S-potentials from colour units in the retina of fish. (*Cyprinidae*). *J. Physiol.* **185**: 536–555.

Penn, R. D. and Hagins, W. A. (1972). Kinetics of the photocurrent of retinal rods. *Biophys. J.* **12**: 1073–1094.

Wyszecki, G. and Stiles, W. S. (1967). *Color Science.* New York: Wiley.

Microspectrophotometry of Visual Pigments in Primate Photoreceptors

E. F. MACNICHOL, Jr, J. S. LEVINE, R. J. W. MANSFIELD, L. E. LIPETZ and B. A. COLLINS

Introduction

Microspectrophotometric (MSP) measurements of visual pigments in primate cones have consistently proven as difficult to obtain as they are desirable. In the quarter-century since the first efforts to obtain absorption spectra from outer segments of individual cones (Hanaoka and Fujimoto, 1957), data of excellent quality and reproducibility have been obtained from dozens of fish species and several amphibians (see, for reviews and examples, Marks, 1963, 1965; Liebman and Entine, 1964; Liebman, 1972; Loew and Lythgoe, 1978; Levine and MacNichol, 1979). The cones of these animals possess outer segments up to 5 μm in diameter and retain their structural integrity for up to 48 hours if they are maintained on ice or refrigerated in dark bottles.

Cones of primates and other terrestrial vertebrates such as turtles and birds are much more difficult subjects for MSP. The outer segments of these photoreceptors are generally of rather small diameter, are extremely fragile, separate easily from their inner segments, and begin to deteriorate rapidly following enucleation. As a result, data on the cone pigments of primates have always been scarce and of less than optimal quality. The earliest MSP records from individual primate cones of humans and macaque monkeys were bleaching difference spectra of parafoveal cones measured axially in the retina. These data, published nearly simultaneously by Brown and Wald (1964) and Marks, Dobelle, and MacNichol (1964), provided convincing evidence for the existence of three cone types, each containing a single visual pigment, and thus provided

COLOUR VISION
ISBN 0 12 000000 0

the first physiological evidence for the Young-Helmholtz trichromatic theory of color vision. However, the location and shape of the spectra obtained from the three cone pigments exhibited considerable variability. These preliminary data (Brown and Wald, 1964; Marks *et al.* 1964; MacNichol 1964; Wald and Brown, 1965), based on less than a dozen receptors in all, placed the wavelengths of maximum absorbance (λ_{max}) of the three cone classes at 440–450 nm for the short-wave cones, 525–540 nm for the middle-wave cones and 555–577 nm for the long-wave cones.

These early absorbance spectra were not sufficiently precise to permit the kind of quantitative comparisons with neural and behavioral data that could provide a satisfactory foundation for understanding the mechanisms of color perception. Simply obtaining a greater number of records would not have provided the necessary precision because of the technical difficulties in early MSP measurements. In addition to the collection of more data, several methodological and technical developments have permitted us to make more accurate determinations of primate visual pigments.

Marks (1963, 1965) and Liebman and Entine (1964) determined with their early measurements that absorbance spectra of good quality could be obtained from goldfish cones with the measuring beam passing transversely through the receptor outer segments. Dobelle, Marks and MacNichol (1969) made some preliminary transverse measurements of individual primate rods and foveal cones, but the poor signal-to-noise ratio caused by the very small diameters of the receptors (0.8 to 1.2 μm) made estimation of pigment λ_{max} values unfeasible. The specific absorbance calculated from these measurements was only $0.008\,\mu\text{m}^{-1}$, considerably less than that of larger rods or cones (0.012 to 0.015). Transverse measurements of the larger, parafoveal cones allow better optical isolation of the outer segment than axial measurements *in situ*, eliminate light scattering by the more proximal layers of the retina, and yield reasonably high optical densities provided that the measuring beam is polarized with the *E*-vector perpendicular to the long axis of the receptor to exploit the dichroism of the outer segments.

A second development, the use of digital computers for automatic control of the MSP instrumentation (Harosi, 1971; Harosi and MacNichol, 1974), enables rapid, repetitive scanning and averaging to decrease both the effects of instabilities in the measuring system and the distortion of spectra due to progressive pigment bleaching during each measurement. The use of low photon-flux densities in the measuring beam minimizes bleaching and helps eliminate distortion caused by light-absorbing photoproducts, but causes a decrease in the signal-to-noise ratio for each scan. This problem necessitated another pair of innovations which are especially important when dealing with small receptors; photon-counting to decrease drift due to high voltage variations, and refrigeration of the photocathode to decrease thermal electron emission, which is further decreased by the use of focusing magnets that limit the effective area of the photocathode by a factor of about 50. The replacement of the customary tungsten-halogen light source for the measuring beam with a stabilized xenon-arc significantly increases the energy available for measurement in the blue, violet, and ultraviolet regions of the spectrum, considerably improving the signal-to-noise ratio in the region critically important for accurate measurements of blue-absorbing cones.

Another alteration to the original equipment was the development and implementation of specialised, interactive computer programs for on-line data gathering and analysis. These programs, which streamline both data gathering and analysis procedures, greatly improve the efficiency of the MSP operators and permit the application of rigorous criteria in data-quality control. All these improvements in instrumentation have been incorporated in a computer-controlled photon-counting microspectrophotometer (PMSP) (MacNichol, 1978) and successfully applied to the cones of numerous non-primate species (Levine and MacNichol, 1979).

In addition to difficulties in measurement, another problem plaguing MSP work on primate cones is the rapid deterioration of primate retinae following enucleation. The sixth development has been a procedure for partial glutaraldehyde fixation that was shown to maintain the structural integrity of cone outer-segments without significantly bleaching the visual pigments of a number of fish species (Levine, Goodman and MacNichol, 1981). There seemed a reasonable possibility that such a technique could be successfully applied to the primate retina.

There still remained the problem of the extreme fragility of primate cone outer-segments. A number of dissection techniques developed in our laboratory during work on fish and turtle retinae were applied to primate tissues, where they were found to greatly increase the yield of measurable photoceptors.

In the course of these developments, and as we began our initial reanalysis of primate material, several other investigators have succeeded in expanding the existing data base on human and primate visual pigments. In a series of recent papers, Dartnall and his colleagues (Bowmaker, Dartnall, Lythgoe and Mollon, 1978; Bowmaker, Dartnall and Mollon, 1980; Bowmaker and Dartnall, 1980) have reported the results of extensive surveys of cone visual pigments from rhesus, cynomolgus and human retinae.

In the present study we present results for cynomolgus and rhesus photoreceptors using the computer-controlled, photon-counting microspectrophotometer and incorporating all the technical and procedural developments described above. Some data on the same material were obtained by our colleague F. I. Harosi using a different instrument, the dichroic microspectrophotometer (DMSP) (Harosi, 1982). Dr Harosi has kindly allowed us to present some of his unpublished results.

Materials and Methods

Animals

Eyes were obtained from two species of macaque monkey from several sources. The majority were feral male and female cynomolgus (*Macaca fascicularis*) aged 3 to 5 years and weighing 2.5 to 3.5 kg. Additionally, both feral male juvenile rhesus (*Macaca mulatta*) aged 1.5 to 3 years weighing 2 to 3 kg and mature female rhesus aged 6 to 12 years and weighing 5 to 8 kg of either feral or domestic origin were examined. For at least 3 months prior to sacrifice the monkeys were maintained on a diet of Purina monkey chow *ad libitum*, supplemented by fresh fruit. The monkeys obtained from Flow Laboratories (MacLean, Va.) were dark-adapted overnight and then given a lethal dose of the euthanasic agent T61 (Webster) and enucleated under dim red light. Otherwise the monkeys were tranquilized with ketamine hydrochloride followed by a surgical dosage of sodium phenobarbitol and then dark adapted for at least 15 minutes prior to enucleation. Following enucleation the monkeys were given a lethal dose of sodium phenobarbital or T61.

Fresh Material

Fresh eyes obtained from Flow Laboratories were removed from the animals under dim red light, wrapped in metal foil, placed on ice, and shipped by air to Boston. For material obtained in this manner, the first retinal piece was usually examined on the PMSP between 6 and 8 hours post-enucleation. Four fresh retinae were obtained from animals sacrificed in dim red light in the Boston–Woods Hole area; in these cases experiments began anywhere from 1 to 3 hours post-enucleation.

The foveal region was located in fresh retinae using retinal landmarks visible under dim red light and infrared illumination. Preparations for the MSP were made from the parafoveal areas of the retina by cutting out small (*c.* 1 mm^2) pieces of tissue with iridectomy scissors and removing this tissue to a drop of Ringers on a large coverslip. This tissue was dissected into smaller pieces either by cutting it between a pair of curve-tip scalpels drawn across each other or by pulling the tissue apart with forceps. The smaller pieces thus obtained were then individually removed to a drop of Ringers on another coverslip either by picking them up with forceps or by gently transferring them in a constant volume pipette. With different retinae in various stages of deterioration either the "rough" or "gentle" technique might provide the best preparations. Once the tissue was prepared as described, it was ringed with silicone oil and squashed with another coverslip.

Fixed Material

Since the number of records obtainable from fresh samples was usually limited by the rapid deterioration of cone outer segments, most of the material was lightly fixed (30 to 60 sec) in 2% gluteraldehyde in cold, buffered primate Ringers. This procedure had been shown earlier (Levine *et al.*, 1981) to preserve fish cone outer-segments without significantly bleaching or otherwise altering visual pigments. Retinal material fixed in this manner retained measurable visual pigment for up to two weeks when stored in buffered primate Ringers in the dark on ice or in a refrigerator, permitting extended time for data gathering. Several retinae treated in this manner were obtained through the courtesy of M. Neuringer of the Oregon Regional Primate Center as well as from Flow Laboratories.

Although partial fixation greatly extended the useful life of the tissue samples, it also altered their consistency, necessitating changes in the techniques used to prepare the tissue for MSP. In an effort to free cone outer-segments from the forest of rod outer-segments that surrounded them in fixed tissue, some preparations were made by embedding the fixed tissue in agarose, quick-freezing it in liquid nitrogen, and then sectioning the material with a cryostat microtome (all under dim red light). Other preparations were made by placing small samples of tissue on a coverslip as previously described and mercilessly teasing the tissue into tiny fragments before covering with the second coverslip. Preparations were then forcibly squeezed and sheared by moving the coverslips between the fingers. In the long run, the latter, simpler technique provided a better yield of measurable cone outer-segments than the more elaborate cryostat procedure.

Measuring Procedure

The photon-counting microspectrophotometer at the Laboratory of Sensory Physiology, Marine Biological Laboratory, Woods Hole, MA, whose essential features have been described elsewhere (MacNichol, 1978) has been somewhat modified. In its current configuration, light from a 100 W tungsten-halogen lamp or a 150 W xenon arc, polarized by a Glan-Thompson prism, enters a grating monochromator which, under computer control, scans the visible spectrum in 0.75 second, repetitively at 1 second intervals. The spectral light illuminates a modified Zeiss microscope equipped with Nikon CF apochromatic optics. The image of a pair of crossed slits, adjustable both in width and position, is demagnified and projected onto the plane of the specimen by a 10× eyepiece and a 40× oil immersion objective. A 100× immersion objective focuses the slit image projected on the specimen plane in such a way that the image can be directed to either viewing or measuring devices. For viewing, the slit image is projected on an infrared-sensitive vidicon (Panasonic S4113) in a closed circuit TV system, while an infrared light-source illuminates the field of the microscope to facilitate specimen examination and critical focusing. For measurement, the field illumination is turned off, and the measuring beam is used to illuminate a photomultiplier tube equipped with an extended red-sensitive photocathode (EMI 9658R), mounted in a thermoelectrically cooled housing (Pacific Instruments Co.). The measuring slit is positioned so that as the polarized measuring beam passes transversely through the receptors, the *E*-vector is oriented perpendicularly to the long axis of the outer segment.

The monochromator is periodically calibrated using either a mercury-cadmium lamp (Osram) or a Balzer P7 multiple-peak interference filter. The power supplies for the photomultiplier (Pacific Instruments Co.) and the tungsten-halogen light source are well regulated, and the xenon arc uses photo-feedback control (Oriel).

A computer (Data General Nova 2/10) with dual diskette drives runs the experiment and, at the operator's discretion, can display the data on a storage oscilloscope (Tektronix 603), store the data on disk, or print them out on a line printer. In order to facilitate comparisons among pigment spectra (see below), the monochromator scans linearly in frequency from 400 to 800 THz (750 to 375 nm). The frequency is read into the computer using an eleven-bit absolute shaft-position encoder (Itek). Photon pulses from the photomultiplier are fed via a fast preamplifier and pulse-height discriminator (Ortec) to a 16 bit counter which is read into the computer at 5 THz intervals.

Interactive programs written with a BASIC compiler specifically configured for the instrument are used for data gathering and data analysis. Using our BASIC program "DGATH", the PMSP scans through the spectrum as described, dividing the spectrum into 81 bins 5 THz wide, with two additional bins for dark counts between scans. Photoelectron counts are added to each bin in computer memory during a scan, and the sum divided by the total number of scans to give the average count. First, twenty or more "blank" scans are made through a clear area of the preparation. Then a variable number of "sample" scans (usually 3 to 20) are made through each receptor outer segment. The computer then calculates the optical density of each bin, using the algorithm O.D. = $\log_{10}$ (average blank counts minus average dark counts)/ (average sample counts minus average dark counts). The resulting curve is automatically scaled to fit the oscilloscope screen. When desired, outer segments may be bleached, using either the measuring beam or an auxiliary beam incorporating a shuttered tungsten lamp and a xenon strobe-flash. Bleaching difference curves are calculated using the pre-bleach scan through the receptor as the "sample" scan and the post-bleach scan as the "blank" when calculating absorbance.

After each receptor was measured, the position of the measuring spot within it was examined on the TV screen for change in position. Records showing obvious motion artifacts were discarded.

Data Analysis Procedure

1) Raw data are retrieved from disk files using our "DANAL" BASIC program. The optical densities of the 81 frequency bins are calculated as described above, and the record is displayed on an oscilloscope screen simultaneously with a previously generated template curve (described below). The X and Y components of the template curve can be stretched and shifted to move the plotted template curve as necessary along the X- and Y-axes by manipulating four manually-operated potentiometers which serve as analog inputs to the computer. The template curve can thus be matched for a critical best fit with the data, at which point interpolation of the "stretching" and "shifting" factors permits accurate calculation of λ_{max}, bandwidth, and maximal optical density.

2) At this point in the analysis procedure, rigorous selection of suitable records is necessary to eliminate curves distorted by focusing errors, build-up of photoproducts or extensive scattering of the measuring beam. Frequency-related light-scattering superimposed on visual pigment spectra raises short-wave absorbance and shifts the apparent λ_{max} in the short-wave direction. Focusing errors and interference from cells or cell fragments in the path of the measuring beam can either elevate or depress the long-wave portion of the curve, also shifting the apparent λ_{max}. For this reason, only records whose shapes conformed well to the accepted shape of visual pigment absorption spectra were selected for analysis.

During the early stages of these investigations, raw records from primate cones were compared with a template curve generated (as described below) from excellent records obtained from the very large cone outer segments of local species of marine fishes containing Vitamin A1-based visual pigments. In each case, the primate data were plotted on the oscilloscope screen along with a template generated from an A1 cone-pigment with a λ_{max} in the general region of the spectrum where the primate pigments were located. Any records exhibiting significant deviations from the shape of the A1 template were rejected. Note that because these templates are easily shifted along the frequency axis on which the data are plotted, there is no *a priori* bias towards selecting records with a particular λ_{max}.

Once an acceptable number of good quality spectra of each primate receptor type had been selected and averaged, a new template was generated to fit those data as closely as possible, and this "custom" template was used to assist in selecting all further records. The importance of rigorous selection at this stage of analysis will be elucidated further in the Discussion.

3) Records that pass this selection procedure may then be entered into an averaging array. Whenever a raw record is included in this array, the program averages the values calculated for the λ_{max}, bandwidth, and optical density of that record with those of all other records included in the average, and

calculates the mean and standard deviation for each of these parameters. At the same time, the photon counts of the latest record are averaged point by point with those of previous records of the same pigment type. In this manner, mean optical density and standard deviation are calculated for each 5-THz interval.

4) At the discretion of the operator, the contents of this averaged array may be plotted with the same template, or a new template may be generated to match the new data more precisely (see below). Either choice allows the calculation of the λ_{max}, bandwidth, and optical density of the *averaged data array*. Comparison of these parameters with those calculated from the individual records permits estimates of the cell-to-cell variation among records.

5) The description and intercomparison of pigment spectra was facilitated by the use of template curves (Dartnall, 1953; Harosi, 1976). Our templates are smooth, mathematically generated curves which contain twice as many points (one each 2.5 THz) as the data arrays, and thus simplify the visual matching procedure. The formula that generates the templates is due to Harosi (1976) who found that the absorptance spectra of visual pigments (plotted on a reciprocal wavelength scale) could be described accurately by the linear summation of three Gaussian functions. Harosi calculated these parameters by an analytical best-fit method using a large computer. We utilize a visual fitting method facilitating on-line data analysis. Averaged data and an existing template are displayed simultaneously on the oscilloscope screen. The mean, amplitude, and bandwidth of each of the three Gaussian components are varied manually through the A/D converter, and the continuously recalculated template curve is fitted to the averaged data by eye.

Results

Rods

Records were obtained from 25 individual rods. Three morphological classes of rods were found in the retinae of both macaque species: conventional rods with an outer-segment diameter of about 1 μm, what we have called "small super rods" with outer-segments of about 1.5 μm diameter and inner-segments more spherical and slightly longer than those of conventional rods, and "large super rods" (Harosi, 1982) with long, cylindrical outer-segments of 1.5−2.5 μm diameter and inner-segments of roughly the same dimensions as those of identified red and green cones. A single, wide-body super rod and a cluster of small super rods are illustrated in Figs 1a and b.

All three morphological classes of rods appeared to contain the same visual pigment, a rhodopsin with λ_{max} at about 502 ± 2 nm. Since larger diameter outer segments yield spectra with greater signal-to-noise ratios and less distortion due to diffraction and scattering of the measuring beam, the best

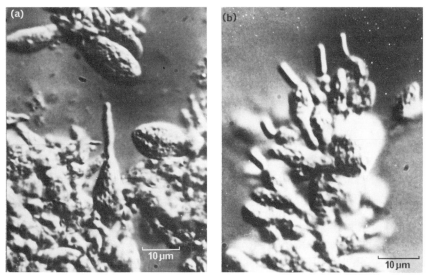

FIG. 1 (a) Nomarski photomicrograph of wide-body super rod. (b) Nomarski photomicrograph of cluster of small super rods.

records were obtained from super rods. Of the 25 records obtained, 5 spectra from cynomolgus rods and 5 spectra from rhesus rods were selected for detailed analysis on the basis of the criteria described in the Methods section. The averaged rod spectra for both macaque species are shown in Fig. 2.

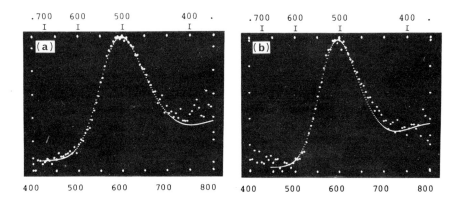

FIG. 2 (a) Averaged cynomolgus rod spectra plotted with template. (b) Averaged rhesus rod spectra plotted with template.

No significant differences were observed between the rod pigments of the two monkey species. The mean transverse absorbance for the cynomolgus super rods was 0.053, and for the rhesus rods was 0.049. The λ_{max} values for these averages of records taken from individual photoreceptors were 502 ± 2 nm for cynomolgus and 503 ± 2 nm for rhesus, while the λ_{max} obtained from groups of rods measured *en masse* with a large measuring beam was 499 ± 1 nm ($n = 6$). The bandwidth at half maximal absorbance for the individual rods was 129 THz for cynomolgus and 118 for rhesus. The Dartnall nomogram predicts an intermediate value (125 THz) for pigments at this wavelength.

Cones

Records from 107 identifiable cone outer segments associated with identified inner segments were saved on disk files. In order to merit being saved, records had to exhibit an absorption curve with the main photopigment absorption peak higher than any other point on the curve, and had to exhibit an optical density of greater than 0.020. Any record in which there was unquestionable evidence of distortion due to focusing errors, motion artifacts, or scattering problems was discarded; records in which possible distortion was not as clear-cut were saved for later comparison with A1 pigment templates as described in the Methods section. Records of this type were classified according to rough estimates of their λ_{max} values into major groups termed (for convenience) "red", "green", and "blue".

It was sometimes possible to study in the Nomarski interference microscope the morphology of cones whose spectra had just been measured. This was done by comparing Polaroid photographs of the TV screen with the microscope image. Fig. 3a shows the spectrum of a red cone whose morphology is identified in Fig. 3b taken from the infrared television screen and illustrated in detail in the Nomarski photomicrograph, Fig. 3c.

From these records of both fresh and fixed receptors, 48 cone spectra were selected for detailed analysis on the basis of the criteria described in the Methods section. As an example of the quality of the records that were selected for this analysis, see Figs 4a and b. Figure 4a shows the best individual cone spectrum included in the red cone average, and Fig. 4b shows an example of the least acceptable of those records used in the average. This record shows a smaller signal-to-noise ratio and greater apparent density in the short-wave region of the spectrum owing to light scatter in the preparation. These records are shown with superimposed A1 pigment template curves generated as described in the Methods section.

Many records exhibiting a clearly defined λ_{max} and reasonably high optical density were not considered for detailed analysis because scattering and/or focusing problems in the preparation systematically distorted the curves and

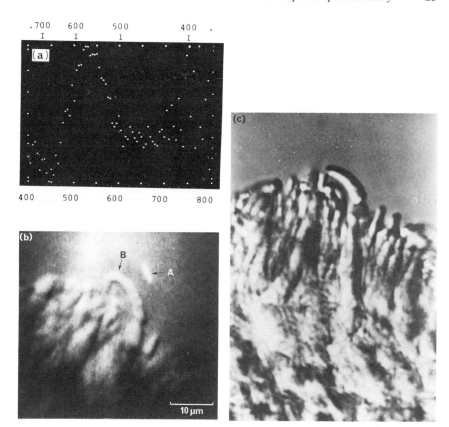

FIG. 3 (a) Individual cynomolgus red-cone spectrum obtained in fixed preparation. (b) Photograph of the same preparation on the screen of the infrared TV.
Arrows: A, measuring beam in blank position; B, Outer-segment that was
measured. (c) Nomarski photomicrograph of the same red cone.

shifted the apparent λ_{max}, usually in the short-wave direction. Figure 4c shows
an individual record that was not included in the final analysis because of
distortion, presumably due to Rayleigh and Mie scattering. These scattering
functions increase sharply as wavelength decreases.

The errors that can be introduced into a data set through the inclusion of
spectra distorted by this type of scattering are considerable. Figures 4d and
4e show the same average of several red cone spectra distorted by scattering.
In Fig. 4d, this distorted average is *fitted* as accurately as possible to a primate
red cone template by stretching and shifting the template to fit the average on
both sides of the peak. When treated in this manner, the average as given by
the template parameters, shows a mean λ_{max} of 556 nm.

Figure 4e shows the same data set *plotted* with the normal red cone pigment
template adjusted laterally to fit the longwave side of the main peak. Note that

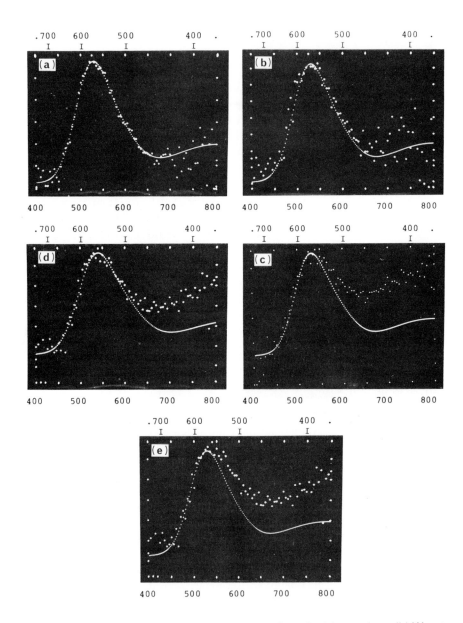

FIG. 4   (a) Best individual red-cone spectrum plotted with template. (b) Worst acceptable individual red cone spectrum plotted with template. (c) Unacceptable individual "red cone" spectrum exhibiting significant short-wave scatter and concomitant shift in apparent λ_{max}. (d) Average of distorted "red cone" spectra *fitted* with red pigment template (see text). (e) Average of distorted "red cone" spectra *plotted* with native red-cone template (see text).

the long-wave limb of the scatter-affected data curve matches the template quite well, but that the short-wave side rises higher and higher away from the template towards the short-wave end of the spectrum. If this spectrum were accepted and included in our analysis of the red cone pigment, and plotted in the manner depicted in Fig. 4d it would have shifted the mean λ_{max} of the average significantly in the short-wave direction, and would have more than doubled the observed individual variation in λ_{max} values for red cones. In the example shown, the elevation of the short-wave end of the curve is not nearly as great as that present in records that have often been considered acceptable in other studies. However, as in Fig. 4d these data are fitted to a template only in the region around the peak, the λ_{max} obtained was 556 nm. As shown in Fig. 4e, fitting the long-wave limb only to the undistorted red cone template gave a λ_{max} of 567 nm, a not insignificant difference. Recalling that 567 is the λ_{max} of our red average, it might be possible to salvage some of our unacceptable data by fitting only the long-wave edge to our average template, without altering its width, only its position. However, we have not chosen to do this.

Other distortions – caused primarily by focusing errors – may have the effect of shifting the putative λ_{max} of the observed spectrum in the long-wave direction. If "short-wave shift" errors are carefully balanced with "long-wave shift" errors when selecting records for final analysis, the *mean* λ_{max} of the final average may be unaffected, but the half-bandwidth of the average will be artificially large, and the variations in λ_{max} ascribed to individual cones – and hence the reported standard deviation – will be greatly increased by these errors in measurement.

Red Cones

A total of 55 red cone records were obtained: 20 from fresh cynomolgus tissue, 4 from fresh rhesus tissue, 26 from fixed cynomolgus retina and 7 from fixed rhesus retina. From these, 7 fresh cynomolgus, 6 fixed cynomolgus, 4 fresh rhesus and 1 fixed rhesus red cone spectra were selected for detailed analysis. The 7 fresh cynomolgus cones yielded a mean transverse absorbance of 0.038. The 6 fixed cynomolgus red cones yielded a mean transverse absorbance of 0.026. The 4 fresh rhesus cones yielded a mean transverse absorbance of 0.032. The bandwidth of the cynomolgus fresh red cone average was 114.5 THz; that of the rhesus fresh red cone average was 120 THz.

The λ_{max} values for all these records clustered tightly about a value near 567 nm. There was no significant difference between fresh and fixed material, and there was no significant difference between rhesus and cynomolgus red cone pigments.

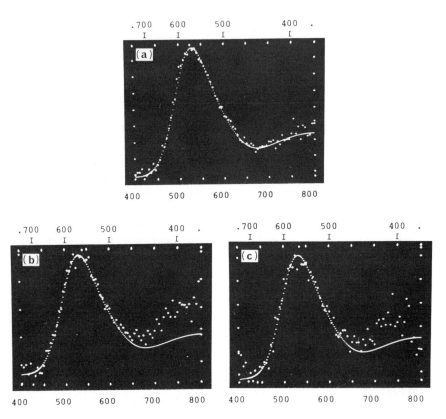

FIG. 5 (a) Fresh cynomolgus red-cone average. (b) Fixed cynomolgus red-cone average. (c) Combined fresh and fixed rhesus red-cone average.

Green Cones

A total of 35 green cones were measured; 15 fresh and 12 fixed cynomolgus "normal" greens, and 8 fixed "anomalous" cynomolgus greens (see below). Of these, 11 fresh and 3 fixed cynomolgus "normal" greens, and 8 fixed cynomolgus "anomalous" greens were suitable for detailed analysis. The fresh cynomolgus greens yielded a mean transverse density of 0.030. The λ_{max} of this averaged group was 532 ± 2 nm, with a bandwidth of 125.3 THz. The λ_{max} of the fixed green cones was also 532 nm with a standard deviation of 5. In addition to these "normal" green receptors, we also found a group of cells exhibiting a λ_{max} of 543 ± 4 nm, which correspond to an anomalous green pigment found by Bowmaker *et al.* (1978) in rhesus. We did not obtain a sufficiently large number of good quality records from the rhesus material to make a similar analysis.

In contrast to the single cluster of λ_{max} values for the red cones, the mean absorbances of the green cones were grouped into two clusters: one in the region around 532 nm and another in the region around 545 nm.

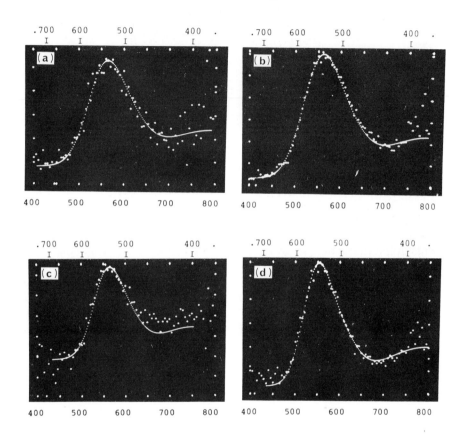

FIG. 6 (a) Typical individual fresh cynomolgus green-cone record. (b) Average of fresh cynomolgus green cones. (c) Average of fixed cynomolgus green cones. (d) Average of cynomolgus "anomalous" green cones (fixed only).

Blue Cones

A total of 8 blue cones were measured: 5 in fresh cynomolgus retinae and 3 in fixed cynomolgus preparations. Of these, only three of the fresh records were suitable for detailed analysis. The λ_{max} of this average was 429 ± 4 nm, and the half-bandwidth was 141 THz. The mean transverse absorbance was

0.022. Figure 7a shows an example of a record from a typical blue cone. Figure 7b shows the average of all three cones fitted with a template curve.

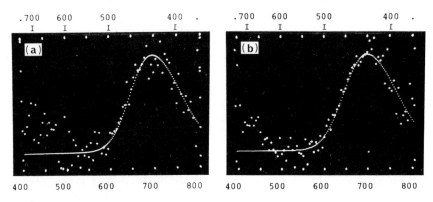

FIG. 7   (a) Individual fresh cynomolgus blue-cone spectrum. (b) Average of fresh cynomolgus blue-cone records.

A number of structures in the primate retina were found to contain non-bleachable pigments absorbing in the short-wave region of the spectrum. The hemoglobin of readily identifiable erythrocytes is optically dense and has a characteristic main absorption at 414 nm. The cytochrome C of mitochondria which are densely packed at the distal end of photoreceptor inner segments also has a well-known absorbance spectrum peaking at about 415 nm. Other components of the respiratory chain also peak in this region, so that the mitochondrial peak is considerably broader than that of cytochrome, and thus more nearly resembles a visual pigment. In order to demonstrate that a pigment absorbing in the short-wave region of the spectrum is in fact a visual pigment, it must not only possess a characteristic shape, but it must also be shown to be bleachable. An example of a blue cone pigment is shown in Fig. 8.

Figure 8a shows a fresh cynomolgus blue cone measured by Dr F. I. Harosi on his dichroic microspectrophotometer. Figure 8b shows a bleaching difference record obtained from the same cone. Figure 8c shows a spectrum from the same cell taken after the bleach.

Discussion

Four major classes of photoreceptors were encountered in the macaque retina as summarized in Table 1. The fixation procedure did not appear significantly to distort the main peak of the pigment spectra, although optical scattering in the glutaraldehyde-fixed material tended to be greater than in fresh retinae. Although we obtained no rhesus green cone spectra suitable for quantitative study, the best rhesus green cone spectra exhibited parameters similar to those

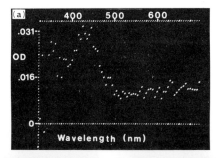

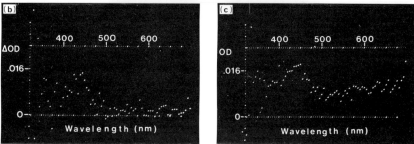

FIG. 8 (a) Individual fresh cynomolgus blue cone record. (b) Bleaching difference record from the same cone. (c) Post bleach measurement of same cell.

of the cynomolgus monkey. We have as yet found no blue cones in the rhesus material, but another investigator in our laboratory has encountered one rhesus blue cone with λ_{max} of 430 nm (Harosi, 1982). Within the limits of our present data base the photopigments of rhesus and cynomolgus monkeys appear to be similar.

Our inference of cross-species similarity is supported by the results of previous studies. Table 2 summarizes previous MSP data on primate rods and cones and compares it with the results of the present study.

Early axial MSP studies on human and rhesus retinae in the 1960s provided the first indications that (within the limits of the techniques employed and the small samples obtained) there were no systematic differences between the two species. However, as Liebman (1972) pointed out, the estimates of λ_{max} provided by those early studies were probably no more accurate than ± 20 nm. More recent measurements over the last four years have succeeded in substantially reducing experimental errors in measurement, and as yet have revealed no systematic differences between the visual pigments of rhesus and cynomolgus monkeys. Bowmaker, Dartnall, Lythgoe and Mollon (1978) measured a sample of 25 rods and 82 cones in rhesus monkey and found values for λ_{max} to be 502 ± 2.5, 565 ± 2.5 and 536 ± 3.5 for rods, red cones, and

TABLE 1   Summary of macaque photoreceptor pigments found in the present study

Receptor type	Rhesus Fresh	Rhesus Fixed	Cynomolgus Fresh	Cynomolgus Fixed
Rods				
max (nm)	503 ± 2		503 ± 2	
Bandwidth				
(THz)	118		129	
(cm^{-1})	3929 ± 300		4296 ± 300	
number	5		5	
Red cones				
max (nm)		564 ± 3	568 ± 2	565 ± 2
Bandwidth				
(THz)		111	115	121
(cm^{-1})		3696 ± 300	3830 ± 175	4029 ± 275
number		5	7	6
Green cones type 1				
max (nm)			532 ± 2	532 ± 5
Bandwidth				
(THz)			125	119
(cm^{-1})			4163 ± 100	3963 ± 250
number			11	3
Green cones type 2				
max (nm)				543 ± 4
Bandwidth				
(THz)				109
(cm^{-1})				3630 ± 200
number				8
Blue cones				
max (nm)			429 ± 4	
Bandwidth				
(THz)			141	
(cm^{-1})			4695 ± 250	
number			3	

and green cones. No blue cones were encountered in their original sample. Bowmaker, Dartnall and Mollon (1980) examined a sample of 12 rods and 38 cones from cynomolgus monkey and found values of λ_{max} to be 500 ± 1.6 nm, 567 ± 6.1 nm, 533 ± 3.9 nm and 415 nm for rods, red cones, green cones and blue cones. Except for the presence of blue cones, these estimates do not differ significantly from those for rhesus visual pigments. Comparing these results with those of the present study we find general agreement on the major classes of visual pigments of these Old World primate species and humans.

TABLE 2 Summary of MSP Data on λ_{max} of primate rods and cones

Method	Species	Rod	Red cone	Green cone	Blue cone	Reference
Axial (patch)	human and rhesus		565 565	535 527		Brown and Wald (1963)
Axial (single)	human and rhesus		570	535	445	Marks, Dobelle and MacNichol (1964)
Axial (single)	human and rhesus		577	540	450	MacNichol (1964)
Axial (single)	human	505	555	525	450	Brown and Wald (1964)
Axial (single)	human		565	529	440	Wald and Brown (1965)
Sonicated foveal suspension	rhesus		573	526		Murray (1968)
Axial and transverse	human and rhesus	498	575–580	535	440	Liebman (1972)
Transverse (single)	rhesus	502 ± 2.5	565 ± 2.5	536 ± 3.5		Bowmaker, Dartnall, Lythgoe and Mollon (1978)
Transverse (single)	cynomolgus	500 ± 1.6	567 ± 6.1	533 ± 3.9	415	Bowmaker, Dartnall and Mollon (1980)
Transverse (single)	human	498 ± 3.3	563 ± 4.7	534 ± 3.7	420 ± 4.7	Bowmaker and Dartnall (1980)
Transverse (single)	cynomolgus	502.5 ± 2	567.5 ± 2	531.8 ± 2 (543 ± 4)[a]	429 ± 3.5	Present study
Transverse (single)	rhesus	503.4 ± 2	564.4 ± 3			Present study

a Anomalous green cones.

Spectral Bandwidths

Dartnall (1953) noted that the absorption spectra of visual pigments became narrower as the λ_{max} shifted to the long-wave region of the spectrum. He showed that they have nearly similar shapes if plotted on a frequency scale, and provided a nomogram based on rhodopsin. The averages of goldfish cones published by Marks (1963, 1965) plotted with points calculated by the Dartnall nomogram show clearly that the blue-pigment curve is too broad to fit the nomogram, the green curve fits well and the red curve is too narrow. Liebman and Entine (1968) specifically studied the question. They showed that at both the long- and short-wave ends of the spectrum, the measured spectra of dehydroretinal-based visual pigments deviated significantly from the nomogram. From the accumulated evidence, Ebrey and Honig (1977) showed that for both retinal-based pigments and dehydroretinal-based pigments, bandwidth expressed on a reciprocal-wavelength scale (cm^{-1}) increased systematically as ($1/\lambda_{max}$) increased. Our results for the four classes of macaque visual pigments span a considerable range of λ_{max} and can be used to test this relation in primates as shown in Fig. 9.

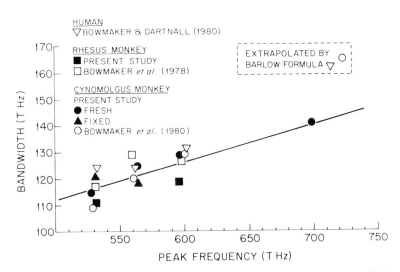

FIG. 9   Bandwidth of primate pigments as functions of λ_{max} (both in THz).

Figure 9 shows bandwidth as a function of λ_{max} when both are plotted on frequency axes. The estimates of bandwidths obtained from the template curves fitted to our data are shown as filled symbols. The solid line drawn through the data represents a least-square linear regression fit to the data of the present study; it has a correlation coefficient of 0.88. To a good approximation, our data indicate a linear relation between bandwidth and frequency.

For comparison, estimates of the bandwidths for the primate data obtained by Dartnall and his colleagues (Bowmaker *et al.*, 1978; Bowmaker *et al.*, 1980; Bowmaker and Dartnall, 1980) are shown as open symbols. For rod, red cone and green cone pigments these estimates were obtained from the text or read from the graphs as necessary. In the case of the blue cones, where the necessary data points on the short-wave limb of the curve were missing, the estimates were obtained by extrapolation from the published data using the $\lambda^{-0.25}$ relation proposed by Barlow (1982). This extrapolation is conservative; a simple linear extrapolation yields a value of about 175 THz.

For the rod, red cone and green cone visual pigments, the two sets of data are interspersed, suggesting (within the limits of experimental variability) that both macaque and human visual pigments have the same bandwidths. For the blue cone visual pigment there is a considerable difference in the estimates. Other estimates of vertebrate A1 blue cone pigments lie at an intermediate location near 150 THz (Harosi, 1975).

Anomalous Visual Pigments

On the basis of psychophysical evidence, a number of researchers have suggested the existence of different classes of cone pigments that differ only slightly in their λ_{max} and bandwidth (Alpern and Moeller, 1977). This means that an individual who would not be diagnosed as color-defective by standard screening tests such as the Farnsworth-Munsell 100-hue test may have in his retina red or green cone pigments that differ from the pigments of normal trichromats. Indeed, sensitive *in vivo* measures of the ratio of red and green absorptances such as the Rayleigh match can disclose minor differences between the color perceptions of such observers and normals. In the case of the blue cones our sample is too small to indicate the existence of subpopulations (see discussion on blue cones) but for the other receptors the samples are of sufficient size that large subpopulations could be discerned.

Anomalous Green Cones

There was no direct evidence for the existence of any anomalous pigments until Bowmaker *et al.* (1978) found a clear bimodal distribution in their sample of 19 green rhesus cones. The majority of cones clustered around 534 nm, but a second group clustered around 541–542 nm. No such bimodal distribution was evident in their distribution for rhesus red cones. We too, found strong evidence for the existence of anomalous green pigments, but in our case the anomalous records were obtained from a cynomolgus retina (Fig. 10). Our green cones λ_{max} values span 20 nm from 528 nm to 551 nm but the majority of the cones cluster near 532 nm. If the major peak is considered to represent a single subpopulation and the distribution beyond 537 a second subpopulation, then the second group is centered around 543 nm, close to the mean reported by Bowmaker *et al.* (1978) for rhesus anomalous green cones. Our anomalous recordings were obtained from a fixed retina, but in view of the concordance between fixed and fresh λ_{max} values in other cases (including normal green cones), the anomalous green cones were probably not a fixation artifact. All these curves passed our analytical selection procedure and were, in our opinion, relatively free of measurement errors. These data thus support the conclusion of Bowmaker *et al.* (1978) that there exist anomalous green pigments in macaques.

Anomalous Red Cones

Bowmaker *et al.* (1980) found that their distribution of λ_{max} values for red cones in cynomolgus spanned 21 nm, a far greater range than might be expected from experimental errors in measurement. In a double-blind study of a squirrel monkey whose Rayleigh match indicated a red–green anomaly, Jacobs, Bowmaker and Mollon (1981) found a clear bimodal distribution in the values for the red cones. One cluster centered at 568 nm and a second cluster centered at 552 nm. Clearly, since our study did not include any individuals shown to be color-anomalous, our data are not directly comparable with those of Jacobs *et al.*, but we believe that some of our results are pertinent to the question of variation in cone pigments.

As described earlier in Results and as illustrated in Fig. 4, distortion of absorbance spectra by scattering and focusing problems can shift the apparent λ_{max} of such spectra significantly. We have chosen a series of red-cone records to illustrate this point, but the same types of errors can affect spectra from all cone types. Had we not applied rigorous selection criteria to our sample of recordings from red cones, we might well have reported the existence of two red-cone populations, rather than one. We certainly would have reported a much larger variation in measured red-cone pigment λ_{max}, and would have ascribed that variation to actual differences among cells, rather than to errors in measurement. We therefore feel that careful scrutiny of all records analyzed is essential to any discussion of variation in visual pigment. The overall quality of records analyzed is clearly as important as the number of records taken.

Blue Cones

Previous axially-measured bleaching-difference spectra of three human blue cones gave λ_{max} values of 445 nm (Marks *et al.*, 1964), 450 nm (Brown and Wald, 1964) and 440 nm (Wald and Brown, 1965). More recent transverse absorbance spectra gave λ_{max} values of 420 nm and 412 nm for the cynomolgus

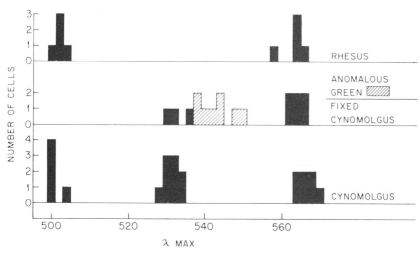

FIG. 10   Histogram for λ_{max} values of rods, green and red cones.

monkey (Bowmaker *et al.*, 1980) and 415 nm, 422 nm and 424 nm for humans (Bowmaker and Dartnall, 1980). Our three measurements yielded values of 430 nm, 430 nm and 426 nm (Harosi also obtained 430 nm for 2 cones). The early data obtained by differential bleaching probably *overestimated* the value of λ_{max} owing to transient photoproducts. Additionally, the low axial absorbances indicated that the measuring beams in the early studies were not perfectly aligned with the axis of the outer-segment, so the results may also exhibit distortions due to optical factors.

The results obtained by Dartnall and his colleagues, on the other hand, may *underestimate* the peak of the blue-cone spectrum because of light scattering that increases rapidly toward the short-wave end of the spectrum. This scattering cancels out in a bleaching-difference spectrum. If we assume that the blue-cone spectrum published by Bowmaker and Dartnall (1980) is typical of their data on this cell type, the significant amount of scattering not removed by the subtraction of light scattered by other components of the receptor than visual pigment would significantly shift the apparent λ_{max} in the short-wave direction. A reanalysis of this record which removes an estimated scattering function from the curve shown (Bowmaker and Dartnall, 1980, Fig. 1), suggests that the actual λ_{max} could be 10 to 15 nm in the long-wave direction from that reported.

Additionally, estimates of blue-cone spectral sensitivity have been made from psychophysical measurements which take into account the optical filtering of the lens and spectral broadening due to self-screening. These estimates do not predict the existence of a blue-cone pigment absorbing maximally around 415 nm, but rather a pigment with maximal absorbance near 430 nm (Smith and Pokorny, 1975; Ebrey and Honig, 1977; Boynton, 1979).

Conclusion

Clearly, although we feel we have made considerable progress in describing the visual pigments of primate rods and red- and green-sensitive cones (Fig. 11), many more experiments are needed to clarify the properties of blue-receptor populations and anomalous red and green receptors.

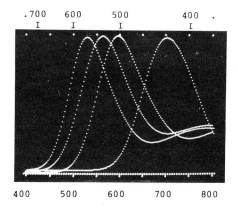

FIG. 11   Visual pigment templates generated to fit cynomolgus rod and cone pigment averages obtained in our recent experiments.

It is our firm belief that the kind of rigorous selection criteria we have presented here must be used to screen out misleading distortions in absorbance spectra. Numerous problems plague MSP studies of small receptors including scatter, focusing difficulties, floating debris from the pigment epithelium, wandering red blood cells, and mitochondria containing high concentrations of respiratory pigments. Without critical screening of records during analysis, spectra obtained from the narrow, often deteriorating outer segments of primate and human cones can easily mislead us into overestimating both cell-to-cell and inter-individual variations in visual pigments, and may also cause consistent errors in estimations of λ_{max}. Although existing fixation techniques are not totally free from problems, it is our hope that they will increase access to primate and human retinae from individuals with documented visual anomalies and deficiencies. In any case, we are rapidly approaching the point where we will be able to examine the manner in which photoreceptor responses and retinal circuitry combine sufficiently to understand the basic mechanisms upon which color perception is based.

Acknowledgements

Support was obtained from a grant from the National Eye Institute and from the Rowland Foundation and other non-governmental sources. Some of our best data were obtained by Mr Steven L. Goodman. We thank Dr F. I. Harosi for providing us with three unpublished records.

References

Alpern, M. and Moeller, J. (1977). The red and green cone visual pigments of deuteranomalous trichromacy. *J. Physiol., Lond.* **266**, 647–675.

Barlow, H. B. (1982). What causes trichromacy? A theoretical analysis using comb-filtered spectra. *Vision Res.* **22**, 635–643.

Bowmaker, J. K. and Dartnall, H. J. A. (1980). Visual pigments of rods and cones in a human retina. *J. Physiol., Lond.* **298**, 501–511.

Bowmaker, J. K. and Mollon, J. D. (1980). Primate microspectrophotometry and its implications for colour deficiencies. In *Colour Vision Deficiencies V* (ed. Verriest, G.), pp. 61–64.

Bowmaker, J. K., Dartnall, H. J. A. and Mollon, J. D. (1980). Microspectrophotometric demonstration of four classes of photoreceptor in an Old World primate, *Macaca fascicularis. J. Physiol., Lond.* **298**, 131–143.

Bowmaker, J. K., Dartnall, H. J. A., Lythgoe, J. N. and Mollon, J. D. (1978). The visual pigments of rods and cones in the Rhesus Monkey, *Macaca mulatta. J. Physiol., Lond.* **274**, 329–348.

Boynton, R. M. (1979). *Human color vision.* Holt, Rinehart and Winston, New York.

Brown, P. K. and Wald, G. (1964). Visual pigments in single rods and cones of the human retina. *Science* **144**, 45–51.

Dartnall, H. J. A. (1953). The interpretation of spectral sensitivity curves. *Brit. med. Bull.* **9**, 24–30.

Dobelle, W. H., Marks, W. B. and MacNichol, E. F. Jr. (1969). Visual pigment density in single primate foveal cones. *Science* **166**, 1508–1510.

Ebrey, T. G. and Honig, B. (1977). New wavelength dependent visual pigment nomograms. *Vision Res.* **17**, 147–151.

Hanaoka, T. and Fujimoto, K. (1957). Absorption spectrum of a single cone in carp retina. *Jpn. J. Physiol.* **7**, 276–285.

Harosi, F. I. (1971). *Frog rhodopsin* in situ: *orientational and spectral changes in the chromophores of isolated retinal rod cells.* PhD Thesis. The Johns Hopkins University, Baltimore, Maryland.

Harosi, F. I. (1975a). Absorption spectra and linear dichroism of some amphibian photoreceptors. *J. Gen. Physiol.* **66**, 357–382.

Harosi, F. I. (1975b). Microspectrophotometry: The technique and some of its pitfalls. In *Vision in fishes* (ed. Ali, M. A.), pp. 43–54. Plenum Press, New York.

Harosi, F. I. (1976). Spectral relations of cone pigments in goldfish. *J. Gen. Physiol.* **68**, 65–80.

Harosi, F. I. (1982). Recent results from single-cell microspectrophotometry: Cone pigments in frog, fish and monkey. *Color Research and Application* **7**, 135–141.

Harosi, F. I. and MacNichol, E. F. Jr. (1974). Visual pigments of goldfish cones; spectral properties and dichroism. *J. Gen. Physiol.* **63**, 279.

Jacobs, G. H., Bowmaker, J. K. and Mollon, J. D. (1981). Behavioural and microspectrophotometric measurements of colour vision in monkeys. *Nature* **292**, 541–543.

Levine, J. S. and MacNichol, E. F. Jr (1979). Visual pigments in teleost fishes: Effects of habitat, microhabitat, and behavior on visual system evolution. *Sensory Processes* **3**, 95–131.

Levine, J. S., Goodman, S. L. and MacNichol, E. F. Jr (1981). Cone pigments: Aldehyde fixation for microspectrophotometry. *Inv. Ophthalmol. Vis. Sci. Suppl.* **20**, 104.

Liebman, P. A. (1972). Microspectrophotometry of photoreceptors. In *Handbook of Sensory Physiology, Vol. VII/1* (ed. Dartnall, H. J. A.), pp. 481–528. Springer, Berlin.

Liebman, P. A. and Entine, G. (1964). Sensitive low-light-level microspectrophotometer: detection of photosensitive pigments of retinal cones. *J. opt. Soc. Am.* **54**, 1451–1459.

Liebman, P. A. and Entine, G. (1968). Visual pigments of frog and tadpole (*Rana pipiens*). *Vision Res.* **8**, 761–775.

Loew, E. R. and Lythgoe, J. N. (1978). The ecology of cone pigments in teleost fishes. *Vision Res.* **18**, 715–722.

MacNichol, E. F. Jr (1964). Retinal mechanisms of color vision. *Vision Res.* **4**, 119–133.

MacNichol, E. F. Jr (1978). A photon-counting microspectrophotometer for the study of single vertebrate photoreceptor cells. In *Frontiers in Visual Science* (eds Cool, S. J. and Smith, E. L.), pp. 194–208. Springer, New York.

MacNichol, E. F. Jr, Feinberg, R. and Harosi, F. I. (1973). Colour discrimination processes in the retina. In *Colour '73: Proceedings of the 2nd Congress of the International Colour Association*, pp. 191–251. Adam Hilger, London.

Marks, W. B. (1963). *Difference spectra of visual pigments in goldfish*. PhD Dissertation, Dept of Biophysics, Johns Hopkins University, Baltimore.

Marks, W. B. (1965) Visual pigments of single goldfish cones. *J. Physiol., Lond.* **178**, 14–32.

Marks, W. B., Dobelle, W. H. and MacNichol, E. F. Jr (1964). Visual pigments of single primate cones. *Science* **143**, 1181–1183.

Murray, G. C. (1968). *Visual pigment multiplicity in cones of the primate fovea*. PhD Dissertation, Johns Hopkins University, Baltimore, Md.

Smith, V. C. and Pokorny, J. (1975). Spectral sensitivity of the foveal cone photopigments between 400 and 500 nm. *Vision Res.* **15**, 161–171.

Wald, G. and Brown, P. K. (1965). Human color vision and color blindness. *Cold Spring Harb. Symp. quant. Biol.* **30**, 345–361.

Wyszecki, G. and Stiles, W. S. (1967). *Color Science*. Wiley, New York.

Variations in Color Vision Among Nonhuman Primates

G. H. JACOBS

Introduction

In the face of the immense literature on human color vision it is startling to discover how little we know of color vision in our fellow primates. Of course, there are good reasons for this disparity. Not the least of these are the obvious difficulties encountered in studies of color vision with subjects who are sometimes slow to appreciate and respond to simple psychophysical instructions. Clearly, assessments of color vision in nonhuman primates are not for the impatient. Despite the impediments to its acquisition, knowledge of color vision in nonhuman primates could prove most useful. On the practical side, understanding of their color vision could be exploited in studies of color vision mechanisms that are difficult in our own species. But beyond that, knowledge about color vision in our close relatives might also lead to some insights into the evolution of this capacity, and perhaps to some understanding of the utility of color vision in the context of normal behavior.

Over the past few years my laboratory has been engaged in the testing of color vision in nonhuman primates. As a result, we believe we have a good picture of color vision in one New World species, and outline sketches for two other species. The most interesting aspect of these results is the discovery of a significant degree of within-species variation in color vision in New World primates. The intent of this paper is to present a summary view of variations in color vision among and within nonhuman primate species. Of necessity the coverage is quite selective in some respects. It also lacks an extensive bibliographic justification, but that is available in a recently published review (Jacobs, 1981).

Before embarking on a discussion of studies of nonhuman color vision, it is worth a reminder that there is an almost universal tendency in such experiments to use the human color vision types as the basis for classification of nonhuman subjects. That tendency is not resisted here. Even so, however, it is well to keep in mind that the human color vision categories may not always be the best descriptors for nonhuman color vision.

Color Vision in Old World Monkeys and Apes

The generalization usually offered about color vision in the Old World monkeys and apes is that the modal color vision of all species is identical to that of our species. This generalization had its origin in Grether's (1939, 1940) pioneering studies of color vision in chimpanzees and macaque monkeys. Despite a few inconsistencies in the results of these experiments, Grether found that all of the representatives of both of these genera performed in color tests much like human trichromats who were equivalently tested. Since these early experiments there have been several other investigations of color vision in macaque monkeys (see Jacobs, 1981). None have provided any persuasive evidence for disputing the claim that macaque color vision is very similar to that of the normal human trichromat.

Granted that the color vision of the macaque monkey and the average human is very similar, is it possible to go further and conclude that they are identical? What is perhaps the most discerning color vision comparison between the two genera so far available is given in Fig. 1. Shown there are results from a Rayleigh match determination in which subjects were tested to find what red/green mixtures were indiscriminable from a standard yellow (DeValois, Morgan, Polson, Mead and Hull, 1974). The curves in Fig. 1 plot asymptotic performance in that test. The points of poorest discrimination represent the Rayleigh match locations, and it is clear that they are very similar for macaques and humans equivalently tested. However, the average macaque monkey in this test made Rayleigh matches shifted slightly greenward from that of the average human. Note also that the entire function for the monkey is displaced toward the green side; it is not just that the monkeys made more errors around the same match point.

Whether this slight variation in Rayleigh matching between humans and macaques shown in Fig. 1 is a significant finding or not is uncertain. However, a further indication that it may be a consistent one can be seen in results obtained by Oyama, Furusaka and Kito (1979). The Rayleigh matches they obtained from four macaque monkeys also appear to be shifted slightly toward the green relative to the matches made by normal human trichromats. This possible difference is interesting in light of recent microspectrophotometric

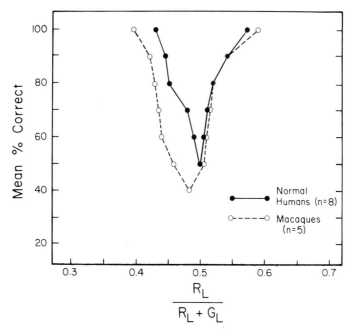

FIG. 1 Performances of macaque monkeys and normal human trichromats in a Rayleigh-type discrimination. The plotted points are asymptotic discrimination levels in a test where subjects were required to discriminate various mixtures of red and green light from a standard yellow light. The points of poorest discrimination indicate the locations of the Rayleigh matches. Data replotted from DeValois *et al.* (1974).

measurements of cone photopigments in the two genera: whereas the cone pigments for various macaque monkeys all show absorbance peaks at 415–420, 535 or 565 nm (Bowmaker, Dartnall, Lythgoe and Mollon, 1978; Bowmaker, Dartnall and Mollon, 1980), the same three classes of cone pigments measured in human retinas are all peak-shifted slightly towards the shorter wavelengths (Mollon, 1982; Dartnall, Bowmaker and Mollon, this volume).

Beyond the macaque monkeys, however, the evidence supporting the claim that Old World monkeys and apes are normally trichromatic is limited. This is quite simply because very few other animals in this group have ever been examined. The results from the species that have been tested do not appear to differ from those reported for the macaques. So the claim for normal trichromacy in Old World monkeys and apes rests on good studies of several macaque species, Grether's results on chimpanzees, very small numbers of tests on a few other representative species, and an absence of any evidence counter to the standard conclusion.

Since there are not extensive data on many Old World species, it is clearly premature to discuss seriously the possibility of within-species variations in this group. Nevertheless, if these species are normally trichromatic, like our own, one wonders if there might also be minority populations within these species analogous to human color defectives. No evidence for any such within-species variations has yet been published. However, the total number of macaques whose color vision has been thoroughly examined is relatively small (perhaps about twenty individuals), and if the frequency of a defect is low it could easily have escaped detection. At least for macaques it would seem that if within-species variations in color vision exist, the frequency of such variations is not likely to be greater than it is in our own species.

Color Vision in New World Monkeys

Unlike the studies of color vision on Old World monkeys and apes, which presently appear to lead to a consensus conclusion, research on color vision in the New World monkeys is remarkable for its lack of a consistent outcome. There is reason to believe that this inconsistency can now be understood.

History

Informative research on color vision in New World monkeys dates from Grether's (1939) investigation of the *Cebus* monkey. From the discovery of an apparent neutral point, Grether concluded that *Cebus* has dichromatic color vision, probably protanopia. A later study of an additional animal led to the same conclusion (Malmo and Grether, 1947). However, studies by Gunter, Feigenson and Blakeslee (1965) and by DeValois and Morgan (see Jacobs, 1981) led to a quite contrary conclusion. DeValois and Morgan's experiment indicated that *Cebus* monkeys are protanomalous trichromats, while Gunter *et al.* reported that some of their monkeys performed like protan humans, others like deutan humans, and still others made errors in color discriminations that did not permit a classification of their color vision.

Investigations of another common cebid species, the squirrel monkey (*Saimiri sciureus*), also produced inconsistent outcomes. By virtue of their inabilities to discriminate between some pairs of spectral stimuli, Miles (1958) concluded that squirrel monkeys are protanopic dichromats. Subsequent tests by Jacobs (1963) and by DeValois and Morgan (1974), however, did not support this claim. Rather, based on the results of wavelength discrimination, saturation discrimination and Rayleigh match determinations, these investigators were led to the conclusion that squirrel monkeys are protanomalous trichromats.

Finally, in his original investigation, Grether (1939) had also tested a third New World species, the spider monkey (*Ateles*). This animal had very acute hue discrimination, good enough to indicate that its color vision was a normal trichromacy.

Although this listing is not complete, it illustrates the lack of consistent conclusions about color vision in New World monkeys. These studies indicate that these monkeys are neither monochromatic nor tritanopic, but beyond that all of the other major categories of human color defective vision have been suggested as appropriate descriptors of their color vision.

Research on the Squirrel Monkey

Experimentation on the squirrel monkey (*Saimiri sciureus*) has involved making detailed measurements of increment thresholds and color discriminations. The impetus for this research was my discovery of substantial between-animal variations made during single unit recordings from the lateral geniculate nucleus of this species (Jacobs, 1983a), and the consequent suspicion that this variability might reflect individual variations in visual capacity. Psychophysical measurements have been completed on more than fifty individuals.

The presence of within-species variation in the squirrel monkey has been established by measurements of increment sensitivity to 540 and 640 nm lights added to achromatic adapting backgrounds. The details of the experimental paradigm are given elsewhere (Jacobs, 1983b). The essential result is summarized in Fig. 2 which plots differences in log threshold to the two test wavelengths for squirrel monkeys and humans equivalently tested. It can be seen that, in contrast to the small spread in threshold differences among humans, there is a very large variation in threshold differences among squirrel monkeys − individual values cover a range of nearly 1.5 log units. It is also apparent that the variation among monkeys is gender-related. Many of the female monkeys had small 540−640 nm threshold differences, values not significantly different from the corresponding human results. On the other hand, all of the male monkeys and a minority (*ca.* 30%) of the female monkeys showed much greater threshold differences. The differences between these two groups are highly significant. Note also in Fig. 2 that the two groups of subjects differ in the distribution of their threshold differences: the sensitive female monkeys show relatively little spread while the distribution for the insensitive monkeys is much broader and, perhaps, suggestive of the presence of some subgroups.

Several direct tests of color vision confirm that the variations in visual sensitivity among squirrel monkeys are paralleled by striking variations in color vision. Individual squirrel monkeys may have either dichromatic or trichromatic color vision, and within these two broad categories several distinct subtypes may be discerned. At the present it appears that there are at least five different color vision phenotypes represented in this species.

Figure 3 shows the results from two color vision tests run on five squirrel monkeys, each animal there representing a different color vision phenotype. The wavelength discrimination functions for the two monkeys shown in the

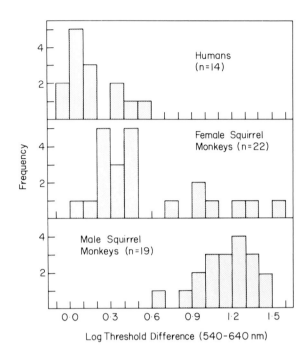

FIG. 2 Summary of increment threshold measurements made on squirrel monkeys in a behavioral test situation. Plotted are the differences in threshold for 540 and 640 nm test lights. These stimuli were presented as flashes of light added to an achromatic adapting field. The top panel shows results obtained from a group of normal human trichromats who were tested in the same situation as the monkeys.

top panel of Fig. 3 have the twin minima and general form associated with trichromatic color vision, although one of these animals (S7) was poorer at discriminating among the long wavelengths than the other monkey (S2). Results from an anomaloscope test are shown in the bottom panel. Both S2 and S7 made discrete anomaloscope matches, thus verifying that their color vision is trichromatic. However, the matches for the two were quite different. S2 required more green light in the red + green = yellow match than did normal human trichromats, while S7 required significantly more red light. In terms of the usual human classification scheme, S2 would be judged a mildly deuteranomalous trichromat, S7 a protanomalous trichromat. The middle panel in Fig. 2 shows wavelength discrimination functions for the other three animals (S5, S22, S31). Their functions are all very similar, each having the single minimum near 500 nm that is characteristic of the dichromatic observer. The dichromacy of these monkeys is verified by the results of the anomaloscope test shown in the bottom panel — all accepted the full range of mixture

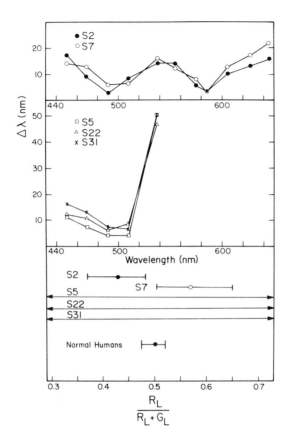

FIG. 3 Results from behavioral tests of color vision for five squirrel monkeys. The top two panels show wavelength discrimination functions for each animal. The monkeys whose results are shown in the top panel are trichromats; those whose results are plotted in the middle panel are dichromats. The bottom panel summarizes the results of a Rayleigh match determination in which monkeys were examined for their abilities to discriminate various mixtures of red (625 nm) and green (536 nm) lights from a standard yellow light (585 nm). The average Rayleigh match for 41 normal human trichromats is indicated by the solid circle; the total range of matches obtained from this group is indicated by the horizontal line. For S2 and S7 the symbols indicate the midpoints of the red/green mixture range which was indiscriminable from the yellow, while the horizontal lines show for each animal the mixture range over which successful discrimination was impossible. None of the other three monkeys (S5, S22, S31) was able to discriminate any red/green mixtures from yellow.

combinations. Although S5, S22, and S31 behaved nearly identically in the color tests, we believe their dichromacies are distinctive. The basis for this conclusion is the substantial differences among these monkeys in the increment threshold test. Since the color vision tests indicated these animals to be dichromatic then, by the conventional argument, they have only a single class of photopigment in the green to red portion of the spectrum, and hence if that pigment is the same for all three animals then their threshold differences to 540 and 640 nm lights should also be identical. In fact, these values were greatly different: 0.66 log units for S31, 0.91 log units for S5, and 1.3 log units for S22. We conclude that each of these animals has a different photopigment in the middle to long wavelength portion of the spectrum. On the basis of these threshold differences, and consideration of the cone photopigments believed to underlie human dichromacy, it could be argued that S31 is like a human deuteranope, S22 is like a human protanope, and S5 has dichromatic color vision that does not correspond to any of the usual human dichromatic categories.

Although it is not yet possible to specify the relative representations of the five color vision phenotypes in a large population of squirrel monkeys, or indeed even be confident that there are not still other distinct types remaining to be discovered, it is at least abundantly clear that substantial within-species variations in color vision and visual sensitivity are characteristic of the squirrel monkey. It is noteworthy that a recent project, involving microspectrophotometric measurements of the cone photopigments of squirrel monkeys whose color vision had been previously established, shows that these color vision variations are directly traceable to the types of cone photopigments found in the retinas of individual animals (Jacobs, Bowmaker and Mollon, 1981; Bowmaker, Mollon and Jacobs, this volume).

Spider Monkeys

I noted previously that the spider monkey (*Ateles*) had been identified by Grether (1939) as possessing excellent, trichromatic color vision. Recently, two spider monkeys have been examined in tests of color vision much like those used for the squirrel monkeys. We found that both of these animals had trichromatic color vision, but neither was exactly like the normal human trichromat nor were the two identical to each other (Blakeslee and Jacobs, 1982). Evidence justifying this conclusion is summarized in Fig. 4.

The wavelength discrimination functions for the two monkeys have those features typically associated with trichromatic color vision. Throughout most of the spectrum the results for the two animals are indistinguishable, except at the very longest wavelengths where A2 had clearly poorer color vision than A1. On the anomaloscope test (bottom panel, Fig. 3) the trichromacy of both subjects is apparent. By comparison with normal human trichromats, however, A1 can be classified as having a mild deuteranomaly while A2, displaced in the opposite direction, is protanomalous.

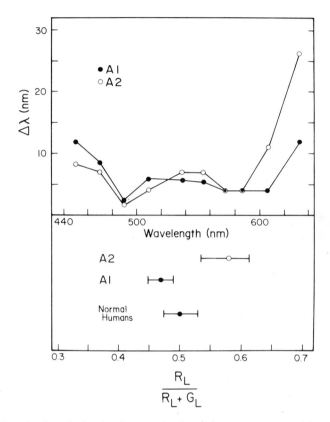

FIG. 4   Results from behavioral tests of color vision run on two spider monkeys. The top panel shows the results for wavelength discrimination tests while the bottom panel gives Rayleigh matches for the two monkeys and for normal human trichromats. The details for the Rayleigh match determinations are as explained in Fig. 2.

Platyrrhine Color Vision: Is Variability the Rule?

The earlier, contradictory results from experiments done to establish the nature of color vision in South American monkeys naturally led to the assumption that some of these results must be in error. Now, however, it is very clear in the case of the squirrel monkey, and strongly suggested for the spider monkey, that these species are characterized by widespread individual variations in color vision capacities. Other cebid species may be similar, and so it is possible to reach the happy conclusion that the earlier experiments which produced contradictory outcomes were in fact all correct; that each had sampled different subjects from among the possible color vision phenotypes characteristic of these species. Whether this also is the correct conclusion is not known, but the best present guess is that there are considerable within-species variations in color vision among the New World monkeys. It should be emphasized that although it is reasonable to suspect widespread within-species variations in color vision among South American monkeys, it seems unlikely that these variations will exactly mirror those seen among squirrel monkeys. Even with limited data some species differences may be discerned. Thus, although we have found individuals formally classifiable as deuteranomalous and protanomalous among both squirrel and spider monkeys, the spider monkeys have significantly keener color vision as judged by the fact that their wavelength difference thresholds are uniformly much smaller than those measured on squirrel monkeys.

Given the lack of critical data establishing its presence in many species, it is perhaps premature to address the question of why New World monkeys show significant individual variations in color vision. In terms of underlying mechanisms, measurements of cone photopigments in the squirrel monkey indicate the presence of three different classes of pigments absorbing maximally in the middle to long wavelengths (Jacobs, Bowmaker and Mollon, 1982). Two of these classes (with λ_{max} of 536 and 564 nm) appear very similar to the two classes of cone pigments routinely found in the retinas of Old World monkeys. The third class ($\lambda_{max} = 550$ nm) is unique. In accord with their variations in color vision, individual squirrel monkeys have either two of these pigments (536, 550 or 550, 564) or only one of them (either 536, 550 or 564). One might hazard the prediction that these same pigment classes, occurring singly or in combinations will also be found in the retinas of other South American monkeys.

The Question of Prosimian Color Vision

Not much is known about color vision in the third of the major primate groups, the *Prosimii* (Jacobs, 1981). On the argumentative grounds that this group might include those contemporary species that most closely resemble the common ancestors from which all present day primates have evolved, it is obviously of great interest to learn about their color vision. Most of the prosimians are nocturnal, and would therefore not be expected to have very highly developed color capacities. However, some lemur species are diurnal and thus provide an attractive target for investigation.

Two ring-tailed lemurs (*Lemur catta*) have recently been subjects in a series of color vision tests conducted in my laboratory (Blakeslee and Jacobs, in preparation). Although the sample size is smaller than ideal, we believe we have nevertheless obtained a reasonable impression of color vision in this species. It was, first of all, not difficult to show that these animals can make discriminations between equiluminant pairs of wavelengths, i.e., that they have some color vision. However, as judged by the size of the difference thresholds measured in a wavelength discrimination test, that color vision must be very poor indeed. Wavelength differences of 25 nm or more were routinely required to support successful discrimination, and these values did not change greatly as a function of spectral location. The absence of a spectral neutral point, and our ability to demonstrate differential chromatic adaptation in the green to red part of the spectrum convinced us that the lemur can be formally classified as trichromatic. However, by the usual standards, that trichromacy is not normal. In an anomaloscope match of $540 + 645 = 570$ nm, the lemurs both made matches that were displaced far to the red side relative to normal human trichromats tested in the same situation. We conclude that lemurs certainly do not have keen color vision (perhaps due to low cone densities), but in terms of formal classification they are most like protanomalous trichromats. Insofar as the lemur can be taken as representing prosimian color vision, it would appear that color vision among the prosimians is more closely akin to that seen in New World monkeys than that characteristic of the Old World monkeys.

Conclusions

Even this brief review should serve to convince the reader that there is much more to be learned about color vision in the nonhuman primates. The evidence suggests, in sum, that there is little variation in color vision among the Old World monkeys and apes. All these species appear to have acute color vision and to be trichromatic. The similarities in color vision among these species seem to reflect both a similar photopigment basis and similar neural processing. The question of whether the great similarity between the color vision of humans and Old World monkeys still allows for a slight (but discernable) difference was raised earlier. Results obtained from studies of color vision in prosimians indicate that their color vision is both qualitatively and quantitatively different from that of other Old World primates.

In contrast to the picture for the Old World monkeys, where consistency appears the rule, the present interpretation of results from New World monkeys indicates that there are substantial within-species variations in color vision. This variation is established for squirrel and spider monkeys, and appears very probable for *Cebus* monkeys. Whether the extent and nature of the variation within each species is the same is not known. This variation can be taken to suggest that contemporary South American monkeys may be representative of a different stage in the evolution of color vision systems than that seen in the Old World monkeys. Whether this is so or not, these animals provide a natural resource for investigating several fundamental questions about color vision, including the relationships between visual environment and color vision variation and the biological bases of color vision variations.

Acknowledgements

I thank Barbara Blakeslee for her helpful comments on the manuscript. This research was supported by the National Eye Institute (EY–02052).

References

Blakeslee, B. and Jacobs, G. H. (1982). Color vision in the spider monkey (*Ateles*). *Folia Primat.* **38**, 86–98.

Bowmaker, J. K., Dartnall, H. J. A., Lythgoe, J. N. and Mollon, J. D. (1978). The visual pigments of rods and cones in the rhesus monkey (*Macaca mulatta*). *J. Physiol.* **274**, 329–348.

Bowmaker, J. K., Dartnall, H. J. A. and Mollon, J. D. (1980). Microspectrophotometric demonstration of four classes of photoreceptor in an old world primate, *Macaca fascicularis*. *J. Physiol.* **298**, 131–143.

DeValois, R. L. and Morgan, H. C. (1974). Psychophysical studies of monkey vision. II. Squirrel monkey wavelength and saturation discrimination. *Vision Res.* **14**, 69–73.

DeValois, R. L., Morgan, H. C., Polson, M. C., Mead, W. R. and Hull, E. M. (1974). Psychophysical studies of monkey vision. I. Macaque luminosity and color vision tests. *Vision Res.* **14**, 53–67.

Grether, W. F. (1939). Color vision and color blindness in monkeys. *Comp. Psychol. Monogr.* **15**, 1–38.

Grether, W. F. (1940). Chimpanzee color vision. *J. Comp. Psychol.* **29**, 167–192.

Gunter, R., Feigenson, L. and Blakeslee, P. (1965). Color vision in the cebus monkey. *J. Comp. Physiol. Psychol.* **60**, 107–113.

Jacobs, G. H. (1963). Spectral sensitivity and color vision of the squirrel monkey. *J. Comp. Physiol. Psychol.* **56**, 616–621.

Jacobs, G. H. (1981). *Comparative Color Vision.* Academic Press, New York.

Jacobs, G. H. (1983a). Differences in spectral response properties of LGN cells in male and female squirrel monkeys. *Vision Res.* (In press).

Jacobs, G. H. (1983b). Within-species variations in visual capacity among squirrel monkeys (*Saimiri sciureus*): Sensitivity differences. *Vision Res.* **23**, 239–248.

Jacobs, G. H., Bowmaker, J. K. and Mollon, J. D. (1981). Behavioural and microspectrophotometric measurements of colour vision in monkeys. *Nature* **292**, 541–543.

Jacobs, G. H., Bowmaker, J. K. and Mollon, J. D. (1982). Colour vision variations in monkeys: Behavioural and microspectrophotometric measurements on the same individuals. *Documenta Ophthalmologica Proceedings Series* **33**, 269–280.

Malmo, R. B. and Grether, W. F. (1947). Further evidence of red blindness (protanopia) in cebus monkeys. *J. Comp. Physiol. Psychol.* **40**, 143–147.

Miles, R. C. (1958). Color vision in the squirrel monkey. *J. Comp. Physiol. Psychol.* **51**, 328–331.

Mollon, J. D. (1982). Color vision. *Ann. Rev. Psychol.* **33**, 41–85.

Oyama, T., Furusaka, T. and Kito, T. (1979). Color vision in men and animals. *Sci. Amer.* (Japanese edition), December, 98–110.

Kind and Intensity of Selection at the Colour Vision Loci

H. KALMUS

Our views on the evolution of colour vision and on the occurrence of deviant colour vision in human populations may need to be changed as a result of the recent discovery in a sample of squirrel monkeys (*Saimiri sciureus*) of five variant types. The individual differences in the monkeys are presumably genetic in origin and some of the variant types, in respect of their cone pigments and behavioural responses to colour, appear to resemble congenitally anomalous or dichromatic human observers (Jacobs, Bowmaker and Mollon, 1981; Jacobs, this volume; Bowmaker, Mollon and Jacobs, this volume). Time permits me to deal with only two questions: (1) How the genetical polymorphism – the coexistence of alleles at frequencies far above mutation rates – at the human colour vision loci is maintained, and (2) why the gene frequencies occurring at these loci differ between populations.

Complete answers to these questions require investigations of the physical nature and action of the mutational and selective processes implicated as well as calculations of the numerical effects various intensities of these processes might have on gene frequencies irrespective of their physical nature. Any consideration of the population genetics of colour blindness must start from two awkward facts: (1) Mutation rates at the colour vision loci cannot be measured because one can never be sure that an "isolated" occurrence of a colour blind man is the result of a freshly arisen mutation. (2) Selection against the sex-linked forms of colour blindness is too weak for changes to be directly measured in successive generations (Kalmus, 1965). Measuring changes in the force of selection are even further out of reach. As a consequence quite different explanations are possible to account for the incidence of the several types of deficient colour vision and for its global variations. Hypotheses may implicate only mutation rates, only selective forces, or a combination of both.

In the absence of selection the frequency of two alleles A_1 and A_2 at equilibrium are

$$m_1 = q_2$$
$$m_2 = q_1,$$

where m_1 is the mutation rate from A_1 to A_2, m_2 the rate of the "back mutation" from A_2 to A_1, q_1 the frequency of A_1, and q_2 the frequency of A_2. If m_1 is larger than m_2, A_2 will be the more frequent allele and vice versa. To maintain the frequency of the deuteranomaly gene at 4%, as found in European populations, would require a rate of mutation (back mutation) from deuteranomaly to normal 24 times as frequent as its opposite. To maintain the deuteranopia, protanopia and protanomaly genes, each at 1% frequency would require 99 times as many back mutations as their opposites. From what is known about mutations this is highly improbable.

Turning therefore to selection for an explanation, the most natural assumption is, that it operates in favour of the most frequent, the "normal" alleles.[1] This is usually implicit in previous explanations of the incidence of hereditary colour blindness and in particular in Post's (1962) hypothesis, accounting for the greater incidence of colour blindness among culturally advanced peoples, as compared with primitive gatherer-hunters. Post believes that the strong selection against the deficiency genes, which previously had kept these rare, became relaxed when people took to agriculture or a pastoral existence. Detection by colour of fruit, prey and predators became less vital with the change of subsistence; the colour blindness genes, formerly quickly eliminated, could then multiply.

Apart from a trivial error in Post's calculations (Kalmus, 1965), his hypothesis could be criticised on several grounds even before the recent findings by Jacobs *et al.* (1981): (1) The force of selection necessary to keep the frequency of the colour blindness genes near the mutation rates during the gatherer-hunter phase would have been unbelievably high −as high as that which until recently eliminated nearly all haemophilic men from procreation. Table 1 shows the disadvantages of the four sex-linked colour vision genes and of one of the genes responsible for haemophilia in present day conditions.

(2) The "relaxation of selection" hypothesis proceeds from the proposition that the gatherer-hunters from whom we derive were as free of colour blindness as Post claims are present day tribes at this cultural stage. For this there is no possibility of proof; furthermore Adam (1969) has shown that colour blindness exists in some such small tribes. Its absence in others may perhaps be due to a loss by chance of the rare alleles responsible for defects in colour vision in the small populations of such primitive tribes rather than to selection.

TABLE 1   Disadvantage $s = 3m/q$ of sex linked genes for maintaining them at frequency q; Mutation rate $m = 1:40,000$.

Gene	q	s
Deuteranomaly	0.04	3/1600
Deuteranopia	0.01	3/400
Protanopia	0.01	3/400
Protanomaly	0.01	3/400
Haemophilia	0.0001	3/4

On the other hand the great and consistent differences in the frequency of colour blindness between most large European and Asiatic samples – about 8% of the males – and most African and Amerindian samples, with about half that value, seem unlikely to be due to drift, but ought to be accounted for by differences in the forces of selection operating over hundreds of generations. The physical nature of these forces is anybody's guess. Also differences in mutation rates of the various populations cannot *a priori* be excluded. (3) It is by no means certain that the entire loss of fitness engendered by the colour blindness genes must be mediated by the most obvious manifestations, the losses in colour discrimination. Other –pleiotropic – effects of the genes, perhaps also affecting (increasing?) the fitness of heterozygotic females may enter into the gene equilibria.

In discussing the consequences, the discovery of the polymorphic colour vision of *Saimiri* might have for hypotheses of the evolution of colour blindness in man, I shall for the time being however accept the generally held notion that it is predominately the deficiency in colour discrimination which causes the loss of fitness; in other words that "nature" uses the same features when sorting out the colour blind hemizygotes and homozygotes as the ophthalmologist, and that other gene effects are of minor consequence.

But whether that is so or not, Post's assumption, that the colour blindness genes must have been much less frequent in our primitive past, is no longer tenable. On the contrary polymorphic colour vision, that is the coexistence in the population of several alleles at the colour vision loci at frequencies much higher than the mutation rate, might have been of long standing among our ancestors, possibly long before they could be considered anthropoids.

There is some indication (Jacobs; Bowmaker *et al.*, this volume) that Old World primates tend to have three kinds of cone pigments rather similar to those of normal human trichormats, while New World monkeys seem in this respect to be different and rather more variable. This would seem to indicate that in the phylogeny of primates colour vision polymorphism might have been prevalent in periods of species divergence. In any case we have now two species – man and *Saimiri* – in which such polymorphisms are manifestly present, and we can speculate, what sort of changes in habitat and habits might have altered the selective forces in favour of one or the other type of colour vision. When some early simians changed from nocturnal to diurnal activity, selection of the genes which control the cone pigments might have grown more intensive, gradually weeding out anything inferior to normal trichromacy. At a later stage perhaps a move from green, shady forest to open savannah might have again shifted the equilibrium at the colour vision loci. At present such speculations are rather insubstantial, because we do not know enough of the variability of colour vision among the primates. But one can hope that the application of modern microphotospectrometry, electrophysiology and psychophysics will soon provide more information, on which to base firmer hypotheses. Comparable studies, trying to relate the habitats and habits of a number of fish species have recently been summarized by Levine and MacNicol (1982). However, I feel that as a geneticist I must point out that all these evolutionary speculations depend on the differences in cone pigmentation and colour vision of nonhumans being indeed genetical. Proof of this by breeding experiments is as yet lacking.

Concluding this brief exposition it appears that we can be reasonably sure of only a few facts: (1) That man is not the only trichromatic primate, nor the only one to show polymorphisms of colour vision. (2) That the frequencies of the sex-linked forms of colour vision deficiency differ significantly between large samples of different populations. (3) That at present any reduction of fitness, if it exists, is so small as not to be measurable. Thus we do not know how stable the equilibria at the colour vision loci are, whether frequency changes there are reversible, what the past conditions have been, which lead to the different gene frequencies between the great groups of humanity. Finally we do not know whether urban life and industrialization have altered the selective pressures at the colour vision loci. The discovery of a second colour vision polymorphic primate species has not narrowed, but rather widened the scope for thinking about the evolution of colour vision and for further experimentation.

Note

1. This assumption need not always apply. A prey or predator cryptically adapted to hide from the normal eye of man, may be more easily discovered by some colour blind individuals, just as some forms of war time camouflage were more easily penetrated by such observers.

References

Adam, A. (1969). A further query on colour blindness and natural selection. *Soc. Biol.* **16**, 197–202.

Jacobs, G. H., Bowmaker, J. K. and Mollon, J. D. (1981). Behavioural and micro-spectrophotometric measurements of colour vision in monkeys. *Nature* **292**, 541–543.

Kalmus, H. (1965). *Diagnosis and Genetics of Defective colour vision.* Pergamon, Oxford.

Levine, J. S. and MacNichol, E. F. Jr (1982). Color vision in fishes. *Sci. American*, February 1982, 108–117.

Post, R. A. (1962). Population differences in red and green colour vision deficiencies; a review and a query on selection relaxation. *Eugen. Quart.* **9**, 131–146.

Microspectrophotometric Results for Old and New World Primates

J. K. BOWMAKER, J. D. MOLLON and G. H. JACOBS

Over the past few years we have been measuring, by microspectrophotometry, the absorbance spectra of the visual pigments of primates, from both the Old and the New World. The aims of these investigations were to establish with some precision the shape and spectral locations of the rod and cone visual pigments and to determine whether variations occur in the location of the peak sensitivities (λ_{max}) of these pigments either between species or within species. In the case of one species, *Saimiri sciureus*, we have been able to secure both behavioural and microspectrophotometric measurements from the same ten individual animals.

The microspectrophotometer is a modification of the instrument designed by P. A. Liebman for the former MRC Vision Unit at the University of Sussex (Liebman and Entine, 1964; Knowles and Dartnall, 1977). One beam is passed transversely through a receptor outer segment while a second beam, the reference beam, is passed through an adjacent area containing no cells. The dimensions of the beams could be adjusted to accommodate the dimensions of a particular cell, but were typically about 2 μm × 3 μm. To increase the proportion of light absorbed by the outer segments, the measurements were made with the *e*-vector of the beams perpendicular to the long axis of the outer segments. In the earlier measurements absorbance spectra were obtained by scanning from 700 to 400 nm and back to 700 nm, the double scan taking about 20 sec, and the output was displayed on an X−Y recorder. In the more recent measurements, after the addition of a DEC-MNC-11 laboratory computer, the monochromator was programmed to step from 700 to 390 nm in 2-nm steps and then to return making measurements at the interleaved wavelengths.

COLOUR VISION
ISBN 0 12 000000 0

The animals were obtained from a number of sources. Before enucleation they were either sedated with phencyclidine hydrochloride or narcotized with ketamine and then sacrificed with an overdose of pentabarbitone sodium. Measurements normally began within 1–2 hours after death, but in some cases not until 4–5 hours after death, depending on the source of the animal; measurements continued for up to twelve hours after death. The preparation of tissue has been described previously (Bowmaker, Dartnall and Mollon, 1980).

In the present paper we summarize data from three species of Old World monkey, two types of macaque, *Macaca mulatta* and *M. fascicularis* (Bowmaker, Dartnall, Lythgoe and Mollon, 1978; Bowmaker *et al.*, 1980), and the baboon, *Papio papio*; and from two species of New World monkey, the capuchin monkey, *Cebus apella* and the squirrel monkey, *Saimiri sciureus*.

In the case of the macaque species the absorbance spectra were analysed by first drawing by eye a smooth curve through the trace obtained from the cell and another through the baseline trace obtained by passing both beams through an adjacent, tissue-free area of the preparation. The difference between the two curves, sampled at 10 nm-intervals, was used to calculate an absorbance spectrum and from the latter the λ_{max} was estimated as described previously (Bowmaker *et al.*, 1980). The data from *P. papio* and the *S. sciureus* were obtained after the addition of the computer and were analysed slightly differently. From the stored data points at each nm, pairs of absorbances for adjacent wavelengths were first averaged. Each of a set of twenty such values on the long-wave limb (corresponding to 40 nm and to per cent absorbances in the range approximately 45–90%) was then referred to an appropriate nomogram to establish the λ_{max}; this operation amounts to finding where the nomogram must be placed on a wavelength abscissa to yield the absorbance value under consideration. The twenty individual estimates of the λ_{max} were then averaged to give the values entered in the histograms.

Old World Monkeys

The microspectrophotometric measurements of the Old World monkeys have established the presence of three cone types with maximum absorbance at about 565 nm, 535 nm, and 420–430 nm. In *M. mulatta* we have analysed records from 219 cones and 80 rods obtained from 17 animals. (Results from the first five animals have been published previously, Bowmaker *et al.*, 1978.) The cones fell into two groups, 92 long-wave cones with a mean λ_{max} at 566.2 ± 4.8 nm and 127 middle-wave cones with a mean λ_{max} at 534.8 ± 4.8 nm. No clear evidence was found for short-wave receptors. The distribution of the λ_{max} values of individual receptors is shown in Fig. 1. Some 58% of the long-wave receptors and 61% of the middle-wave receptors lie within 3 nm of the mean values, but the outliers of the distributions cover a

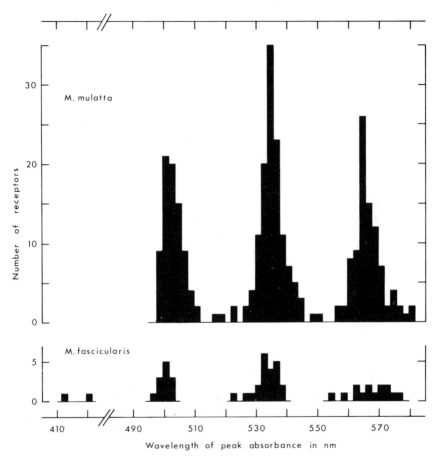

FIG. 1   Distribution of values of peak sensitivity of all individual records from 17 rhesus monkeys (upper panel) and from six eyes from cynomolgus monkeys (lower panel). The bin size is 2 nm. The λ_{max} of an individual record was obtained by fitting an appropriate nomogram to the absorbance spectrum as described in the text.

total of 25 nm for the long-wave and 35 nm for the middle-wave cones with no complete break between the distributions of the two classes. Most of the outliers are drawn from one animal and we have no grounds for discarding these records.

Similar data have been obtained from the closely related cynomolgus macaque, *M. fascicularis* (Bowmaker *et al.*, 1980) from which records for 12 rods and 38 cones from six different eyes were analysed. The rods had a λ_{max} of 500.1 ± 1.6 nm with a transverse absorbance ranging from 0.016 in cells of small diameter to 0.06 in large cells. The 38 cones fell into three distinct groups: 14 of the outer segments had values of λ_{max} ranging from 554 to 575 nm (Fig. 1) with a mean of 567.0 ± 6.1 nm whereas 22 cells yielded λ_{max} values from 521 to 538 nm with a mean of 533.3 ± 3.9 nm. When cells with high short-wavelength absorbance were excluded from the sample, the mean λ_{max} for the middle-wavelength cones shifted slightly to 535 nm (cf. MacNichol *et al.*, this volume). The remaining two outer segments, morphologically indistinguishable from the others, gave λ_{max} values between 410 and 420 nm with a mean transverse absorbance of 0.015. The mean absorbance spectra for the four classes of receptor from *M. fascicularis* are shown in Fig. 2. The λ_{max} values that we obtain for the two macaque species are in good agreement with the recent independent measurements of MacNichol *et al.* (see this volume); the only instance of a large discrepancy occurs in the case of the short-wave cones, for which data are limited.

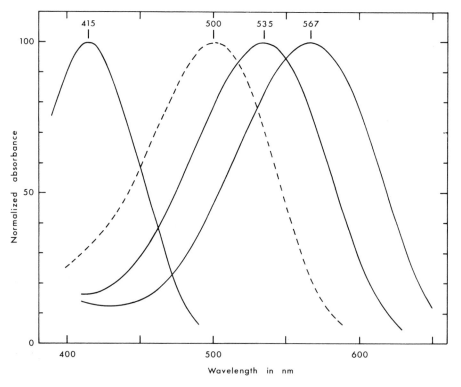

FIG. 2   Mean absorbance spectra for the four classes of receptor cell in *Macaca fascicularis*. The solid curves are for three classes of cone, the dashed line for the rods. The curve for the middle-wavelength cones is based on a selected subset of 16 cells (see text).

In the baboon, *Papio papio*, we have analysed spectra from a total of 144 receptors obtained from five animals. Again these fall into four classes, rods and 3 types of cones (Fig. 3). Analysis of 35 rods yielded a λ_{max} of

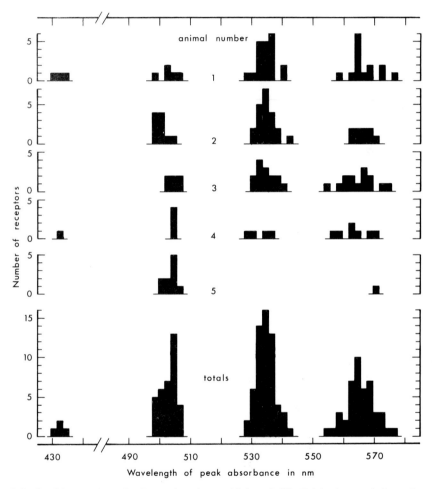

FIG. 3   Distribution of values of peak sensitivity of all individual records from five baboons. The bin size is 2 nm. The λ_{max} for an individual record was obtained using the method described in the text.

502.9 ± 2.4 nm. The long-wave cones had a mean λ_{max} of 565.5 ± 3.6 nm ($n = 45$) and the 60 middle-wave cones had a mean λ_{max} of 534.7 ± 3.2 nm. Four cones were found absorbing maximally at short wavelengths, with a mean λ_{max} of 432.5 ± 1.7 nm.

These results from Old World primates show a remarkable consistency. The mean λ_{max} values for the rods lie close to 500 nm within a 3 nm range, and similarly, the long-wave and middle-wave cones have maxima close to 565 nm and 535 nm falling within a range of only 2 nm in both classes. Less agreement is found between the short-wave cone data where the range is about 15 nm. However, these so-called "blue" cones are rare and only 6 out of a total of 493 receptors have been analysed. In addition, at short wavelengths, the signal to noise ratio of the microspectrophotometer is very low so that analysis becomes more difficult with a subsequent uncertainty as to the exact location of the λ_{max}.

It seems increasingly likely that the Old World monkeys, though very consistent among themselves, are not the exact model for human trichromats that they have sometimes been taken to be. Rather, their photopigments tend to have λ_{max} values several nm longer than those found for the majority of human observers (see Table 1, and Dartnall, Bowmaker and Mollon, this volume).

New World Monkeys

The first New World monkey that we examined, a single male specimen of *Cebus apella*, confirmed the classical view of the Platyrrhini, that their colour vision corresponds to that of human protanopes. We were able to identify only a single class of cones in the red−green region of the spectrum with a mean λ_{max} of 534.3 ± 1.6 nm ($n = 19$), a value very similar to that obtained for the middle-wave receptors of the Old World monkeys. No short-wave receptors were found. The rods also gave a mean λ_{max} similar to other primates with a value of 499.3 ± 3.6 nm ($n = 18$).

However, as has become quite clear from behavioural results (see Jacobs, this volume), the classification of colour vision in New World monkeys is much more complicated and raises many interesting questions. In a collaborative study we have examined a group of ten squirrel monkeys, *Saimiri sciureus*, in which, from behavioural studies, there occur clear variations in colour vision similar to those found in the small percentage of the human population that is considered colour deficient. Correspondingly, we have found, by microspectrophotometric analysis, systematic variability in the spectral locations and number of the cone pigments between the individual monkeys.

The behavioural tests, carried out in GHJ's laboratory in Santa Barbara (see Jacobs, this volume) included wavelength discrimination, Rayleigh matches and measurements of sensitivity at 540 nm and 640 nm. The tests were all carried out in a forced-choice discrimination apparatus in which the monkeys viewed three circular, trans-illuminated panels. They were taught to touch one of the three panels which was illuminated differently from the other two, in order to receive a food pellet. Which of the three panels was positive (i.e. differently illuminated) varied randomly from trial to trial. The behavioural results were not known to the microspectrophotometrists. The animals were flown to London where the microspectrophotometric measurements were made. It proved possible to obtain up to 75 records from a single animal. (Preliminary reports of the results from the first two and first six monkeys have already been published, Jacobs, Bowmaker and Mollon, 1981, 1982.)

From the microspectrophotometric data at least four cone visual pigments were identified. The short-wave cone type was rare, as it is in Old World primates, with only 14 being identified out of a total of about 475 cones, and none being found in two of the ten animals. The mean λ_{max} of these cells was 433.5 ± 2.5 nm, a value similar to that found for *P. papio*. In all animals we recorded rods with maximum absorbance at approximately 500 nm (Table 1).

TABLE 1 λ_{max} of primate visual pigments

	Short	Rod	Middle		Long
Old World					
Macaca mulatta	?	503	535		566
M. fascicularis	415	500	535		567
Papio papio	433	503	535		566
Homo sapiens[*]	419	496	531		558
New World					
Cebus apella	?	499	534		
Saimiri sciureus					
S2, 3, 19	432	501		550	564
S7	433	499	535	545	
S1, 21, 22, 25	435	499	535		
S5	433	503		549	
S24	?	501			562

[*]   Data from Dartnall, Bowmaker and Mollon, this volume.

In six of the animals we found only one class of cone in the red–green region of the spectrum, rather than the two we have found in all of the individual Old World monkeys. However, the spectral location of the single pigment was not constant (Fig. 4). In four monkeys, S1, 21, 22 and 25, it appeared to be very similar, the mean λ_{max} values being 537, 534, 535 and 535 nm. This cone type corresponds with that found in the single *Cebus* monkey and also with the middle-wave cones of the Old World monkeys. On this basis these four dichromats can be classified as protanopes, if the analogy with human colour vision is valid. Such a diagnosis is basically in concordance with the behavioural evidence. Animals S21, 22 and 25 failed to make a Rayleigh match, being

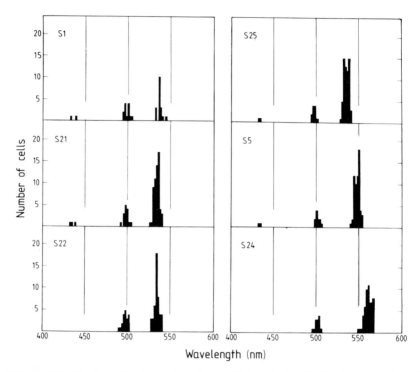

FIG. 4   Distribution of values of peak sensitivity of all individual records from 6 squirrel monkeys that had only a single pigment in the red–green region of the spectrum. S1, 21, 22 and 25 are assumed to contain the same pigment, λ_{max} 535 nm. The mean λ_{max} for S5 is 549 nm and for S24 is 562 nm.

unable to distinguish a pure red or green from yellow, a failure echoed in the wavelength discrimination functions for S21 and S22, which show good discrimination up to about 525 nm, with a minimum at about 490 nm (Fig. 5), but with increasingly poorer discrimination at longer wavelengths. The fourth of this group S1, proved slightly problematical in that after extensive trials it was able to make a Rayleigh match, accepting a very wide range of mixtures on the protan side of the normal human match. In addition, the wavelength discrimination function of S1, although showing only a single minimum at about 490 nm, showed better discrimination than S21, 22 and 25 at wavelengths above 525 nm (Fig. 5). We must leave open the possibility that S1 was an extreme protanomalous subject.

The remaining two dichromats, S5 and S24 were found to have their single pigment in the red–green range at longer wavelengths than the protans. S5 contained a pigment with λ_{max} 549 nm whereas S24 contained a pigment with λ_{max} 562 nm. The longer-wave pigment is similar to the long-wave pigment found

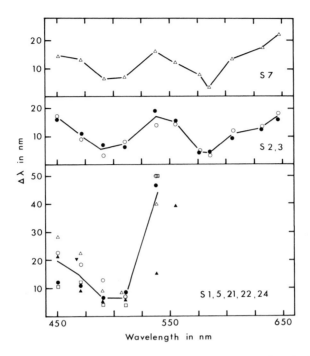

FIG. 5 Wavelength discrimination functions for eight individual squirrel monkeys. The values (Δλ) indicate the magnitude of the wavelength change required at each spectral location to support discrimination between two equiluminant spectral lights at a criterion level of 70% correct. The values are averages for differences in both spectral directions except at 452 nm.

S7, S2 and S3 are diagnosed as trichromats while S1, 5, 21, 22 and 24 are diagnosed as dichromats. S1, possibly severely protanomalous, is represented by the filled triangles in the bottom panel. S19 and S25 were not run on this test.

in Old World monkeys, but the class of cone with λ_{max} 549 nm has not been reported from other primate species. Behaviourally, S5 and S24 did not differ: they were unable to make a Rayleigh match and both showed only a single minimum at 490 nm in their wavelength discrimination function (Fig. 5). However, they differed from the protanopes in that they were more sensitive at 640 nm, as would be expected from the spectral location of their pigments. In terms of human colour vision, S24 would be classified as a deuteranope and S5 may correspond to the rare type of human dichromat said to accept matches of both protanomalous and deuteranomalous observers and thought to share the "anomalous" pigment with them both.

The remaining four squirrel monkeys had distributions of cones in the red–green range that were clearly different from the previous six animals (Fig. 6). None of the distributions show the well separated long- and middle-wave

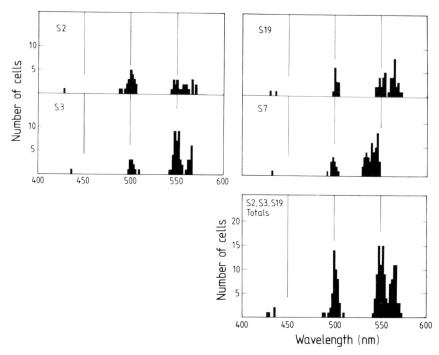

FIG. 6 Distributions of values of peak sensitivity of all individual records from four squirrel monkeys shown behaviourally to be trichromatic. S2, 3 and 19 are thought to be similar, having two presumptive pigments in the red–green range with λ_{max} at 550 and 564 nm. S7, a behaviourally protanomalous animal, has presumptive pigments with λ_{max} at 535 and 545 nm.

cones found in Old World primates, but they can be distinguished from the distributions of the six behavioural dichromats by their variance: the standard deviations of the dichromats are in the limited range of 2.4 to 4.2 nm, whereas the standard deviations of the other four monkeys are in the range 5.2 to 8.5 nm.

Three of the animals S2, 3 and 19 had long-wave receptors in a similar range with clear indications at least in S3 and S19 of a bimodal distribution, a suggestion supported by the total distribution obtained by summing the data from the three animals (Fig. 6). On the assumption that the distribution represents two separate classes of cone we took the mean of the individual λ_{max} values of the two hypothetical classes and obtained λ_{max} values of about 550 and 564 nm (Table 1). The longer of the two pigments corresponds with the long-wave pigment of the Old World primates and the pigment of the dichromat S24, whereas the shorter of the two corresponds with the pigment of the dichromat S5.

The suggestion that S2, 3 and 19 were trichromatic is in agreement with the behavioural results. Wavelength discrimination functions are available for S2 and 3, and show good discrimination over the entire range tested with two minima at about 490 and 580 nm (Fig. 5). All three animals accepted a limited range of Rayleigh matches, though lying to the deutan side of the normal match. The three monkeys can thus be classified, in human terms, as deuteranomalous.

The fourth animal of this group, S7, had receptors with a range of λ_{max} values from about 530 to 550 nm, clearly different from the three deuteranomalous monkeys, with an indication, though slight, of a bimodal distribution. On this slender evidence we divided the distribution into two hypothetical classes of cone with mean λ_{max} at 535 and 545 nm. The shorter of the two presumptive pigments corresponds to the middle-wave pigment of Old World primates and with the pigment of the four squirrel monkeys diagnosed as protanopes. The longer of the two pigments may correspond with the shorter of the two pigments found in the deuteranomalous animals (Table 1).

The tentative suggestion from the microspectrophotometric data that S7 is trichromatic is supported by the behavioural tests. The wavelength discrimination of S7 was good throughout the entire spectral range tested with two minima at about 500 and 580 nm (Fig. 5). The monkey could also make a Rayleigh match, accepting a limited range of mixtures on the protan side of the normal human match.

Thus in contrast to the Old World primates, squirrel monkeys show large variations in their colour vision that are due to variations in the cone pigments in the red–green range. At least three classes of cone, with peak sensitivities at about 535, 550 and 564 nm are present, singly or in pairs, in correspondence with the presence of dichromatic or anomalous trichromatic vision, giving at least five behavioural types. It is interesting that we have not found an animal that resembles a normal human observer or an Old World primate.

References

Bowmaker, J. K., Dartnall, H. J. A., Lythgoe, J. N. and Mollon, J. D. (1978). The visual pigments of rods and cones in the rhesus monkey, *Macaca mulatta*. *J. Physiol.* **274**, 329–348.

Bowmaker, J. K., Dartnall, H. J. A. and Mollon, J. D. (1980). Microspectrophotometric demonstration of four classes of photoreceptor in an Old World primate, *Macaca fascicularis*. *J. Physiol.* **298**, 131–143.

Jacobs, G. H., Bowmaker, J. K. and Mollon, J. D. (1981). Behavioural and microspectrophotometric measurements of colour vision in monkeys. *Nature (Lond.)* **292**, 541–543.

Jacobs, G. H., Bowmaker, J. K. and Mollon, J. D. (1982). Colour vision variations in monkeys: behavioural and microspectrophotometric measurements on the same individuals. In *Colour Vision Deficiencies VI* (ed. Verriest, G.). Junk, The Hague.

Knowles, A. and Dartnall, H. J. A. (1977). The photobiology of vision. In *The Eye*, Vol. 2B (ed. Davson, H.). Academic Press, New York.

Liebman, P. A. and Entine, G. (1964). Sensitive low-light-level microspectrophotometer: detection of photosensitive pigments of retinal cones. *J. opt. Soc. Am.* **54**, 1451–1459.

Microspectrophotometry of Human Photoreceptors

H. J. A. DARTNALL, J. K. BOWMAKER and J. D. MOLLON

Material

Through the co-operation of surgeon and patients we have obtained human eyes for examination by microspectrophotometry. The eyes were removed because of malignant growths. Only those cases in which a substantial portion of the retina (including fovea) was uninvaded by the tumour were suitable. We report results from the first seven such eyes.

One eye (number 1, see Table 1) was removed under red light, while two others (numbers 4 and 7) were exenterations, and were taken complete with eyelids sutured together. The remaining four eyes were removed under the full glare of the operating lights. The eyes were dissected under deep red light, and 1 mm² portions of the retina, close to (and including) the fovea, were taken and prepared in the usual way (Bowmaker, Dartnall and Mollon, 1980) for examination of the photoreceptors. Transverse measurements were made of the absorbance spectra of the outer segments of the rods and cones, using a Liebman microspectrophotometer (for description see Knowles and Dartnall, 1977).

From this material 173 records of different outer segments were obtained. It was easy to recognise the outer segments of the rods, and all 44 examples had spectra with λ_{max} (wavelength of peak absorbance) close to 496 nm. The outer segments of the cones, however, were assigned to three classes simply according to their λ_{max}, since we were unable to distinguish the classes morphologically. Sixty-nine of them peaked between 550 and 570 nm and were designated "reds", 49 were "greens" (peaking at 520−540 nm) and 11 were "blues" (415−425 nm).

COLOUR VISION
ISBN 0 12 000000 0

Precise values of λ_{max} were not calculated for 26 (15%) of the 173 records. This was either because their signal-to-noise ratios were very low (transverse density < 0.01) or because the traces were irregular through drifting of cells into or out of the beams. The remaining 147 acceptable records (see Table 1) gave the following mean results:

rods $\lambda_{max} = 496.3 \pm 2.3$ nm $(n = 39)$;
"red" cones $\lambda_{max} = 558.4 \pm 5.2$ nm $(n = 58)$;
"green" cones $\lambda_{max} = 530.8 \pm 3.5$ nm $(n = 45)$;
"blue" cones $\lambda_{max} = 419.0 \pm 3.6$ nm $(n = 5)$.

Absorbance Spectra of the Photoreceptors

The mean absorbance spectra of these four classes of photoreceptor are shown in Fig. 1. From left to right these four curves refer to "blue" cones (419 nm), rods (496 nm), "green" cones (531 nm) and "red" cones (558 nm).

It is appropriate here to emphasize the unfamiliar way in which the spectra of Fig. 1 have been plotted. It has become usual over the years to plot the spectra of visual pigments against a scale of frequency rather than one of wavelength. This practice stems partly from considerations of Quantum Theory and partly from a nomogram (Dartnall, 1953) which was constructed on the supposition that on the frequency basis all visual pigments had the same shape of absorbance spectrum. In 1968, however, Liebman and Entine showed that the spectra of frog and tadpole photoreceptors, as determined by the microspectrophotometric method, were progressively narrower on this scale as the peak wavelength (λ_{max}) advanced towards longer wavelengths. We confirmed this for the four pigments of the cynomolgus monkey and showed that the band-width of the spectrum was linearly related to the spectral location of the peak on a frequency scale (Bowmaker, Dartnall and Mollon, 1980). More recently Barlow (1982), also using our cynomolgus data, made the capital observation that the shapes of the spectra can be made very similar by plotting them in another way – namely to an abscissal scale of the fourth root of wavelength.

It is on this scale that the mean absorbance spectra of the four kinds of photoreceptor are plotted in Fig. 1. It is clear from the figure that Barlow's observation also holds closely for the human pigments, the continuous curves drawn through the data being of exactly the same shape in each case. This standard curve is, in fact, the mean of the four curves drawn through each set of points separately. Data for drawing the standard curve, and hence for constructing the absorbance spectrum of any visual pigment based on retinal are given in Table 2.

TABLE 1 Details of the results. "Mean density" is the mean transverse optical density at λ_{max}

Eye number	1	2	3	4	5	6	7	All
Sex	male	male	male	male	female	female	female	
Age	46	43	58	70	34	74	63	
Rod outer-segments								
Number	11	5	1	13	1	8	0	39
Mean λ_{max}	496.5	497.2	496.0	496.2	494.0	495.9	–	496.3 ± 2.3 nm
Mean density	0.035	0.027	0.025	0.044	0.033	0.045	–	0.039 ± 0.011
"Blue"-cone outer-segments								
Number	3	1	0	1	0	0	0	5
Mean λ_{max}	419.3	419.0	–	418.0	–	–	–	419.0 ± 3.6 nm
Mean density	0.037	0.024	–	0.023	–	–	–	0.032 ± 0.011
"Green"-cone outer-segments								
Number	11	2	5	13	2	9	3	45
Mean λ_{max}	532.7	532.5	527.6	530.7	534.5	529.0	530.7	530.8 ± 3.5 nm
Mean density	0.033	0.026	0.040	0.036	0.032	0.040	0.030	0.035 ± 0.008
"Red"-cone outer-segments								
Number	20	5	3	8	2	9	11	58
Mean λ_{max}	560.9	561.4	552.0	553.1	556.0	556.3	560.0	558.4 ± 5.2 nm
Mean density	0.027	0.021	0.029	0.033	0.029	0.034	0.023	0.028 ± 0.007

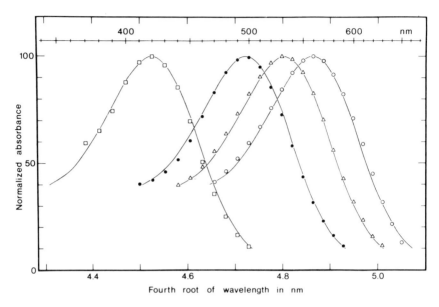

FIG. 1 The mean absorbance spectra of the four human photoreceptors. Squares, the "blue" cones $(\lambda_{max} = 419.0 \pm 3.6$ nm, mean of 5); filled circles, the rods $(\lambda_{max} = 496.3 \pm 2.3$ nm, mean of 39); triangles, the "green" cones $(\lambda_{max} = 530.8 \pm 3.5$ nm, mean of 45); plain circles, the "red" cones $(\lambda_{max} = 558.4 \pm 5.2$ nm, mean of 58). The curves are all exactly the same shape and were calculated from the data tabulated in Table 2. Note inset scale of wavelengths.

Spectral Distribution of the Photoreceptors

As already mentioned the values of λ_{max} in each of the four groups of photoreceptors were spread over considerable ranges of wavelength. In Fig. 2 these distributions are shown in histogram form for each of the seven eyes separately, and also as totals. The eyes 1, 2, 3 and 4 were from male patients, and 5, 6 and 7 from females. There is no obvious difference between the sexes. The absence of the uncommon "blue" cones in females is only apparent — not real. In fact in one female eye (no. 6) two examples of bleachable "blue" cones were found, but the records were not good enough for the precise computation of λ_{max}, and consequently do not appear in Fig. 2.

In Fig. 2 the mean values of λ_{max} for the four kinds of photoreceptor are shown by the four vertical dashed lines. There are only five examples of the "blue" cone, the λ_{max} ranging from 414–424 nm. With so few examples, there is little one can say about the distribution of λ_{max}. In the case of the other receptors, however, there are perhaps sufficient numbers of observations to warrant some cautious remarks about distribution. Thus it is at once clear

TABLE 2   Data for constructing the Absorbance Spectrum of any visual pigment, based on retinal and of known λ_{max}

Absorbance A (% maximum)	$\lambda_A^{1/4} - \lambda_{max}^{1/4}$
40	-0.216
50	-0.157
60	-0.128
70	-0.098
80	-0.073
90	-0.048
95	-0.031
95	$+0.033$
90	$+0.047$
80	$+0.068$
70	$+0.085$
60	$+0.099$
50	$+0.114$
40	$+0.130$
30	$+0.149$
20	$+0.174$
10	$+0.211$

Example. Suppose $\lambda_{max} = 535$ nm. Consequently $\lambda_{max}^{1/4} = 4.809$ and 80% (say) absorbance on the short-wave side of the maximum occurs at a wavelength λ_A given by $\lambda_A^{1/4} - 4.809 = -0.073$, i.e. at 503 nm.

from Fig. 2 that whereas the mean λ_{max} for rods coincides with the most frequent value this is not so with the "green" and "red" cones. In both these cases, the mean values of λ_{max} occur where there is a dip in the distribution frequency.

In order to take the examination of λ_{max} distribution a stage further the histograms for the rod, "green" cone and "red" cone populations have been re-plotted on a larger scale in Fig. 3, together with interpretative statistical functions.

The 39 rod records give a mean λ_{max} value of 496.3 nm and a standard deviation of ± 2.3 nm. The dashed curve in Fig. 3 is what one would expect from these statistics when the distribution is normal. The normality of a distribution can be conveniently assessed, when n is small, by Shapiro and Wilk's (1965) analysis of variance test. Application of the test to our rod data showed no evidence of non-normality ($W = 0.969$, $p = \sim 0.5$).

The 45 "green" cone records give a mean λ_{max} of 530.8 nm and a standard deviation of ± 3.5 nm. The distribution (if normal) to be expected from these values is given by the dashed curve in Fig. 3; it does not seem to be a satisfactory

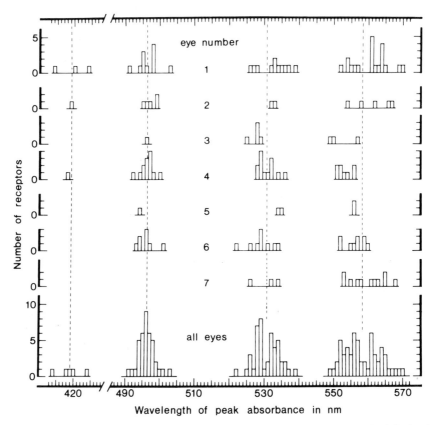

FIG. 2   Spectral distributions of the human photoreceptors. The vertical dashed lines give the mean values of λ_{max} for the four kinds of receptor. See also Table 1.

description. Does this mean that the distribution is not normal? Are there subpopulations of "long" and "short" green cones?

If we divide the 45 "greens" into two groups according to whether λ_{max} lies above or below 530.5 nm we obtain 23 "longs" with a mean λ_{max} of 533.7 nm and standard deviation of ± 2.1 nm, and 22 "shorts" with a mean of 527.8 and standard deviation of 1.8 nm. The expected distribution for *two* such normal populations is given by the double-hump continuous curve in Fig. 3.

This might be thought to describe the actual distribution of λ_{max}-values better than the single-hump (dashed) curve. But when Shapiro and Wilk's test is applied to the "green" cone data the *W* value of 0.976 is obtained, close to the value of 0.973 given for the 0.5 probability level. Thus, perhaps surprisingly, there is no evidence for non-normality. It is clear that when the mean values of two normal populations are close in relation to their standard

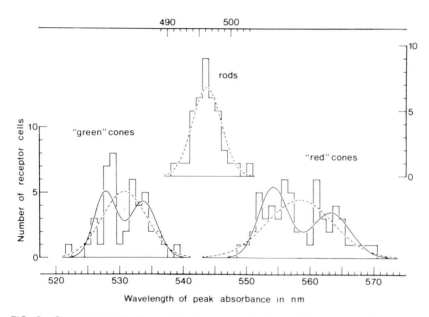

FIG. 3   Spectral distributions of the human rods, "green" cones and "red" cones interpreted in terms of their statistics. The dashed-line curves give the normal distributions expected from the relevant means and standard deviations. The double-hump continuous curves drawn through the "green" and "red" cone data give the expectations if the respective populations are regarded as containing "long" and "short" subpopulations. For further explanation see text.

deviations the test will not easily distinguish the combination from a single normal distribution having its mean between the two.

The 58 "red" receptors yield a mean λ_{max} of 558.4 nm with a standard deviation of ± 5.2 nm. The normal distribution corresponding to these statistics is given by the dashed curve in Fig. 3. It seems to be a poor description of the population distribution, even worse than in the case of the "green" cones. Application of the Shapiro and Wilk test confirms that distribution of the "red" cone population is significantly non-normal ($W = 0.940, p = \sim 0.02$).

If we divide the 58 "reds" into two groups according to whether the λ_{max} lies above or below 558.4 nm we obtain 27 "longs" with mean $\lambda_{max} = 563.2$ ± 3.1 nm and 31 "shorts" with mean $\lambda_{max} = 554.2 \pm 2.3$ nm. The expected distribution for such a population is given by the continuous double-hump curve for "reds" in Fig. 3. It seems to be a fair approximation to the actual distribution.

Spectral Location of "Red" Cones, and Red Sensitivity

When the microspectrophotometric examination of the first four eyes (see Fig. 2) had been completed it was noticed that the results obtained with the first and fourth eyes showed differences as regards the average spectral locations of the "red" cones. It was thought possible that these differences were large enough to have visual significance. Consequently the vision in the remaining eyes of patients 1 and 4 was tested psychophysically. Each patient completed a number of clinical tests of colour vision comprising: (a) pseudo-isochromatic plates, including the Ishihara (9th edn), the Okuma (Amoriex Co., Tokyo), the Farnsworth tritan plate, and an unpublished tritan plate kindly provided by J. Birch-Cox; (b) the City University test, a booklet version of the Farnsworth Panel D15 test; (c) the Farnsworth-Munsell 100-hue test; and (d) the Nagel anomaloscope. For details of several of these tests see Pokorny, Smith, Verriest and Pinckers (1979).

A reduced version of Stiles' field-sensitivity method (Stiles, 1978) was also used. Detection thresholds were first measured for 666-nm targets presented for 10 msec in Maxwellian view to the dark-adapted fovea. When the absolute threshold had been established the 666-nm target was set to be one $\log_{10}$ unit above the absolute threshold and a steady adapting field, subtending 6.25 degrees of visual angle was introduced. In successive runs the wavelength of the adapting field was either 650 nm or 555 nm and in each run the radiance of the field was adjusted, according to a single staircase procedure, in order to estimate the radiance at which 50% of targets were detected (see Mollon and Polden (1977) for general details of the apparatus).

Both patients gave normal responses on all the pseudoisochromatic plates, and neither made any errors on the City University test. On the Farnsworth-Munsell test, patient 1 had a total error score of 89 on first test and 40 on second; for patient 4 the corresponding values were 115 and 51. These scores are within the ranges for normal observers of the appropriate age groups (Verriest, 1963). Neither patient showed the clustered pattern of errors characteristic of colour defective patients.

On the Nagel instrument the anomalous quotients for patient 1 were 1.09 for a 3.1-deg field and 1.04 for a 1.2-deg field; for patient 4 the corresponding values were 0.98 and 1.08. The range of anomalous quotients for normal trichromats is given as approximately 0.74 to 1.33 by Pokorny *et al.* (1979).

However, although both patients were classified as normal trichromats by all clinical tests of colour vision, there was a clear difference in their relative sensitivities to long-wave fields under the conditions designed to isolate the long-wave pigment. Table 3 shows for each patient the $\log_{10}$ psychophysical ratio, that is the difference between the $\log_{10}$ field sensitivities at 555 nm and 650 nm. The range of values in normal subjects is not known but two other normal trichromats, tested concurrently, gave values of 0.83 and 0.70.

TABLE 3

Patient	log₁₀ psychophysical ratio	
	Measured	Estimated from microspectrophotometry
1	0.56	0.58
4	0.75	0.71

The table also shows for comparison the values of the $\log_{10}$ psychophysical ratio calculated from the absorbances at 555 nm and 650 nm of the "red" cones of the two patients. The estimated values were obtained by assuming that receptors in the central fovea have a length of 35 μm and a specific absorbance of 0.015 μm^{-1}, giving an axial absorbance at λ_{max} of 0.525 (see Bowmaker and Dartnall, 1980). It was also assumed that there was no difference in the pre-receptoral absorption at the two wavelengths. The agreement between the measured and estimated values of the $\log_{10}$ psychophysical ratios is satisfactory, and supports the conclusion from the microspectrophotometric measurements that the "red" cones of patient 1 peak, on average, at longer wavelengths than those of patient 4.

Comparison of a Deutan and a Normal

Some considerable time after completion of the microspectrophotometric examination of the seven eyes described above we were fortunate in being able to examine a 75-year-old deutan the day before enucleation of his right eye. The examination was confined to the left eye as he was not able to perform the tests with his right. This patient (No. 9) made 22 errors with the Ishihara Plates, indicating severe red–green deficiency. On the four diagnostic plates (nos 22–25) he gave three deutan responses and one erroneous but unclassified response ("8" to plate 22). On the screening cards of the Okuma test, he gave 7/7 responses characteristic of the "red–green blind". On the diagnostic cards the classification was "severe deutan".

In the Farnsworth-Munsell 100-hue test his total error score was 220 on the first test and 305 on second. The mean results for this test are shown in Fig. 4 and provide a classical deutan pattern. In fact all tests carried out on this patient were consistent with a deutan defect. The acceptance of all R/G ratios on the anomaloscope (and the setting of a neutral point (at 502–504 nm) in the tungsten spectrum) strongly suggests that he is dichromatic.

The results of the microspectrophotometric examination of portions of the retina of the enucleated eye are equally striking and are also shown in the lower part of Fig. 4. Of the 17 receptors examined 2 were "blue" cones, 5 were rods and 10 were "red" cones. No "green" cones were found. The results obtained

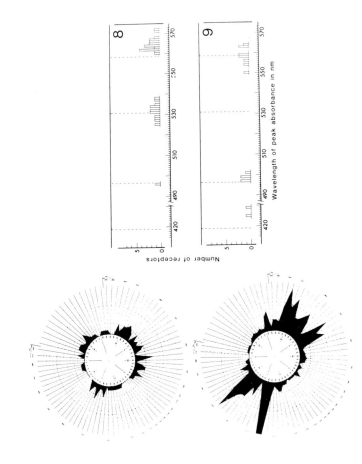

FIG. 4   Correlation between psychophysical and microspectrophotometric measurements on human patients. Results are shown for patient No. 8 (above), a normal trichromat, and for patient No. 9 (below), a deutan. In each case, performance on the Farnsworth-Munsell 100-hue test is shown to the left, and the spectral distribution of photoreceptors is shown to the right. The vertical dashed lines in the right-hand plots have the same spectral locations as those of Fig. 2. Note the absence of "green" cones in the case of patient No. 9.

from a normal patient (No. 8) of age 56 examined by similar procedures just over a month before the deutan are also shown in Fig. 4 (upper part) and provide a useful comparison. On the Farnsworth-Munsell test this patient had a total error score of 102, which is close to the mean for colour normals of this age group (Verriest, 1963), and, indeed, all other tests were consistent in suggesting that he is a normal trichromat. Of the 33 receptors examined by the microspectrophotometer, one was a rod, 13 were "green" cones and 19 were "red" cones. No example of the relatively uncommon "blue" cone was found in this patient, but this is not unusual (cf. Fig. 2). The values of λ_{max} for the "red" cones of patient 8 lie at the long-wavelength end of the distribution of "red" cones in Fig. 2.

The microspectrophotometric results for patient 9 provide direct evidence against the hypothesis that in deuteranopia although both "red" and "green" cones are present in normal proportions, their signals are mixed at a post-receptoral level. This hypothesis – which originates from Fick (1879) – has been resuscitated relatively recently (e.g. Wright, 1967). The present results, however, indicate the absence of "green" (middle-wave sensitive) cones in our deuteranope.

The strength of this conclusion can be approximately assessed in the following way. The first seven (normal) eyes we examined yielded 49 "green" cones and 69 "red" cones. If we assume that these numbers roughly represent the relative proportions of "green" and "red" cones in the foveolar region, then the chance that 10 non-"blue" cones would all be "red" is $(69/118)^{10} = 0.0047$, or less than one in two hundred. Thus the evidence is fairly strong that the deuteranopic eye (in which the 10 non-"blue" cones were indeed all "red") is lacking a cone type. Moreover, the mean λ_{max} of the residual class is 558.4 ± 4.4 nm, precisely the same as the mean value, 558.4 ± 5.2 nm, for the "red" receptors of the seven normal eyes of Table 1. Our conclusions are concordant with those drawn by Rushton (1965) and by Alpern and Wake (1977) from reflection-densitometry measurements.

References

Alpern, M. and Wake, T. (1977). Cone pigments in human deutan colour vision defects. *J. Physiol., Lond.* **266**, 595−612.

Barlow, H. B. (1982). What causes trichromacy? A theoretical analysis using comb-filtered spectra. *Vision Res.* **22**, 635−643.

Bowmaker, J. K. and Dartnall, H. J. A. (1980). Visual pigments of rods and cones in a human retina. *J. Physiol., Lond.* **298**, 501−511.

Bowmaker, J. K., Dartnall, H. J. A. and Mollon, J. D. (1980). Microspectrophotometric demonstration of four classes of photoreceptor in an Old World primate, *Macaca fascicularis. J. Physiol., Lond.* **298**, 131−143.

Dartnall, H. J. A. (1953). The interpretation of spectral sensitivity curves. *Brit. med. Bull.* **9**, 24−30.

Fick, A. (1879). Die Lehre von der Lichtempfindung. In *Handbuch der Physiologie*, Vol. 3 (ed. Hermann, L.), pp. 139–234. Vogel, Leipzig.

Knowles, A. and Dartnall, H. J. A. (1977). *The Photobiology of Vision*, Vol. 2B of *The Eye* (ed. Davson, H.). Academic Press, London and New York.

Liebman, P. A. and Entine, G. (1968). Visual pigments of frog and tadpole *Rana pipiens. Vision Res.* **8**, 761–775.

Mollon, J. D. and Polden, P. G. (1977). An anomaly in the response of the eye to light of short wavelengths. *Phil. Trans. roy. Soc. B* **278**, 207–240.

Pokorny, J., Smith, V. C., Verriest, G. and Pinckers, A. J. L. G. (1979). *Congenital and Acquired Color Vision Defects.* Grune and Stratton, New York.

Rushton, W. A. H. (1965). A foveal pigment in the deuteranope. *J. Physiol., Lond.* **176**, 24–37.

Shapiro, S. S. and Wilk, M. B. (1965). An analysis of variance test for normality (complete samples). *Biometrika* **52**, 591–611.

Stiles, W. S. (1978). *Mechanisms of Colour Vision.* Academic Press, London.

Verriest, G. (1963). Further studies on acquired deficiency of color discrimination. *J. opt. Soc. Am.* **53**, 185–195.

Wright, W. D. (1967). *The Rays are not Coloured*, p. 78. Hilger, Bristol.

Factors Influencing the Color Matches of Normal Observers

D. I. A. MACLEOD and M. A. WEBSTER

The physiological basis for matching lights of different spectral composition is well defined in general outline: incident light undergoes wavelength-dependent filtering in the ocular media and retina and then the transmitted fraction acts on the visual pigments in the three different types of cone, exciting each pigment to the extent that it is absorbed by it. Absorption spectra are known approximately for two prereceptoral screening pigments (the lens and macular pigment) and for the three cone pigments. An observer's match between two fields of light is a match for their action on each of his cone pigments. The matches made by different normal observers are not the same, so the cone pigments or the interposed filters must vary between individuals. We have examined normal variation in color matching with the aim of gaining quantitative information about the typical substrate of color matching as well as about the ways it varies from one normal person to another.

When a limited number of underlying factors is responsible for variation in a larger number of measured quantities, the techniques of factor analysis can be helpful in identifying them, by establishing for each factor in turn how much it influences each measured variable. This information can be used either to pick out the important factors from a larger set which on *a priori* grounds might be considered relevant, or to refine initial assumptions about a factor once it has been confirmed as an influential one. The power of the technique in both these respects is especially well realized in its application to color matching, probably because the factors affecting matching are limited in number as the factor analytic model requires; and yet the dependence of the

COLOUR VISION
ISBN 0 12 000000 0

observed variables (amounts of matching primaries) on the underlying factors is not intuitively very simple, and neither the precise absorption spectra of the pigments nor the ways in which they vary among normal individuals are definitely known.

The only information used in factor analysis is the matrix of correlation between the measured variables. A high (positive or negative) correlation between two variables can occur only to the extent that they depend on a common underlying factor or factors. Thus the pattern of correlations contains evidence about the nature of the operative factors. The correlations between each variable and each of the underlying factors, termed the factor *loadings*, jointly determine the correlations between the variables themselves. All the information in the correlation matrix may be captured by representing each variable by a point in a space where each operative factor is represented by a different axis and the coordinates of the points are given by the corresponding factor loadings. Factor analysis generates a set of factor loadings to account more or less adequately for the observed correlation matrix using a relatively small number of underlying factors.

The color matching variables used in our analysis are the amounts of three spectral primaries needed to match exactly each in turn of a series of test lights ranging across the spectrum. The particular data chosen are the ones collected by Stiles and Burch (1959) using 10° fields and 49 observers. Their results are expressed as the energies of three primaries of 441 nm, 526 nm and 645 nm needed to match a series of 32 test lights of unit energy spanning the spectrum from 392 nm to 714 nm. The data for individual observers were kindly made available by Dr F. J. J. Clarke of the National Physical Laboratory. The subjects were run in two groups under slightly different conditions. Very small corrections for monochromator slit width differences (provided by Stiles and Burch) were applied to make the data for the two groups comparable. Along with the 3×32 variables making up the color-matching functions of each observer we included the observer's age as a 97th variable in the analysis.

Factors were initially extracted using a standard (SPSS) computer program package. The statistical significance of the extracted factors could be roughly gauged on the assumption that "real" factors (unlike ones that merely absorb random error in the data) will modify the color-matching variables by continuous functions of wavelength so that their loadings will show a systematic dependence on wavelength. By inspection at least 10 factors were clearly genuine by this criterion and a factor space of 11 dimensions (defined by the first 11 extracted factors) was chosen for further analysis. The arrangement of the 97 variables in this space is given by taking the 11 factor loadings for each variable as Cartesian coordinates for the point representing it, but the axes corresponding to the factors can be rotated arbitrarily (with resulting changes in the factor loadings and hence in the interpretation of the factors) without affecting the fit to the correlation matrix. We initially fixed the factor axis orientations using the standard VARIMAX criterion. The rotation chosen is one that maximizes the order in the pattern of factor loadings, seeking to produce a maximal number of very large or near zero loadings. The rationale is a very general one. The underlying factors presumably vary in importance, some being generally influential and others less significant; in addition, different variables will be predominantly affected by different factors. An incorrect rotation would have a levelling effect on the coordinates, tending to obliterate the inequalities in the true factor loadings that result from the varying importance of the factors and from the selective relationship between the measured variables and the factors influencing them.

After rotation using the VARIMAX criterion, the first 6 factors almost immediately "made sense". These account for about 75% of the variance between individuals in the color-matching functions overall; for the most reliable color-matching functions (e.g. the amounts of red and of green needed to match a yellowish test light) the proportion of variance rises to over 90%.

Despite the use of a large field (with instructions to disregard the central macular area defined by Maxwell's spot), the most important factor was macular pigmentation (Fig. 1), which can be identified as such mainly because its influence is greatest in the blue–green region of the spectrum, where macular pigment density is greatest. When the amount of a primary is negative because the primary has to be mixed with the test light, the factor loading are correspondingly inverted, and this accounts for the zero crossings at the primary wavelengths. The overall polarity of the factor is such that the greater an observer's macular pigmentation the lower his factor score. A high-scoring observer would require more green (and more negative red) to match a blue–green test, as shown by positive and negative loadings respectively on these primaries in that spectral region. As a check on the identification of this factor, theoretical loadings for a macular pigment factor were calculated assuming the absorption spectrum tabulated in Wyszecki and Stiles (1967). For each color-matching variable, the variance of the logarithms of the primary energies attributable to observer variation in macular pigment density was calculated, and this was divided by the observed variance in log energy. The square root of the result was the predicted variable-factor correlation or factor loading. Our reason for making predictions for the *logs* of the primary energies (for this and for other factors) is that these predictions are not upset by incorrect assumptions about other prereceptoral factors or about the visual pigment spectra. These assumptions can affect the mean predicted color-matching functions, and their absolute variances, but not the variances of their logarithms. The predicted loadings are all proportional to the assumed standard deviation of macular pigment density in the normal population; set at 0.11 as a first guess, this was later chosen for a least squares fit to the observed loadings, yielding the value 0.12. The analysis provides no evidence about mean macular pigment density. The agreement between the

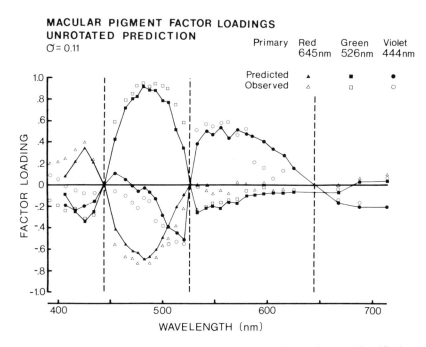

FIG. 1   Loadings of the amounts of three primaries on a factor identified as macular pigment density, plotted as a function of the test wavelength matched. Closed symbols show loadings theoretically expected for a macular pigment factor. A least squares fit requires a standard deviation of 0.12 in density rather than the value shown.

observed and predicted loadings shown in Fig. 1 not only establishes macular pigment density as an operative factor but also speaks well for the efficacy of the VARIMAX criterion in converging on an appropriate factor rotation without any prior assumptions as to the nature of the factors.

Perhaps not surprisingly, another extracted factor corresponded to lens pigment density, as shown by its predominating influence at the violet end of the spectrum. A standard deviation of 0.21 in density at 400 nm was indicated. Correlations of macular and lens pigment density with age were 0.34 and 0.24 respectively, not statistically significant. But there were few very old or young observers.

Of the remaining 4 identified factors, one was assumed to represent rod intrusion since its only strong influence was on the amounts of desaturating blue primary needed with long-wavelength test lights. The remaining three factors were collectively about as important as the two prereceptoral factors; they were each identified as representing shifts in the absorption spectrum of one of the cone pigments (see below). The question whether the six factors vary independently or in a correlated fashion from one observer to another was investigated by requesting an oblique rotation instead of an orthogonal one (using for the DIROBL parameter a value of zero, which encourages moderate inter-factor correlations). The resulting factor pattern was still approximately orthogonal and broadly similar to the one produced by allowing orthogonal rotations only. Correlations between factors were not significant: for example 0.18 between lens and macular pigment density and 0.26 between wavelengths of peak absorption for long-wave and mid-spectral pigments. Thus it seems reasonable to suppose that the factors vary independently of one another.

To check quantitatively the spectral shift interpretation of the three remaining factors, we assumed that different observers' visual pigments, though differing slightly in spectral placement, have absorption spectra of similar shape when plotted against wavenumber, the shapes assumed being the ones of Smith, Pokorny and Starr (1976). There was good agreement between observed and predicted loadings for the factors corresponding to shifts in the midspectral and short-wavelength sensitive pigments. But in the case of the long-wavelength sensitive pigment (Fig. 2) the agreement, though encouraging, was far from perfect. Reasons for the disagreement should be discoverable if the factor identification is to be sustained.

One way that the disagreement could arise is that the VARIMAX criterion may have failed to yield an appropriate factor rotation. This possibility was tested in two ways. First, we generated a theoretical set of factor loadings for the five main factors tentatively identified, omitting rod intrusion of the six mentioned since we were unable to make quantitative predictions for that factor. In the resulting 5-dimensional space the axis orientations were then allowed to vary to satisfy the VARIMAX criterion. It turned out that only slight rotations away from the theoretically fundamental orientations were called for by the VARIMAX criterion, so that the errors of prediction seen in Fig. 2 were little affected. The fact that only the observed loadings (and not the predicted ones) in Fig. 2 have undergone a VARIMAX rotation is therefore not the reason for the disagreement. Second, we subjected the observed factor pattern to a theoretically guided rotation instead of the VARIMAX rotation. To do this we computed functions of the color-matching variables that should on theoretical grounds be unaffected by one or other of the postulated factors. For instance, the ratio of the energies of two primaries at any test wavelength, divided by the same ratio at any other wavelength, is a measure that (as von Kries argued) should not be affected by prereceptoral filter factors. Similar measures can be constructed for factors that affect only one visual pigment: these factors must leave unaffected the excitation of the other cone pigments by the matching field, since the match, though different thanks to the alteration in one absorption spectrum, must remain a match for the unchanged pigments in order to be visually accepted. By computing, for instance, the excitation

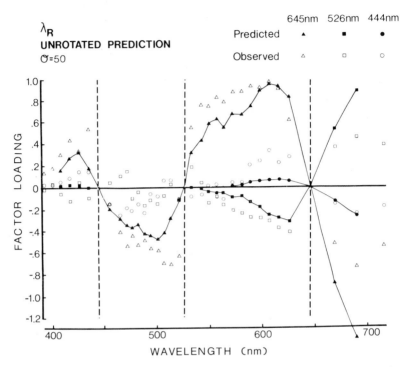

FIG. 2 Loadings for a factor initially identified as a peak shift in the long-wavelength sensitive pigment, with corresponding predictions. Disagreement in the red partly reflects rounding error in the assumed pigment absorption spectrum; substantial disagreements in the green are also correctable by revising the estimated absorption spectrum (see text and Fig. 4).

of the typical midspectral or short-wave pigments by the mixture of primaries chosen by an individual to match some test light, we obtain a measure that should have zero loading on any factor that changes only the red-sensitive pigment, no matter what the nature of the change. The rod intrusion factor should have zero loadings on matches made with fields that saturate the rod system. We defined a sufficient number of theoretically unaffected measures for each of the six tentatively identified factors, and using the VARIMAX rotation as a starting point made further rotations by trial and error to minimize, for each factor, the ratio of the sum of squares of the loadings on the "theoretically unaffected" items to the sum of squares of all loadings for that factor. This rotation yielded a pattern of observed loadings little different from the one yielded by the VARIMAX criterion. The deviations from prediction in Fig. 2 were not substantially affected and indeed the loadings from the theoretically guided rotation differed from the VARIMAX pattern by less than the expected effects of sampling error on the factor pattern. Once again the implication is that the VARIMAX criterion has produced a rotation very close to the theoretically appropriate one.

The possibility that the long-wave visual pigment varies in density rather than in spectral placement was considered, but predictions from that hypothesis (Fig. 3) are even worse than those in Fig. 2 (and allowing a VARIMAX rotation of the predicted factor pattern only increases the disagreement). The hypothesis of density variation fails even more badly to account for the loading of the midspectral and short-wave visual pigment factors.

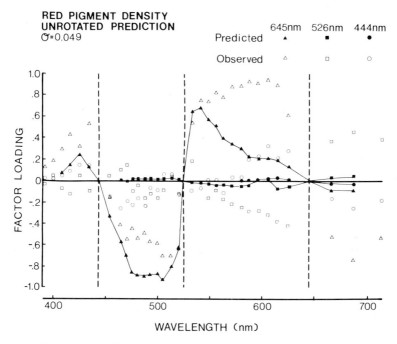

FIG. 3   The factor of Fig. 2 compared with predictions for density variation in the long-wavelength pigment. The density hypothesis qualitatively resembles the peak shift hypothesis in its predictions for this factor, but it fails by not predicting enough influence on matches to long-wavelength test lights.

It could be argued, however, that individual differences in density would most probably be correlated in the three cone pigments, as they would if outer segment length varied appreciably from one observer to another. In that case the density variation should yield a single factor rather than three orthogonal ones. Predicted loadings for such a common density factor do not resemble any of the sets of loadings obtained by the VARIMAX criterion. We find, however, that the VARIMAX rotation tends to absorb some common density variance, when present, into other factors so that a minor role for correlated density variations (standard deviation up to 0.03 in density or about 2 μm in outer segment length) cannot be excluded. Indeed in one of the theoretically guided rotations much of the variance left over from the six major identified factors was accounted for by a factor with a loading pattern resembling that for common density, and its loadings were high enough to suggest a standard deviation of about 0.03.

Reverting to the spectral shift interpretation of the factor of Fig. 2, it seemed possible that the predictions might be improved by revising the estimated absorption spectrum of the pigment, since of course the effect of a shift depends on what is shifted. To allow maximum flexibility in revising the estimated absorption spectrum we considered spectra obtained by multiplying the Smith-Pokorny-Starr estimate by an 11th order polynomial in wavenumber. The coefficients of the polynomial were varied for a least squares fit to the observed loadings of Fig. 2. To assist convergence the polynomial was built up from Tchebycheff-Hermite polynomials as components since these would be roughly mutually orthogonal when multiplied by the visual pigment spectrum. In this procedure the pigment spectrum is not constrained to be consistent with the color-matching functions but is only required to generate appropriate individual variation in their logarithms, yet the result (Fig. 4) is credible as an estimate of the absorption spectrum of the long-wave sensitive cones. This slight revision of the Pokorny-Smith-Starr estimate reduces the r.m.s. error of prediction of the factor loadings to 0.075, allowing the spectral shift hypothesis to be maintained for long-wavelength as well as midspectral and short-wavelength cones.

We also considered a modified form of the shift hypothesis, in which the absorption spectrum is translated on a scale of *log* wavenumber (or log wavelength). This assumption was suggested by the same data that recently led Barlow (1982) to a similar proposal, that shape is invariant on a scale given by a low power of wavelength. The log shift assumption called for almost the same amendments to the absorption spectrum as did the wavenumber shift (Fig. 4), so the absorption spectrum required to account for individual variation with the spectral shift hypothesis does not depend critically on the scale on which the shift is supposed to occur.

The alternative hypothesis of density variation could not be made consistent with the data by allowing modification of the absorption spectrum for best fit. The "absorptions" required became negative at some wavelengths, and still the fit to the data remained poor.

The estimation of the absorption spectrum through the spectral shift hypothesis has the distinctive merit of being direct, or independent of assumptions about preceptoral filtering (provided that it is the predicted variance in the *logs* of the color-matching functions that is considered). The usual estimates are made indirectly by correcting visual sensitivities for preceptoral

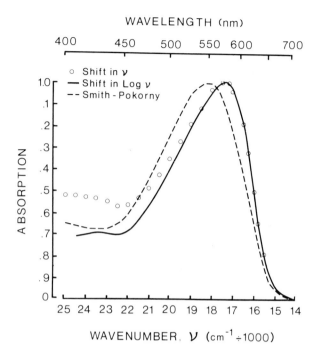

FIG. 4   Dashed line shows the pigment absorption spectrum that generated the predictions of Fig. 2. Open circles show the revised spectrum that best fit the observed loadings of Fig. 2 (r.m.s. error = 0.075) with variations in its placement on a wavenumber axis. Continuous line is best-fitting spectrum assuming variable placement on a log axis (r.m.s. error = 0.097).

filtering, and the estimate of Smith, Pokorny and Starr is typical in showing for the long-wavelength sensitive pigment a shorter wavelength sensitivity peak than the one estimated from the peak shift hypothesis. Seeking other similarly direct psychophysical evidence on the absorption spectrum to help decide between the alternative estimates, we turned to data on the breakdown of color matches due to pigment bleaching, plausibly explained by self-screening in the photolabile visual pigments (Wyszecki and Stiles, 1980). We were able, with the help of polynomial modifications of the absorption spectrum, to fit the bleaching-induced changes in the Wyszecki color matches on the hypothesis that the changes result from self screening, but the long-wave cone absorption spectrum needed to accomplish this (Fig. 5) resembles Wyszecki and Stiles' own estimate, and also the estimate from the peak shift hypothesis of individual variation, in being displaced to long wavelengths relative to the indirect estimates. The estimates could be reconciled by invoking a filter factor that reduces sensitivity at long wavelengths. No such screening pigment is known, but another relevant factor, poorly understood, is introduced by waveguiding

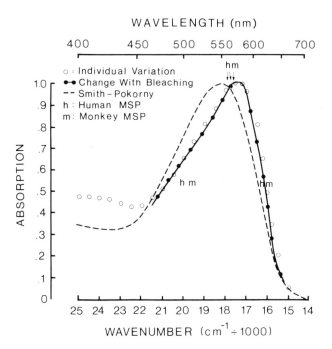

FIG. 5 Open circles are from Fig. 4; closed circles show long-wavelength absorption spectrum estimated from the change in color matches due to bleaching in one observer. h and m show half-height points and peak positions for human and monkey microspectrophotometry.

of light within the outer segment layer. Since receptor dimensions are of the same order as the light wavelength it is not unreasonable to suppose that the fraction of light transmitted within the outer segment, where it can be absorbed in visual pigment, may decrease with increasing wavelength. The required loss in the red is only about 0.15 log units. A discrepancy similar in magnitude and direction appears when rod sensitivity is compared with spectrophotometric data on rhodopsin (Bowmaker and Dartnall, 1980). Interestingly, van Loo and Enoch (1975) report that rod spectral sensitivity changes when light is directed obliquely at the retina. The change they report is enough to make oblique psychophysical sensitivity match the spectrophotometric data after correction for lens absorption. Perhaps the presumed waveguide factor is less influential if axial stimulation is avoided.

If the waveguide interpretation is correct the "direct" psychophysical estimates of the absorption spectrum in Fig. 4 and 5 might be consistent with transverse microspectrophotometry. This comparison is made in Fig. 5 where h and m plot the half-height points on the average MSP absorption spectra from human and monkey cones (Bowmaker and Dartnall, 1980; Bowmaker,

Dartnall and Mollon, 1980). The wavelengths of peak absorption, also indicated, are probably a less reliable basis for comparison, since they depend critically on assumptions about the shape of the absorption spectrum. On the whole the MSP data appear to agree with the "direct" psychophysical estimates of Fig. 4 and 5 at least as well as they do with psychophysical sensitivities with corrections for lens and macular pigmentation.

The standard deviations of spectral peak position needed for a good fit to the factor loadings were 1.32 nm for the long-wave sensitive pigment, 0.73 for the midspectral pigment and 0.89 nm for the short-wave sensitive pigment. These values are so small as to indicate that only a small proportion of the variance among single cones observed with MSP can represent variation between individuals, but they are consistent with other psychophysical evidence on variability between individuals, both defective (Alpern and Wake, 1977; Alpern and Pugh, 1977) and normal (Eisner and MacLeod, 1981). The factor scores gave no clear indication of the fine-grain clustering in spectral placement suggested by Eisner and MacLeod. Coarser clustering is inconsistent with the small observed standard deviations. The standard deviations of spectral position could conceivably be less than the values given above if density variations or other factors are responsible for some of the matching variance that we attribute to variations in spectral placement of the cone pigments; but they cannot be appreciably greater since that would imply greater variability in matching than was observed by Stiles and Burch.

Acknowledgement

Supported by NIH grant EY 01711.

References

Alpern, M. and Pugh, E. N. Jr (1977). Variation in the action spectrum of erythrolabe among deuteranopes. *J. Physiol., Lond.* **266**, 613–646.

Alpern, M. and Wake, T. (1977). Cone pigments in human deutan colour vision defects. *J. Physiol., Lond.* **266**, 595–612.

Barlow, H. B. (1982). What causes trichromacy? A theoretical analysis using comb-filtered spectra. *Vision Res.* **22**, 636–644.

Bowmaker, J. K. and Dartnall, H. J. A. (1980). Visual pigments of rods and cones in a human retina. *J. Physiol., Lond.* **298**, 500–511.

Bowmaker, J. K., Dartnall, H. J. A. and Mollon, J. D. (1980). Microspectrophotometric demonstration of four classes of photoreceptor in an Old World primate, Macaca fascicularis. *J. Physiol., Lond.* **298**, 131–143.

Eisner, A. E. and MacLeod, D. I. A. (1981). Flicker photometric study of chromatic adaptation: selective suppression of cone inputs by colored backgrounds. *J. opt. Soc. Am.* **71**, 705–718.

Smith, V. C., Pokorny, J. and Starr, S. J. (1976). Variability of color mixture data –
    I. Interobserver variability in the unit coordinates. *Vision Res.* **16**, 1087–1095.
Stiles, W. S. and Burch, J. M. (1959). N.P.L. colour-matching investigation: final
    report (1958). *Optica Acta* **6**, 1–26.
van Loo, J. A. Jr and Enoch, J. M. (1975). The scotopic Stiles-Crawford effect.
    Vision Res. **15**, 1005–1010.
Wyszecki, G. and Stiles, W. S. (1967). *Color Science*, Wiley, New York.
Wyszecki, G. and Stiles, W. S. (1980). High-level trichromatic color matching and
    the pigment-bleaching hypothesis. *Vision Res.* **20**, 23–38.

How Do Sets of Color-Matching Functions Differ?

VIVIANNE C. SMITH, JOEL POKORNY and QASIM ZAIDI

Introduction

There are currently three "standard" sets of color-matching functions (CMFs) characterizing 2° foveal color vision. These are the 1931 CIE, the Judd (1951) version of the CIE and the Stiles (1955) functions. The 1931 CIE used spectral coefficients collected by Wright (1929) and Guild (1931). Wright obtained spectral coefficients for the NPL "white", a white of about 4800 K. The two data sets were transformed to the same primaries, those of the RGB observer (Wyszecki and Stiles, 1967) but normalized to the NPL white. The data were then converted to color matching functions by Wright's method which assumed that the luminosity function was a linear combination of the CMFs. The 1924 CIE relative photopic luminous efficiency factor was used as the luminosity function. The data were subsequently transformed to the RGB and XYZ primary systems. When it became evident that the CIE 1924 standard luminous efficiency function underestimated the luminosity of many observers at wavelengths below 460 nm, Judd (1951) derived revised luminosity values based on data obtained in several laboratories during 1945–1950. These new values were combined with the data of Gibson and Tyndall (1923) on which the 1924 standard observer had in part been based. Judd (1951) then used these new luminosity values to revise the color matching functions.

The color matching functions of Stiles (1955) were obtained with the NPL trichromator and represent pilot data for ten observers. The functions are reported for an equal-energy spectrum. Subsequently, a calibration correction was reported in Stiles and Burch (1959).

COLOUR VISION
ISBN 0 12 000000 0

The CIE observer is used by color theorists to derive sets of color fundamentals or spectral sensitivities of presumed cone photoreceptors. Concern that the CIE luminosity was not representative of an "average" observer led naturally to the use of the Judd (1951) revision (e.g., Thomson and Wright, 1953; Vos and Walraven, 1971; Smith and Pokorny, 1975). Recently, Estévez (1979) has suggested that the Stiles (1955) pilot data may be a better data set for color-modelling purposes. Data from individuals are not available for either the CIE or the Stiles (1955) observers. The CIE observer that combines photometric and colorimetric properties has the advantage to the color theorist that it allows prediction of luminosity by a linear combination of cone fundamentals. This operation is justified to the extent that heterochromatic luminances are additive (e.g., Dresler, 1953; Wagner and Boynton, 1972; Eisner and MacLeod, 1981). However, criticism may be directed at the fact that the spectral coefficients were characteristic of different observers than the luminosity values. A major disadvantage of the Stiles (1955) data set is that the luminance level of the different test wavelengths varied considerably owing to the use of an equal-energy spectrum. There is the possibility that the data are contaminated by rod intrusion (see, for example, Estévez, 1979).

In this communication we ask the question, "To what extent do the three data sets differ?" If the data sets differ only by differences in ocular media transmission then the three sets are essentially equivalent for color-modelling purposes. If more serious differences are found, some rational choice would have to be made as to the preferred set.

Evaluation of the Color-Matching Functions

Our first step was to evaluate differences in the three sets of color matching functions. Our null hypothesis was to assume that the three data sets differ only in pre-retinal screening factors.

The pre-retinal screening factors we allowed were the lens and the macular pigment. For lens we used the density spectrum, LN, tabulated by Wyszecki and Stiles (1967). Van Norren and Vos (1974) noted that this tabulation is consistent with the Boettner and Wolter (1962) data for total pre-retinal ocular media (i.e., cornea, lens and vitreous humor). Van Norren and Vos (1974) reviewed existing studies of the ocular media and recommended a density function for total ocular media that differed from the Wyszecki and Stiles (1967) tabulation only below 420 nm. For macular pigment we used the density spectrum, MP, tabulated by Wyszecki and Stiles (1967). This tabulation is similar to one suggested by Vos (1972) after an extensive review of the literature on macular pigment.

According to the null hypothesis, the ratio of two sets of CMFs will be equal to the ratio of the pre-retinal transmittances. If the null hypothesis is correct, this ratio of the transmittances, which will be in transmittance units, can be fit by the antilog of a linear combination of lens, LN, and macular pigment, MP. A set of color-matching functions, CMF(I), can then be adjusted to another set, CMF(II), by multiplying the first set by a pre-retinal screening factor, T^*.

$$CMF(II) = CMF(I)T^* \tag{1}$$
$$T^* = 10^{(K_1 LN + K_2 MP)} \tag{2}$$

We have chosen to work with T^*, the inverse of the ratio of transmittances, so that the weights, K_1 and K_2, have a convenient interpretation. K_1 and K_2 will be proportional to the difference between observers in optical pathlength through the lens and macular pigments respectively.

This calculation may be made for each CMF individually and for an average of the three CMFs. The two sets of color matching functions must be expressed in the same primary and normalization system. The average may be a simple sum or a weighted average of the three primaries. We used equal energy CMFs in the Stiles primary system (15,500, 19,000 and 22,500 cm^{-1}) and a simple average of the three functions.

We made three comparisons: we adjusted the CIE to the Judd; we adjusted the Stiles to the Judd; and we adjusted the Stiles to the CIE. We calculated the logarithmic ratio for each comparison pair and found the values of K_1 and K_2 that minimized the square of the errors in the linear equation:

$$\log [CMF(II)/CMF(I)] = K_1 LN + K_2 MP + error \tag{3}$$

The results are expressed in Table 1 and the three tabulations of T^* are given in Table 2. In the comparison of the CIE to the Judd, the CIE observer showed more lens pigmentation but less macular pigment than the Judd observer.

TABLE 1   Differences in optical densities of lens and macular pigment between different sets of CMFs*

Set I	Set II	Lens		Macular pigment	
		K_1	O.D. difference at max.	K_2	O.D. difference at max.
CIE	Judd	0.611	0.733	−0.299	−0.148
Stiles	Judd	0.288	0.346	−0.085	−0.042
Stiles	CIE	−0.323	−0.387	0.214	0.106

* K_1 and K_2 are the coefficients derived in Equation 3.
   Lens and macular pigment are expressed in density units at their maxima (i.e., 1.2 at 25,000 cm^{-1} for the lens and 0.495 at 21,700 cm^{-1} for the macular pigment.)
   A positive number means that Set I had higher optical density than Set II.
   A negative number means that Set I had lower optical density than Set II.

The Judd observer, as intended by the corrections, is characterized by a lower lens factor than the CIE observer. Additionally, Judd built slightly higher macular pigment into his revised observer. These calculations confirm a similar observation of Stiles (1955) concerning the Judd observer.

In the comparison of the Stiles to the Judd observer, the Stiles observer showed more lens and slightly less macular pigment. Finally, in the comparison of the Stiles observer to the CIE observer, the Stiles observer showed less lens but more macular pigment.

The values in Table 1 depend on the normalization of CMFs. We also checked the effect of WDW normalization. This normalization reduces the contribution of the ''red'' primary CMF to the unweighted average. The main trends of the data were the same but the derived values of lens and macular pigment differed slightly.

Figures 1 to 3 show the set II CMFs (continuous lines) compared with the set I CMFs (symbols) multiplied by the factors T* given in Table 2 and renormalized at each primary. In each figure the symbols show minor deviations from the solid lines. Few of the differences appear systematic. There is no statement of interobserver variability for the three sets of CMFs. None of the deviations exceed the interobserver variability of the Stiles and Burch (1959) 10° data or the Viénot (1980) 10° data.

Our conclusion from this analysis is that the CIE, the Judd and the Stiles observers differ primarily in lens and macular pigmentation. Judd's correction was intended to do more than add inert pigments. However, the residual deviations are not great.

Fundamentals Derived from the CMFs

Given the conclusion that the three sets of CMFs are characterized by the same underlying set of cone visual photopigment spectra, we can now ask whether a candidate set of fundamentals can fit the CIE and Stiles observers. We chose to evaluate our set of König fundamentals (Smith and Pokorny, 1975) derived from the Judd (1951) observer. Identical results were obtained using the analytical functions described by Boynton and Wisowaty (1980).

Our first step was to transform the copunctal points characteristic of the Smith and Pokorny (1975) fundamentals to the Stiles primary system. These copunctal points are shown in Table 3. The solution equations for the fundamentals can be solved by inverting the matrix of the copunctal points. This solution gives arbitrary heights and the three fundamentals should be normalized. Table 3 shows the solution equations for the Judd observer normalized to unit sensitivity. Fundamentals based upon the same copunctal points but other color-matching functions are obtained using the weighted CMFs and normalizing. The solution equations for the CIE and Stiles observers are shown in Table 4. There are no free parameters in determining the shape of the

COLOR MATCHING FUNCTIONS
CIE VS JUDD

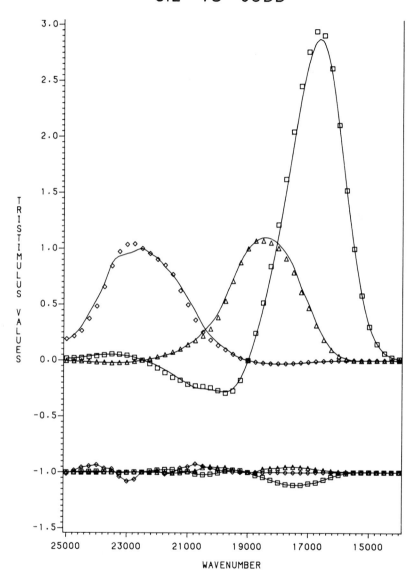

FIG. 1 The top panel shows the Judd CMFs as solid lines and the CIE CMFs adjusted for lens and macular transmission to the Judd CMFs as symbols. The primaries are P_1, 15000; P_2, 19000; P_3, 22500 wavenumber (cm^{-1}). The bottom panel shows the errors centered on -1.0. Symbols: □, $\bar{p}_1$; △ $\bar{p}_2$; ◇ $\bar{p}_3$.

COLOR MATCHING FUNCTIONS
STILES VS JUDD

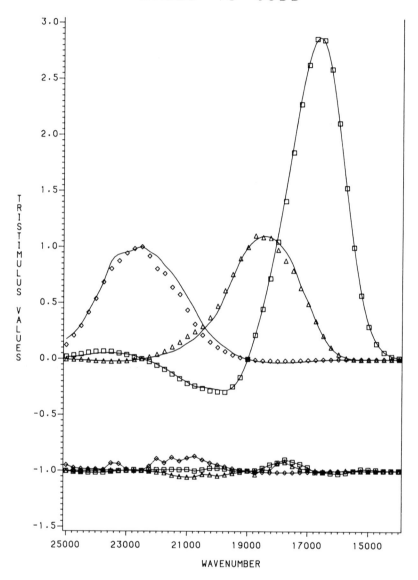

FIG. 2 Comparison of Judd [solid lines] and Stiles [symbols] CMFs. The Stiles CMFs were adjusted for lens and macular transmission to the Judd. Symbols: □, $\bar{p}_1$; △ $\bar{p}_2$; ◇ $\bar{p}_3$.

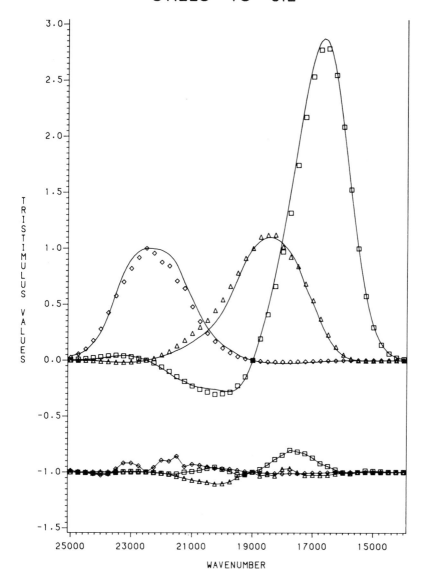

FIG. 3 Comparison of CIE [solid lines] and Stiles [symbols] CMFs. The Stiles CMFs were adjusted for lens and macular transmission to the CIE. Symbols: $\square$, $\bar{p}_1$; $\triangle \bar{p}_2$; $\diamond \bar{p}_3$.

TABLE 2   Values of T* to minimize differences between color-matching functions

Wavenumber (cm⁻¹)	CMF(I): CIE CMF(II): Judd	CMF(I): Stiles CMF(II): Judd	CMF(I): Stiles CMF(II): CIE
25000	5.0988	0.4277	2.1807
24750	3.9185	0.4934	1.9334
24500	3.0920	0.5613	1.7357
24250	2.4746	0.6347	1.5706
24000	2.0093	0.7145	1.4356
23750	1.6843	0.7900	1.3307
23500	1.4560	0.8580	1.2492
23250	1.2968	0.9139	1.1851
23000	1.1984	0.9546	1.1440
22750	1.1176	0.9926	1.1094
22500	1.0435	1.0354	1.0804
22250	1.0027	1.0591	1.0619
22000	0.9583	1.0896	1.0442
21750	0.9450	1.0984	1.0380
21500	0.9394	1.0987	1.0322
21250	0.9378	1.0958	1.0276
21000	0.9506	1.0830	1.0295
20750	0.9324	1.0948	1.0209
20500	0.9210	1.1013	1.0143
20250	0.9387	1.0842	1.0178
20000	0.9897	1.0419	1.0312
19750	1.0456	0.9997	1.0453
19500	1.0956	0.9649	1.0572
19250	1.1160	0.9504	1.0607
19000	1.1312	0.9394	1.0627
18750	1.1326	0.9367	1.0609
18500	1.0996	0.9511	1.0458
18250	1.0938	0.9537	1.0432
18000	1.0880	0.9564	1.0406
17750	1.0766	0.9618	1.0354
17500	1.0653	0.9671	1.0303
17250	1.0541	0.9725	1.0252
17000	1.0432	0.9779	1.0202
16750	1.0376	0.9807	1.0176
16500	1.0289	0.9851	1.0135
16250	1.0213	0.9889	1.0100
16000	1.0159	0.9917	1.0075
15750	1.0106	0.9944	1.0050
15500	1.0053	0.9972	1.0025
15250	1.0000	1.0000	1.0000
15000	1.0000	1.0000	1.0000
14750	1.0000	1.0000	1.0000
14500	1.0000	1.0000	1.0000
14250	1.0000	1.0000	1.0000
14000	1.0000	1.0000	1.0000

TABLE 3   Coefficients to derive Judd-based König fundamentals in Stiles primary system

Copunctal points:	p_1	p_2	p_3
Deuteranope	1.3741	-0.3868	0.0127
Protanope	1.0226	-0.0233	0.0070
Tritanope	0.0507	-0.0606	1.0099

Solution equations:

$$S_R = 0.2034\bar{p}_1 + 0.7239\bar{p}_2 + 0.0332\bar{p}_3$$
$$S_G = 0.0205\bar{p}_1 + 0.9022\bar{p}_2 + 0.0531\bar{p}_3$$
$$S_B = \phantom{0.0205\bar{p}_1 + {}} 0.0293\bar{p}_2 + 1.000\bar{p}_3$$

TABLE 4   Solution equations to derive fundamental sensitivities to the CIE and Stiles observers in the Stiles primary system

CIE observer

$$S_R = T^* (0.1870\bar{p}_1 + 0.6723\bar{p}_2 + 0.0309\bar{p}_3)$$
$$S_G = T^* (0.0187\bar{p}_1 + 0.8204\bar{p}_2 + 0.0483\bar{p}_3)$$
$$S_B = T^* (\phantom{0.0187\bar{p}_1 + {}} 0.0302\bar{p}_2 + 0.9202\bar{p}_3)$$

T^* is tabulated in Table 2 (Column 2)

Stiles observer

$$S_R = T^* (0.2067\bar{p}_1 + 0.7355\bar{p}_2 + 0.0338\bar{p}_3)$$
$$S_G = T^* (0.0193\bar{p}_1 + 0.8496\bar{p}_2 + 0.0500\bar{p}_3)$$
$$S_B = T^* (\phantom{0.0193\bar{p}_1 + {}} 0.0304\bar{p}_2 + 0.9202\bar{p}_3)$$

T^* is tabulated in Table 2 (Column 3)

fundamentals, the solution equations differ only in the setting of the peaks to unity. The resulting fundamentals are plotted in Fig. 4 and 5 and compared with the Smith and Pokorny (1975) fundamentals derived from the Judd observer. The fundamentals derived from the CIE observer show a good fit to those derived from the Judd observer although there is residual deviation of the B fundamental at short wavenumbers. The comparison of the fit of the fundamentals derived from the Stiles observer to those derived from the Judd observer shows some deviations, generally not exceeding 0.2 logarithmic units. For the R and G fundamentals the fits are good at short wavenumbers and the major deviations occur near 21,500 cm^{-1}. The B fundamental shows more serious deviations for wavenumbers below 18,500 cm^{-1}. Estévez (1979) pointed out that the difficulty with the B fundamental occurs because the spectrum locus in the chromaticity chart is not described by a straight line at short

CONE SENSITIVITY FUNCTIONS

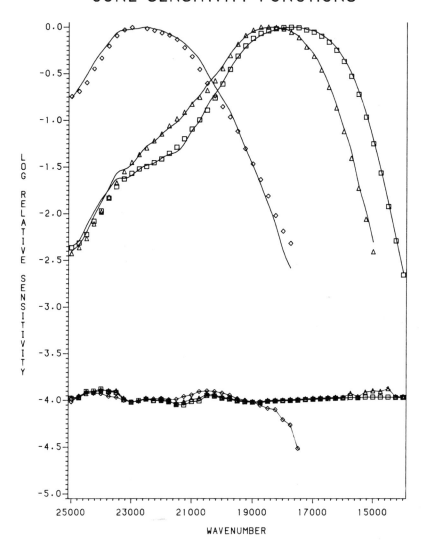

FIG. 4   The top panel shows the Smith-Pokorny (1975) fundamentals as solid lines and the fundamentals derived from the CIE observer as symbols. The bottom panel shows the difference between the two sets of log relative sensitivities centered at −4.0. Symbols: □, R; △, G; ◇, B.

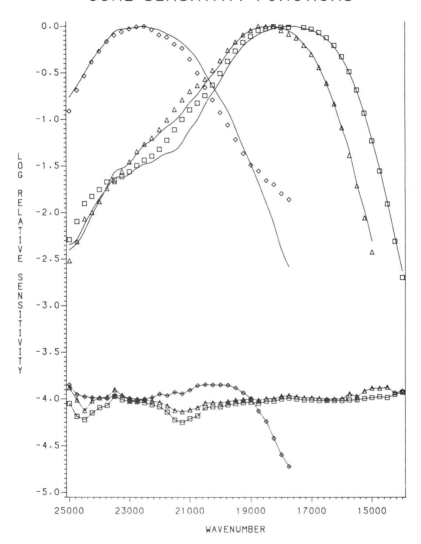

CONE SENSITIVITY FUNCTIONS

LOG RELATIVE SENSITIVITY

WAVENUMBER

FIG. 5   Comparison of Smith-Pokorny (1975) fundamentals [solid lines] and the fundamentals derived from Stiles average observer [symbols]. Symbols: □, R; △, G; ◇, B.

wavenumbers. Estévez suggested that rod intrusion in the Stiles (1955) pilot data is one potential cause of such nonlinearity. He noted that similar non-linearity was present in the original Guild (1931) and Wright (1929) data. This was smoothed in the process of deriving the CIE observer. If the B fundamental is truncated at 18,750 cm^{-1} (533 nm), the deviations are within 0.2 log units.

From the above analysis we conclude that the major sources of variation between the various sets of color-matching functions are the prereceptoral filters, the lens and the macular pigment. It may be noted that the derived differences fall within normal physiological variability. The macular pigment variation is relatively small. The lens values for the Judd (1951) and Stiles (1955) observers are characteristic of younger eyes than the CIE observer. We consider that the CIE (1931), the Judd (1951) and the Stiles (1955) observers are essentially equivalent for color-modelling purposes.

Acknowledgement

This work was supported in part by NEI Grants Ey 00901 and Ey 01876.

References

Boettner, E. A. and Wolter, J. R. (1962). Transmission of the ocular media. *Invest. Ophthal.* **1**, 776–783.

Boynton, R. M. and Wisowaty, J. J. (1980). Equations for chromatic discrimination models. *J. opt. Soc. Am.* **70**, 1471–1476.

Dresler, A. (1953). The non-additivity of heterochromatic brightness. *Trans Illum. Eng. Soc., Lond.* **18**, 141–156.

Eisner, A. and MacLeod, D. I. A. (1981). Flicker photometric study of chromatic adaptation: Selective suppression of cone inputs by colored backgrounds. *J. opt. Soc. Am.* **71**, 705–718.

Estévez, O. E. (1979). On the fundamental data-base of normal and dichromatic color vision. Thesis, Amsterdam, Krips Repro Meppel.

Gibson, K. S. and Tyndall, E. P. T. (1923). Visibility of radiant energy. U.S. Bureau of Standards. Scientific paper No. 475, **19**, 131–191.

Guild, J. (1931). The colorimetric properties of the spectrum. *Phil. Trans. roy. Soc., Lond.* A **230**, 149–187.

Judd, D. B. (1951). Secr. Rep. "Colorimetry and artificial daylight". In Proc. 12th Session C.I.E., Stockholm, Vol. I, Techn. committee, No. 7.

Norren, D. van and Vos, J. J. (1974). Spectral transmission of the human ocular media. *Vision Res.* **14**, 1237–1244.

Smith, V. C. and Pokorny, J. (1975). Spectral sensitivity of the foveal cone photo-pigments between 400 and 500 nm. *Vision Res.* **15**, 161–171.

Stiles, W. S. (1955). Interim report to the Commission Internationale de l'eclairage, Zurich, 1955 on the National Physical Laboratory's Investigation of colour-matching (1955), with an appendix by W. S. Stiles and J. M. Burch. *Optica Acta* **2**, 168–181.

Stiles, W. S. and Burch, J. M. (1959). N.P.L. colour matching investigation: Final report (1958). *Optica Acta* **6**, 1–26.

Thomson, L. C. and Wright, W. D. (1953). The convergence of the tritanopic confusion loci and the derivation of the fundamental response functions. *J. opt. Soc. Am.* **43**, 890–894.

Viénot, F. (1980). Relations between inter- and intra-individual variability of color matching functions. Experimental results. *J. opt. Soc. Am.* **70**, 1476–1483.

Vos, J. J. (1972). Literature Review of human macular absorption in the visible and its consequences for the cone receptor primaries. Soesterberg, Rep. Inst. Perception TNO Report No. 1972-17.

Vos, J. J. and Walraven, P. L. (1971). On the derivation of the foveal receptor primaries. *Vision Res.* **11**, 799–818.

Wagner, G. and Boynton, R. M. (1972). Comparison of four methods of heterochromatic photometry. *J. opt. Soc. Am.* **62**, 1508–1515.

Wright, W. D. (1929). A re-determination of trichromatic coefficients of the spectral colours. *Trans. opt. Soc.* **30**, 141–164.

Wyszecki, G. and Stiles, W. S. (1967). *Color Science.* John Wiley & Sons, New York.

Can Variation in Macular Pigment Account for the Variation of Colour Matches with Retinal Position?

F. VIÉNOT

Introduction

Colorimetry is based on visual trivariance, but a different colorimetric system is required according to whether a 2-deg or a 10-deg field is considered. This is so even if the level of illumination is restricted to the photopic domain. In general the difference in colour matches can be explained by the presence of macular pigment, which is more dense in the fovea. But, as Stiles (1955) states, "the difference is not wholly explicable by assuming receptor systems with identical (or linearly related) spectral sensitivities under uniform pigment layers of different densities".

In this paper, we first review briefly the various factors relevant to the differences found for large and small fields. Next, we present measurements of colour matching and of macular pigment density, both of which were obtained from the same observers; and, finally, we compare the results.

Colour-Matching Data at Various Retinal Locations

Moreland and Cruz (1959) made "asymmetric" matches between an extra-foveal spectral test and a foveal reference mixture (30 td, dark surround). They reported that the spectral locus is markedly reduced with increasing eccentricity; this modification was already visible at 10 deg. Wright (1946), carrying out symmetric matches on a 2-deg bipartite field, pointed out that changes occur in the spectral coefficient curves at 4 deg eccentricity: the negative red lobe is less pronounced, the blue more so. These trends were confirmed by Moreland (1955) at an eccentricity of 10 deg. The same type of change in the red lobe was reported by Stiles (1955) for a 10-deg centrally-fixated field when chromaticity coordinates were compared with those for a 2-deg field.

The chromaticity of the white point as matched in a 10-deg centrally fixated field is nearer to the white point for a 1 deg 20' field at 2.5 deg or 5 deg eccentricity than to the point for a small foveal test (Ruddock, 1963). Similarly, Pokorny, Smith and Starr (1976) suggest that tritan colour matches are determined neither by the extreme perimeter nor by the very centre of a centrally fixated field.

Maxwell's Spot

Maxwell's spot is seen by about 80% of observers. Several methods have been adopted to reduce its disturbing effect on colour matching with 10-deg bipartite fields: observers may be asked to ignore the spot (Stiles, 1955) or to make the best overall match (Nimeroff, 1964), or the centre of the field may be masked off (Speranskaya, 1959).

Spencer (1967) describes a halo with a diameter of about 2.5 deg that is present in all observers who see Maxwell's spot. The central zone, 30' in diameter, varies considerably in brightness from one observer to another. The halo is generally attenuated more rapidly than the centre. A high correlation exists between the threshold of Maxwell's spot, measured on a dichroic background after white or blue adaptation, and the observer's white point.

According to Clarke and Trezona (1975), Maxwell's spot is no longer visible when tetrachromatic matches are carried out with a blue or a violet test stimulus. This was denied by Palmer (1978) who found that the spot became all the more visible as the deviation between the blue and the violet radiations entering the mixture increased. He also noted that photometric matches on a 10-deg field differ by 7%, depending on whether Maxwell's spot disturbs the centre or whether the field is uniform.

Although Maxwell's spot is no longer seen at very high levels, the matches obtained at such levels do still differ for a 2-deg and a 10-deg field (Wyszecki, 1978).

Macular Pigment and its Relation to Maxwell's Spot

Subjective measurements of the absorption of the macular pigment are based on the differential measure of visual performance in the fovea and in the parafovea. In making such measurements, it is crucial to eliminate all variation that is of receptoral origin.

The density of the macular pigment changes rapidly between the centre of the foveola and small retinal eccentricities. Ruddock (1963) estimated the density along a meridian, in one highly pigmented observer, from the displacement of the white point in the chromaticity diagram. For a series of dark-adaptation curves obtained at 10 deg, 6 deg, 2 deg, 1 deg, 0.6 deg, and in the foveolar centre, Wald (1960) recorded the cone threshold for violet and yellow lights. The variation of the profiles between 0 deg and 2 deg indicated that the violet test was absorbed by the macular pigment. The estimation of macular pigment density by the threshold method is questioned by Stabell and Stabell (1980) who prefer to derive it from the elevation of the spectral sensitivity curve measured by flicker at short wavelengths; they report that the density of the macular pigment changes rapidly from 0 deg to 3 deg and stabilizes between 3 deg and 7 deg. Williams, MacLeod and Hayhoe (1981b) isolated the green cone mechanism by presenting their tests on a purple background. They determined the foveal distribution of the macular pigment by subtracting the green cone sensitivity map, obtained with a very small test of 420 nm, from the map obtained at 538.5 nm. Its profile agreed with the details of Maxwell's spot given by the same observer, for whom a slight central dip having a 3.6' diameter corresponded to the subjectively brighter centre, and a very dense halo having a 25' diameter corresponded to the darker halo. The results of Wooten (1981) were obtained by using heterochromatic flicker above the flicker fusion frequency of the blue mechanism; a red adapting background was used to isolate the response of the green cones. Naylor and Stanworth (1954) established that the main cause of Haidinger's brushes must be absorption by orientated macular pigment. They then plotted its areal distribution, which corresponded to the observer's Maxwell spot.

It is evident that a close correspondence exists between the distribution of the macular pigment and Maxwell's spot; however, a few discrepancies must still be explained. Spencer (1967) concluded from her studies that the halo of the Maxwell spot is attributable to the macular pigmentation, but that the cause of the central structure is less certain. It should be noted that all the macular pigment density profiles traced by various authors flatten out at about 2 deg eccentricity; but in the foveolar centre they are sometimes smooth, sometimes peaked, and sometimes notched.

The role of the macular pigment in colour matching can be reduced to that of an inert filter capable of modifying the spectral energy distribution of the stimuli. Recourse to the WDW system for calculating the spectral chromaticity coordinates allows the effects of this filter to be masked. In this case, any change of the spectrum locus would reflect only a change in the spectral sensitivity of the receptors. These properties have often been turned to for controlling the role of the macular pigment. Thus, the observers of Ruddock (1963) all yielded the same spectrum locus, although they differed in their pigmentations. A complication is the possibility that the macular pigment might be located in cone outer segments, a hypothesis introduced by Smith *et al.* (1976) to explain some colour-matching and spectral sensitivity data.

Rod Participation

Several authors (Wright, 1946; Speranskaya, 1959; Stiles and Burch, 1959) have considered the likely contribution of the rods in colour-matching data for large or extrafoveal fields. In addition, Moreland (1955), Clarke (1960) and Nimeroff (1964) report an additivity failure related to eccentricity, less pronounced with large fields, which they attribute to rod-cone interaction. This, however, is not the opinion of Stabell and Stabell (1977). Making measurements during the cone plateau period, they ruled out the contribution of the rods and showed in one observer, at an eccentricity of 5 deg, between 3 and 100 trolands, that the spectral chromaticity coordinates r and g of wavelengths longer than 460 nm do not change between the fovea and 5 deg eccentricity.

Large-field trichromacy in dichromatic subjects has been shown to be mediated by the rods acting as a third colour mechanism (Smith and Pokorny, 1977). However, Nagy's (1970) work on dichromats suggests that the participation of rods in matching stops at luminances below those producing rod saturation: the upper limits of rod participation were 160 scotopic td in a deutan and 40 in a protan observer. According to Aguilar and Stiles (1954), saturation of the rods occurs at about 2000 scotopic td.

Individual Variability

For large fields, inter-individual variations were reported by Stiles and Burch (1959). In a theoretical study of Stiles' results on 2-deg fields, Smith *et al.* (1976) showed that the profile of chromaticity coordinate dispersion over the spectrum is characteristic of the cause of that dispersion. To account for interobserver variability, they postulated variation in the optical density of the cones, or in the wavelength of peak sensitivity, or in both factors, along with the variation of the macular pigment. They considered the same model for the 10-deg data compared to the 2-deg data and concluded that in the periphery there is a reduction of the macular pigment and of the concentration of the visual pigment (Pokorny *et al.*, 1976). In studying the yellow matches made by 7 trichromats and 12 anomalous trichromats, Alpern (1979) obviated the differences in eye media and suggested that "the extinction spectra of the cone pigments sensitive to long and medium wavelengths might differ from one trichromat to the next".

In an earlier paper (Viénot, 1980), we noted fairly broad intra-individual dispersion which, for 10 observers, followed approximately the same tendencies over the spectrum. We mentioned significant intra-individual correlations between the red and the green colour-matching functions, more frequent than between either of them and the blue function. But, at the inter-individual level such correlations were not found.

Finally, let us note that microspectrophotometric recordings (Bowmaker and Mollon, 1980; see also Dartnall, Bowmaker and Mollon, this volume) reveal that there may be distinct populations within the same class of cones, each having a slightly different peak sensitivity; the variation may occur within as well as between retinae.

Experimental Results

In order to verify that the variation in macular pigment can account for the variation of colour matches with retinal position, the same observers were tested for their colour-matching functions at foveal and perifoveal locations and for the density of their macular pigment across the retina.

A. Colour Matching at Foveal and Perifoveal Locations

For the first experiment, the equipment and the matching procedure have been described elsewhere (Viénot, 1980). Quasi-monochromatic radiations are obtained with interference filters. Primaries are set at 466 nm, 526 nm and 627 nm. A 30-deg bipartite field is seen in Maxwellian view. Variously shaped stops may be inserted to define the limits of the coloured bipartite field (Fig. 1,

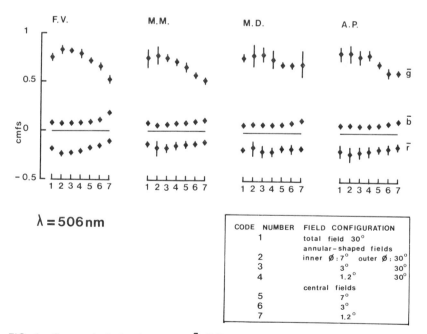

FIG. 1   Spectral tristimulus values $\bar{b}, \bar{g}, \bar{r}$ for test wavelength 506 nm, related to various configurations of the matching field. The inset indicates the retinal area covered by the matching field.

inset). A white field alternates with the coloured field every eight seconds and serves to renew the adaptation state of the retina however long a matching operation may last.

Four observers having normal colour vision took part in the experiment. They were 34, 22, 20 and 20 years old. Matches were repeated over ten sessions by the first observer and over five sessions by the other three.

An example of spectral tristimulus values is shown for one test wavelength (Fig. 1). The general trend is obvious: the spectral tristimulus values slightly increase or decrease from periphery to fovea. The total match tristimulus values are intermediate between the results for the peripheral and for the central configurations. Note that the exclusion of the small central region (1.2 deg) hardly changes colour matching.

The macular pigment is probably preponderant in modifying the match from the periphery to the fovea. It acts as an inert, spectrally selective filter, and so results in a selective attenuation of the fluxes reaching the photoreceptors. If such a filter is the only relevant factor, the logarithmic value of the ratio of two spectral tristimulus values should vary in the same way with stimulus configuration whatever the test wavelength that is being matched. Indeed, the shape of such curves for the present data does appear to remain constant (Fig. 2), except for the 668 nm match. (A likely explanation of this exception might be rod intrusion.)

We tested the hypothesis concerning the identity of the shape of the curves by an analysis of variance. Results for the 668-nm radiation were omitted from

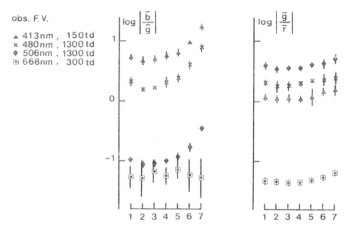

FIG. 2   Logarithms of the absolute value of the ratios of the colour-matching functions and dispersion, related to the various retinal areas in one observer (code number as in Fig. 1). For clarity's sake, only four wavelengths are reported. Estimates of the retinal illumination of the field for each test wavelength are also reported.

the analysis since they were clearly divergent. The analysis of variance nevertheless revealed the existence of an interaction between the test wavelength to be matched and the stimulated retinal area in three observers. Results are presented in Fig. 3.

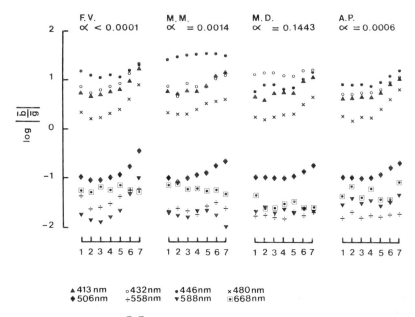

▲413 nm ○432nm ●446nm ×480nm
◆506nm ÷558nm ▼588nm ▣668nm

FIG. 3 Log-value of $|\bar{b}/\bar{g}|$ related to various retinal areas (code number as in Fig. 1) in the four observers. The level of significance (shown as α at the top of each panel) excludes the results for 668 nm because of the likely intrusion of the rods.

B. Distribution of the Macular Pigment

Optical density was determined by comparing the spectral sensitivity of the green cones at foveal and extrafoveal locations, using heterochromatic flicker photometry. A red (Wratten No. 70) adapting background having a troland value of 1100 trolands was steadily presented to adapt chromatically the red cones. The alternation rate of the flicker was 25 Hz, in order to eliminate the blue cone response. The pair of alternating wavelengths were 466 nm and 526 nm (the same wavelengths as the blue and green primaries in the former experiment). The measurements were made at locations spaced 1 deg apart, between 0 deg and 6 deg, along the left and the right hemi-meridians. A control experiment was conducted on a purple (Wratten No. 35) background. Since no significant difference was found, the results for the red and purple backgrounds were combined.

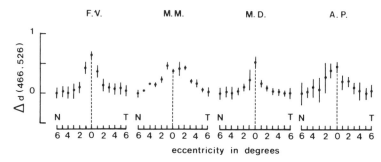

FIG. 4   Distribution at 466 nm and 526 nm of the difference in density of the macular pigment in the horizontal meridian (N : nasal and T : temporal), relative to the value of 6 deg eccentricity. Number of sessions: obs FV : 10, obs MM : 3, obs MD : 8, obs AP : 6.

Figure 4 shows the difference in density of the macular pigment at 466 nm and 526 nm, relative to the value at 6 deg eccentricity. The bars represent standard deviations.

Discussion

The plots of the logarithmic value of the ratio of the blue to the green spectral tristimulus values show a strong curvature, which reflects the presence of macular pigment. However, the analysis of variance indicates significant differences in the shapes of the curves, which may reveal the participation of some other factors in the variation of colour matches with retinal position.

We emphasize the similarity between the results of our two studies in which totally different techniques were used. Although the test field did not cover the same retinal areas, it should be noted that in both experiments the curves suggest a variation of similar form and extent in the density of the macular pigment. It should also be noted that the plots reflecting macular pigment density are characteristic of the individual observers.

What further factors may be operative in causing the difference between large and small colour-matching fields? There is the possibility that small-field matches are altered by a change in cone sensitivity near the centre of the visual field. For our results, in agreement with the suggestions of Ruddock (1963). Pokorny *et al.* (1976), and Williams *et al.* (1980a), show that the receptors at the peripheral limits of the field tend to dominate colour matches. If the cones play a role in modifying matches, this could arise only from a deformation in the action spectrum, which could be due to either a lengthening of the cones in the fovea (bringing about a self-screening effect) or an increase in photopigment density.

There is another problem to be considered. Most of the models aimed at explaining changes in colour matching assume a concentric distribution of both macular pigment and receptor sensitivity. However, in their study on the distribution of blue mechanism sensitivity throughout a 1-deg region, Williams *et al.* (1981b) demonstrated a marked asymmetry in B cone sensitivity between the inferior temporal side and the superior nasal side; the distribution of macular pigment was also not perfectly concentric. Irregularities of fixation might also introduce asymmetries (Le Grand, 1967). These considerations have implications for colour matches with a bipartite field. If the macular pigment is not symmetrically distributed to the right and the left of the bipartite field, the profile of the curve showing the logarithmic value of the ratio of the blue to the green spectral tristimulus values would take two different shapes according to whether the blue primary was on the left or the right.

The possibility of an asymmetry in the receptor mechanisms also exists. It would be interesting to evaluate their sensitivity on the left and the right in the same observer. Matches obtained with a bipartite field are usually called "symmetric", but once we allow that there may be an asymmetry in retinal sensitivity, we should treat such matches as being obtained with different retinal surfaces and call them asymmetric.

In conclusion, it does not seem reasonable to rely on a circular symmetry of the factors capable of modifying matches in and around the fovea. This asymmetry could be the reason why it is always difficult completely to explain the differences between matches obtained for a 2-deg and a 10-deg field. This question should be further investigated, whatever be the model tested to explain the variation of colour matches with retinal position.

References

Aguilar, M. and Stiles, W. S. (1954). Saturation of the rod mechanism of the retina at high levels of stimulation. *Optica Acta* **1**, 59.

Alpern, M. (1979). Lack of uniformity in colour matching. *J. Physiol., Lond.* **288**, 85–105.

Bowmaker, J. K. and Mollon, J. D. (1980). Primate microspectrophotometry and its implications for colour deficiencies. In *Colour Vision Deficiencies V* (ed. Verriest, G.), pp. 61–64. Adam Hilger, Bristol.

Clarke, F. J. J. (1960). Extrafoveal colour metrics. *Optica Acta* **7**, 355–384.

Clarke, F. J. J. and Trezona, P. W. (1975). Towards general systems of colorimetry and photometry based on the tetrachromatic colour match. C.I.E. publ. No. 36 (1976), Paris.

Le Grand, Y. (1967). *Form and Space Vision*. Indiana University Press, Bloomington and London.

Moreland, J. D. (1955). The perception of colour by extrafoveal and peripheral vision. PhD thesis, University of London.

Moreland, J. D. (1972). Peripheral colour vision. In *Handbook of Sensory Physiology* (ed. Jameson, D. and Hurvich, L. M.), Vol. VII/4, pp. 517–536. Springer-Verlag, Berlin and New York.

Moreland, J. D. and Cruz, A. (1959). Colour perception with the peripheral retina. *Optica Acta* **6**, 117–151.

Nagy, A. L. (1980). Large-field substitution Rayleigh matches of dichromats. *J. opt. Soc. Am.* **70**, 778–784.

Naylor, E. J. and Stanworth, A. (1954). Retinal pigment and the Haidinger effect. *J. Physiol., Lond.* **124**, 543–552.

Nimeroff, I. (1964). Colorimetry in parafoveal fields. I. Color matching functions. *J. opt. Soc. Am.* **54**, 824–832.

Palmer, D. A. (1978). Maxwell spot and additivity in tetrachromatic matches. *J. opt. Soc. Am.* **68**, 1501–1505.

Pokorny, J., Smith, V. C. and Starr, S. J. (1976). Variability of color mixture data – II. The effect of viewing field size on the unit coordinates. *Vision Res.* **16**, 1095–1098.

Ruddock, K. H. (1963). Evidence for macular pigmentation from colour matching data. *Vision Res.* **3**, 417–429.

Smith, V. C. and Pokorny, J. (1977). Large-field trichromacy in protanopes and deuteranopes. *J. op. Soc. Am.* **67**, 213–220.

Smith, V. C., Pokorny, J. and Starr, S. J. (1976). Variability of color mixture data – I. Inter-observer variability in unit coordinates. *Vision Res.* **16**, 1087–1094.

Spencer, J. A. (1967). An investigation of Maxwell's spot. *Br. J. physiol. Opt.* **24**, 103–147.

Speranskaya, N. I. (1959). Determination of spectrum color coordinates for twenty-seven normal observers. *Optics Spectrosc.* **7**, 424–428.

Stabell, B. and Stabell, U. (1977). The chromaticity coordinates for spectrum colours of extrafoveal cones. *Vision Res.* **17**, 1091–1094.

Stabell, U. and Stabell, B. (1980). Variation in density of macular pigmentation and in short-wave cone sensitivity with eccentricity. *J. op. Soc. Am.* **70**, 706–711.

Stiles, W. S. (1955). Interim report to the Commission Internationale de l'Eclairage. *Optica Acta* **2**, 168–181.

Stiles, W. S. and Burch, J. M. (1959). NPL colour-matching investigation: final report. *Optica Acta* **6**, 1–26.

Viénot, F. (1980). Relations between inter- and intra-individual variability of color-matching functions. Experimental results. *J. opt. Soc. Am.* **70**, 1476–1483.

Wald, G. (1960). Analysis of retinal function by a two-filter method. *J. opt. Soc. Am.* **50**, 633–641.

Williams, D. R., MacLeod, D. I. A. and Hayhoe, M. M. (1981a). Foveal tritanopia. *Vision Res.* **21**, 1341–1356.

Williams, D. R., MacLeod, D. I. A. and Hayhoe, M. M. (1981b). Punctate sensitivity of the blue-sensitive mechanism. *Vision Res.* **21**, 1357–1375.

Wooten, B. R. (1981). Spectral absorbance and distribution of the macular pigment. Proceedings of 4th European Conference on Visual Perception, Gouvieux, France.

Wright, W. D. (1946). *Researches on Normal and Defective Colour Vision*. Henry Kimpton, London.

Wyszecki, G. (1978). Color matching at moderate to high levels of retinal illuminance: a pilot study. *Vision Res.* **18**, 341–346.

A Note on Theory of the Stiles-Crawford Effects

M. ALPERN

The brightness, as well as the color, of a light depends upon its angle of incidence on the retina. These two phenomena are known as the Stiles-Crawford Effects of the first (SCE I) and second (SCE II) kind respectively. Forty-five years after its discovery (Stiles, 1937) it is remarkable that theory – a single paper excepted – has utterly failed to deal with the color effect. There is a body of theory dealing with the subset of SCE II data known as the "hue shift", but it is the subset ignored by such theory which proves crucial to understanding the whole. Experiments providing quantitative data on this whole are again found in only a single paper. It is the same paper (Enoch and Stiles, 1961).

Drs Kenji Kitahara, Ryutaro Tamaki and I have studied its implications in some depth. In Cambridge I summarized the findings of three papers (Alpern and Kitahara, 1983; Alpern, Kitahara and Tamaki, 1983; Alpern and Tamaki, 1983) which lead to the strong inference that a fundamental assumption of the Enoch and Stiles theory – or, somewhat less strongly, any *unified* theory of the two Stiles-Crawford Effects – is false. Documenting that conclusion is difficult with present space constraints. Even if it were not, it must be done in a journal with severe referees.

Journals appropriately reject redundancy, so this paper summarizes a single aspect of the work excluded from the first of these papers, when it proved overly long.

To understand SCE II, Alpern and Kitahara (1982) measured the intensity effect (SCE I) for each of the three species of foveal cones (upon which their observer's color vision presumably depends) operationally defined by the field sensitivities of the three Stiles mechanisms $\Pi_j(\mu)$, where j = 3, 4 and 5. The details are given in their paper. In brief, the field sensitivity of a monochromatic background of wavenumber $(\mu)^{-1}$ (i.e. its radiance effecting tenfold threshold elevation) in succession entering the eye at different points r along a horizontal chord through the pupil center, was measured throughout the spectrum for each mechanism.

The results of a single set of such measurements (j = 3, μ^{-1} = 24,988 cm^{-1}) are plotted at the bottom of Fig. 1. In the figure ordinates are log

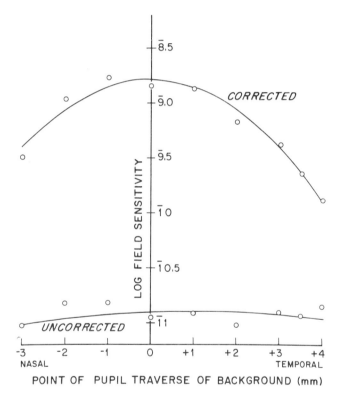

FIG. 1   Log$_{10}$ of the field sensitivity of Π_3 for backgrounds μ^{-1} = 24,988 cm^{-1} entering the entrance pupil at different positions r along the horizontal chord through its center. The data plotted below are obtained from the radiances measured at the cornea, those above are corrected for different pathlengths through this observer's lens. The curves are the computer optimized fits to Equation (1) which minimizes the r.m.s. deviations. Its equation is $S(r)$ = 10.911 ± 0.048 + (0.007 ± 0.0066) $(r - 1.02 ± 13.86)^2$ for the lower curve and $S(r)$ = 8.787 ± 0.042 + (0.0691 ± 0.006) $(r + 0.117 ± 0.097)^2$ for the upper curve. The former accounts for almost none (i.e. 0.24%), the latter for 95% of the variance of field sensitivity with r.

field sensitivities, photons $^{-1}$ (400.2 nm) sec deg^2; the abscissas specify the points (r) in the plane of the entrance pupil through which the background beam traversed the optics of the eye. Stiles (1939) "tentatively" suggested quantifying the directional sensitivity (SCE I) of each mechanism for every background by a variant of his Equation (10) which reduces to

$$S_j(\mu) = -\log \Pi_j(\mu) - \varrho_j(\mu) (r - r_0)^2. \tag{1}$$

With these symbols $10^{-S_j(\mu)}$ is the field sensitivity of the j mechanism for backgrounds μ traversing the pupil position r and $\Pi_j(\mu)$ is that sensitivity for the most effective pupil point r_0. The solid line through the results plotted at the bottom of Fig. 1 has this equation fitted by computer to minimize the squares of the deviations of these experimental data. Because the parabola is so flat it accounts for only 0.24% of the variance in sensitivity shown in the figure.

These results are appreciably distorted by the facts that the light path of the background through the edge of the lens is much shorter than the path traversed by the foveal chief ray, and that for this observer, and this background, only 0.78% of the radiance in the chief ray striking the front of his lens emerges at the lens–vitreous interface. Alpern and Kitahara (1983) measured the spectral density of their observer's lens correcting for pathlength differences for every r, μ and j. The corrected field sensitivities (for the same data set) are shown by the circles above in Fig. 1.

The computer fit of Equation (1) to the corrected values in this figure is a satisfactory quantification of the results; it accounts for 95% of the variance in the data. Alpern and Kitahara (1983) found for their subject that for every μ and j, Equation (1) similarly provided accurate descriptions of the $S(r)$ relationship after correction for losses in the observer's lens. The dependency of the directional sensitivity (SCE I) with field wavenumber of each mechanism was completely described by the $\varrho_j(\mu)$ of these computer fits to the corrected $S(r)$ data. It is noteworthy that invariably $\varrho < 0$.

These results are here evaluated in terms of current theories of the wavelength dependencies of the Stiles-Crawford effect of the first kind (SCE I). The approach is described by Zwas (1979); details will be found in his paper and in the references he cites. Zwas (1979) considered two approaches to the directional theory of a single cone species: (1) the self-screening model which Enoch and Stiles (1961) (see also Walraven and Bouman, 1960) applied to calculations of spectra inferred from color matching and (2) the wave-guide hypothesis of Snyder and Pask (1973).

Theory

Self-Screening Model

The visual pigment of each photoreceptor is supposed to be concentrated in relatively high density (D_m) at the wavenumber of peak absorbance (Brindley, 1953; 1955; Alpern, 1979). The full density $D(\mu)$ achieved by the entire outer segment length is exposed to normally incident light, but obliquely incident light traverses a much smaller length of outer segment and exposes a much less dense pigment as a consequence. Light which passes through a given outer segment and then passes out into the surround is assumed lost to the visual act, as if for example each outer segment were encased in an opaque pigment sheath. [Sheathing is a recognized ultrastructural feature of human and other mammalian cone, but not rod, outer segments (Walls, 1934; Steinberg and Wood, 1974) but it is not opaque. If however, its index of refraction were appreciably higher than that of the immediate outer segment surround n_s it might perform the same optical function.] The fraction of light passing down the outer segment lost to surrounding tissue is quantified by the "leakage density" A, which is wavenumber independent, increasing with increasing obliquity and zero for normally incident light. The resulting equation (Enoch and Stiles, 1961; Zwas, 1979) is:

$$-\varrho(\mu) = \frac{1}{(r - r_0)^2} \log \left[\left(\frac{D(\mu) + A}{D(\mu)} \right) \left(\frac{1 - 10^{-D(\mu)}}{1 - 10^{-[D(\mu) + A]}} \right) \right] . \tag{2}$$

For a receptor in which self-screening occurs, the directional effect will be least at the wavenumber most strongly absorbed by its visual pigment.

Wave-Guide Model

A wavenumber dependency of photoreceptor directional sensitivity is implicit in the first suggestion (by Toraldo di Francia, 1948, 1949a, b) that wave optics is essential for SCE I theory because of constraints imposed by the size of human fovea cones. Twenty-five years elapsed before an explicit quantitative theory appeared (Snyder and Pask, 1972; 1973).

Simon (1970) proposed a simpler model based on diffraction theory. It can easily be extended to make the prediction that ϱ will vary directly with the square of the wavenumber of the background. This relation fails to provide a reasonable description of the results for the wavelength dependency of the directional sensitivity of any of the mechanisms studied here and analysis turned to the more complex waveguide model of Snyder and Pask.

A cone in this model has a circular cross section with cylindrical outer segment of diameter d_0 and of uniform index of refraction n_0, the index of refraction of the inner segment n_i is also uniform. Note that $n_s < n_i < n_0$.

The inner segment is conical with a maximum diameter d_i tapering to d_0 at the inner–outer segment junction. Light travels along this model in the form of discrete patterns, or *modes*. Some of the light remains inside but a fundamental property of a mode is that part of its light is transmitted outside the receptor. Depending upon the mode, the fraction of light inside the inner segment may go to zero during the cone traverse. The light in these modes is radiated to the surrounding medium and lost. For modes which do not radiate, the taper funnels the light to the inner–outer segment junction. Mode 1 and mode 2 are the most important. For normal incidence only mode 1 is excited but as the angle of oblique incidence increases, mode 2 becomes excited and mode 1 becomes less important. The directional properties are determined by summing the total modal power which can be absorbed by the visual pigment in the outer segment. This is the modal power at the inner–outer segment junction which can be sustained by the outer segment structure. The relevant equations are derived by Snyder and Pask (1972, 1973).

Results

The $\varrho_j(\mu)$ ($j = 3, 4, 5$) data of Alpern and Kitahara (1983) have been analyzed following methods described by Zwas and the best fitting parameters of the two theories together with the r.m.s. deviations from the best fitting $\varrho_j(\mu)$ theoretical curves for each mechanisms and each theory are summarized in Table 1. Space constraints obviate illustrating the confrontation of each data set with each theory, but the same features generally characterize all three mechanisms and only the $\varrho_5(\mu)$ results are given here as representative of both the facilities and the difficulties of this approach to the Alpern and Kitahara (1983) data.

The open circles in Fig. 2A are Alpern and Kitahara's (1983) $\varrho_5(\mu)$ data obtained by computer application of Equation (1) to $\Pi_5 S(r)$ results corrected for losses in the lens. The lines specify the limit of one standard error on each side of the mean. The dashed curve in the figure was obtained by drawing an eye-fitted smooth curve through the $\Pi_5(\mu)$ action spectrum for $r = r_0$ and assigning to this spectrum a peak density $D_m = 0.6 \log_{10}$ units and a leakage density $A = 1.6 \log_{10}$ units and substituting directly into Equation (2). This is the best fitting prediction of the self-screening theory. The points deviate from this curve with an r.m.s. deviation of 5.95×10^{-3} (Table 1, row 3, column 4).

The solid curve through these same data is the best waveguide curve fit to those results. It is generated by inner segment parameters given in A–2 in Table 1, once the constraints provided by the other parameters of the model are imposed (see Appendix).

Self-screening theory applied to these data predicts for each mechanism that $D_m = 0.6$ for $r = r_0$ and that D_m is negligibly small for $r - r_0 = 3.5$ mm.

TABLE 1   Directional and spectral properties of foveal mechanisms (data of Alpern and Kitahara, 1982)

	$\Pi_3(\mu)$	$\Pi_4(\mu)$	$\Pi_5(\mu)$
A. Theory of $\varrho_j(\mu)$			
1. Self-Screening			
D_m (common log units)	0.6	0.6	0.6
A (common log units)	2.2	1.55	1.6
r.m.s. deviations $\times 10^3$	7.64	7.82	5.95
2. Wave-Guide			
d_j (μm)	2.285	2.622	2.690
n_j	1.3505	1.3540	1.3533
r.m.s. deviations $\times 10^3$	9.25	5.87	6.82
B. Nomogram Fit to Action Spectra			
1. $r - r_0 = 0$			
μ_m^{-1} (cm^{-1})	23,082	19,107	17,635
D_m (common log units)	0.0001	0.312	0.1526
r.m.s. deviations	0.134	0.0965	0.0482
n	16	27	21
2. $r - r_0 = 3.5$ mm			
μ_m^{-1} (cm^{-1})	23,113	19,107	17,659
D_m (common log units)	0.0001	0.0001	0.0781
r.m.s. deviations	0.182	0.144	0.0709
n	16	18	21

To evaluate these expectations we have followed Pugh and Sigel (1978) who used the minimization routine STEPIT (Chandler, 1965) to fit visual pigment nomograms to Stiles' Π mechanisms. Following procedures described in their paper we have fit each one of the six action spectra of interest $j = 3, 4$ and 5 for $r = r_0$ and for $r - r_0 = 3.5$ mm. Each of these data sets was corrected not only for losses in the lens but also for losses in the observer's macular pigment (obtained from *ad hoc* experiment) and remaining eye media as described by Alpern and Kitahara (1983). Ebrey and Honig's (1977) long- and short-wave nomograms were used for $j = 5$ and 3 respectively and the Dartnall nomogram (Wyszecki and Stiles, 1967) for $j = 4$; each nomogram had a linear long-wave extension. The routine adjusted the peak wavenumber for $(\mu)_m^{-1}$ and D_m (along with a scaling factor) to minimize the deviations of the log sensitivity action spectrum from the best-fitting theoretical absorption spectrum. The resulting parameters for each of these curves are summarized in Part B of Table 1.

The density $(D_m = 0.6)$ required to fit the $\varrho_j(\mu)$ relation is not to be found in the fit of either $\Pi_3(\mu)$, $\Pi_4(\mu)$ or $\Pi_5(\mu)$. The closest agreement $[\Pi_4(\mu)]$ is still

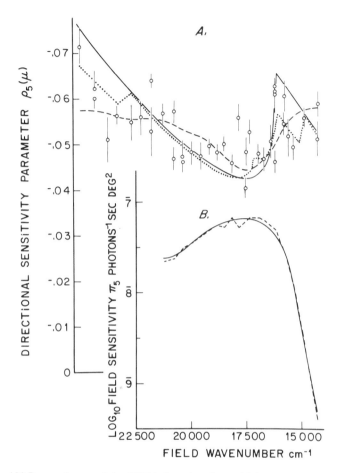

FIG. 2 (A) Dependency of the SCE I directional sensitivity parameter $\varrho_5(\mu)$ upon background wavenumber. The circles are the mean values ± 1 sem of the corrected Π_5 data of Alpern and Kitahara (1983). The dashed line describes the best fitting self-screening prediction with $\mu_m = 573.4$ nm, $D_m = 0.6$ and $A = 1.6$ respectively (Table 1). The solid line illustrates the best fitting curve from wave-guide theory setting $d_i = 2.69$, and $n_i = 1.3533$ (along with $n_s = 1.34$; $n_0 = 1.39$; $d_0 = 1.5\,\mu$m obtained as described in the Appendix). The dotted line is calculated from a modified wave-guide theory in which the directional sensitivity is determined by pooling responses from four subsets of Π_5 cones with slightly different d_i and n_i parameters, including the one used to determine the solid line. The others are 1.353, 2.55; 1.3527, 2.75 and 1.36, 2.75 respectively.

(B) Dashed line: Alpern and Kitahara (1983) field sensitivity corrected for losses in the cornea, aqueous, lens, vitreous and macular pigment for $\Pi_5(\mu)$ $r = r_0$ over the range of background wavenumbers the nomogram can be applied. The solid line is the optimized fit of the Ebrey-Honig long-wave, nomogram obtained by the method outlined in the text. This has $\mu_m^{-1} = 17,635$, $D_m = 0.1526$. Given the precision of the agreement (r.m.s. deviations = 0.0482) the latter value is measurably smaller than $D_m = 0.6$ expected from the fit of the self-screening theory to the results in (A).

too small by a factor of two. But in this case the action spectrum peaks at μ_m^{-1} = 19,107 cm^{-1} while the smallest value for $-\varrho_4(\mu)$ occurs at 18,149 cm^{-1}. The discrepancy (equivalent to more than 25 nm) is sufficient to reject the fundamental tenet of self-screening that the receptor be directionally least, and spectrally most, sensitive at the same wavenumber, even if both $\Pi_4(\mu)$ and $\varrho_4(\mu)$ curve fitting had yielded the same D_m.

In the case of both $\varrho_3(\mu)$ and $\varrho_5(\mu)$ self-screening fits the variation of the directional sensitivity parameter with field wavenumber better than waveguide theory (Table 1). But self-screening is inconsistent with the action spectra of these mechanisms.

In Fig. 2B the solid curve represents the pigment absorption spectrum obtained by applying the STEPIT routine to $\Pi_5(\mu)$, $r = r_0$; the dashed line represents this corrected Π_5 field sensitivity for the spectral range the nomogram can be applied. The fitting procedure yields a good description of the corrected $\Pi_5(\mu)$ field sensitivity, though we are often told (Wald, 1964; Eisner and MacLeod, 1981) that the $\Pi_5(\mu)$ spectrum is too broad to represent the "true" absorption spectrum of a pigment. Paradoxically it is the fact that it is *not broad enough* which rejects self-screening theory applied to the wavelength variation in directional sensitivity (SCE I) of this mechanism. The D_m selected by STEPIT to fit the dashed lines, in Fig. 2B was only 0.1526, (row 8, column 4); self-screening theory fit to results in Fig. 2A required 0.6. On the other hand for $r - r_0 = 3.5$, the measured spectrum is broader than expected if (as required by that theory) the density were negligibly small. The double contradiction tips the balance towards the Snyder-Pask alternative as the more reasonable theoretical account of the wavelength variation in directional sensitivity of Π_5, despite the fact that r.m.s. deviations of the data in Fig. 2A from the (solid) curve generated by waveguide theory is larger than it is for the self-screening curve.

The high r.m.s. deviations in the waveguide fit can be traced to the sharp discontinuity in the theoretical curve at wavenumbers at which (for obliquely incident light) a mode sustained at higher wavenumber is abruptly lost. Snyder and Pask (1973) related this difficulty to the implausible simplification that all photoreceptors have identical parameters. They suggested pooling responses from individual receptors with slightly different parameters to broaden the peak at this critical wavenumber.

The dotted line in Fig. 2A illustrates such a modification applied to $\varrho_5(\mu)$. This curve was obtained by pooling responses of four subsets of Π_5 cones with slightly different n_i, d_i parameters, including the subset yielding the solid curve in the figure. The fit is considerably improved – r.m.s. deviations = 5.04×10^{-3}. [The responses pooled were assumed proportional to the logarithm of photon absorptions, not the Snyder and Pask assumption that they are directly proportional to the photon absorptions (r.m.s. deviation = 6.55×10^{-3}).] Considering the number of additional parameters available the improvement is hardly surprising and it is pointless to press curve-fitting beyond the observation that deviations of the theory from measurements in the neighborhood of the critical wavenumber are insufficient grounds for categorically rejecting the Snyder-Pask theory. But attempts to generate a more realistic, and considerably smoother, waveguide curve based on distributions of n_i, d_i values must await a better understanding of the physiology of the pooling process.

With regard to the comparison of alternative simple theories of $\varrho_3(\mu)$, an evaluation analogous to that applied to ϱ_5, leads to a similar conclusion. Nonetheless Enoch and Stiles' (1961) grounds for rejecting self-screening theory applied to short-wave sensitive cones prove grossly inconsistent with the $\varrho_3(\mu)$ data. There is both a trivial and a fundamental cause for this inconsistency. The former is that Enoch and Stiles depended upon the literature to estimate losses in their observers' lens and these estimations were almost certainly too conservative at the violet spectrum extreme. The latter is that Enoch and Stiles' inferences were drawn from matching, not thresholds (Alpern, Kitahara and Tamaki, 1983).

The computer minimization routine fit to the $\Pi_3(\mu)$ spectrum $r = r_0$ yields a D_m at the lower limit of available values (0.0001). A further case against $\Pi_3(\mu)$ self-screening follows from a comparison of the long-wave end of the field sensitivity spectra for $r = r_0$ and $r - r_0 = 3.5$. Results were obtained at seven backgrounds for $\mu^{-1} \leq 20,751$ cm^{-1}. These data were remarkably well fit (for $r = r_0$, accounting for all but 0.245%, for $r - r_0 = 3.5$ for all but 1.58%, of the variance) with a straight line on a plot of log field sensitivity against μ^{-1}(cm)$^{-1}$, consistent with Stiles' (1948) theory of spectral sensitivity curves. For r_0 the slope of this line was $- 1.02 \times 10^{-3}$; but for $r - r_0 = -3.5$ it was -0.9×10^{-3}, a significantly ($t = 2.86$, $0.05 > \varrho > 0.02$) shallower value. But from the predicted densities self-screening theory requires it to be steeper!

Discussion

Taking advantage of the full power of the theory of self-screening it is possible to exclude it as a viable explanation for the SCE I wavelength dependency of each of the mechanisms studied by Alpern and Kitahara (1983). The elimination process leaves only the weaker theory, i.e. guiding waves by cone structure. The theory is weaker because it yields parameters, the consistency of which can be evaluated only by considering that structure. The process requires the ability both to identify the absorption spectrum of the visual pigment in the outer segment of individual photoreceptors, and to discriminate subtle morphological differences between them. This combination of technical competences is so far to be found only in the study of Baylor and Fettiplace (1975) on single cones of the turtle retina. They report that "... The dimensions of cones were found to be scaled approximately in proportion to the wavelength of maximum sensitivity. Red receptors were largest, green receptors intermediate and blue receptors smallest''. For the diameters of the inner (*and* the outer) segments these ratios were: 1.65 : 1.28 : 1 while for the λ_{max}s they were 1.4 : 1.22 : 1.0. This trend is also found in the waveguide analysis of the present results (Table 1). The ratios of μ_m are 1.3 : 1.2 : 1.0. The ratios of the diameters of the inner segment in row 4, Table 1 are 1.18 : 1.15 : 1.0; for the outer segment (Fig. 3, see Appendix) these ratios are 1.33 : 1.33 : 1.0. [The model outer segment diameter is only constrained by a lower limit (see Appendix). The subtle distinctions between $\Pi_4(\mu)$ and $\Pi_5(\mu)$ possible with inner segment diameter can not be made between outer segment diameters of these two mechanisms by this analysis.]

Further study can decide whether these rough agreements are more than coincidental. The theory is too simple and its fit to the data (r.m.s. deviations in row 6, Table 1) is not especially impressive. Still, that two such widely different approaches on two such diverse species converge to qualitatively, and at least approximate quantitatively, similar inferences, suggests that efforts to exclude the hypothesis that human short-wave sensitive cones are smallest and long-wave sensitive cones the largest of the three species of foveal cones might prove worthwhile. It is remarkable that problems of this sort are now capable of experimental resolution, as other papers in this volume make clear.

Appendix

Fitting the Snyder-Pask Waveguide Model to $\varrho_i(\mu)$ Data

The five free parameters available to confront theory with data, make the waveguide analysis vulnerable to the criticism that its ratio (assumptions made)/(facts explained) is too large. However, the requirement of *biological realism* reduces the curve fitting parameters sufficiently to make it comparable to self-screening theory.

Obviously one cannot suppose the index of refraction of the surround n_s different for each cone species; it must be fixed at a biologically plausible value. Arbitrarily set $n_s = 1.34$. Secondly, the requirement that only the modal power which can be sustained by the outer segment structure is relevant for vision, specifies a set of boundary conditions above which variations in d_0, n_0 do not influence theoretical predictions. In a plot of d_0 against n_0, any set of parameters falling in the area above this boundary limit is equally useful and in so far as the theory is concerned one set is neither better nor worse than another within these constraints.

The two smooth curves showing d_0 as a function of n_0 in Fig. 3 specify these boundary limits found in the present analysis [the lower curve for $\Pi_3(\mu)$, the other for $\Pi_4(\mu)$ and $\Pi_5(\mu)$]. But the index of refraction n_0 should correspond realistically to *in vivo* measurements. Sidman (1957) in Barer's (1957)

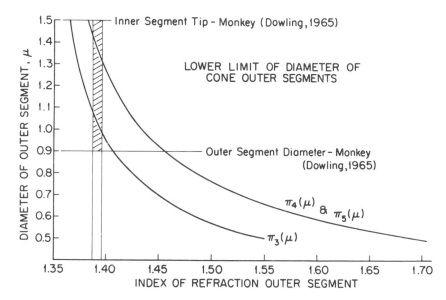

FIG. 3   Lower limit estimates of the value of d_0 (ordinate in μm) and n_0 acceptable in fitting the waveguide model to the ϱ_j against (μ) data of Alpern and
Kitahara (1983). Any value d_0, n_0 falling above the lower curve [for $\Pi_3(\mu)$] and
above the upper curve [for $\Pi_4(\mu)$ and $\Pi_5(\mu)$] yield the curves through their $\varrho_j(\mu)$
results when used with the d_i, n_i and n_s values specified (Table 1). Any value of
d_0, n_0 falling below the respective curves shown here when used with those
other parameters no longer define the same $\varrho_j(\mu)$ relation. The vertical straight
lines represent estimates of n_0 obtained by Sidman (1957) in Barer's (1957)
laboratory. The upper horizontal line is the diameter of the outermost tip of the
inner segment of rhesus foveal cones measured by Dowling (1965), the lower
horizontal line is his estimate of the diameter of the outer segment of monkey
foveal cones. In the model these two dimensions must be equal. The cross-hatched
rectangle defined by these four lines specifies a biologically realistic range and
suggests outer segments of short-wave sensitive cones may prove thinner than
the outer segments of medium- and long-wave sensitive cones.

laboratory suggested the limits of n_0 between 1.387 and 1.396. Two vertical
lines have been drawn in Fig. 3 at these abscissa values. Similarly ultra structure data on foveal cones provide constraints on the outer segment diameter;
Dowling (1965) specifies the outer tip of the inner segment as 1.5 μm and the
diameter of the inner tip of the outer segment as 0.9 μm in rhesus (*Macaca
mulatta*). Horizontal lines are drawn at these ordinates in Fig. 3 because the
inner–outer segment junction has the same dimension in the model (whether
defined by the innermost tip of the outer segment or the outermost tip of the
inner segment). The cross-hatched rectangle in Fig. 3 defines the area specified
by these constraints. The result indicates a domain of possible outer segment

diameters for short-wave sensitive cones impossibly small for long- and medium-wave sensitive cones (Fig. 3). This paper arbitrarily uses $n_0 = 1.39$, $d_0 = 1.5 \mu m$.

Acknowledgements

Assisted by grant EY-00197-24 from the National Eye Institute. I am indebted to the collaboration of Kenji Kitahara, M.D. and Ryutaro Tamaki, M.D. in the experiments which yielded the results analyzed here, to E. N. Pugh, Jr for providing the STEPIT program used to analyze the field sensitivity spectra and to Fred Zwas for helpful discussions.

References

Alpern, M. (1979). Lack of uniformity in colour matching. *J. Physiol.* **288**, 85–105.

Alpern, M. and Kitahara, K. (1983). The directional sensitivities of the Stiles' color mechanisms. *J. Physiol., Lond.* **338** (In press).

Alpern, M., Kitahara, K. and Tamaki, R. (1983). The dependence of the color and the brightness of a monochromatic light upon its angle of incidence on the retina. *J. Physiol., Lond.* **338** (In press).

Alpern, M. and Tamaki, R. (1983). The saturation of monochromatic lights obliquely incident on the retina. *J. Physiol., Lond.* **338** (In press).

Barer, R. (1957). Refractometry and interferometry of living cells. *J. opt. Soc. Am.* **47**, 545–556.

Baylor, D. A. and Fettiplace, R. (1975). Light path and photon capture in turtle photo-receptors. *J. Physiol.* **248**, 433–464.

Brindley, G. S. (1953). The effects on colour vision of adaptation to very bright lights. *J. Physiol.* **122**, 332–350.

Brindley, G. S. (1955). A photochemical reaction in the human retina. *Proc. phys. Soc. B* **68**, 862–870.

Chandler, J. P. (1965). STEPIT. Quantum chemistry exchange program. Department of Chemistry, Indiana University, Bloomington, Indiana.

Dowling, J. E. (1965). Foveal receptors of the monkey retina: fine structure. *Science, N.Y.* **147**, 57–59.

Ebrey, T. G. and Honig, B. (1977). New wavelength dependent visual pigment nomograms. *Vision Res.* **17**, 147–151.

Eisner, A. and MacLeod, D. I. A. (1981). Flicker photometer study of chromatic adaptation: selective suppression of cone inputs by colored backgrounds. *J. opt. Soc. Am.* **71**, 705–718.

Enoch, J. M. and Stiles, W. S. (1961). The colour change of monochromatic light with retinal angle of incidence. *Optica Acta* **8**, 329–358.

Pugh, E. N., Jr and Sigel, C. (1978). Evaluation of the candidacy of the Π-mechanisms of Stiles for color-matching fundamentals. *Vision Res.* **18**, 317–330.

Sidman, R. L. (1957). The structure and concentration of solids in photoreceptor cells studied by refractometry and interference microscopy. *J. biophys. biochem. Cytol.* **3**, 15–30.

Simon, J. (1970). Un nouveau modèle destiné à l'interprétation de l'effect Stiles-Crawford. *Vision Res.* **10**, 1471–1476.

Snyder, A. W. and Pask, C. (1972). Light absorption in the bee photoreceptor. *J. opt. Soc. Am.* **62**, 998–1008.

Snyder, A. W. and Pask, C. (1973). The Stiles-Crawford effect–explanation and consequences. *Vision Res.* **13**, 1115–1137.

Steinberg, R. H. and Wood, I. (1974). Pigment epithelial cell ensheathment of cone outer segments in the retina of the domestic cat. *Proc. R. Soc. B* **187**, 461–478.

Stiles, W. S. (1937). The luminous efficiency of monochromatic rays entering the eye pupil at different points and a new colour effect. *Proc. R. Soc. B* **123**, 90–118.

Stiles, W. S. (1939). The directional sensitivity of the retina and the spectral sensitivities of the rods and cones. *Proc. R. Soc. B* **127**, 64–105.

Stiles, W. S. (1948). The physical interpretation of the spectral sensitivity curve of the eye. In *Transactions of the Optical Convention of the Worshipful Company of Spectacle Makers*, pp. 97–107. Spectacle Makers Company, London.

Toraldo di Francia, G. (1948). Per una teoria dell'effecto Stiles-Crawford. *Nuovo Cimento* **5**, 589–590.

Toraldo di Francia, G. (1949a). The radiation pattern of retinal receptors. *Proc. phys. Soc., Lond. B* **62**, 461–462.

Toraldo di Francia, G. (1949b). Retina cones as dielectric antennas. *J. opt. Soc. Am.* **39**, 324.

Wald, G. (1964). The receptors of human color vision. *Science* **145**, 1007–1016.

Walls, G. L. (1934). Human rods and cones. *Arch. Ophth.* **69** (new series 12), 914–930.

Walraven, P. L. and Bouman, M. A. (1960). Relation between directional sensitivity and spectral response curves in human cone vision. *J. opt. Soc. Am.* **50**, 780–784.

Wyszecki, G. and Stiles, W. S. (1967). *Color Science: Concepts and Methods, Quantitative Data and Formulas*. Wiley, New York.

Zwas, F. (1979). Wavelength variation in directional sensitivity of the long- and medium-wave sensitive foveal cones of red–green dichromats. *Vision Res.* **19**, 1067–1076.

Raster-Based Colour Stimulators

R. W. RODIECK

Exchange Stimulation

A few years ago, William Rushton and I investigated rod–cone interaction at the level of cat retinal ganglion cells, using a method of light exchange (Rodieck and Rushton, 1976a, b). The great majority of cat ganglion cells receive signals from rods and from a single (green) cone type. Because only two photoreceptor types were involved, we were able to devise a simple optical apparatus that neatly exchanged an orange light for a white light. If the intensity of the white light was adjusted so that it activated the rods to the same degree as did the orange light, then there was no rod response to the light exchange, and we could show that the observed response was due entirely to the cones. If the two lights were made equal for the cones, then the cone response to the exchange of orange and white lights was abolished, and we could show that the observed response was due entirely to the rods. In this way we were able to investigate the response of ganglion cells to both rod and cone stimulation at the same level of ambient illumination. This notion is illustrated in the HRR pseudoisochromatic plates and is discussed by Estévez and Spekreijse (1982).

Although our apparatus was suitable for investigating many questions about the response characteristics of rod and cone signals and their interaction at the ganglion-cell level, it had a feature that limited the range of problems that could be investigated. For example, when an exchange spot was centred in the receptive field of a cell, and the orange and white light made equal for the rods, then, although the response to the light exchange was due entirely to the cones, the centre of the cell's receptive field still received what was in effect a steady

COLOUR VISION
ISBN 0 12 000000 0

stimulation of the rods over this region. In the case of an off-centre receptive field, this steady rod stimulation could be sufficient to suppress the firing of the cell, thereby rendering it unresponsive to the cone stimulation.

The basic problem lay in the fact that the spot was superimposed upon the background. What was needed was to embed the spot within the background, so that the array of cones could be presented with, say, a field containing a flashing spot, while at the same time the array of rods was presented with a uniform and unchanging field. We realized that the same principles extended to three spectrally different photoreceptors stimulated by three spectrally different lights; this would allow stimulation of each photoreceptor type in isolation, and was thus relevant to investigations of colour.

I investigated a number of ways of realizing such stimuli. While theoretically possible using conventional optics, the light losses through the apparatus were considerable, the calibration critical, and the range of stimuli limited. Moving paper figures of some spectral reflectance before a background of another spectral reflectance, both illuminated by three spectrally distinct lights, two of whose intensities could be controlled, offered another possibility. But edge effects appeared to be difficult to eliminate, and again the range of stimuli that could be presented was limited, and did not encompass those stimuli conventionally used to analyse receptive fields.

The approach that showed the greatest possibilities was to present the stimuli on the screen of a high resolution colour CRT. Only two of the three beams were necessary for studying the interaction of rod and green-cone signals in cats, but all three could be used to study foveal colour vision in primates. It thus appeared possible, at least in principle, to present to the array of green cones a field containing a grating, moving bar, flashing spot, etc., while at the same time the arrays of red and blue cones would be presented with a uniform and unchanging field.

The left-hand side of Fig. 1 illustrates this possibility. The three cartesian axes represent the photon stimulation of the red, green and blue cones. Each of the three phosphors of the colour CRT differentially activates these three cone types to different degrees, and each corresponds to three different directions in this cone space. The radiance of each phosphor corresponds to a length along its direction, and thus represents a vector. The stimulation of the three cone types is represented by the vector sum of the phosphor vectors. In this way any point in cone stimulation space can be reached within the solid bounded by the three phosphor vectors. Since we are considering cone inputs, rather than cone outputs, no assumption of linearity is required for the cones.

Consider a background represented by point "B" in the right-hand side of Fig. 1. All the points along the vertical line through this point are indistinguishable to the red cones, and are likewise indistinguishable to the blue cones. Colours realizable within the domain of phosphor primaries are indicated by a thickening of this vertical line. If the spectral sensitivities of these two cone

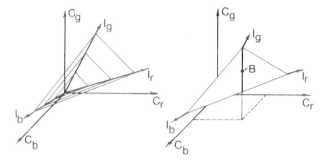

FIG. 1   Mapping of colour phosphors onto cone stimulation space. The orthogonal axes C_r, C_g and C_b are the stimulus strengths (effective photon catches) of the three cone types. The three phosphors of a colour CRT map onto this space as fixed directions, specified by their relative spectral distribution and the spectral sensitivities of the three cone types. The radiance of each phosphor can thus be represented by a vector, I_r, I_g and I_b. Left: With reference to the domain of cone stimulation space, the domain of realizable colours corresponds to the triangular solid bounded by the phosphor directions. Right: An example of how stimulation can be restricted to a single cone type. A vertical slice is taken through the domain of realizable colours, and within the triangle so formed, a vertical line is dropped from the upper corner to the lower base. The part of this line that lies in the domain of realizable colours is thickened, and a background point, B, is placed midway along this part. Colours of different contrast above and below this background produce the same stimulation as the background for the red cones, C_r, and this is also true for the blue cones, C_b. Thus, with reference to the background, these colours generate a nonzero stimulus only for the green cones, C_g.

types is uniform across the field, then the screen of the CRT could be painted with a palette of colours lying along this line, greens, greys and purples, that would not be detected by the arrays of either of these cone types. Such a line thus corresponds to a deuteranopic pseudoisochromatic line, as do all vertical lines in this space that intercept the solid of realizable colours. Points on the vertical line near the background point "B" represent low contrast stimuli to the green cones, and of course zero contrast stimuli to the remaining cone types. In a like manner, other slices through the cone input space allow isolation of the red and blue cones.

The points at which the vertical line intercepts the solid of realizable colours represents maximum positive and negative contrast for the green cones under these conditions. Calculations, based upon cone spectral sensitivities and the phosphor spectral radiances of commercial CRTs, showed that stimuli having contrasts as large as 0.43 to the green cones could be presented in this way, while the maximum contrasts attainable to isolated stimulation of the red and blue cones were 0.43 and 0.95, respectively. These values are less than the theoretical maximum obtainable with monochromatic lights, but are nevertheless quite strong stimuli and this gave some hope to the approach.

Thus encouraged, I embarked upon a project to construct a visual stimulator, based upon a colour CRT, that would selectively activate single photoreceptor mechanisms. There are a number of technical issues that need to be dealt with, and the remainder of this talk concentrates on what have proved to be the most important of these.

Control of Screen Intensity

The critical problem in exchange stimulation is to ensure that certain photo-receptor types are not stimulated, and this implies that one must be able to control the radiances of the three phosphors to a high degree. On consideration, it is clear that it is their relative values at a given point on the screen that is critical, rather than some minor change in the total radiance with position on the screen. This is an issue of colour alignment, and without going into the details, modern CRTs, designed for high-resolution graphics, meet this requirement, at least within the central region of the screen. Another aspect of colour alignment is that each of the three beams of the CRT activate only its phosphor, or at least activate all three in the same ratio throughout the screen. Again, without going into details, this requirement can also be satisfied.

The problem then reduces to the control of these intensities, and the essence of the problem is shown schematically in Fig. 2. The screen radiance for a given

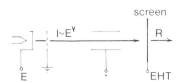

FIG. 2   Schematic diagram illustrating the main factors that determine screen radiance in a CRT. The beam current, I, is mainly controlled by the cathode-to-control-grid voltage, E, via a power-law relation. For a given screen voltage, EHT, the screen radiance, R, is linearly related to beam current, I, over the range of beam currents we use. However the screen radiance depends strongly on the EHT voltage, which must be well regulated to ensure that a change in the radiance of one beam of a colour CRT does not affect the radiances of the other two beams.

beam depends on both the beam current and the accelerating voltage (EHT). Unless the EHT supply is well-regulated the current of one beam will reduce it, thereby affecting the intensities of the other two beams. Thus, in order for the three beams to be independent it is necessary for the EHT voltage to be insensitive to total beam current. This specification is not found in commercial television sets, which make them unsuitable for this type of application unless the EHT supply is rebuilt.

If the EHT voltage is constant then the screen radiance is exactly proportional to beam current up to a saturation point that is higher than we need to reach. The beam current is determined in turn by the grid-to-cathode voltage for this beam, and control of cathode voltage is the normal means of setting beam radiance. Unfortunately, there is a highly nonlinear relation between grid-to-cathode voltage (E) and beam current (I), having the following form:

$$I \sim E^{\gamma}$$

In commercial television broadcasting there is an inverse nonlinear correction applied prior to transmission. In certain situations it may be possible to current drive the cathode, thereby exploiting the linear relation between beam current and screen radiance. Some form of capacitive neutralization is then necessary to compensate for the cathode-to-grid capacitance of about 35 pF, which would otherwise take beam current away from the screen during current transitions.

Otherwise one must determine the voltage necessary to produce the desired screen radiance. If the stimulus is sufficiently simple, such as a uniform spot, then the radiance can be measured directly and set. But for most stimuli, such as sinusoidal gratings or transitions, a spectrum of intensities is required. We have tested the accuracy of the above equation by monitoring both screen radiance and cathode voltage and found it accurate to within the limits of our measurements. This allows the required cathode voltages for each intensity to be calculated, given the value of the factor γ. We have tested the stability of this factor with time, and found it to drift in value over a period of hours. It thus becomes necessary to experimentally determine the value of this factor for each beam during each session. Automatic methods can be devised to quickly determine the value of this factor, so that this is not as bad a situation as it might first appear.

Frame and Field Rates

The way in which successive television images are displayed, developed in the late 1930s, represents an interesting interplay between the physiological requirements of the viewer, the limitations of the electrical circuitry of the time, the previously established frequency of the power mains, and a neglected physiological discovery made by cinematographers.

The television image consists of a sequence of frames, each composed of a series of horizontal lines. In broadcasting, it is presented successively in two parts, a field consisting of the odd horizontal lines, followed by a field consisting of the even horizontal lines. Since there are two fields for each frame, the rate of presentation of fields is twice the frame rate.

The reason for separating the frame into two successive fields is entirely physiological. The developers of cinematography had discovered that the rate of repetition of static images necessary to produce the effect of smooth movement (frame rate) is significantly slower than the rate required to eliminate flicker (field rate). The frames of the film are photographed at 24 Hz, and pass through the projector at the same rate. The shutter closes to bring a frame into the projection area, and then closes again in the middle of the period during which the frame remains within this area. This extra closing of the projector's shutter effectively presents each frame twice, increasing the rate at which images are displayed from 24 Hz to 48 Hz. Without this trick of doubling the fundamental Fourier component of the flicker, cinematography would require twice the film and half the exposure time in the camera.

In the same way the splitting of the frame into two interdigitating and successive fields doubles the frequency of the fundamental fourier component of the television display. In books on television broadcasting it is stated that this procedure works because the eye is unable to resolve the difference between the odd and even lines. But this explanation begs the question of why so many lines are needed. In fact, one can stand close enough to the screen to clearly see each of the lines, and nevertheless be unable to detect any flicker in these lines. However if a single line is presented then the flicker is quite noticeable. Apparently the mechanism that sets the flicker threshold has a larger summation area than does the mechanism that sets the threshold for spatial acuity. As far as I have been able to determine, this phenomenon has not been investigated psychophysically and has no demonstrated physiological explanation.

The field rate for commercial broadcasting is always set at, or very close to, the frequency of the a.c. power lines – 50 Hz for Europe and Australia, and 60 Hz for the United States. This is done so that any effect of the stray electromagnetic field of the a.c. power will be synchronized with the field rate, rather than beating with it. For our purposes the important effect is the influence of the a.c. signal on the deflection of the electron beam. If the field rate is a submultiple of the mains frequency, then whenever the beam has reached a certain point on the screen it will be at the same point relative to the phase of the a.c. mains, and thus be deflected by it by the same amount. Thus, at a given position on the screen the lines of the odd field will be shifted to the same degree as those of the even field. This allows manufacturers to place the power transformer close to the cathode-ray tube without noticeably distorting the interlacing of odd and even lines.

An interesting historical sidelight comes from the fact that one of the factors underlying the original choice of the frequency of the a.c. mains was that the frequency be high enough that an incandescent bulb did not appear to flicker. Since incandescent and fluorescent bulbs glow twice on each full power cycle, the fundamental fourier component in their light output is at twice the mains frequency. Furthermore, the glow of incandescent bulbs dies relatively slowly, so that the relative amplitude of the fundamental fourier component is small. Considering the variety of light-emitting devices to be later tied in some way to the mains frequency, it is fortunate that the choice of this frequency was so conservative with respect to the flicker of "Edison bulbs".

Nevertheless, with the fundamental fourier component of the broadcasting field rate having a frequency half that of incandescent bulbs, combined with a much larger amplitude (because of short persistence of the screen phosphors), the images on television receivers have a noticeable flicker, particularly for peripheral vision.

Broadcast field rates, however well tolerated by viewers, are nevertheless too low to be employed in raster devices used to investigate the visual process. One well-known problem, appearing in the related area of raster graphics, is that a thin horizontal line will appear only on the odd or the even field and will thus have a repetition rate at half the field rate, producing quite an annoying flicker. Modern raster graphics devices have thus abandoned the broadcast standard, and employ a frame consisting of a single field that is repeated at the mains frequency. The number of horizontal lines is retained by halving the period of each line. The flicker of a single line is then no worse than the flicker of the entire screen in normal broadcasting.

A more fundamental problem arises when raster display devices are used as visual stimulators in the investigation of the visual process in experimental animals. Cats, monkeys, and perhaps many other small animals have cells with flicker-fusion frequencies higher than those of humans, and these cells readily synchronize their firing to the broadcast field rate. Quite paradoxical effects can be obtained. For example, in my first attempt to use a raster stimulator, I recorded from a cell that, using conventional stimuli, was an off-centre X cell, being suppressed by a bright spot in the centre of its receptive field, and activated by a dark one. But when a raster-generated spot was placed in the centre of the receptive field, the cell was strongly activated, firing synchronously with the field rate. Presumably it was responding to the "off" of each field. Most of the cells studied in that first experiment readily followed the 50 Hz field rate, and I was led to rebuild the apparatus, increasing the field rate to 200 Hz, which eliminated the effect.

A following of a 60 Hz field rate has been noted for cells in the parvocellular layers of the monkey LGN (R. Young, personal communication). Furthermore, monkeys, who readily show optokinetic nystagmus to moving stripes on a rotating drum, fail to respond to moving stripes on a television screen (R. Boothe, personal communication).

If the field rate is to be increased above the mains frequency, then the effect of the electromagnetic field of the mains must be minimized for the reasons described above. Fortunately, high-quality colour monitors are available that reduce the spurious effect of the mains to an acceptable level. There are then two general approaches to increasing the field rate. The first is to increase the horizontal line frequency. For commercial television monitors this requires rewinding the horizontal deflection coils and rebuilding the horizontal deflection circuitry. However special-purpose colour monitors are becoming available with much higher line frequencies. The frequency response of the device used to generate the video signal must also be increased, and for reasons I will discuss, this is a difficult, but not intractable problem.

The second approach is to leave the frame rate unchanged, but increase the number of fields per frame from two to four (or more). Modification of the colour monitor is reduced to halving the value of a capacitor in the vertical deflection oscillator. Modification of the device used to generate the video signal is still required, but these changes are more concerned with alteration of the logic than with attempts to boost the frequency response. This approach does not avoid the single-line problem mentioned earlier, and in this way limits the range of visual stimuli. Furthermore, the minimal region of the screen encompassing the full field rate is increased from two lines to four. A consideration of the visual factors involved indicates that one should not get into any new visual problems by adopting this approach, and testing humans and cats with a colour monitor modified in this way has confirmed this view. At worst, the viewing distance must be doubled, thereby halving the angle subtended by the screen. This is acceptable when studying single visual neurons. For these reasons I have followed this latter approach.

Spatial Resolution of Colour CRTs

The spatial detail of the image is ultimately limited by spacing of the phosphors on the screen of the colour CRT. Currently, tubes are available having a spacing as small as 0.31 mm between phosphor dots of the same colour. Along a horizontal line this is reduced to 0.27 mm, or a spatial frequency of 37 dots cm^{-1}. With a screen viewing width of 19″ (48 cm), this gives some 1800 dots across the screen. For a horizontal line frequency of 31.5 kHz, the time between dots is about 15 nsec. In order to change the signal over this period requires a minimum high-frequency response of the associated colour monitor of about 60 MHz for each of the R, G and B input channels.

Image Generation

The continuing decline in the price of digital memory has made the digital representation of images ubiquitous, as illustrated by video games and home computers. The screen is represented digitally by means of a "frame buffer" consisting of a two-dimensional array of unit cells, termed pixels. The frame buffer is read once per frame and its contents mapped onto the screen of the colour monitor. Each pixel consists of a number of bits of memory, the larger the number of bits the greater the range of values that the pixel can take. In simple monochrome systems the intensity on the screen is directly determined by pixel values, which form a "grey scale". However a more powerful approach is to use the pixel value as an address to a look-up table, in which a value is stored that corresponds to the screen intensity.

Figure 3 is a schematic representation of the system that I am using, which uses a look-up table for the intensities of each of the three phosphors. This

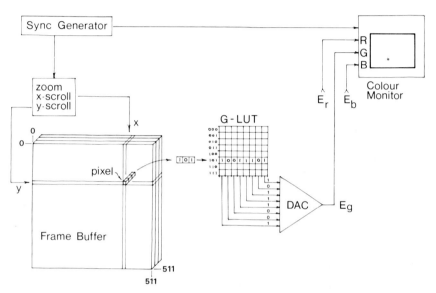

FIG. 3   Schematic diagram of the three main components of a device used to generate the video signals for a raster-display system for coloured stimuli. The frame buffer consists of an array of digital memory that is mapped onto the screen of the colour monitor. Each digital location in the frame buffer is termed a pixel, and the position of each pixel on the display screen is offset by the two scroll registers, while its size is determined by the contents of the zoom register. The value of the pixel is used as an address to look-up tables, containing the intensity values for the R, G and B signals to the colour monitor. Only the G look-up table is shown.

diagram illustrates how the value of a given pixel, in this case 5, is used as the address for each of the R, G and B look-up tables, and how the value contained in this location in the G look-up table is converted to a voltage to form one of the inputs to the colour monitor. In this diagram each pixel consists of 3 bits, allowing access to 8 locations in the look-up table, and thus to 8 possible colours on the screen. In my system each pixel actually consists of 8 bits, allowing access to 256 locations in the look-up tables, and thus up to 256 different colours on the screen. Each value in the look-up table also happens to consist of 8 bits, allowing a resolution of about 0.4% in the voltage produced by the digital-to-analog converter. Because of the non-linear characteristics of the voltage-to-intensity conversion, described above, the resolution at low intensities is finer than this value, and coarser than it at high intensities.

The look-up table is much smaller than the frame buffer, and changing the R, G and B values at a given address modifies all the parts of the screen whose pixels contain that address. As an example, consider a uniform spot presented on a uniform background. The frame buffer need contain only two values, one for the background and one for the spot. Assume that the background corresponds to a pixel value of 0, and the spot to a pixel value of 1. The R, G and B values contained in address 0 of the look-up tables thus specify the background colour, while those in address 1 specify the colour of the spot. To make the spot disappear, it is only necessary to load address 1 with the three values contained in address 0. Likewise the spot can be made to vary sinusoidally in time by successive modification of the contents of address 1. If the contents of the look-up tables are modified during the presentation of a field, then a noticeable "glitch" appears in the stimulus. For this reason all modification of these tables is restricted to the 2 ms or so between the presentation of successive fields (i.e. during the vertical retrace period). By modifying the circuitry of the device I am using, it has proved possible during this period to reload the R, G and B values at 60 addresses in the look-up tables and thus modify 60 colours on the screen. This allows for the dynamic presentation of more complex stimuli, such as temporal contrast modulation of sinusoidal gratings.

The other feature of this device is the zoom/scroll circuitry. This controls the manner in which the frame buffer is mapped to the screen. The two scroll registers determine the starting position for reading the frame buffer, and by successively modifying their contents the image on the screen can be made to move in any direction. They can be likened to the stage controls on a microscope. The zoom value controls the size of the displayed pixel, and can be likened to the turret of condensors on a microscope. For moving stimuli, we usually use a zoom factor of 2; this prevents stimuli that have moved off the screen to the right from reappearing at the left. For stationary stimuli that change only in colour we use a zoom factor of 1 to maximize spatial resolution.

By placing four of the eight planes of frame-buffer memory under zoom/scroll control, and holding the other four planes fixed, it proves possible to move patterns on the screen, while leaving other patterns fixed. By different loadings of the look-up table, it is possible to have the moving patterns move in front of, or behind the fixed patterns, as well as to produce a variety of other effects.

The state of the image processor is entirely determined by the contents of the zoom/scroll registers, of the look-up tables, and of the frame buffer. Due to the large number of pixels contained in the frame buffer, and because of limitations in our device, we are unable to modify more than a small part of this memory during the vertical retrace period, so that in practice we vary only the three zoom/scroll registers, or the look-up tables during stimulus presentation. We refer to this constraint as the "static frame buffer". There is such a rich variety of visual stimuli that can be presented by modifying only the zoom/scroll registers and the look-up table that we have not been much concerned with the constraint of a static frame buffer. For example a spot can be made to grow slowly in size or to oscillate sinusoidally in size by means of successive change to the contents of the look-up tables. The static-frame-buffer constraint is a feature of our device, rather than a fundamental limitation of such devices. Array processors are available that can reload the entire frame buffer on every frame, and these are used in flight simulators, where the view that the pilot sees is dynamically determined by his use of the controls. Currently, such devices increase the cost of the image processor by a factor of about 10.

The device I am using is a Lexidata 3400 video image processor that has been modified to increase the loading speed of the look-up tables, to improve the linearity and stability of the video outputs, and to increase the field rate from 60 to 120 Hz. This latter modification mainly involves the redesign and manufacture of a number of programmable read-only memory chips.

With 512 pixels/horizontal line, the period of each pixel is about 100 nsec. In this time the output of the frame-buffer memory is strobed from a shift register to form an address to the look-up table memory, and the digitally stored beam voltages are read from this second memory to form the inputs to the digital-to-analog converters. A doubling of the frequency response of the system would require fitting this sequence of events into a 50 nsec period, and this is the difficulty I alluded to earlier in discussing the possibility of doubling the horizontal line frequency in the device I possess. However there is no fundamental limit with regard to the rate of pixel presentation; an increase in frequency response by a factor of four (i.e. 25 nsec pixel^{-1}) is currently available, and significantly faster devices are technically feasible. At present the limitations of raster-display systems are entirely set by the specifications of the colour monitor, rather than by the circuitry generating the video signals.

Imposed Constraints

There are so many possible ways of using an apparatus of this type that it is useful to consider constraints that can serve to sharpen one's approach. Figure 4 illustrates the constraints that we have adopted. As shown in the diagram at the left, an arbitrary point in the stimulus space is designated as the "background" colour. The "background vector" has its tail at the origin of the stimulus space, and its head at the chosen point. Any other point in this space corresponds to a "stimulus colour", and the "stimulus vector" is defined as having its tail at the background point and its head at the stimulus point. "Stimulus contrast" is defined to mean the ratio of the magnitude of the stimulus vector to that of the background vector. This definition reduces to the conventional definition when these two vectors are parallel, that is when there is only an intensity change.

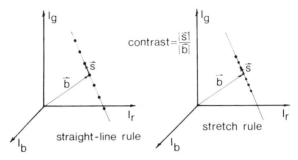

FIG. 4   Constraints that can be imposed on the range of stimuli that can be generated by colour stimulators. The "straight-line rule" states that all the colours on the screen map along a straight line in phosphor-radiance space, which is equivalent to requiring that they map to a straight line in cone-input space. The "stretch rule" states that when the positions of the colours change with time they all do so by a specified proportion of their distance from the background point. The rationale for these constraints is discussed in the text.

The first constraint we have imposed is that the palette of colours on the screen is restricted to those lying on a straight line of arbitrary direction that passes through the background point. The direction of the line determines the relative magnitude and sign of the stimulus to each of the three cone types. There exists a plane in this space, passing through the background point, within which all the stimulus colours produce the same effect as the background does on one of the photoreceptor types, such as the red cones. If the screen were painted with a palette of the colours lying in this plane then the pattern they produce would not be distinguished by the array of red cones. There exists another plane in this space, also passing through the background point, within which all the colours are equivalent for another photoreceptor type, say the blue cones. The intersection of these two planes is a straight line, passing through the background point, along which all the colours are equivalent for both the red and the blue cones. Thus, in the foveolar region, or elsewhere when rods do not contribute, any response to stimulus colours lying along this line must be due entirely to the green cones. Neurons that do not receive from the green cones would not respond to such stimuli. It was the possibility of experimentally determining the direction of this line and using stimuli along it to analyse receptive fields in terms of their cone inputs that originally prompted the design of the apparatus I am using. Broadly, the constraint that the colours should lie along a straight line in a linear stimulus space isomorphic with cone input space appears to be a basic stimulus configuration for the analysis of receptive fields into spectral mechanisms, and for investigation of the interaction of these mechanisms when their signals are combined. Land-type experiments, by contrast, require a palette broadly scattered throughout the stimulus space and the "straight-line rule" is not applicable.

Whereas the "straight-line rule" constrains how colours can vary spatially, another rule, which we term the "stretch rule" constrains how they can vary temporally. Because of the straight-line rule, any change in colour at a given point on the screen can be expressed as a time-varying scalar coefficient on the magnitude of the stimulus vector, which we term the "stimulus modulation function" at that point. The "stretch rule" states that the stimulus-modulation function at any point on the screen is the same as at any other point on the screen. The stretch rule is shown diagramatically in the right-hand side of Fig. 4. Consider a rubber band that is cut and tied at its middle at the background point in this stimulus space. Colours (Newton's small masses) are placed along this band, which is held straight by the first rule. As the rubber band is stretched equally on each side of the background point, the colours move together toward and away from the background point, preserving their relative order and moving at a rate proportional to their distances from the background point. The stretch rule ensures that, for example, a sinusoidal grating retains its sinusoidal spatial character, whatever temporal changes might take place.

Programming and Associated Hardware

In the investigation of the receptive-field properties of single cells, we have found it useful to employ a graphics tablet (Summagraphics Bit Pad) with a hand-held cursor to move patterns such as bars and spots on the screen. By means of a button on the cursor, the pattern can be made to flash. A transparent, electrically-conducting screen placed before the CRT is useful in reducing electrode pickup of the horizontal scan frequency.

Because receptive fields can be located anywhere in the visual field, it is necessary to optically direct them to the centre of the display screen. We accomplish this by means of a mirror gimbaled about its centre. The mirror centre can be temporarily marked, and it can be positioned so that the receptive field is approximately centred at this temporary mark. A telescope and pair of right-angle prisms is brought into place so that when an observer looks through the telescope it is as if his eye were positioned at the centre of the screen. The observer sees the temporary mark on the mirror, and looking through the mirror sees the relevant pupil. The mirror is then rotated under screw control about its gimbals to bring the pupil into coincidence with the temporary mark, which is then removed. Receptive fields having an approximate radial symmetry are then located with greater accuracy by passing an edge through the receptive field at six angular orientations spaced 60 degrees apart.

Programming considerations form a topic in themselves; however the following points deserve at least brief comment. Patterns are constructed in the frame buffer by primitive routines that, for example, draw a line of a given pixel value from one point on the screen to another point. The Special Interest Group on Graphics of the Association for Computing Machinery (SIGGRAPH-ACM) publishes standards for these primitives. Program design based on standards naturally aids program portability. We use a variety of display devices, including incremental plotters, storage scopes, graphics terminals, etc., and have found it worthwhile to develop an interactive and device-independent graphics system, based upon the SIGGRAPH-ACM standards, that controls the output to the various display devices, including the color stimulator.

The program we use in experiments with the color stimulator generates and presents the stimuli, and acquires and analyses the responses. It contains routines that call on the primitives to load the frame buffer with a spot, generate a sinewave change in contrast, and so on. These routines are selected by the user, who can either enter a command name on a terminal that calls the routine, or request that a file be read containing a list of such commands, which are then invoked. This approach has proved to be a good balance between flexibility and ease of use.

Acknowledgements

This study was supported in part by NIH Research Grant No. EY-02923 from the National Eye Institute, in part by the E. K. Bishop Foundation, and in part by a James S. Adams Scholar award from Research to Prevent Blindness Inc.

References

Estévez, O. and Spekreijse, H. (1982). The "silent substitution" method in visual research. *Vision Res.* **22**, 681–691.

Rodieck, R. W. and Rushton, W. A. H. (1976a). Isolation of rod and cone contributions to cat ganglion cells by a method of light exchange. *J. Physiol., Lond.* **254**, 759–773.

Rodieck, R. W. and Rushton, W. A. H. (1976b). Cancellation of rod signals by cones and cone signals by rods in the cat retina. *J. Physiol., Lond.* **254**, 775–785.

Discreteness Artifacts in Raster Display Systems

WILLIAM B. COWAN

1. Introduction

Experiments in colour vision generally use stimuli that are spatial or temporal patterns of coloured light produced by modulating the spectral, spatial, and/or temporal characteristics of one or more fields of steady white light. Various devices: filters, monochromators, masks, beamsplitters, shutters, etc. perform the modulation, often under the control of a laboratory computer. When the stimulus must be altered, whether as part of the experimental protocol or to produce different stimuli for a different experiment, the computer (or a human operator) alters analogue parameters which provide continuous variation of the stimulus. This technique of stimulus control has a major disadvantage. Since mechanical and optical devices are difficult to build with more than a few degrees of freedom, they must usually be specially made for a given stimulus configuration, which is costly in time and money.

Recent advances in computer technology now make available a radical alternative for stimulus production. They allow the stimulus to be stored in high-speed semiconductor memory. It is easily modulated by changing the contents of the memory, in just the way that data is altered within a computer program. Because the alteration is fast, complicated stimuli and complex real-time methods of controlling them are possible. And new stimulus configurations and modulation methods can be produced quickly, without the need for construction of mechanical and optical components. Thus, this method of stimulus generation obviates the usual difficulties associated with the traditional methods. Any technology has artifacts and problems of calibration which must be understood before it can be used with confidence. With this technology the major artifacts are discreteness artifacts. They arise because the stimulus must be broken down into a finite number of discrete blocks (areas, times, and colours) in order to be stored in a finite memory. In this paper I will discuss discreteness artifacts as they apply to raster display systems. The inexpensive availability of these systems is a recent phenomenon, and their performance is undergoing constant improvement, but their basic configuration seems unlikely to change greatly. If so, the sources and sizes of discreteness will remain calculable by methods used to address the properties of currently available systems. I will not discuss calibration problems, because they are specific to whatever device is used to transform the memory representation into light, and are bound to change as device technology changes. This is occurring very rapidly, making it difficult to say which, if any, of the technical details of calibration are of lasting relevance.

2. Components of a Raster Display System

Before discussing the origin and magnitude of discreteness artifacts, we should clarify terminology by looking at the functional components of a raster display system (Fig. 1). The host is a general purpose computer, running application

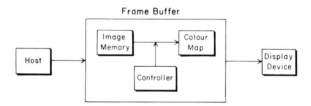

FIG. 1   Functional components of a raster display system.

programs written by the experimenter. It makes up and controls the stimulus by sending data over a high speed link (the order of a million bytes/second) to the frame buffer, and may monitor responses as well. The frame buffer is a large amount of high-speed memory plus several data channels. The memory stores, in a way to be discussed below, one or more images. It is accessed continuously, the information flowing through its internal data paths being used to make up a video signal representing the stimulus. The video signal goes to the display device, which accepts a video signal and makes up the corresponding colour picture. Currently, the most popular device of this kind is the shadow mask cathode ray tube (CRT). It is unreliable, expensive to manufacture, not susceptible to easy improvement, and, most serious of all, has optical properties that are neither well understood nor consistent.

Because display devices are so variable, and because they may be replaced by completely different technology at any time, we will omit them from this discussion, concentrating on the frame buffer, in which discreteness is inherent. Within it, design trade-offs between spatial, temporal, and colour resolution and cost determine a level of discreteness that the display device cannot appreciably improve. To discuss the frame buffer we assume a perfect display device. Its face is completely filled by small regions, normally rectangular, called pixels. Each region is a solid colour defined by the video signal.

Now, let us examine the internal organization of the frame buffer. Its simplest version has three components: image memory, colour maps, and a controller. The image memory is a two-dimensional array of memory registers, one to a pixel. Each register stores an index. The size of image memory is defined by: x-resolution, R_x, the number of pixels per line; y-resolution, R_y, the number of lines per image; and depth, D, the number of bits in each memory register. Thus, the index at each pixel may take on 2^D distinct values. Each index corresponds to a register in the colour map (also called a colour look-up table). These registers contain the intensities which will be given to the red, green and blue components (primaries) of the image of any pixels that have the appropriate index. Each register has L bits of colour resolution per primary. Note that the number of distinct index values, 2^D, determines the number of distinct colours that may be concurrently present in the stimulus; the number of possible colours, from which each colour is chosen, is $2^L \times 2^L \times 2^L$. Making up the video signal − getting index numbers from image memory, associating them to entries in the colour map, inserting synchronization signals, etc. − is done by the controller. To do this it must have timing and sequencing information, how many and which pixels and lines to send, and for how long. To be able to vary these quantities, as we shall see, adds to the performance of the display.

To recapitulate, the frame buffer has three functional parts: image memory, colour map, and controller. Spatial properties of the stimulus are limited by the image memory, and by the controller, temporal properties by the controller, and colour gamut properties by the colour map.

3. Spatial Artifacts

Spatial artifacts arise because any stimulus generated by a raster graphics system consists of a finite pattern of discrete regions. Continuous gradients cannot be produced. We would like to know when the deviation from continuity is significant. The answer lies in the relationship between spatial properties of the display and spatial properties of the visual system. Since spatial processing in the human visual system is not completely understood, we assume that it is limited by a low-pass spatial frequency filter. Then the question "To what extent can we independently manipulate all spatial frequencies that pass through the filter (including phase relationships)?" is definite enough to have an answer.

Clearly, we must know the spatial frequency content of the desired stimulus, and how it compares to that of its raster representation. Given raster resolution, R_x pixels by R_y pixels, where each pixel is x_0 by y_0, the overall display size is $R_x x_0$ by $R_y y_0$. Any stimulus of these dimensions can be exactly represented as a product of two infinite Fourier sums. For simplicity consider the x-direction only. The continuous stimulus $s(x)$ is

$$s(x) = A_0 + \sum_{n=1}^{\infty} A_n \cos(k_n x) + \sum_{n=1}^{\infty} B_n \sin(k_n x) \tag{3.1}$$

where $k_n = 2\pi n/(R_x x_0)$ and the coefficients A_n and B_n are determined in the usual way (Churchill, 1963). The raster representation $s'(x)$ is not exactly the

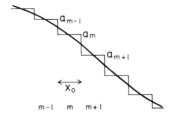

FIG. 2   Part of a continuous stimulus, $s(x)$, shown by the smooth line, and its raster representation, $s'(x)$, shown by the set of steps.

same, consisting of a number of steps (Fig. 2). If the mth step has height a_m, then

$$s'(x) = \sum_{m=1}^{R_x} a_m (\theta(x - m x_0) - \theta(x - (m-1)x_0)) \tag{3.2}$$

where $\theta(x)$ is the step function ($\theta(x) = 1$, $x > 0$; $\theta(x) = 0$, $x < 0$). We can calculate the Fourier representation of $s'(x)$ to be

$$s'(x) = A_0' + \sum_{n=1}^{\infty} A_n' \cos(k_n x) + \sum_{n=1}^{\infty} B_n' \sin(k_n x) \tag{3.3}$$

with

$$A_n' = \frac{1}{\pi n} \sum_{m=1}^{R_x} a_m (\sin(mk_n x_0) - \sin((m-1)k_n x_0))$$

$$\tag{3.4}$$

$$B_n' = \frac{-1}{\pi n} \sum_{m=1}^{R_x} a_m (\cos(mk_n x_0) - \cos((m-1)k_n x_0))$$

Now, the continuous stimulus and its raster representation are the same to the extent that we can choose the a_m such that $A_n' = A_n$ and $B_n' = B_n$. This amounts to

$$\frac{1}{\pi n} \sum_{m=1}^{R_x} a_m (\sin(mk_n x_0) - \sin((n-1)k_n x_0)) = A_n$$

$$\frac{-1}{\pi n} \sum_{m=1}^{R_x} a_m (\cos mk_n x_0) - \cos((m-1)k_n x_0)) = B_n \tag{3.5}$$

which is a set of linear equations for the step heights, a_m. Clearly, R_x variables, a_m, can satisfy only R_x of the infinite set of equations. Choose those of lowest spatial frequency ($n < R_x/2$), since if we choose higher ones we will leave mismatches at whichever of the low frequencies are omitted. Then, the highest value of k_n that can be matched is

$$k_n = \frac{\pi}{x_0} \tag{3.6}$$

The unit of k_n is radians/distance. In terms of the more familiar cycles/distance the limit is $1/2x_0$.

Take note of four items:

1) The same analysis performed in two dimensions gives the simultaneous limits $1/2x_0$ in the x-direction and $1/2y_0$ in the y-direction.

2) The usual observation that a raster display can generate spatial frequencies up to its minimum subdivision is not quite correct. It can generate any spatial frequencies, at the cost of leaving others arbitrary. When no low frequencies are left arbitrary, it can generate frequencies up to that of half its smallest subdivision.

3) It is not true that raster displays can generate only subharmonics of their smallest subdivision. Subharmonics are easy to generate, since Equation (3.5) is easy to invert for subharmonics, but any frequency below the limit can be generated. Equation (3.5) can be used to generate them. The difficulty of using it can be alleviated by writing Equation (3.5) in matrix form, inverting the matrix (which can be very large) once, and using the inverted matrix any time that step heights are needed.

4) The same theorem can easily be proved for pixels that deviate from the ideal pixel shape, as do those in real displays. All that changes are the coefficients of each a_m in Equation (3.5).

Now we are ready to relate raster display properties to actual stimuli. Here the key elements in the stimulus are the field size, F, and the highest spatial frequency that must be controlled, f_0. (Note that if a spatial frequency must be absent from a stimulus its absence requires control.) With the R_x by R_y display, the field size is adjusted by moving the eye position until the display occupies the field size. That is, $R_x x_0 = F$. And, since $1/2x_0$ is the highest spatial frequency that can be controlled by the display, $R_x/2 = Ff_0$. For example, if the field size is to be $10°$ and R_x is 512, then f_0 is 25.6 cycles deg^{-1}. Table 1 gives a few more representative values.

These values show that for large stimuli the highest possible resolution is

TABLE 1   Highest controllable spatial frequency for several field sizes and display resolutions

Field size	Display resolution		
	256	512	1024
10°	12.8	25.6	51.2
2°	64.0	128	256
1°	128	256	512

needed for experiments examining spatial vision; for smaller stimuli modest resolution is quite satisfactory. Phenomena such as hyperacuity (Westheimer, 1976), if mediated by spatial frequency amplitude analysis, involve spatial frequencies of 400 cycles deg^{-1} and are beyond the scope of raster display technology. On the other hand, if mediated by phase analysis of lower frequencies, these displays can be used.

Three practical conclusions can be drawn from this analysis:

1) Display resolution (which is strongly correlated with display cost) must be chosen with particular stimuli in mind.

2) Displays which allow the reconfiguration of memory to different resolutions greatly increase the range of experiments that can be done.

3) The computational effort to solve Equation (3.5) can be great. It shrinks drastically for periodic stimuli with periods that are multiples of $1/x_0$. Some off-the-shelf displays allow continuous variation of x_0 by software. Such displays can make any stimulus have a multiple of $1/x_0$ for its period.

4. Temporal Artifacts

Temporal artifacts arise in raster systems for much the same reasons as spatial artifacts. That is, the desired stimulus is a continuous function of time, but is approximated by a discrete stream of impulses. By analogy with the spatial case, treat the temporal response of the eye as if it is limited by a filter that passes low temporal frequencies; Fourier analyse the desired stimulus; and take over to the time domain the theorem about spatial frequencies. Specifically, if the display produces complete pictures (frames) at $1/t_0$ Hz, all Fourier components up to $1/2t_0$ Hz can be produced exactly. Note that the commonly-made statement that raster systems produce only subharmonics of a fundamental frequency $(1/t_0)$ is not true.

The application of these results to raster display systems is more complicated than in the case of spatial artifacts. This is because temporal modulation can be perceived at relatively high frequencies: around 60 Hz for large fields at 100 Trolands (Kelly, 1961). Thus, while frame rates of this order, which are readily available, are adequate for the presentation of steady stimuli, they are inadequate for time-varying stimuli which need rates of 120 to 150 Hz. To achieve such speeds, which is possible with some off-the-shelf systems, note that the critical display parameter is line rate, the rate at which new lines are produced. For example, a 60 Hz frame rate is produced by drawing 500 lines at a 30 KHz line rate. If the controller puts out only 250 lines, the frame rate is 120 Hz. We are trading off *y*-resolution, number of lines, for frame rate. In this way frame rates as fast as desired can be produced. This procedure also gives virtually continuous control of the frame rate. There is no gain in available stimuli, but for periodic stimuli, the computational effort (for the solution of Equation (3.5)) can be greatly reduced. The reduction can be important, particularly for a small host calculating in real time. Two notes of caution are necessary:

1) There is always a point where the rate gets too fast for the display device to hold its synchronization. It varies widely from one device to another, and is not usually advertised by their manufacturers.

2) Many display systems, when the number of lines is reduced, keep frame rate the same by putting out blank lines at the end of each frame. Displays which have only this method, often called windowing, of changing the number of lines, cannot operate at other than standard repetition rates.

5. Colour Artifacts

The colour of any area in the stimulus is taken from the colour map. Quantities stored there have discrete values, so colour is not continuously adjustable; the display produces a finite set of discrete points in colour space. Using what is known about colour discrimination we can get an idea of when the discreteness is significant.

Suppose the colour map to have L bits per primary per index. Then the smallest proportional difference occurs when a single step is taken from the highest intensity. The difference is $1/2^L$. When the primary is at a fraction q ($0 < q < 1$) of this intensity (value $q2^L$) the proportional difference is $1/q2^L$. Thus, a stimulus requiring steps with a proportional difference smaller than p, can be made down to an intensity $q2^L$, where $p = 1/q2^L$. For a given p, the greater L is, the smaller q can be, and the greater the dynamic range of the primary. Thus, even if L is large enough that the smallest proportional difference is less than p, the colour performance may be inadequate if the stimulus needs a lot of dynamic range (i.e. must use a wide range of intensities).

Looking at Weber fraction data (Wysecki and Stiles, 1967, p. 507), we see that a proportional difference in the neighborhood of 1% is near threshold. Suppose we want there to be two minimal steps to threshold ($p = 0.005$), and if the colour map has 8 bits per primary per index, then $q = 0.78$, and only the top 22% of the possible primary intensities can be used. Increasing L to

10 decreases q to 0.20. The top 80% of primary intensities can be used. When gamma correction (see Rodieck, this volume), an important factor with CRT display devices, is considered, the disparity between 8 and 10 bits is even greater. With $\gamma = 2$ even the smallest steps do not meet the criterion for $L = 8$, while for $L = 10$, $q = 0.39$, and 85% of the range of primary intensity is available.

Similarly, among equiluminous colours, discreteness artifacts can severely limit the gamut within which continuous adjustment is possible. This effect, when blue colours must form part of the stimulus set, is particularly strong for saturated reds and greens. But, the magnitude of the artifacts depends critically on the stimulus set desired and, beyond the fact that increasing L decreases them, nothing very general can be said.

The figures given here are only an example; the artifacts vary widely from application to application, and should be calculated anew for each stimulus. What does not vary is the borderline nature of 8 bits per primary per index. Sometimes it is acceptable; sometimes, as here, not. By contrast, 10 bits per primary per index is almost always good enough; 6 bits per primary per index almost always inadequate. In any case, the number of bits per primary per index is a critical parameter to maximize; even 12 is not too many.

6. Conclusions

Any stimulus generation technology has its limitations, and it is important for users and potential users to know and respect them. We have discussed some limitations inherent in the frame buffer of raster display systems. They preclude some types of stimuli (e.g. simultaneous high temporal and spatial frequencies, threshold stimuli with small colour maps, etc.), but there remain many experiments that can utilize the convenience of these systems. Our analysis shows that features considered unimportant by many users, such as 10 bit per primary per index colour maps, reconfigurable image memory, variable numbers of lines per field, etc., increase the performance of such systems for colour vision research.

In all this the display device has not been considered. Its properties, the artifacts it creates, and the difficulties involved in calibrating it are certain to remain areas of rapid change in the years to come.

Acknowledgements

I would like to thank Dr P. Cavanaugh of l'Université de Montréal, who introduced me to video technology, and Dr G. Wyszecki, who read a first draft of this paper and helped to improve its expression.

References

Churchill, R. V. (1963). *Fourier Series and Boundary Value Problems*. New York, McGraw-Hill.
Kelly, D. H. (1961). Visual responses to time-dependent stimuli. I. Amplitude sensitivity measurements. *J. opt. Soc. Am.* **51**, 422–429.
Westheimer, G. (1976). Diffraction theory and visual hyperacuity. *Am. J. Optom. Physiol. Opt.* **53**, 362–364.
Wyszecki, G. and Stiles, W. S. (1967). *Color Science*. New York, Wiley.

A Minimum Motion Technique for Judging Equiluminance

STUART ANSTIS and PATRICK CAVANAGH

This article evaluates a new technique based on apparent motion (Anstis, 1980) for matching the luminance of different colours. This method supplements the established methods for measuring spectral sensitivity to different hues, namely heterochromatic flicker photometry and minimum-border (Wagner and Boynton, 1972). The minimum motion technique has the advantage of simplicity when used for adjusting colour luminances on television displays.

Consider two coloured square-wave gratings, one made of red and green bars, the other of dark yellow and light yellow bars. If the red/green grating is suddenly replaced by the dark yellow/light yellow grating which is displaced one quarter-cycle (half a bar width) to the right, then the grating will appear to jump to the left if the green bars are lighter than the red bars but to the right if the red bars are lighter than the green. If the red bars were made equiluminous with the green bars, then there is no reason to pair off the dark yellow bars with either the red or the green bars; so no consistent apparent motion will be seen.

A computer-generated television display presented red/green gratings interleaved with dark yellow/light yellow gratings in a four-stroke cycle (Fig. 1) which produced continuous AM to the left or right, or no motion at equiluminance. Subjects found it fairly easy to set the red and green bars to equal luminance, as the direction of the grating motion indicated in which direction a correction should be made in order to approach equiluminance.

The first experiment consisted of matching the luminance of the coloured bars in the test grating (red and green in this case) by adjusting their relative

COLOUR VISION
ISBN 0 12 000000 0

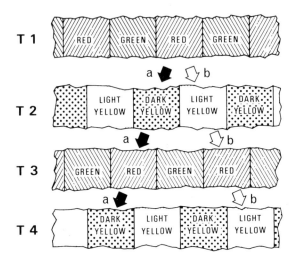

FIG. 1   Four coloured gratings were exposed in a repetitive sequence, at times T1 through T4, on the screen of a computer-controlled TV. Positions of the gratings were superimposed, not displaced vertically as illustrated. Each grating was displaced sideways by one-quarter cycle (half a bar width) from its predecessor. Direction of apparent motion, shown by the arrows, depended on the luminance of the bars. (a) When the red bars were darker than the green bars, the dark red bars in the grating at time T1 (or T3) appeared to jump leftward to the dark yellow bars in the grating at time T2 (or T4). (b) Conversely when red bars were lighter than the green bars they appeared to jump rightward to the light yellow bars.

luminance until no consistent motion was seen, either to the left or to the right. The interleaved light yellow/dark yellow grating that contained the fixed luminance difference was actually a mixture of the two colours to be matched, i.e. yellow in the case of a red/green match. The vertical yellow bars were produced by a dithering technique in which pairs of the 512 horizontal raster lines within each bar were alternated between the red and green of the red/green grating. The horizontal lines within each bar were below the threshold of resolution, so they were spatially summated by the visual system into a metameric yellow. The red and green were made slightly lighter than in the red/green grating to produce the light yellow bars, and slightly darker to produce the dark yellow bars. This procedure ensured that the light/dark (yellow) gratings had the same average hue and luminance as the red/green gratings. This was designed to minimize flicker and hold adaptation level constant, thus optimizing the conditions for motion detection.

Experiment 1: Equating Luminance by Minimum Motion

The luminances of red and green were matched for minimum motion by the method of constant stimuli. A square-wave grating of red and green bars of spatial frequency 2.5 cycles deg^{-1} was set up on the TV screen (P22 phosphor; CIE chromaticity coordinates red $x = 0.68$, $y = 0.32$; green $x = 0.28$, $y = 0.60$). The gratings were 2 deg × 2 deg in a dark surround, and a white cross on a blue 6-min square served as the central fixation point. The gratings were alternated at 5 Hz in a four-stroke cycle of two red/green and two dark yellow/light yellow gratings (Fig. 1). The green bars were held constant at 13.4 cd m^{-2} as measured by a Spectra photometer, and the red bars were set to a range of luminance values between 8 and 12 cd m^{-2}. The contrast of the yellow grating was 6.25% and its average luminance was always equal to the average luminance of the red/green grating. On each trial the red bars were randomly set to one of the test luminance values and the subject reported whether the apparent motion of the stimulus was to the left, right, or neither. The response "neither" was defined to include ambiguous motion, no motion, two super-imposed gratings apparently moving in opposite directions, or motionless flicker such as one would see in a counterphase flickering grating. The two authors were the subjects; the technique has also been successfully demonstrated to dozens of observers.

Each luminance value for red was presented a total of ten times in random order. The responses are plotted as psychometric functions in Fig. 2a. The same procedure was used for blue/yellow gratings (CIE chromaticity coordinates blue $x = 0.15$, $y = 0.07$: yellow $x = 0.51$, $y = 0.44$), interleaved in a four-stroke cycle with two gratings of light and dark grey (spatial mixture of blue and yellow) bars. The yellow bars of the blue/yellow gratings were always at 7.9 cd m^{-2} and the luminance of the blue bars was varied.

Results are shown in Fig. 2b. The red and green bars appeared to have the same luminance (PSE) when the luminance of the red bars was 9.54 cd m^{-2} for subject PC and 10.47 cd m^{-2} for SMA. The PSE for the blue and yellow bars was 10.5 cd m^{-2} for PC and 9.41 cd m^{-2} for SMA. Thus PC was relatively more sensitive to longer wavelengths and less so to shorter wavelengths, than SMA. The indifference interval was quite narrow: the number of "neither" responses fell to one-half maximum when the contrast of the red/green grating deviated from its equiluminous value by 1.6%, averaged across both subjects. The corresponding contrast for the blue/yellow grating was 2.8%.

Experiment 2: Effect of Spatial Frequency

We compared the apparent-motion and flicker techniques using square-wave gratings whose spatial frequencies were 0.625, 1.25, 2.5 and 5 cycles deg^{-1}. For minimum flicker the standard CIE stimulus is a uniform field of 2 deg

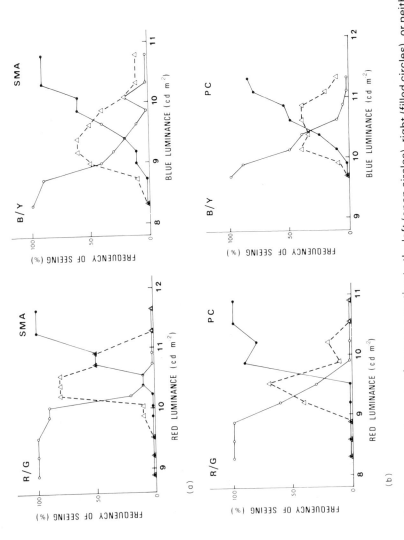

FIG. 2 Left panels: Percentage of reports of apparent motion to the left (open circles), right (filled circles), or neither direction (open triangles), when the luminance of the red bars was varied (abscissa) and green bars were held at a constant 13.4 cd m^{-2}. Display was the four-stroke cycle shown in Fig. 1. Method of constant stimuli.
Right panels: As above for blue/yellow gratings. Yellow bars were kept at 7.9 cd m^{-2} and blue bars were varied. The interleaved gratings (at times T2 and T4 in Fig. 1) were now light and dark grey instead of yellow.

diameter, but in order to evaluate the effects of spatial frequency we used square-wave gratings whose bars were flickering in counterphase between the two colours to be matched. Instead of taking colours in pairs such as red vs. green or blue vs. yellow, we now measured each colour separately, matching the luminance of red to white ($x = 0.30$, $y = 0.30$), then of green to white, then of blue to white. Thus in a grating of red and grey (or white) bars, the red bars suddenly became grey and the grey bars suddenly became red. The alternation rate was 15 Hz, so each grating of the two-stroke counterphase cycle was presented for two TV frames (33 msec). We also included a standard flicker match of each colour in turn against white in a 2-deg uniform field, and each of these three settings was normalized to a value of one in Fig. 3. The temporal rates were matched for flicker and motion, although as we shall see in the next experiment temporal rates are not critical.

For the apparent motion conditions we used the same four-stroke cycle as in Experiment 1. However, the bars of the two coloured gratings in the cycle were now red and achromatic grey, while the bars of the two inter-leaved gratings were light and dark pink. The grey bars had a luminance of 13.6 cd m^{-2}. The pink was made of equal parts of the red and the achromatic grey, and the light and dark bars had the same hue but differed in luminance so the grating had a luminance contrast of 12.5%. The cycling rate was 15 Hz, so each grating in the four-stroke cycle was presented for a single TV frame (16 msec). This gave equivalent velocities ranging from 3 deg sec^{-1} for the 5 cycle deg^{-1} gratings to 24 deg sec^{-1} for the coarsest gratings: the latter gave very fast apparent motion, which looked like rapidly fleeting shadows.

In both conditions the subject adjusted the luminance of the coloured bars by means of a joystick control until he saw minimum motion or minimum flicker. Spatial frequencies and colours were presented in a counterbalanced randomized order, and six readings were taken for each datum point.

Results are shown in Fig. 3. Luminous efficiencies for each colour were plotted relative to that for the uniform field flicker match. Open symbols show results for minimum motion, closed symbols for minimum flicker. Standard errors (SEs) are not shown as they were generally smaller than the symbols used to plot the graphs; the average SEs in relative units for motion and flicker were ± 0.0103 and ± 0.0125 respectively for PC and ± 0.0120 and ± 0.0159 for SMA. The luminances for the standard uniform field flicker matches for red, green and blue against a 13.6 cd m^{-2} white have all been normalized to unity in Fig. 3, but their actual values were 11.77, 15.0 and 14.68 cd m^{-2} respectively for PC and 12.97, 14.47 and 10.47 cd m^{-2} for SMA. The SEs in cd m^{-2} were ± 0.17, 0.05, 0.28 for PC and ± 0.20, 0.11, 0.35 for SMA.

The findings can be summarized as follows: 1) The means and SEs for motion and for flicker are almost indistinguishable. 2) As spatial frequency was increased, the luminous efficiency, relative to white, went up for red, stayed about the same for green, and went down for blue.

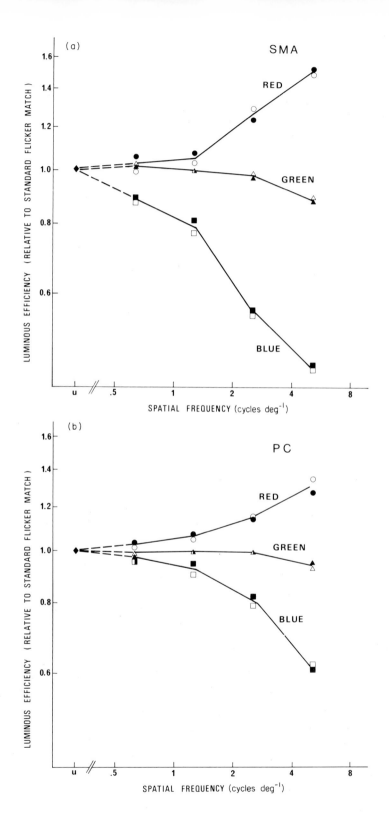

Experiment 3: Effect of Temporal Frequency

In this experiment we compared minimum motion and minimum flicker over a range of temporal frequencies, using similar conditions for the two techniques. We found that minimum motion could be successfully measured over a much wider range of temporal frequencies than minimum flicker could, and in fact gave settings that were largely independent of temporal frequency. The properties of the TV display and the four-stroke cycle limited us to frequencies that were submultiples of 60 Hz (15, 7.5, 3.75, 1.875 and 0.9375 Hz). For the luminance values we were using, good flicker judgements could be made only at 15 and 7.5 Hz. They could not be made at 30 Hz because there was a very wide dead range of luminance settings within which no flicker could be seen, and they could not be made below 7.5 Hz because strong chrominance flicker interfered seriously with judgements of luminance flicker. However, stable judgements of minimum motion could easily be made at frequencies down to 1 Hz or below.

As before, the gratings were red/grey, green/grey or blue/grey, the flicker condition comprised a counterphase flickering grating, and the motion condition comprised a four-stroke cycle. The spatial frequency was held constant at 2.5 cycles deg^{-1}. The temporal frequency of flicker (or drift) was set to 0.9375, 1.875, 3.75, 7.5 or 15 Hz. The effective velocity in the motion condition ranged from 0.375 to 6 deg sec^{-1}.

Results are shown in Fig. 4. Conventions are the same as for Fig. 3. The height of the red, green and blue curves is replotted from the 2.5 cycles deg^{-1} condition of Fig. 3. Where flicker results could be obtained they were virtually identical to motion results. Motion results could be reliably obtained over a much wider temporal range. Temporal frequency, in sharp contrast to spatial frequency, had virtually no effect on the results, since each curve is more or less a flat, horizontal line. The only slight departures from horizontality were not consistent between the two subjects. Red sloped slightly downwards for PC, but upwards for SMA. Blue sloped considerably upwards above 7.5 Hz for PC, but not for SMA.

FIG. 3 (opposite)   Effect of spatial frequency. Red was matched to white in minimum flicker condition (filled circles) by square-wave flicker at 15 Hz in a 2-deg uniform field; and in minimum motion condition (open circles) by interleaving red/grey gratings with pink gratings in the four-stroke sequence shown in Fig. 1. Results for green (triangles) and blue (squares) were collected in the same way. Luminous efficiencies for each colour are plotted relative to their minimum-flicker matches against a 2-deg white uniform field.

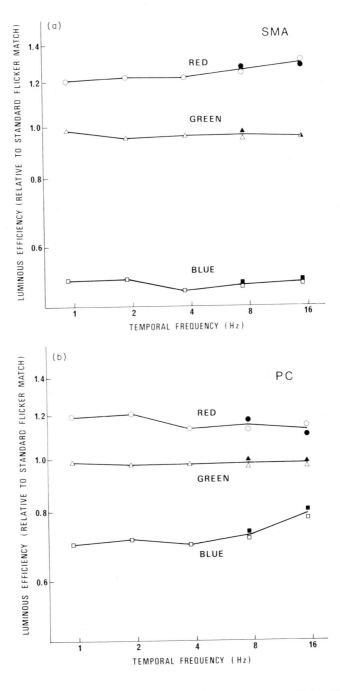

FIG. 4 Effect of temporal frequency on minimum counterphase flicker (filled symbols) and minimum motion (open symbols). Gratings were same as in Fig. 3, except spatial frequency was always 2.5 cycles deg^{-1}. Flicker data could not be collected below 7.5 Hz (see text). Height of each line replotted from 2.5 cycles deg^{-1} condition of Fig. 3.

Discussion

Our conclusions are as follows:

1) The identical luminance matches from flicker and motion suggest that the two phenomena are mediated by the same system. Kulikowski and Tolhurst (1973) and Tolhurst (1973) drew similar conclusions from their experiments on sensitivity to gratings.

2) Calibrations. Our spatial frequency results in Fig. 3 show that there are no luminance matches that will hold over the whole range of spatial frequencies. Calibration procedures should be designed with this in mind and should be tailored to match the experimental stimuli. For instance, 2-deg uniform fields would be an inappropriate choice for calibrating an experiment on fine-grained coloured patterns which contained many high spatial frequencies.

3) Spatial frequency. Our red/grey (or red/white) grating in Experiment 2 can be thought of as a red/black grating interlaced with a white/black grating, and the set of equiluminance matches plotted in Fig. 3 shows the relative luminous efficiency of the two interlaced gratings at different spatial frequencies, i.e. the ratio of the red/black CSF to the white/black CSF. The same is true for green and blue. These CSF ratios indicate the relative contributions of red, green and blue stimuli to the luminance channel at different spatial frequencies. (The method ignores the role of the R, G, B mechanism through which the colours pass.) Thus in Fig. 3 the green curve remains horizontal, indicating that green and white stimuli maintain the same relative inputs to the luminance channel from 1 to 5 cycles deg^{-1}. The red and blue curves slope respectively upwards and downwards, indicating a drop in luminous efficiency at low and high spatial frequencies respectively, compared to white or green. Van Nes and Bouman (1967) and Nelson and Halberg (1979) showed that the CSFs of black/white gratings were the same whether they were viewed directly or through a narrow-band or broad-band red or green filter. These CSFs are presumably mediated by luminance, not chrominance channels.

   Our results for red and green cannot be compared to those of Kelly (1974), Green (1968) or Cavonius and Estévez (1975a, b), as they were examining sensitivities of the colour mechanisms and not, as we were, the inputs of coloured stimuli into the luminance channel.

4) Temporal frequency. Our results show that temporal frequency had little effect on equiluminance settings. This is implied as well by the fact that minimum flicker settings made at 10–20 Hz are virtually the same as minimum border settings made at zero Hz (Wagner and Boynton, 1972). Since minimum motion settings could be made reliably over a wide range of temporal frequencies, the experimenter may choose a single convenient frequency and perform all measurements at that value, independently of

stimulus luminance or colour. The same freedom of choice is not available in minimum flicker matches, as the flicker rate must be chosen to maximize luminance flicker sensitivity, which peaks at 10 Hz for moderate luminance levels, and to minimize chrominance flicker sensitivity, which peaks at 2 Hz (Kelly and van Norren, 1977). In particular Kelly and van Norren (1977) state that the presence of chrominance flicker strongly interferes with the detection of luminance flicker.

We found that equiluminance judgements were unaffected by temporal frequency, using minimum-flicker and minimum motion techniques. However, Kelly (1982) reached the opposite conclusion when he measured the luminance ratio that gave minimum contrast sensitivity for a two-colour grating presented in counterphase flicker, and found that the visual system was relatively less sensitive to red at an 8 Hz flicker rate than at 1 Hz. Minimum-flicker matches cannot be made reliably at these low flicker rates so there is no way to know if they are also influenced by rate in this range. Since the minimum motion technique appears to measure the same system response as minimum flicker, but can operate at lower temporal rates, we used it to test Kelly's (1982) claims, with minimum motion standing in lieu of minimum flicker at low temporal rates. Our results are at variance with Kelly's findings.

5) TV vs. optical systems. Methods of equating colour luminance are important whenever the experimenter wishes to study the chromatic channels independently of luminance (Wagner and Boynton, 1972). The spatial characteristics of chrominance channels have been explored with equiluminous pictures which show losses of resolution (van der Horst and Bouman, 1969), borders (Tansley and Boynton, 1976), depth (Lu and Fender, 1972) and motion (Anstis, 1970; Ramachandran and Gregory, 1978). These studies suggest that information about borders, depth and motion is carried mainly by luminance channels.

Computerised TV graphics systems are becoming increasingly popular, and our new photometric method exploits the advantages that TV systems have over optical techniques. The great strength of optical systems lies in their ability to control stimulus wavelengths very precisely. Monochromatic lights of arbitrarily narrow bandwidths can easily be produced in a way that no TV system, with its inherently broad-band phosphors, can hope to emulate. Where colour vision *per se* is the primary concern, optical presentation remains the method of choice. But for studying spatially distributed stimuli which happen to be coloured, TV has significant advantages. For the control of timing there is not much to choose between the methods since both have their good and bad points. Optical devices allow very brief flashes or extended continuous presentations, but often at the price of elaborate and inconvenient mechanical shutters or high-voltage power supplies. Timing on a computer-controlled TV is restricted to a sampling rate of

50 (or 60) Hz, but within this limitation it is quick and easy to control. But it is in presenting spatially extended coloured pictures, either stationary or moving, that TV systems really come into their own.

6) Advantages of minimum-motion technique. (a) over flicker: Our method of colour matching enables inexperienced observers to make straightforward equalization settings of colour brightness. The direction of motion on the screen tells the subject in which direction he should adjust the luminance. Minimum motion can be used at any desired temporal frequency. (b) over minimum-border: Misalignment of the colour guns is a common TV problem which is difficult to eliminate completely. It produces troublesome edge transients which can rule out the use of minimum-border methods. However, judgements of minimum flicker and minimum motion are unaffected by even quite severe misalignments.

Acknowledgements

This research was supported by Grant A 0260 to SMA and Grant A 8606 to PC, both from the National Science and Engineering Research Council of Canada (NSERC).

References

Anstis, S. M. (1970). Phi movement as a subtraction process. *Vision Res* **10**, 1411–1430.

Anstis, S. M. (1980). The preception of apparent movement. *Phil. Trans. Roy. Soc., Lond. B* **290**, 153–168. Reprinted in *The Psychology of Vision* (eds Sutherland, N. S. and Longuet-Higgins, H. C.). London, The Royal Society.

Cavonius, C. R. and Estévez, O. (1975a). Contrast sensitivity of individual colour mechanisms of human vision. *J. Physiol., Lond.* **248**, 649–662.

Cavonius, C. R. and Estévez, O. (1975b). Sensitivity of human color mechanisms to gratings and flicker. *J. opt. Soc. Am.* **65**, 966–968.

Green, D. G. (1968). The contrast sensitivity of the colour mechanisms of the human eye. *J. Physiol., Lond.* **196**, 415–429.

Kelly, D. H. (1974). Spatio-temporal frequency characteristics of color-vision mechanisms. *J. opt. Soc. Am.* **64**, 983–990.

Kelly, D. H. (1982). Stabilised spatio-temporal threshold surface for chromatic gratings. *Supplement to Investig. Ophthalm.* **22**, 78.

Kelly, D. H. and van Norren, D. (1977). Two-band model of heterochromatic flicker. *J. opt. Soc. Am.* **67**, 1081–1091.

Kulikowski, J. J. and Tolhurst, D. J. (1973). Psychophysical evidence for sustained and transient detectors in human vision. *J. Physiol., Lond.* **232**, 149–162.

Lu, C. and Fender, D. H. (1972). The interaction of color and luminance in stereoscopic vision. *Investig. Ophthalm.* **11**, 482–489.

Nelson, M. A. and Halberg, R. L. (1979). Visual contrast sensitivity functions obtained with colored and achromatic gratings. *Human Factors* **21**, 225–228.

Ramachandran, V. S. and Gregory, R. L. (1978). Does colour provide an input to human motion perception? *Nature* **275**, 55–56.

Tansley, B. and Boynton, R. M. (1976). A line, not a space, represents visual distinctness of borders formed by different colors. *Science* **191**, 954–957.

Tolhurst, D. J. (1973). Separate channels for the analysis of the shape and the movement of a moving visual stimulus. *J. Physiol., Lond.* **231**, 385–402.

van der Horst, G. J. C. and Bouman, M. A. (1969). Spatiotemporal chomaticity discrimination. *J. opt. Soc. Am.* **59**, 1482–1488.

van Nes, F. L. and Bouman, M. A. (1967). Spatial modulation transfer in the human eye. *J. opt. Soc. Am.* **57**, 401–406.

Wagner, B. and Boynton, R. M. (1972). Comparison of four methods of heterochromatic photometry. *J. opt. Soc. Am.* **62**, 1508–1515.

Normal and Deficient Colour Discrimination Analysed by Colour Television

P. EWEN KING-SMITH, GEORGE M. CHIORAN, KEITH L. SELLERS and SARA L. ALVAREZ

Introduction

In this article, we emphasize the advantages of the chromatic test stimuli which can be generated on a colour television. In particular, an "equiluminous" test spot can be generated on a neutral background by brightening one phosphor (e.g. red) at the position of the test spot while another phosphor (e.g. green) is dimmed by an equal luminance step. As there is no luminance difference between the test spot and the surrounding screen, the subject is forced to use colour vision to detect such a stimulus. Thus, a detection threshold can be used to measure colour discrimination. Such mixtures of incremental and decremental test flashes can readily be generated on a colour television display.

Methods

The display system used is illustrated schematically in Fig. 1. A video generator within a North Star Horizon Computer, was used to generate a video signal corresponding to a white disc in the centre of a television frame. The contrast, colour and timing of the spot were controlled by analog outputs applied to Motorola MC1495 analog multipliers. A decremental stimulus component could be generated by reversing the polarity of the analog output to the corresponding multiplier. The luminance and colour of the surrounding screen

COLOUR VISION
ISBN 0 12 000000 0

were not detectably altered by presentation of the test spot. A Sony Trinitron K-1513 colour television was modified to accept separate red, green, blue and synchronizing signals. The luminances and chromaticities of the phosphors and their combination (i.e. the white screen) were measured using a Pritchard Photometer and are given in Table 1. The screen subtended 8 by 6 degrees at a viewing distance of 200 cm.

TABLE 1   Chromaticity and luminance of colour television display

	Chromaticity coordinates			Luminance (cd m^{-2})	
	x	y	z	Photopic	Scotopic
Red phosphor	0.625	0.342	0.033	21.5	10.7
Green phosphor	0.307	0.587	0.106	68.3	157.9
Blue phosphor	0.156	0.069	0.775	9.2	112.1
Combination (white)	0.307	0.316	0.377	99.0	280.7

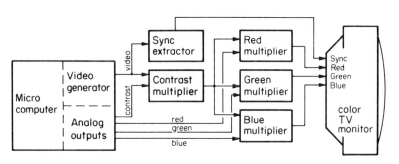

FIG. 1   Block diagram of the colour television display. See text for discussion.

Thresholds were determined by a staircase procedure, with test stimuli of different colours being randomly intermixed, together with blank trials. The different colours were generated by brightening or dimming the red phosphor only, the green phosphor only or by combination of such red and green stimuli in fixed proportions. The plotted results have been corrected for the nonlinear voltage–intensity characteristics of the three phosphor circuits. The subjects used monocular vision with a natural pupil.

Results and Discussion

A. Rod Monochromat

Because a rod monochromat can detect only brightening or dimming of the test spot, his results are particularly simple to interpret. Figure 2 shows thresholds for red–green mixtures for 1 degree, 0.2 sec test flashes. For each combination of red and green, the corresponding threshold has been recorded by plotting the contrast of the green phosphor as a function of the contrast of the red phosphor. Contrast was defined as the luminance increment (or decrement) of the phosphor at the test spot position divided by the surrounding luminance of that phosphor; negative contrasts correspond to decremental stimuli.

It may be seen that the results may be approximated by two parallel straight lines; the upper and lower lines correspond respectively to detection of brightening and dimming. Each of these lines may therefore be described as an "equiluminous line" because every point on the line corresponds to a constant, just detectable increment (or decrement) of luminance. The slope of these lines (about −0.06) is reasonably consistent with the relative scotopic luminances of the red and green phosphors (about 0.07, see Table 1).

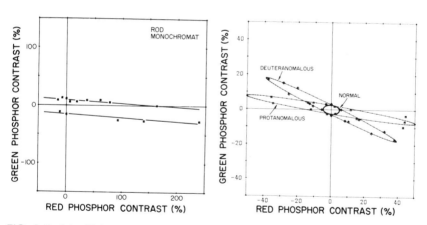

FIG. 2 (Left)   Bichromatic thresholds for red–green mixtures for a rod monochromat. The 1 degree test flash was presented for 0.2 sec.

FIG. 3 (Right)   Bichromatic thresholds for 1 degree, 0.2 sec foveal flashes in protanomalous (squares) and deuteranomalous (diamonds) subjects. The data have been fitted by ellipses and an ellipse for a normal subject is also shown.

B. *Congenital and Acquired Colour Deficiencies*

Squares and diamonds in Fig. 3 give thresholds for a protanomalous and a deuteranomalous subject, respectively, for a 1 degree, 0.2 sec foveal test flash. In comparison to the two parallel lines of the rod monochromat, it is seen that these data can be fitted quite well by ellipses (cf. Noorlander, Heuts and Koenderink, 1981) and a corresponding ellipse for a normal subject is also shown (see also Fig. 4).

Anomalous trichromats give a closed curve (ellipse) rather than the two parallel lines of the rod monochromat because they use a colour-sensitive mechanism (which is lacking in the rod monochromat) to detect flashes near the ends of the ellipse. The ellipses for the anomalous trichromats are very elongated compared to normal and the high thresholds at the ends of the ellipses are presumably due to the poor colour discrimination of these subjects. Thus the length of the ellipse is a measure of colour discrimination threshold. The long flanks of the ellipses are similar to the two parallel lines of the rod monochromat and correspond to detection of brightening or dimming of the test spot. Thus the width of the ellipse is a measure of brightness discrimination.

The ratio of length to width is thus a measure of the ratio of colour to brightness discrimination threshold. This ratio is very variable in anomalous trichromats; in 14 deuteranomalous subjects, the ratio ranged from 3.3 to 27 whereas in 3 protanomalous it ranged from 12 to 63. Data for congenital dichromats can also be fitted by ellipses rather than by two straight lines as might be expected if they have no red–green colour discrimination; we are investigating the cause of this observation.

As in the case of the rod monochromat, the slope of the plot (i.e. the major axis) reflects the relative sensitivity of the subject to the red and green primaries. The slope is smaller for protans than for deutans because they are less sensitive to the red primary (but not as insensitive as the rod monochromat of Fig. 2). For 22 deutans, the slope of the major axis varied from -0.39 to -0.54 whereas for 6 protans it varied from -0.14 to -0.20. Thus the technique discriminates clearly betwen protan and deutan defects.

Among the acquired defects we have studied, have been three cases of optic atrophy which seem to correspond to a selective loss of "tonic" or colour-opponent optic nerve axons (de Monasterio and Gouras, 1975; King-Smith, Rosten, Alvarez and Bhargava, 1980). The ellipses fitted to the red–green plots for these patients had length: width ratios of 5.4, 8.7 and 20 which are much greater than normal (see below). This indicates a selective loss of colour discrimination (rather than a general loss of contrast discrimination) which would be consistent with a selective loss of colour-opponent axons.

C. Normals

Figure 4 shows red–green bichromatic thresholds for a normal subject using both 0.2 and 0.017 sec durations for the 1 degree foveal flash. The fitted ellipse for the brief duration is evidently considerably more elongated and this was confirmed in four other subjects. This may be interpreted as indicating that there is a relatively greater fall of colour threshold than of brightness threshold as the test flash duration is increased – i.e. there is greater temporal integration in the colour system (cf. Regan and Tyler, 1971; King-Smith and Carden, 1976).

The slope of the major axis for the 0.017 sec flash is -0.32 and so lies between the values for protans and deutans (see above). This might be expected for a normal observer who has both red- and green-sensitive cones. The slope of the major axis for the 0.2 sec flash is only -0.14 which lies within the range of protan observers and similar results were obtained in many normal eyes (mean slope derived from 28 subjects was -0.11).

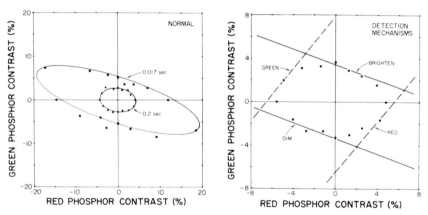

FIG. 4 (Left)   Normal bichromatic thresholds for 1 degree foveal flashes of durations 0.2 sec and 0.017 sec.
FIG. 5 (Right)   The squares are experimental bichromatic thresholds for a normal subject for 1 degree, 0.2 sec foveal flashes. The thresholds of the four postulated detection mechanisms, "brighten", "dim", "red", and "green" are represented by the four straight lines as indicated.

Figure 5 offers a possible explanation of why the major axis is so close to horizontal in this case. The squares correspond to the experimental data for 0.2 sec flashes. The four lines correspond to thresholds of postulated detection mechanisms. The continuous lines represent mechanisms detecting brightening and dimming and they have been drawn at the angle expected from the relative luminances of the red and green phosphors (Table 1). The dashed lines represent colour detecting mechanisms for red and green stimuli. Whenever two mechanisms (e.g. "brighten" and "red") are about equally sensitive, the visual threshold is reduced by probability summation (e.g. Boynton, Ikeda and Stiles, 1964). The colour mechanisms are not at right angles to the brightness mechanisms and so the data points are fitted by a parallelogram with rounded corners. It can be seen that the major axis of the ellipse no longer corresponds to the equiluminous lines of the brightening and dimming mechanisms. Theoretically, the same analysis should apply to the congenital defects of Fig. 3; however, in those cases, the ellipses are so elongated that little error is involved in assuming that the colour detection lines are at right angles to the equiluminous lines.

For these reasons, the colour thresholds for normal subjects were derived, not from the major axis, but from the intersection of the ellipse with the equiluminous line through the origin. The luminance threshold was similarly determined from a line at right angles to this. The ratio of colour to luminance thresholds varied from 0.93 to 3.0 in 28 normal subjects. Thus the best deuteranomalous subject had slightly poorer colour discrimination than the worst normal on this test. It would also seem that the range of variation in deuteranomalous subjects (a factor of about 8.2 times between the highest and lowest colour : luminance ratios in 14 subjects) is greater than in normals (a factor of about 3.2 in 28 subjects).

Acknowledgements

We are grateful for support from the Ohio Lions Eye Research Foundation and the Burroughs Wellcome Fund.

References

Boynton, R. M., Ideka, M. and Stiles, W. S. (1964). Interactions among chromatic mechanisms as inferred from positive and negative increment thresholds. *Vision Res.* **4**, 87–117.

De Monasterio, F. M. and Gouras, P. (1975). Functional properties of the rhesus monkey retina. *J. Physiol.* **251**, 167–195.

King-Smith, P. E. and Carden, D. (1976). Luminance and opponent colour contributions to visual detection and adaptation and to temporal and spatial integration. *J. opt. Soc. Am.* **66**, 709–717.

King-Smith, P. E., Rosten, J. G., Alvarez, S. L. and Bhargava, S. K. (1980). Human vision without tonic ganglion cells? In *Colour Vision Deficiencies V* (ed. Verriest, G.), pp. 99–105. Bristol, Adam Hilger.

Noorlander, C., Heuts, M. J. G. and Koenderink, J. J. (1981). Sensitivity to combined luminance and chromaticity contrast. *J. opt. Soc. Am.* **71**, 453–459.

Regan, D. and Tyler, C. W. (1971). Temporal summation and its limits for wavelength changes: an analog of Bloch's Law for color vision. *J. opt. Soc. Am.* **61**, 1414–1421.

Nonlinear Versus Linear Opponency in Vertebrate Retina

BOB W. VAN DIJK and HENK SPEKREIJSE

Introduction

Although many models of vertebrate color processing have been presented in the literature, no physiological model exists that successfully describes the color processing quantitatively. It is generally assumed that signals originating in different receptor mechanisms superpose in the ganglion cell responses. This concept is expressed e.g. in the notation of receptive field codings with plusses and minuses ($R + G-$ etc.). In the most distal cells (i.e. receptors and horizontal cells) this linearity has been confirmed when the cells are driven by small signals (Tomita, Kaneko, Murakami and Pautler, 1967; Spekreijse and Norton, 1970). At ganglion cell level, however, it is clear that nonlinear color interactions occur. This is demonstrated by the fact that ganglion cell action spectra in general cannot be constructed by algebraic summation of a set of three ganglion cell spectra. To prove this point we took a large set (124) of carp ganglion cell spectra and grouped them in eight different classes on the basis of the wavelengths of peak sensitivity and shapes of the curves. For every class we calculated the mean spectrum. If the color processing in the carp retina is linear then it should be possible with any set of three mean spectra that are independent, i.e. none of the three can be constructed from the two others, to generate the other five mean spectra by algebraic summation. This proved not to be the case. At best we could select three spectra to generate two of the remaining five. On the other hand, a similar approach to horizontal cell spectra gave, as expected, satisfactory fits. So color interactions do not remain linear up to ganglion cell level.

COLOUR VISION
ISBN 0 12 000000 0

For a quantitative study of nonlinear color interactions a precise knowledge of the fundamental spectra (i.e. before any interaction amongst the three receptor classes has occurred) is essential. For the cyprinid retina absorption spectra of all three cone types have been determined by microspectrophotometry (Harosi, 1976). On the basis of these absorption data Harosi proposed a set of three absorption spectra by extrapolating the 1 log unit sensitivity range that can be measured by microspectrophotometry. However, these extrapolated curves disagree with the electrophysiologically determined fundamentals as measured for instance at the horizontal cell level by Norton and Spekreijse (1971). They also seem to disagree with the fundamentals that underlie the ganglion cell responses (Spekreijse, Mooij and Van den Berg, 1981). Caution is indicated in interpreting the latter observation since nonlinear interactions occur before the ganglion cell level, which may alter the shape of action spectra (Sirovich and Abramov, 1977).

In the present study we will first derive the fundamentals underlying ganglion cells responses, using the silent substitution technique to exclude the influence of nonlinear dynamic color interactions. (For a review of this method, see Estévez and Spekreijse, 1982.) Next we will give some examples of nonlinear color interactions that can be seen at the ganglion cell level; and we will demonstrate that these nonlinear interactions can be blocked by Ethambutol application leaving simple algebraic opponent interactions intact.

Methods

Isolated retinas of common carp (*Cyprinus carpio*) are placed in a superfusion chamber, through which a fish Ringer's is pumped continuously. The pH is kept at 7.4, and temperature at 17.5°C. A three beam optical system can project spots and annuli of different sizes from below on the retina. Ganglion cell responses are registered with PtIr electrodes which are lowered from above into the retina. The spikes are shaped and played over a loudspeaker. Shaped spikes are fed into a PDP 11/60 computer which on line produces peri-stimulus time histograms (PSTHs). Responses of single ganglion cells can be registered for up to 11 hours. For a more detailed description of superfusate, stimulation and recording, see Van Dijk and Spekreijse (1983).

Results and Discussion

There exists one class of ganglion cells in carp that receives input from the red cones only. These are the Silent Red ON; Red OFF cells that do not have an apparent spatial opponency.

The spectra of these cells are invariant with response criterion (Fig. 1A) and with intensity and wavelength of background illumination (Fig. 1B). Furthermore, the responses of these cells can always be silenced by two overlapping

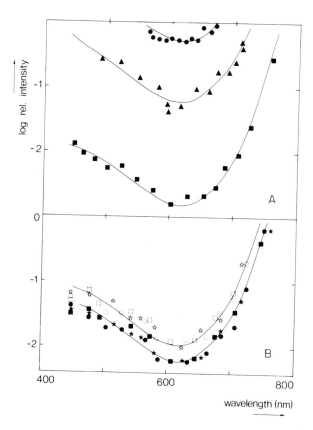

FIG. 1 Silent red ON; red OFF carp ganglion cell. The unit had a maintained activity of 2.3 ± 0.7 spikes per second; the receptive field covered the entire stimulating area (10°). Criterion response spectra were determined with a full field stimulus.

Duty cycle: 800 msec on, 800 msec off. 0 log unit corresponds to 9×10^{16} quanta sec^{-1} m^{-2}.

(A) Response spectra obtained with different criteria for the OFF response: 1 spike per 2 stimuli (■); 2 spikes per stimulus (▲); 10 spikes per stimulus (●). A 500 nm background of 5×10^{14} quanta sec^{-1} m^{-2} was used to eliminate rod intrusion; unless otherwise stated backgrounds covered the entire retina.

(B) Threshold response curves recorded in the presence of different monochromatic backgrounds: 633 nm (○,●); 485 nm (☆,★); 577 nm (□,■). The filled symbols represent OFF responses, the open symbols ON responses. The intensity of the background was chosen such that they would have equal effects on a mechanism with a spectral sensitivity curve as depicted by the drawn lines in A. This intensity was 1.2 log unit above the threshold for this unit without a background present.

alternating spots of different wavelengths whose intensities can be derived from the criterion response spectrum of the cell. These cells thus exhibit linear color processing. The spectrum of this class of ganglion cells was chosen as the red fundamental (continuous curves in Fig. 1).

Knowing this fundamental, it is possible to isolate the blue and green components in ganglion cell responses that are fed either by red and green or by red and blue inputs. (The trichromatic ganglion cells are not considered in this study.) Isolation is achieved by substituting a 694-nm stimulus for the test stimulus of variable wavelength in such a way that no modulation of the red mechanism occurs (silent substitution). Since nonlinear interactions with a sustained (DC) character are not eliminated by this approach, we tested the invariance of the resultant spectra in the presence of various chromatic backgrounds. If a spectrum derives from a single univariant color mechanism, it should have the same shape irrespective of the wavelength and intensity of the background. This proved to be the case. A second test for isolation consisted

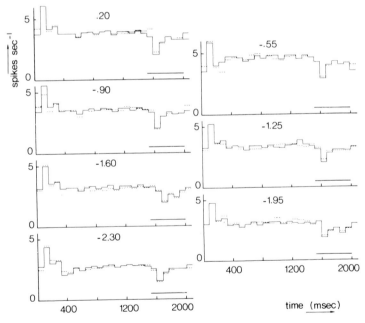

FIG. 2   Peri stimulus time histograms for red silenced stimuli on a center red ON blue OFF; surround red OFF ganglion cell with a maintained activity of 3.0 ± 0.95 spikes per second.

The stimulus is a spot of 2.5° centered in the receptive field and superposed on a 500-nm background to avoid rod intrusion. The PSTHs obtained for 440 nm are depicted in drawn lines, those for 520 nm in dashed lines. The intensity of the stimulus is shown in log units. 0 log unit corresponds to 9×10^{16} quanta $sec^{-1} m^{-2}$.

of monitoring the dynamics of the responses of ganglion cells driven by two color mechanisms, when one of the mechanisms (the red) was silenced. We could demonstrate (Fig. 2) that for various wavelengths differing in intensity by as much as 0.8 log unit, as seen by the silenced red process, the same PSTHs could be observed. This finding indicates that the isolated green and blue spectra are invariant and thus fundamentals. In this way we derived a set of three fundamentals underlying the ganglion cell responses. These fundamentals are shown in Fig. 3 together with the electrophysiological data that are obtained in the cone pedicles (Kaneko, in prep.) and in the horizontal cells (Norton and Spekreijse, 1971) and with the extrapolated optical density spectra of Harosi (1976), corrected for self-screening. As can be seen

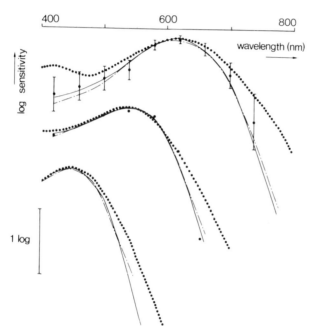

FIG. 3 Carp photopic retinal spectral sensitivity curves. The dotted lines represent the optical density spectra (Harosi, 1976) corrected for self-screening; the maximum densities used for the red, green and blue cones were 0.11, 0.10 and 0.05 respectively. The data points (mean ± SD) are the action spectra measured in cone pedicles by Kaneko (in prep.). The red values are based on 8 cone spectra; the green are the average of 2 cone spectra; the blue data were not consistent and therefore left out.

The interrupted lines represent the action spectra obtained with chromatic adaptation at horizontal cell level (Norton and Spekreijse, 1971). The drawn lines represent the action spectra obtained with the silent substitution method at ganglion cell level.

For clarity the green and blue spectra are shifted respectively 1 and 2 log unit relative to the red spectrum.

all electrophysiological data are alike, but large differences exist between action and absorption spectra. All action spectra are narrower than the extrapolated absorption spectra. This difference can be attributed at the long-wavelength side to the extrapolation procedure Harosi employed (Spekreijse *et al.*, 1981). There is, however, another difference that is most obvious for the red spectra: unlike the absorption spectrum the red action spectrum does not have a cis-peak. This cannot be attributed to calibration errors in either set of data since in the short-wavelength region, where the blue and green spectra agree, the red disagree. An explanation based on the existence of blue-absorbing oil droplets, operating exclusively on the red cones, seems unlikely since such droplets have so far not been reported in fish retina. An explanation of this difference in terms of mixing of blue and green signals at the red cone pedicle, as suggested by Stell and Lightfoot (1975), also seems unlikely, since neither at horizontal cell nor at ganglion cell level does strong chromatic adaptation change the shape of the red spectrum. Finally, whereas the pure red ganglion cells behave highly linearly, their action spectra cannot be generated by sub-tracting green and blue absorption spectra from the red absorption spectrum. An obvious but speculative explanation might be that beta-band and main-band absorption follow different chemical pathways, such that the bleaching is as depicted in the absorption spectrum, but the sensitivity as in the action spectrum.

Examples of Nonlinear Color Interactions

The most commonly observed nonlinear interaction in the carp retina is inhibition. Generally a strong red response inhibits the contribution of green and blue processes to the ganglion cell response (irrespective of its sign: ON or OFF). This inhibition is strongest when the red mechanism is antagonistic to the other color mechanisms. The strength of the inhibition can be influenced by the timing and duty cycle of the stimulus. Stimulation at low frequencies mostly weakens the nonlinear behaviour (Fig. 4). To inhibit the contribution of green and blue processes it is not necessary that the red mechanism itself is strongly modulated or even responsive. The former happens when strong red adaptation is used. In that case the (sub-threshold) small dynamic signals in the red system still suppress the other mechanisms' responses (Fig. 5A). An example where the red system by itself does not respond is demonstrated in Fig. 5B. The red input of this ganglion cell can only be made visible by its inhibition of the blue mechanism. When stimulating with a red (e.g. 625 nm) stimulus no response can be observed. However, when this stimulus is presented together with a blue stimulus it inhibits the response of the blue mechanism (silent inhibition). If a constant output of the blue system is used as criterion, a pure red action spectrum is obtained. This is another illustration of the uni-directional character of color inhibition in carp retina.

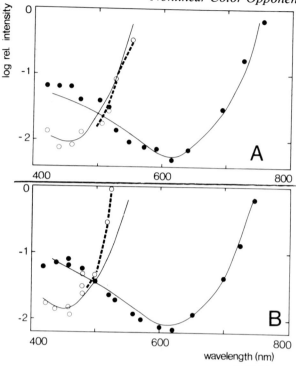

FIG. 4   Influence of stimulus frequency (4A: 1/4 Hz, 4B: 4 Hz) on the opponent
color interaction of a center red OFF blue ON; surround red ON ganglion cell with
a maintained activity of 22.3 ± 6.2 spikes per second. The threshold response
curves are obtained with a 2.5° spot centered in the receptive field (open symbols
ON responses; filled symbols OFF responses) in the presence of a 500-nm background to eliminate rod intrusion (5×10^{14} quanta sec^{-1} m^{-2}). 0 log unit corresponds to 9×10^{16} quanta sec^{-1} m^{-2}.

Effects of Ethambutol on the Nonlinear Color Opponency

Zrenner and Krüger (1981) reported that Ethambutol, a commonly used tuber-
culostaticum, which can cause color anomalies, does not affect the sensitivities
of the receptor mechanisms, but their (opponent) interactions. From this
finding they concluded that Ethambutol probably affects "higher" (cortical)
processing. We tried Ethambutol in low concentrations in our isolated carp
retinas and found that it affects the ganglion cell responses (Van Dijk and
Spekreijse, 1983). We confirmed that Ethambutol does not change the sensitivity of the underlying color mechanisms and we could demonstrate that
Ethambutol weakens selectively the nonlinear interactions, leaving the
algebraic opponency intact. This is exemplified in Fig. 6 where a ganglion cell
criterion response spectrum is depicted for both a small spot (a) stimulating
the receptive field center and for a wide annulus (b) stimulating the surround.

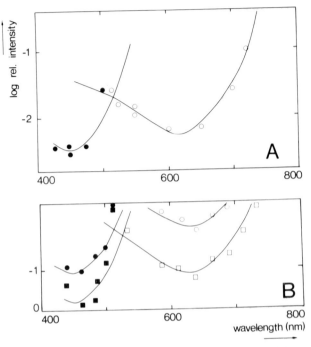

FIG. 5   Examples of inhibition of the blue process by a weak (A) or not responsive (B) red mechanism. (A) The stimulus is a 2.5° spot superposed on a bright (12.6×10^{16} quanta sec^{-1} m^{-2}) 546-nm background (10°). The duty cycle of the stimulus is 500 msec on, 1500 msec off. The silent unit had a red ON blue OFF center and a red OFF surround. (B) Example of silent inhibition. The criterion response spectrum to full field stimulation, duty cycle 1 sec ON 1 sec OFF (filled symbols) does not show a red mechanism. However, a red stimulus inhibits the response to a simultaneously presented blue stimulus. The open symbols depict the criterion response curve obtained by using as the criterion the complete inhibition of a 1 log unit supra-threshold 450-nm stimulus, presented simultaneously.

In this cell the presence of the red mechanism strongly affects the green response. No green response could be recorded for wavelengths longer than 500 nm although the green mechanism by itself peaks at 530 nm. When Ethambutol is applied in different concentrations (Figs 6c–f) the spectra change: the red inhibition on the green mechanism becomes weaker. This effect was reversible. From this finding we concluded that a nonlinear mechanism exists which can be affected by Ethambutol. Since Ethambutol did not influence the maintained activity of the ganglion cell nor the center and surround sensitivities, it is most likely that bipolars or amacrines are affected by Ethambutol and hence the sources of the nonlinear processing.

Finally the similarity of the effects of Ethambutol on color processing in

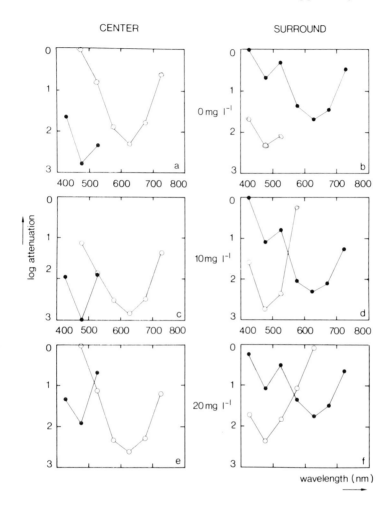

CENTER   SURROUND

FIG. 6 Criterion response spectra for a center red ON, green OFF (left column); surround red OFF, green ON (right column) ganglion cell, when different concentrations of Ethambutol are applied. Center stimulus: 1.8° spot, surround stimulus 4–8°. Duty cycle 1 sec ON, 1 sec OFF. A 500 nm background (4×10^{14} quanta sec^{-1} m^{-2}) was used to eliminate rod intrusion.

man and carp shows that, although their retinas certainly are not identical (e.g. in carp a fovea is absent and the most commonly observed color coding in carp retina, i.e. double opponency has not yet been observed in the primate retina) the isolated carp retina is a good model for some of the electrophysiological processing underlying human color discrimination.

Acknowledgements

We are grateful to Dr Harosi who kindly gave us the actual data of the carp cone absorption spectra and also to Dr Kaneko who provided us with the cone pedicle action spectra. We thank Dr Ringo for critically reading this manuscript. Bob van Dijk was supported by the Dutch Organization for the Advancement of Pure Research (ZWO) through the Netherlands Foundation for Biophysics.

References

Estévez, O. and Spekreijse, H. (1982). The "silent substitution" method in visual research. *Vision Res.* **22**, 681–691.

Hárosi, F. I. (1976). Spectral relations of cone pigments in goldfish. *J. Gen. Physiol.* **68**, 65–80.

Norton, A. L. and Spekreijse, H. (1971). The color coding of S-potentials. Abstracts of Association for Research in Vision and Ophthalmology.

Sirovich, L. and Abramov, I. (1977). Photopigments and pseudo-pigments. *Vision Res.* **17**, 5–16.

Spekreijse, H. and Norton, A. L. (1970). The dynamic characteristics of color-coded S-potentials. *J. gen. Physiol.* **56**, 1–15.

Spekreijse, H., Mooij, J. E. M. and Van den Berg, T. J. T. P. (1981). Photopigments and carp ganglion cell action spectra. *Vision Res.* **21**, 1601–1604.

Stell, W. K. and Lightfoot, D. V. (1975). Color-specific interconnections of cones and horizontal cells in the retina of the goldfish. *J. comp. Neur.* **159**, 473–502.

Tomita, T., Kaneko, A., Murakami, M. and Pautler, E. L. (1967). Spectral response curves of single cones in carp. *Vision Res.* **7**, 519–531.

Van Dijk, B. W. and Spekreijse, H. (1982). Ethambutol changes the color coding of carp ganglion cells reversibly. *Invest. Ophthal.* (In press).

Zrenner, E. and Krüger, C. J. (1981). Ethambutol mainly affects the function of red/green opponent neurons. *Doc. Ophthalmol.* **27**, 13–26.

Colour-Opponent Mechanisms in Cat Retinal Ganglion Cells

M. WIENRICH and E. ZRENNER

Introduction

After several decades of controversy (for references see Granit, 1947; Granit and Tansley, 1948; Donner, 1950; Daw and Pearlman, 1969) behavioural experiments demonstrated relatively recently the ability of cats to discriminate colours (Mello and Peterson, 1964; Sechzer and Brown, 1964; Daw and Pearlman, 1969), the data being obtained only with considerable difficulties (Brown, LaMotte, Shively and Sechzer, 1973; Loop, Bruce and Petuchowski, 1979). Compared to the large amount of behavioural and electrophysiological data available for the monkey (for references see Gouras and Zrenner, 1981; Zrenner, 1983), only little is known about the processing of colour information in ganglion cells of the feline retina. Colour-opponent cells in the cat's lateral geniculate nucleus were first described by Daw and Pearlman (1970); since then investigations of electroretinographical responses (ERG), visual evoked cortical potentials (VECP) and optic nerve responses (ONR) (Rabin, Mehaffey and Berson, 1976; Zrenner and Gouras, 1979a; Schuurmans, 1981, Schuurmans and Zrenner, 1981a, b) as well as single cell recordings at different stages of the visual system have pointed to a trichromatic or at least dichromatic organization of the cat's retina (Ringo, Wolbarsht, Wagner, Crocker and Amthor, 1977; Saunders, 1977; Crocker, Ringo, Wolbarsht and Wagner, 1980; Wienrich and Zrenner, 1981).

This paper presents the results of experiments in which 265 cat retinal ganglion cells were studied with respect to (1) cone input, (2) the presence of

COLOUR VISION
ISBN 0 12 000000 0

colour-opponent interactions between different cone mechanisms, and (3) the incidence of different cell types.[1]

Material and Methods

In 29 adult cats (*Felis catus*, both sexes, 2.5−4.5 kg) extracellular recordings were obtained from 265 retinal ganglion cells. The animals were anaesthetized with sodium pentobarbitone (Nembutal, 5 mg kg^{-1} h^{-1}), paralysed with gallamine triethiodide (Flaxedil, 5 mg kg^{-1} h^{-1}) and artificially respired (30 ml stroke^{-1}, 20 strokes min^{-1}). The cat's head was placed in a stereotactic head holder and a glass microelectrode (tip diameter $<$ 1 μm, 30−100 MΩ) was advanced towards the retina through a small hole cut in the sclera on the temporal side of the limbus (Gouras and Zrenner, 1979; Wienrich, 1982; Zrenner, 1983). In a three-beam light stimulator (Maxwellian view) two beams provided exchangeable test stimuli variable in intensity and wavelength (Wienrich, 1982); the third served as an adaptation beam to saturate rods and to produce chromatic adaptation.

To determine the response characteristics of retinal ganglion cells single unstructured flashes (200 msec duration, 1 Hz) were superimposed on the background adaptation field. The irradiance of the test beams (in quanta sec^{-1} μm^{-2}) was measured with a Pin 1223 photodiode (UDT); the retinal illumination of the adaptation beam (in td) with a Pin 10 AP photodiode (UDT). Standard electrophysiological equipment was used for recording and data processing (Wienrich, 1982).

Results

Figure 1 shows the action spectra of three photopically active receptor mechanisms which dominate the responses of different retinal ganglion cells when appropriate chromatic adaptation (μ) is applied.

Based on a constant threshold criterion, spectral sensitivity is inferred from intensity−response functions: the ganglion cell's sensitivity to a given wavelength (λ) is determined by the irradiance (E) necessary to elicit a constant change in the cell's discharge rate. The sensitivity (log $1/E$) is indicated as log S (quanta^{-1} sec μm^2).

The open symbols represent averaged data points derived from several cells (n) of the same type; the standard deviations are shown as vertical bars. The data points were fitted with pigment nomogram curves (solid lines) according

---

[1] Since spatial and temporal characteristics of retinal ganglion cells lie beyond the scope of this paper, the classification is based on their spectral sensitivity only. Therefore, aspects of linearity and receptive field structure were not taken into account.

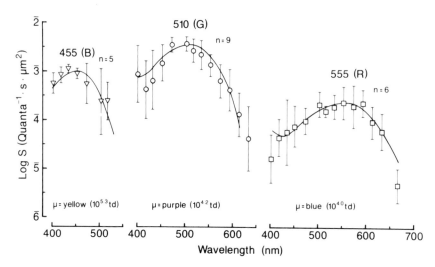

FIG. 1 Spectral sensitivity functions of cat retinal ganglion cells. The data points (open symbols) represent mean values (*n*) obtained from 5, 9 and 6 cells of the same type (error bars show standard deviations) under three conditions of chromatic adaptation (μ; yellow, OG 550, $10^{5.3}$ td, or purple, PAL 630, $10^{4.2}$ td, or blue, BG 28, $10^{4.0}$ td; all filters manufactured by Schott). The sensitivity (*S*) of the three photopically active receptor mechanisms has been matched with pigment nomogram curves (Dartnall, 1953) with maxima at 455, 510 and 555 nm. Test light duration = 200 msec, frequency = 1 Hz, Ganzfeld presentation.

to Dartnall (1953). A short-wavelength sensitive cone mechanism with a sensitivity maximum at 455 nm can be isolated in the presence of yellow adaptation light ($10^{5.3}$ td) which reduces sensitivity of the long wavelength sensitive cones; with purple adaptation light ($10^{4.2}$ td) a middle-wavelength sensitive mechanism with a peak sensitivity at 510 nm determines the cells' threshold while a long-wavelength sensitive cone mechanism with a sensitivity peak at 555 nm can be isolated by blue adaptation light ($10^{4.0}$ td).

Thus three photopically active receptor mechanisms can be detected in the responses of retinal ganglion cells in the cat's visual system, which will be called blue-, green- and red-sensitive mechanisms, although their spectral positions do not coincide with those of macaques or man.

Figure 2 shows the interaction between the blue-sensitive and longer-wavelength sensitive receptor mechanisms that was found in a small number of retinal ganglion cells (*n* = 3). The figure shows an averaged spectral sensitivity function, based on a constant threshold criterion.

In the presence of yellow adaptation (μ; $10^{5.2}$ td), light of short wave-lengths excites these cells (open triangles) while light of longer wavelengths inhibits them (filled triangles, original records are shown below each branch).

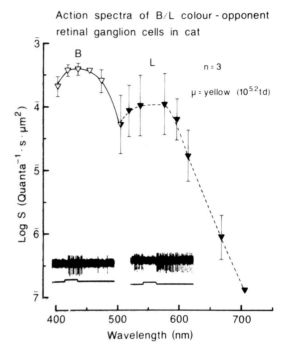

FIG. 2 Averaged action spectra (means ± SD) of three colour-opponent retinal ganglion cells in cat, excited by the blue-sensitive mechanism (B, open triangles, connected with solid lines) and inhibited by longer-wavelength sensitive receptors (L, filled triangles, broken line) during yellow adaptation (μ, $10^{5.2}$ td, OG 550, Schott). The action spectra are based on a constant threshold criterion. Original excitatory and inhibitory responses are shown below.

The curves do not represent nomograms. Light of intermediate wavelength (500 nm) stimulates the blue-sensitive excitatory (B) and the opposing longer wavelength sensitive inhibitory (L) mechanism to approximately the same extent so that they almost cancel each other out. Consequently the cell has a sensitivity minimum near 500 nm (neutral point). Of the cells studied, 3.4% showed antagonism between blue- and longer-wavelength sensitive mechanisms.

Figure 3 shows the spectral sensitivity functions of a rare retinal ganglion cell with trichromatic receptoral input and antagonistic interaction between the green- and the red-sensitive receptor mechanisms.

The action spectra recorded under different adaptation conditions (μ) are based on a constant threshold criterion; representative original responses are given beneath each graph. When the cell is adapted with white light ($10^{6.0}$ td, extreme left) its response to test stimuli up to 590 nm is dominated by an excitatory mechanism (open circles). Stimulation with longer wavelengths inhibits the cell (filled circles). Despite this apparent spectral dichotomy the

Spectral sensitivity functions of a colour-opponent retinal ganglion cell in cat

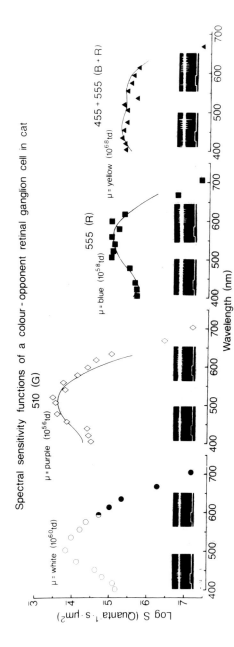

FIG. 3   Spectral sensitivity functions based on a constant threshold criterion from a colour-opponent retinal ganglion cell in cat, which receives input from three spectrally different photopically active receptor mechanisms. Original responses to short- and long-wavelength stimuli are presented underneath each graph. Four different states of Ganzfeld adaptation were used: μ = white, circles, $10^{6.0}$ td, 5500 K; μ = purple, diamonds, $10^{5.6}$ td, Pal 630, Schott; μ = blue, squares, $10^{5.8}$ td, BG 28, Schott, and μ = yellow, triangles, $10^{6.8}$ td, OG 550, Schott.

Excitatory responses are indicated by open symbols, inhibitory responses by filled ones. The mechanisms isolated by chromatic adaptation were matched with Dartnall pigment nomograms (solid lines) with maxima as indicated in nm above each nomogram.

action spectrum does not show the clear sensitivity minimum (neutral point) that usually separates the sensitivity maxima for excitatory and inhibitory mechanisms in colour-opponent cells (cf. Fig. 2). Purple adaptation (second graph from the left) of $10^{5.6}$ td, which definitely suppressed rod activity in cat (Schuurmans and Zrenner, 1981a; Wienrich, 1982), reveals the dominating excitatory mechanism (open diamonds), which matches a 510 nm Dartnall nomogram curve (solid line, G). Adaptation with blue light ($10^{5.8}$ td, second from the right) isolates the inhibitory mechanism (filled squares) which matches the 555 nm Dartnall nomogram curve (R). However, yellow adaptation ($10^{6.8}$ td, extreme right) reveals a third inhibitory mechanism which contributes to the response of the ganglion cell: the data points (filled triangles) could only be matched with a Dartnall pigment nomogram curve derived from a linear addition of 455 and 555 nm nomograms (B + R) despite many trials with combinations of 510 and 555 nm nomograms. Consequently this retinal ganglion cell must receive excitatory input from the 510 nm mechanism and inhibitory input from both the 455 and 555 nm mechanisms.

Figure 4 shows the action spectra of a retinal ganglion cell whose antagonistic receptor input is not obvious under normal daylight conditions (a, white adaptation, $10^{5.0}$ td, 5500 K). The cell is excited at all wavelengths investigated (open circles) with data points roughly matching the 555 nm Dartnall nomogram curve. If, however, chromatic adaptation (μ) is applied (Fig. 4b) two different receptor mechanisms are revealed: during blue adaptation ($10^{4.8}$ td) an excitatory red-sensitive mechanism determines the threshold throughout the visible spectrum with the data points (open circles) matching the 555 nm Dartnall pigment nomogram curve (solid line); whereas during purple adaptation ($10^{4.5}$ td, closed circles) an inhibitory mechanism is revealed whose data points closely follow the 510 nm Dartnall nomogram (broken line). Such a response pattern in colour-opponent cells, where the antagonistic photopic mechanisms are only obvious under certain conditions of chromatic adaptation, we term "hidden opponency". Hidden opponency between the red- and the green-sensitive receptor mechanisms occurred in 9.2% of all cells recorded. This might correspond to the phenomenon of graded cone dominance in the rhesus monkey retina described by Zrenner and Gouras (1979b; see also this volume) and Zrenner (1983).

Figure 5 summarizes the incidence of the different types of cat retinal ganglion cells (white columns) compared with the corresponding cell types in the macaque monkey (*Macaca mulatta*; *M. fascicularis*; hatched columns). The data from the primary cells are based on a population of 108 cells in 11 monkeys studied in a parallel series of experiments with the same equipment (Wienrich and Zrenner, 1981; Wienrich, 1982). The incidence is given in per cent of all cells recorded.

In contrast to the macaque monkey, where about 50% of all cells investigated show overt red/green (R/G) opponent receptor input, in cat only few

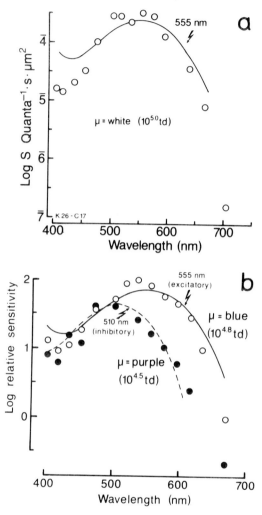

FIG. 4 Action spectra based on a constant threshold criterion of a cat retinal ganglion cell with "hidden opponency" (see text). Excitatory responses are indicated by open circles (a, b), inhibitory ones by filled circles (b). In the presence of white ($10^{5.0}$ td, a) and blue ($10^{4.8}$ td, BG 28, Schott, b) Ganzfeld adaptation (μ) the data points match the 555 nm Dartnall pigment nomogram curve (solid lines). Purple adaptation ($10^{4.5}$ td, PAL 630, Schott) reveals the inhibitory green-sensitive mechanism, the data points matching the 510 nm Dartnall pigment nomogram curve (broken line in b).

retinal ganglion cells ($< 10\%$) receive chromatically antagonistic R/G receptor input. Furthermore, in cat the overwhelming majority (75%) of all tonic ganglion cells (applying the nomenclature of Gouras, 1968) respond in a

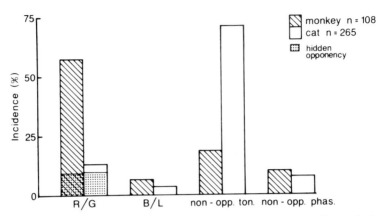

FIG. 5   Incidence (in per cent) of different types of retinal ganglion cells in cat (white columns, 265 cells) compared to those recorded in the same experimental set up from macaque monkey retina (*Macaca mulatta, M. fascicularis*; hatched columns, 108 cells). "R/G" indicates red/green colour-opponent cells; Stippling indicates hidden opponency (cf. Fig. 4). Colour-opponent cells showing antagonism between blue-sensitive and longer-wavelength sensitive cones are indicated by "B/L". "Non-opp. ton." means cells showed *tonic* response characteristics and lacked colour opponency under all chromatic adaptation conditions tested. "Non-opp. phas." cells showed *phasic* response characteristics without colour opponency.

noncolour-opponent fashion, with the receptor mechanisms usually acting synergistically. B/L cells with antagonism between the blue-sensitive and longer-wavelength sensitive cones (G and/or R) and nonopponent phasic cells (Gouras, 1968) are relatively rare in both species (< 10%). The latter presumably do not deal with processing of colour information (Gouras, 1968; Gouras and Zrenner, 1979, 1981; Zrenner, 1983) and are not discussed in this paper. Cat ganglion cells were classified as "phasic" if they responded with a short, transient discharge to all wavelengths tested; all other cells were classified as "tonic".

Discussion

Photopic Receptor Mechanisms

The existence of three spectrally different, photopically active receptor mechanisms has been recently demonstrated in recordings from single retinal ganglion cells of cat (Ringo *et al.*, 1977). Whereas the presence of short- and long-wavelength sensitive cones has been accepted for some time (see Granit, 1947; Daw and Pearlman, 1970; Zrenner and Gouras, 1979a), there has always been doubt as to whether the 510 nm mechanism originates from rods instead of cones. The rod pigment after all shows maximal absorbance at 507 nm (Granit, 1943; Brown and Wald, 1963). Schuurmans and Zrenner (1981a) investigated electroretinographical and cortical responses in cats using chromatic adaptation and found that the 510 nm mechanism possesses the qualities usually attributed to cone mechanisms: first, it is active under conditions of adaptation where rods are clearly saturated. This is in accordance with the present study where purple light saturating rods (Fig. 1) still revealed a 510 nm mechanism. Second, it follows flicker light of 40 Hz, while rods show a flicker fusion frequency of 30 Hz (Dodt and Walther, 1958). Third, it can be demonstrated in the cone dominated VECP and it exhibits typical cone characteristics in ERG responses. Fourth, it shows intensity–response functions and dark adaptation curves resembling those of cones.

Colour Opponent Cells

It does not necessarily follow from the presence of three photopic retinal mechanisms that an animal can discriminate colours, since each individual cone mechanism can transmit information only about the number of photons absorbed. In man, deficiencies caused by toxic drug effects are known, where all three cone mechanisms are unchanged while the function of red/green opponent neurones is affected, leading to severe losses of colour vision (Zrenner and Krüger, 1981). Therefore interaction between two different receptor mechanisms is necessary for good colour vision so that the number of quanta absorbed in each type of receptor can be utilized by the neuronal network to provide information about the colour of an object. Colour-opponent mechanisms have been extensively studied in ganglion cells of the macaque retina (Zrenner and Gouras, 1981; for references see Zrenner, 1983); they have also been demonstrated in cells of the cat's lateral geniculate nucleus (Daw and Pearlman, 1970; Cleland and Levick, 1974). Although it turns out that colour-opponent ganglion cells are difficult to record from in cat retina, we have shown that they do exist, albeit with slight functional and considerable numerical (see below) variations as compared to the monkey. These differences are less pronounced in B/L-antagonistic cells which show very similar response characteristics in cats and monkeys (Wienrich and Zrenner, 1981; full paper in preparation).

R/G-opponent cells are extremely rare in cats. One such cell, which could be studied for long enough to measure spectral sensitivity functions under several conditions of chromatic adaptation, revealed trichromatic input (Fig. 3), which was never observed in R/G-opponent cells of the monkey. Colour-opponent mechanisms in cat apparently possess qualities different from those in the monkey.

Incidence

Apart from the different functional manifestations of colour-opponent mechanisms mentioned above, cats and monkeys also possess them in different numbers (Fig. 5). Interestingly, nonopponent tonic cells in the cat retina occur almost as often as R/G-opponent cells in the monkey retina, while roughly the converse relation is true for the R/G-opponent cells of the cat and the nonopponent tonic cells of the monkey. A possible explanation for this phenomenon could be deduced from the fact that the cat, a nocturnal animal, depends to a large extent on nonopponent retinal mechanisms transmitting information about brightness at low light levels. On the other hand, B/L-antagonistic cells are not only very similar in their response properties and spectral sensitivity functions in both species but also show similar incidence in the retinas of cats and monkeys.

All cells were recorded in the region of the area centralis. There is no part of the cat's retina that is rod-free or where cones even outnumber rods (Steinberg *et al.*, 1973). This rather homogeneous receptor distribution in cat retina might account for the fact that we recorded the different types of retinal ganglion cells from all parts of the central retinal region.

The comparatively small number of cones in the cat's retina (Steinberg *et al.*, 1973) and the weak expression of colour-opponent mechanisms in terms of quality and quantity might account for the difficulties in training cats to discriminate colours (Sechzer and Brown, 1964; Loop *et al.*, 1979).

Acknowledgement

The authors wish to thank the head of the department, Professor E. Dodt, for his continuous support, Mrs M. Granz for excellent technical assistance during the experiments and in preparing the figures, and Dr D. C. M. Taylor for improving the English.

References

Brown, J. L., LaMotte, R. H., Shively, F. D. and Sechzer, J. A. (1973). Color discrimination in the cat. *J. comp. physiol. Psychol.* **84**, 534–544.

Brown, P. K. and Wald, G. (1963). Visual pigments in human and monkey retinas. *Nature* **200**, 37–43.

Cleland, B. G. and Levick, W. R. (1974). Properties of rarely encountered types of ganglion cells in the cat's retina and an overall classification. *J. Physiol.* **240**, 470–492.

Crocker, R. A., Ringo, J., Wolbarsht, M. L. and Wagner, H. G. (1980). Cone contributions to cat retinal ganglion cell receptive fields. *J. gen. Physiol.* **76**, 763–785.

Dartnall, H. J. A. (1953). The interpretation of spectral sensitivity curves. *Brit. Med. Bull.* **9**, 24–30.

Daw, N. W. and Pearlman, A. L. (1969). Cat colour vision: one cone process or several? *J. Physiol.* **201**, 745–764.

Daw, N. W. and Pearlman, A. L. (1970). Cat colour vision: evidence for more than one cone process. *J. Physiol.* **211**, 125–137.

Dodt, E. and Walther, J. B. (1958). Netzhautsensitivität, Linsenabsorption und physikalische Lichtstreuung: der skotopische Dominator der Katze im sichtbaren und ultravioletten Spektralbereich. *Pflügers Arch. Ges. Physiol.* **266**, 166–174.

Donner, K. O. (1950). The spike frequency of mammalian retinal elements as a function of wave-length of light. *Acta Physiol. Scand.* **21**, Suppl. 72, 1–59.

Gouras, P. (1968). Identification of cone mechanisms in monkey ganglion cells. *J. Physiol., Lond.* **199**, 533–547.

Gouras, P. and Zrenner, E. (1979). Enhancement of luminance flicker by color-opponent mechanisms. *Science* **205**, 587–589.

Gouras, P. and Zrenner, E. (1981). Color vision. In *Progress in Sensory Physiology*, Vol. 1 (ed. Ottoson, D.), pp. 139–179. Berlin, Springer Verlag.

Granit, R. (1943). The spectral properties of the visual receptors of the cat. *Acta physiol. Scand.* **5**, 219–229.

Granit, R. (1947). *Sensory Mechanisms of the Retina.* London, Oxford University Press.

Granit, R. and Tansley, K. (1948). Rods, cones and the localization of pre-excitatory inhibition in the mammalian retina. *J. Physiol., Lond.* **107**, 54–66.

Loop, M. S., Bruce, L. L. and Petuchowski, S. (1979). Cat color vision: the effect of stimulus size, shape and viewing distance. *Vision Res.* **19**, 507–513.

Mello, N. K. and Peterson, N. J. (1964). Behavioural evidence for color discrimination in cat. *J. Neurophysiol.* **27**, 323–333.

Rabin, A. R., Mehaffey, L. and Berson, E. L. (1976). Blue cone function in the retina of the cat. *Vision Res.* **16**, 799–801.

Ringo, J., Wolbarsht, M. L., Wagner, H. G., Crocker, R. and Amthor, F. (1977). Trichromatic vision in the cat. *Science* **198**, 753–754.

Saunders, R. McD. (1977). The spectral responsiveness and the temporal frequency response (TFR) of cat optic tract and lateral geniculate neurons: sinusoidal stimulation studies. *Vision Res.* **17**, 285–292.

Schuurmans, R. P. (1981). *Colour vision in cat: the spectrally different mechanisms and their interaction as recorded from the arterially perfused eye and visual cortex.* PhD Thesis, University of Amsterdam.

Schuurmans, R. P. and Zrenner, E. (1981a). Chromatic signals in the visual pathway of the domestic cat. *Doc. Ophthal. Proc. Series.* Vol. 27 (eds Spekreijse, H. and Apkarian, C. P. A.), pp. 27–40. Den Haag, Junk.

Schuurmans, R. P. and Zrenner, E. (1981b). Responses of the blue sensitive cone system from the visual cortex and the arterially perfused eye in cat and monkey. *Vision Res.* **21**, 1611–1615.

Sechzer, J. A. and Brown, J. L. (1964). Color discrimination in the cat. *Science* **144**, 427–429.

Steinberg, R. H., Reid, M. and Lacy, P. (1973). The distribution of rods and cones in the retina of the cat (*Felis domesticus*). *J. comp. Neurol.* **148**, 229–248.

Wienrich, M. (1982). *Vergleichende Untersuchungen zur Verarbeitung chromatischer Reize in retinalen Ganglienzellen von Makaken und Katzen.* PhD Thesis, University of Giessen.

Wienrich, M. and Zrenner, E. (1981). Chromatic signals in retinal ganglion cells: cat versus monkey. *Pflügers Arch.* **389** (*Suppl.*) R29 (Abstract).

Zrenner, E. (1983). Neurophysiological aspects of color vision in primates: comparative studies on simian retinal ganglion cells and the human visual system. In *Studies of Brain Function*, Vol. 9 (eds. Braitenberg, V., Barlow, H. B., Bullock, T. H., Florey, E., Grüsser, O.-J. and Peters, A.). Berlin, Springer Verlag.

Zrenner, E. and Gouras, P. (1979a). Blue-sensitive cones of the cat produce a rodlike electroretinogram. *Invest. Ophthalmol. Visual Sci.* **18/10**, 1076–1081.

Zrenner, E. and Gouras, P. (1979b). Cone opponency in tonic ganglion cells and its variation with eccentricity in rhesus monkey retina. *Invest. Ophthalmol. Visual Sci. (ARVO Suppl.)* **18**, 77 (Abstract).

Zrenner, E. and Gouras, P. (1981). Characteristics of the blue-sensitive cone mechanism in primate retinal ganglion cells. *Vision Res.* **21**, 1605–1609.

Zrenner, E. and Krüger, C. J. (1981). Ethambutol mainly affects the function of red/green opponent neurons. *Doc. Ophthal. Proc. Ser.* Vol. 27 (eds. Spekreijse, H. and Apkarian, C. P. A.), pp. 13–25. Den Haag, Junk.

Neurophysiological Aspects of Colour Vision Mechanisms in the Primate Retina

E. ZRENNER

Colour vision subserves the ultimate purpose of the visual system, the detection of objects and their spatial relationships. Since the borders of objects sometimes have the same luminance as their background, only the capacity of distinguishing illuminated areas by the wavelength composition of the light quanta reflected enables the visual system to detect these objects. Furthermore, the differences in the spectral reflectance of objects and their backgrounds are often very subtle, so that the ability to discriminate adjacent colours must be outstanding in order to permit optimal performance in a spectrally more or less homogeneous environment.

This paper provides a short review of present knowledge concerning the processing of chromatic information in the primate retina. For major recent reviews about colour vision, with large reference lists, see Gouras and Zrenner (1981b), Mollon (1982), and Zrenner (1983). Moreover, some new concepts will be outlined which point to the wide range of stimulus-dependent variability in the antagonistic interaction between spectrally different cone mechanisms; the colour-opponency in a certain retinal neurons is not immutable, but varies considerably with temporal and spatial properties of the objects to be coded.

Some recent morphological data clarify the retinal circuit we are dealing with when recording from ganglion cells. Figure 1 summarizes the combined morphological and electrophysiological efforts of Nelson, Famiglietti and Kolb (1978) to understand the functional role of the separation of off- and on-pathways in mammals. By injecting horseradish peroxidase or procion yellow into electrophysiologically classified cells, they found that the dendrites of

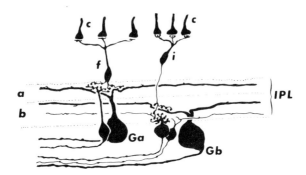

FIG. 1   Diagram of on- and off-pathways in the mammalian retina; for explanation see text (from Nelson, Famiglietti and Kolb, 1978).

on-centre ganglion cells (Ga), which are excited by light, always branch in the inner two-thirds of the inner plexiform layer (IPL, sublamina b) whereas off-centre ganglion cells (Gb), which are inhibited by light, always branch in the outer one-third of the IPL (sublamina a). A morphological topography of on- and off-ganglion cells was recently given by Wässle, Peichl and Boycott (1981).

This clear layering is valid for the large ganglion cells, which correspond to the phasic units in monkey retina (Gouras, 1968) that respond only with a brief transient discharge to any change of light. It is also valid for the small ganglion cells, which correspond most probably to the tonic units, which exhibit colour-opponency and sustained responses.

On- and off-ganglion cells receive their input from very distinct bipolar cells. The so-called invaginating cone bipolar cell (i), which puts its dendritic processes in the cone pedicle (c), provides the depolarizing on-pathway while the flat cone bipolar cell (f), which just touches the cone pedicle, provides the off-pathways (Nelson, Kolb, Robinson and Mariani, 1981).

Thus, there is a clear vertical and horizontal organization of the on- and off-pathways that signal brightness and darkness. Although most of these data were obtained in cat retina, there exists strong morphological evidence that this dichotomy holds in the monkey retina as well (Mariani, 1981).

Rods have several ways of producing ganglion cell responses, either by direct contacts with cones (Nelson, 1977), or via their own rod bipolar cell (Nelson, Kolb, Famiglietti and Gouras, 1976), or by contacting horizontal cell terminals (Nelson, Lützow, Kolb and Gouras, 1975), thus sharing pathways with cones. There are very new morphological data from Mariani (1982) and electrophysiological data from Zrenner, Nelson and Mariani (1983) in depolarizing primate biplexiform ganglion cells which, having been recorded intracellularly, were stained with horseradish peroxidase. Approximately 2 per cent of all ganglion cells in Rhesus monkey (Mariani, 1982) have a long dendritic process that bypasses bipolar cells and directly contacts rods, a previously

A

Radial section

B

Circuit

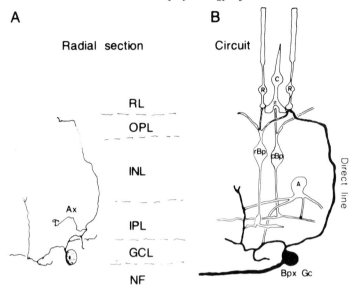

50 μm

FIG. 2 (A) Radial section though a biplexiform ganglion cell (GCL) in the Rhesus monkey retina, stained with horseradish peroxidase. One of several fine dendritic processes arises from the main dendritic arborization, ascends radially through the inner plexiform and nuclear layer (IPL and INL) to the outer plexiform layer (OPL) where it terminates at rod spherules (RL).

(B) Schematic circuit. The biplexiform ganglion cell's (Bpx Gc) ascending dendrite forms a direct line to rod spherules (r), forming the central element of a triad. According to Mariani (1982) it has conventional synapses with amacrine cells (A) and rod bipolar cells (rBp). Direct connections with cone (c) bipolar cells (cBp) are unknown. From Zrenner, Nelson and Mariani (1983).

undescribed pathway (see Fig. 2), which could play a yet unknown role in rod–cone interaction and in colour vision.

In order to identify the receptors that have input to a certain ganglion cell, selective chromatic adaptation can be used. Figure 3 shows spectral sensitivity functions of three populations of retinal ganglion cells obtained in collaboration with Dr Marion Wienrich (full paper in preparation); sensitivity is based on a constant threshold criterion, i.e., the reciprocal of the number of quanta $sec^{-1} \mu m^{-2}$ necessary to evoke a fixed change in impulse rate at the various wavelengths (usually 40 spikes per second). If the pigments of the red- and the blue-sensitive cones are bleached strongly with purple light (μ), one cell population reveals input from the green-sensitive cones (G, circles) with a sensitivity maximum at 535 nm; if the pigments of the green- and red-sensitive cones are bleached by a strong orange–red adapting light, a second cell population is revealed with input from the blue-sensitive cones (B, triangles), and a sensitivity

Spectral - sensitivity functions in rhesus monkey

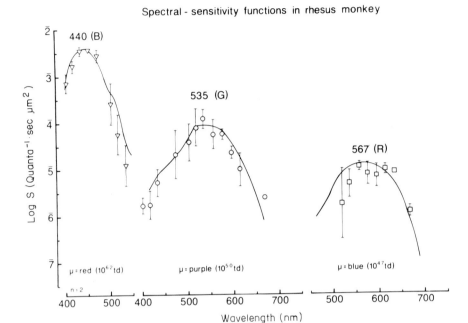

FIG. 3 Action spectra of three populations of retinal ganglion cells of Rhesus monkey based on a constant threshold criterion (see text) for monochromatic wavelengths (stimulus size 15°, duration 200 msec). Isolated by the appropriate background illumination (μ, Schott filter RG 630, PAL 630 and BG 28), three spectrally different cone mechanisms are revealed ($n = 3$ cells, mean ± standard deviation. The functions are compared with the pigment absorption spectra (solid lines) of Bowmaker, Dartnall and Mollon (1980), obtained by microspectrophotometry in macaque photoreceptors, with λ_{max} values indicated on the top of each function (reported by Wienrich and Zrenner, 1981, full paper in preparation).

maximum at 440 nm. The data thus obtained fit reasonably well the corrected spectral data of Bowmaker, Dartnall and Mollon (1980) over a rather large part of the visible spectrum (solid lines). If strong steady short-wavelength adapting lights are used, the red-sensitive cone mechanism is revealed in another cell population (R, squares) with a maximum at 567 nm. This technique is sufficient to identify clearly the cone mechanisms that have input to a colour-opponent ganglion cell, although it is not a perfect method as seen in the deviations from the red-sensitive cones' action spectrum, a deviation that points to some weak opponent processing, narrowing the spectral sensitivity function. The spectral identification of the cone mechanisms involved is − we think − an indispensable prerequisite for understanding the underlying retinal circuitry.

If instead of a chromatic background light, homogeneous white light is used, then the interaction of cone mechanisms can be seen and a totally different

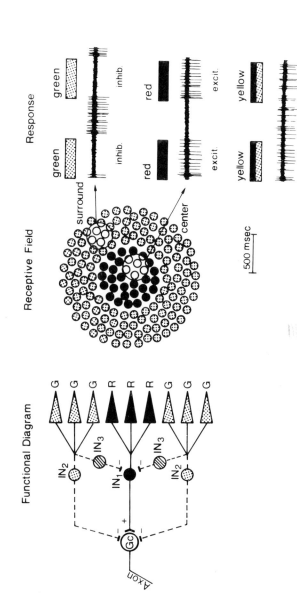

FIG. 4 Simplified functional diagram, receptive field structure and responses of a colour-opponent ganglion cell (Gc). In this cell, the red-sensitive cones in the centre act excitatorily (+), the green-sensitive cones in the surround act inhibitorily (−) via interneurons (IN₁ − IN₃). Yellow light, which stimulates both red- and green-sensitive cones, produces no modulated response to light, since excitation and inhibition cancel each other out. The stimuli, with duration indicated by the bars on the right side, cover the entire receptive field. The number of receptors (stippled or filled circles) is arbitrary. The separation of the spectrally different receptors at the border of centre and surround is not as abrupt as depicted here for simplification (from Zrenner, 1983).

picture emerges. Figure 4 shows a schematic, rather simplified diagram of the circuitry, receptive field structure, and responses of a red/green colour-opponent cell (as described by De Valois, 1965; Wiesel and Hubel, 1966; Gouras, 1968; and many others). Red light projected on to the receptive field (RF), predominantly stimulates the red-sensitive cones in the centre (filled circles). They excite the ganglion cell (GC) via interneurons (IN₁), so that during the entire duration of the stimulus (black bar) a tonic increase of discharge rate is observed. Green light stimulates predominantly the green-sensitive cones in the surround (stippled circles). They inhibit the cell (−) through other interneurons (IN₂ and IN₃), namely horizontal and bipolar cells, so that a tonic phase of inhibition is seen in the cell's response (stippled bar). Yellow light stimulates about equally the centre and surround, so that excitation and inhibition cancel each other. This is the so-called neutral point. No light-modulated change in discharge rate is observed (mixed stippled/solid bar). Of course there are limitations in this linearity of cancellation and more detailed considerations about the circuitry involved are given elsewhere (see Gouras and Zrenner, 1981b; Zrenner, 1983).

To summarize, colour opponent neurons are inhibited in one part of the spectrum, excited in another, with a neutral point in between, as Ewald Hering had postulated already in 1878. The broad sensitivity function of the receptors is thus divided into two rather specifically responding spectral parts. It is worthy of note that already by this rather simple arrangement of cone interactions in the retina the detection of differences in hue is improved considerably. For instance, when looking for strawberries in a green field of leaves, the berry and the almost equiluminous leaves stimulate the red and green cones with only slight gradual differences. In the receptors themselves, no strong neuronal signal is produced. However, if a red/green-opponent cell is stimulated by the strawberry, it is excited; if it is stimulated by the leaves, it is inhibited. It *reverses* its polarity and thus provides the strongest neuronal signal possible. Thereby colour-opponent cells are very well suited to code for even subtle differences in hue.

Figure 5 shows the spectral sensitivity functions of the various tonic cell types in the presence of a white adapting light, so that the cones can interact as they do in normal daylight. Sensitivity is based on a constant threshold criterion: at each wavelength, the irradiance (quanta sec^{-1} μm^{-2}) was determined which is necessary to obtain either a certain impulse increment for on-responses (open symbols, representing excitation) or an impulse decrement for off-responses (closed symbols, representing inhibition); the reciprocal of this value was plotted as sensitivity on the ordinate. Some red/green-opponent cells (top) with overt opponency have a sensitivity maximum near 610 nm for excitatory responses, a second peak at 500 nm for inhibitory responses, and a neutral point at 565 nm. Such cells make up about 40% of all tonic cells. The bandwidth of each spectral branch is smaller than an individual cone

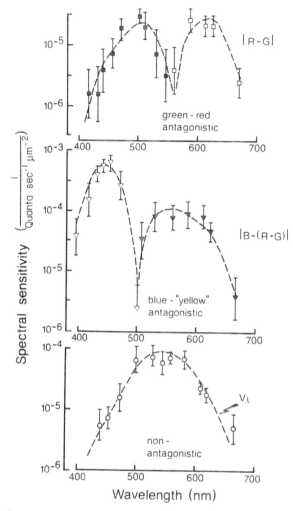

FIG. 5   Action spectra of 8 R/G-opponent (squares), 3 B/L-opponent (triangles) and 3 nonantagonistic (circles) tonic ganglion cells, recorded in the presence of a white (5500 K) Ganzfeld background (20,000 td); mean ± one standard deviation as indicated. Open symbols indicate thresholds of excitatory responses, i.e., just detectable spike frequency increments in response to increments of the test flashes' (15° in diameter) irradiance. Closed symbols indicate thresholds of inhibitory responses, i.e., just detectable spike frequency *dec*rements in response to increments of irradiance. Since the neutral point varies among individual cells (see Zrenner and Gouras, 1979 and this volume), the standard deviation increases in this neutral zone. Only cells with overt cone opponency were included (modified from Zrenner, 1983).

function (cf. Fig. 3); however, it can rather nicely be described by a linear subtraction of the R and G functions of Fig. 3 as indicated by the broken lines derived from the functions given by Bowmaker, Dartnall and Mollon (1980). The second type of red/green-opponent cells (not shown here) is very similar in spectral sensitivity except that the short-wave spectral branch mediates excitation, while the long-wave branch mediates inhibition; this cell type constitutes about 30% of the tonic ganglion cells in Rhesus monkey. In two-thirds of both cell types the red-sensitive cones form the centre of the receptive field, whereas in about one third the green-sensitive cones are found in the centre. Off-centre cells are less common than on-centre cells (see Gouras and Zrenner, 1981a, b; Zrenner, 1983).

There is another very distinct cell type, almost exclusively excited near 440 nm and maximally inhibited near 560 nm, as shown in the centre of Fig. 5. Its action spectra can be rather well described by a linear subtraction of the B function and by an additive combination of the R and G functions shown in Fig. 3. It is therefore called "blue/yellow"-opponent. Its incidence is low (about 10% of tonic cells), its receptive field size is larger, its latency is longer, and its flicker fusion frequency is lower than that of red/green cells (see Zrenner and Gouras, 1981; Zrenner, 1983 for a detailed discussion).

These colour-opponent cells respond *qualitatively* differently in the several spectral regions and are therefore not very well suited for comparing the brightness of two spectrally different stimuli. There is, however, a third cell type, constituting about 20% of tonic cells, which responds in a non-colour-antagonistic manner, either with excitation or inhibition. Its sensitivity closely follows the daylight luminosity function (V_λ, Fig. 5, bottom). This cell type is very well suited to detecting brightness or darkness, and is closely related to the spectral sensitivity function of the phasic ganglion cells shown in Fig. 6. However, the latter have the highest incidence in the retinal periphery (Zrenner, 1983, Fig. 3.15), and respond to any luminance change of any wavelength with a short monotonic transient discharge. Phasic cells probably serve as luminance difference detectors, coding optimally only for an event in the retinal periphery, so that we can direct our central retina, with all the capabilities inherent in its colour-opponent cells, to this event for analysis.

In the literature it is often suggested that opponent cells with two-peaked spectra serve to build up a colour channel, while cells with the single-peaked broadband spectra build up a luminance channel (for references see Zrenner, 1983). The next figures demonstrate that this separation is not so strict, and that under certain circumstances colour-opponent cells can act as luminance detectors as well. As described earlier (Zrenner and Gouras, 1978; Gouras and Zrenner, 1979), colour-opponent cells change their action spectra with temporal frequency of stimulation. Figure 7 gives an example: At low flicker frequencies (5 Hz, triangles), red/green colour-opponent cells have two sensitivity maxima, one for excitation and one for inhibition, with a broad neutral

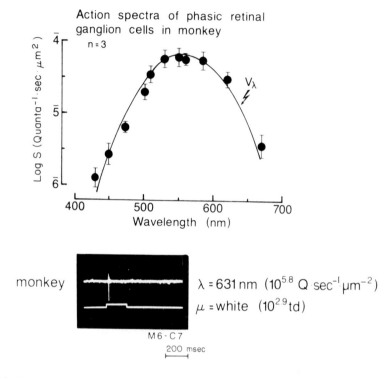

Action spectra of phasic retinal ganglion cells in monkey

n = 3

monkey $\lambda = 631\,nm$ $(10^{5.8}\,Q\,sec^{-1}\mu m^{-2})$

μ = white $(10^{2.9}\,td)$

M6-C7

200 msec

FIG. 6 Action spectra of 3 phasic ganglion cells; mean ± one standard deviation. Photopic relative luminous efficiency function (V_λ) indicated by solid line. An original recording is shown below, parameters as indicated (obtained in collaboration with M. Wienrich).

zone in between where the cells' spectral sensitivity is low. At higher flicker frequencies (30–33 Hz, crosses), the wavelengths of the neutral zone become most effective in all cells, so that the spectral dichotomy and colour-opponency is lost. The spectral sensitivity function becomes broadband and single-peaked and resembles that of the luminance detecting cell shown above. This spectral transition occurs in every colour-opponent cell we have studied so far. The mechanism that produces this sharp change in sensitivity is shown at the top of Fig. 7: the increase in sensitivity in the midspectral region is based on a phase shift between the centre and surround responses of colour-opponent cells (Zrenner and Gouras, 1978; Gouras and Zrenner, 1979). In this figure, the spike density of a colour-opponent cell is represented by a d.c. signal. At low frequencies (5 Hz), the excitation provided by the centre (622 nm) and the inhibition provided by the surround (456 nm) are almost 180° out of phase; the sum of both responses is therefore zero at low frequencies and the cell shows no modulated response to light. At higher frequencies a latency change occurs,

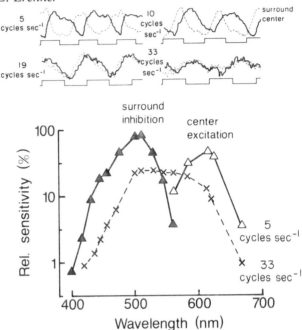

FIG. 7   Action spectrum of a red/green colour-opponent ganglion cell, based on a flicker threshold criterion at low (5 Hz, triangles) and at high (33 Hz, crosses) frequencies of stimulation in the presence of a white adapting light of 30,000 td. As reported by Zrenner and Gouras (1978) and Gouras and Zrenner (1979), these cells lose colour-opponency at higher flicker frequencies owing to a phaseshift between centre and surround (shown above).

which is different for the centre and surround, so that the phases of inhibition and excitation slowly synchronize. Near 29 cycles sec⁻¹ this synchronization is almost perfect and the sum of the two responses results in a very strong flicker response, especially for wavelengths that stimulate centre and surround equally strongly.

Consequently, this phase shift turns the cell's antagonism between the centre and surround mechanisms into a synergism. Therefore, since centre and surround do the same thing at the same time, the spatial- as well as the colour-opponency is lost. At higher flicker frequencies *all* cells are single peaked and broadband. This might explain why the daylight V_λ luminosity function obtained by *flicker* photometry, is such a simple, stable, and single-peaked curve. But it also suggests that the V_λ function is a rather artificial function, not at all reflecting the normal trichromatic spectral sensitivity function under normal, i.e. *nonflickering*, daylight conditions.

If the daylight spectral sensitivity function is measured with single flashes of long duration, a three-peaked function emerges (Sperling and Harwerth, 1971; King-Smith and Carden, 1976; Zrenner, 1977; Zrenner and Krüger, 1981).

The dips directly reflect the ongoing antagonistic interactions between the centres and surrounds of colour-opponent cells. Apparently, the V_λ function is produced only when the centre and surround excitation of colour opponent cells is synchronized.

Having observed this transition from colour-opponent processing to achromatic processing, one is very much tempted to look into the reverse phenomenon, i.e. the transition from an achromatic to a coloured sensation as occurs in the Fechner-Benham top (see Fechner, 1838 and Benham, 1895; and Fig. 8, left). Attempting to explain this flicker-induced illusion of colour, one has to emphasize that all such discs use, as an indispensable prerequisite, black and white sectors which, when rotated, produce flickering light. This kind of intermittent stimulation, however, causes the colour-opponent ganglion cells' centre and surround excitation to synchronize, so that colour-opponent processing is lost; from a certain frequency range on they are all in the synergistic mode of processing as shown at the top of Fig. 7 at 19 Hz. The stripes, however, introduced in the Fechner-Benham top as well as in their simplified analogues (centre and rightmost patterns, after von Campenhausen, 1968a, b) produce an additional phase shift in some of the cells, when their centres and surrounds are appropriately located, as indicated in Fig. 8. If this additional phase shift

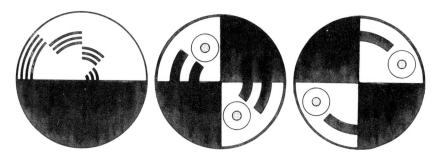

FIG. 8   (Left) Fechner-Benham top in an original version. Rotation of the black and white disk at certain frequencies produces the illusion of relatively desaturated coloured rings.

(Centre) Simplified Fechner-Benham top after von Campenhausen (1968a, b); the additional black stripes in the white field introduce a phrase shift between the responses of the centre and surround in the receptive field and can restore the antagonism in colour-opponent cell (indicated by concentric circles).

(Right) Another type of simplified Fechner-Benham top, introducing phase shifts also between centre and surround, however, in the opposite direction (from Zrenner, 1983).

of centre and surround comes close to 180°, it causes these cells to change from their flicker-induced synergism back into antagonism; they are then in the mode observed with stationary stimuli, as shown at the top of Fig. 7 at 5 Hz. Since the signal at the output of the retinal cell is indistinguishable from that produced by a stationary hue, it could well be interpreted by cortical detectors as a colour signal; owing to the well-known effects of simultaneous colour contrast, this colour can become particularly strong when seen adjacent to another coloured ring, produced by neighbouring cells which are in a slightly different mode of processing the centre- and surround-signals, depending on the length of the stripes included in the original Fechner-Benham top.

It is not surprising then that the visual system can be made to see colours, when stimulated by an achromatic pattern which, by flickering black and white areas, first synchronizes centre and surround excitation and then by introducing additional patterns gradually desynchronizes it back to different grades of colour-opponent processing. Further discussion is given by Zrenner (1983).

On the other hand, this synchronization between centre and surround excitation is achieved not only by flickering stimuli but also by flashes of short duration as shown in Fig. 9. If a light is switched on and instantly switched

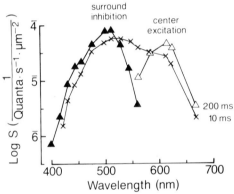

FIG. 9   Action spectra of a colour-opponent ganglion cell (R$^+$/G$^-$), based on a spike frequency increment threshold criterion for stimuli of long (200 msec, triangles) and short duration (10 msec, crosses) in the presence of a white adapting light of 30,000 td (from Zrenner, 1983).

off again, the on- and off-discharges in ganglion cells occur quasi-simultaneously; this can be considered as a special way of synchronization of centre and surround responses. Indeed, if an individual ganglion cell is stimulated first with flashes of long duration (triangles in Fig. 9), then with flashes of short duration (crosses), the action spectrum changes from its colour-opponent spectral dichotomy of excitation and inhibition to a broadband function (Zrenner, 1983). Apparently, colour-opponency is lost if an object is presented only briefly. Indeed, for flashes of short duration, we cannot very well detect the stimulus colour, as has been observed in psychophysical experiments by King-Smith and Carden (1976, 1978) and in visually evoked cortical potential experiments by Zrenner (1977). However, there is no need to invoke two anatomically different channels for luminance and chromaticity, as often suggested; one type of cells, the tonic colour-opponent type, can code both parameters interchangeably.

A similar enhancement, also probably due to a synchronizing effect, can be observed in the spatial domain. In experiments performed in collaboration with Dr Marion Wienrich (full paper in preparation), we moved equiluminous blue/red borders over the receptive field of red/green colour-opponent ganglion cells of Rhesus monkey (Fig. 10). Since the chromaticity change of the border first stimulates the surround and approaches the centre of the cells' receptive field only with a delay, synchronization of the excitation of the centre and the postinhibitory excitation of the surround can occur at certain velocities of border movement. Indeed, with increasing velocity, the cells' responsiveness

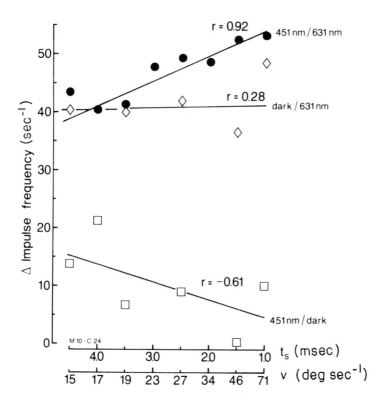

FIG. 10   A red/green colour-opponent ganglion cell of Rhesus monkey is stimulated by an equiluminous chromatic border (451 nm and 631 nm) with different velocities (v in deg sec^{-1}). The impulse frequency increases with velocity (dots), while it decreases or stays constant, when one of the border-forming areas is switched off (dark condition, open symbols). Regression line with correlation coefficient as indicated (reported by Wienrich and Zrenner, 1981; full paper in preparation). The second abscissa (t_s) indicates step interval time of the motor drive on a *linear* scale.

to equiluminous chromatic borders (dots in Fig. 10) *increased*, while it remained constant or even decreased when one of the two areas that formed the border was "blacked out" in control experiments (open symbols in Fig. 10), although this condition introduces a very strong brightness gradient.

From these experiments one would predict a psychophysical counterpart, namely that equiluminous colour borders moved at a certain velocity should become visible at lower thresholds than a comparable pattern with a high brightness gradient, as far as the "chromatic channels" are concerned.

In conclusion: special attention is drawn to the fact that colour-opponency as observed in individual cells of primate retina is not a fixed characteristic. Although there are several clearly distinct cell types with differently wired inputs from spectrally well-defined cones, their colour-opponent interaction can vary considerably, depending on the spatial characteristics (size, position) or temporal properties (duration and repetition rate) of the stimulus. Colour-opponent cells can switch instantly to nonopponent processing. Though colour-opponent cells under these circumstances lose their ability to detect differences in wavelength composition, they are much better equipped to follow the object's luminance changes up to much higher frequencies. Synchronization of the excitatory phases of centre and surround provides a stronger response modulation than either mechanism could achieve singly. Taking into account the physical properties of the stimulus to be coded, colour-opponent retinal ganglion cells show a surprising functional *plasticity*; in a way, they adapt to the tasks imposed by the physical characteristics of the objects to be analysed. This adaptability to the task required is usually attributed to the function of higher neurons; it is rather surprising to find such a versatile mechanism built already into the visual system's peripheral neurons.

Acknowledgement

I am very grateful to Professor Dr E. Dodt for continuous support of the project, to Professor P. Gouras for many exciting discussions, to Dr Marion Wienrich for dedicated participation and to Mrs Breitenfelder and Mrs Granz for expert technical assistance.

References

Benham, C. E. (1894–5). The artificial spectrum top. *Nature* **51**, 113; 200.
Bowmaker, J. K., Dartnall, H. J. A. and Mollon, J. D. (1980). Microspectrophotometric demonstration of four classes of photoreceptor in an old world primate, *Macaca fascicularis*. *J. Physiol.* **298**, 131–143.
Campenhausen, C. von (1968a). Über die Farben der Benhamschen Scheibe. *Z. vergl. Physiol.* **60**, 351–374.
Campenhausen, C. von (1968b). Über den Ursprungsort von musterinduzierten Flickerfarben im visuellen System des Menschen. *Z. vergl. Physiol.* **61**, 355–360.

De Valois, R. L. (1965). Analysis of color vision in the primate visual system. *Cold Spring Harbor Symp. Quant. Biol.* **30**, 567–579.

Fechner, G. T. (1838). Über eine Scheibe zur Erzeugung subjektiver Farben. *Ann. Physik. Chemie* **45**, 227–232.

Gouras, P. (1968). Identification of cone mechanisms in monkey ganglion cells. *J. Physiol., Lond.* **199**, 533–547.

Gouras, P. and Zrenner, E. (1979). Enhancement of luminance flicker by color-opponent mechanisms. *Science* **205**, 587–589.

Gouras, P. and Zrenner, E. (1981a). Color coding in primate retina. *Vision Res.* **21**, 1591–1598.

Gouras, P. and Zrenner, E. (1981b). Color vision: A review from a neurophysiological perspective. In *Progress in sensory physiology*, Vol. 1 (ed. Ottoson, E.), pp. 139–179. Berlin, Springer Verlag.

Hering, E. (1878). *Zur Lehre vom Lichtsinne*, pp. 107–141. Wien, Carl Gerold's Sohn, See also: E. Hering (1920): *Grundzüge der Lehre vom Lichtsinne*. Berlin, Springer Verlag.

King-Smith, P. E. and Carden, D. (1976). Luminance and opponent-color contributions to visual detection and adaptation and to temporal and spatial integration. *J. opt. Soc. Am.* **66**, 709–717.

King-Smith, P. E. and Carden, D. (1978). Luminance and opponent-color contributions to visual detection and to temporal and spatial integration. *J. opt. Soc. Am.* **68**, 1146–1147.

Mariani, A. P. (1981). A diffuse, invaginating cone bipolar cell in primate retina. *J. comp. Neurol.* **197**, 661–671.

Mariani, A. P. (1982). Biplexiform cells: ganglion cells of the primate retina that contact photoreceptors. *Science* **216**, 1134–1136.

Mollon, J. D. (1982). Color vision. *Ann. Rev. Psychol.* **33**, 41–85.

Nelson, R. (1977). Cat cones have rod input: A comparison of the response properties of cones and horizontal cell bodies in the retina of the cat. *J. comp. Neurol.* **172**, 109–136.

Nelson, R., Famiglietti, E. V. Jr and Kolb, H. (1978). Intracellular staining reveals different levels of stratification for on- and off-center ganglion cells in cat retina. *J. Neurophysiol.* **41**, 472–483.

Nelson, R., Kolb, H., Famiglietti, E. V. and Gouras, P. (1976). Neural responses in the rod and cone system of the cat retina: Intracellular records and procion stains. *Invest. Ophthalmol.* **15**, 946–953.

Nelson, R., Kolb, H., Robinson, M. M. and Mariani, A. P. (1981). Neural circuitry of the cat retina: cone pathways to ganglion cells. *Vision Res.* **21**, 1527–1536.

Nelson, R., Lützow, A. von, Kolb, H. and Gouras, P. (1975). Horizontal cells in cat retina with independent dendritic systems. *Science* **189**, 137–139.

Sperling, H. G. and Harwerth, R. S. (1971). Red–green cone interactions in the increment-threshold spectral sensitivity of primates. *Science* **172**, 180–184.

Wässle, H., Peichl, L. and Boycott, B. B. (1981). Morphology and topography of on- and off-alpha cells in the cat retina. *Proc. R. Soc., Lond.* B **212**, 157–175.

Wienrich, M. and Zrenner, E. (1981). Chromatic signals in retinal ganglion cells: cat versus monkey. *Pflügers Arch. Suppl.* **389**, R 29.

Wiesel, T. N. and Hubel, D. H. (1966). Spatial and chromatic interactions in the lateral geniculate body of the rhesus monkey. *J. Neurophysiol.* **29**, 1115–1156.

Zrenner, E. (1977). Influence of stimulus duration and area on the spectral luminosity function as determined by sensory and VECP measurements. *Doc. Ophthal. Proc. Series* **13**, 21–30.

Zrenner, E. (1983). Neurophysiological aspects of color vision in primates. Comparative studies on simian retinal ganglion cells and the human visual system. Monograph. *Studies of Brain Function*, Vol. 9 (eds Braitenberg, V., Barlow, H. B., Bullock, T. H., Florey, E., Grüsser, O.-J. and Peters, A.) Berlin, Springer Verlag.

Zrenner, E. and Gouras, P. (1978). Retinal ganglion cells lose color opponency at high flicker rates. *Invest. Ophthalmol. visual Sci.* (ARVO-Suppl.) **17**, 130.

Zrenner, E. and Gouras, P. (1979). Cone opponency in tonic ganglion cells and its variation with eccentricity in rhesus monkey retina. *Invest. Ophthalmol. Visual Sci.* (ARVO-Suppl.) **18**, 77.

Zrenner, E. and Gouras, P. (1981). Characteristics of the blue-sensitive cone mechanism in primate retinal ganglion cells. *Vision Res.* **21**, 1605–1609.

Zrenner, E. and Krüger, C.-J. (1981). Ethambutol mainly affects the function of red/green-opponent neurons. *Doc. Ophthal, Proc. Series*, Vol. 27 (eds Spekreijse, H. and Apkarian, P. A.), pp. 13–25. The Hague, Junk.

Zrenner, E., Nelson, R. and Mariani, H. (1983). Intracellular recordings from a biplexiform ganglion cell in macaque retina, stained with horseradish peroxidase. *Brain Res.* **262**, 181–185.

Cone Opponency in Tonic Ganglion Cells and its Variation with Eccentricity in Rhesus Monkey Retina

E. ZRENNER and P. GOURAS

Introduction

A colour-opponent cell is defined as a cell that is excited by one part of the visible spectrum and inhibited by another. The excitatory and inhibitory spectral zones are separated by the so-called neutral point, where the cell is almost unresponsive, although the different time courses of the opposing cone mechanisms seldom allow the elimination of all transient responses. In most studies it has been shown, however, that under identical conditions the neutral point of the colour-opponent cells is not fixed in one spectral region, but that it can vary considerably, depending upon either the spatial variables (Wiesel and Hubel, 1966; Gouras, 1968; De Monasterio and Gouras, 1975; De Valois, 1972; De Valois and De Valois, 1975) or the temporal properties of the stimulation (Zrenner and Gouras, 1978; Gouras and Zrenner, 1979a; Gielen, 1980).

Even with identical spatial and temporal stimuli and adapting conditions, there is a considerable variation in the neutral point among individual colour-opponent cells (De Monasterio, Gouras and Tolhurst, 1975; Zrenner and Gouras, 1979; Creutzfeldt, Lee and Elepfandt, 1979). The functional implications of these variations have not yet been convincingly accounted for. Histochemical studies point to a higher incidence of green-sensitive cones (Marc and Sperling, 1977), and this is partly supported by electrophysiological studies (De Monasterio and Gouras, 1975) at least for the foveolar region.

COLOUR VISION
ISBN 0 12 000000 0

Although it is well established that the spectrally different cone mechanisms having input to a colour-opponent cell do not act equally strongly in each cell, there are no data on the functional variation of cone dominance in *one* retinal area, nor on the variations of cone dominance across *different* retinal areas.

In the present study we attempted to systematically define in a sample of 385 retinal tonic ganglion cells of Rhesus monkey *how* colour-opponency varies among cells subserving the same area of visual space and whether there is a regularity in these variations with retinal eccentricity. For this purpose we developed a scale for grading more precisely the *dominance* of the cone mechanisms feeding colour-opponent cells.

Methods

In anesthetized and paralysed Rhesus monkeys we recorded extracellularly from retinal ganglion cells with glass microelectrodes, inserted through a scleral hole. Two independent light beams were projected onto the retina in Maxwellian view through a modified fundus-camera: one beam, with monochromatic lights of variable irradiance flashed 200 msec every 1.5 sec, served as the test beam; the other served as a steady adaptation beam with red, yellow and blue broadband filters, providing a retinal illumination of about 300,000 td (for details see Gouras and Zrenner, 1979a). In some cases also white adaptation of 30,000 td was used to suppress rod activity. Small rings and spots were projected onto the retina in order to map the cells' receptive fields. The responses were amplified, averaged and transformed into spike frequency histograms.

Results

The responses of a colour-opponent cell that does not overtly exhibit an antagonism between red and green sensitive cones are shown in Fig. 1A. Spike frequency is plotted against time for two wavelengths (622 nm and 456 nm), presented for 200 msec with slightly suprathreshold irradiances in the presence of a white background. If the test spot (20° in diameter) is covering the entire receptive field (left column) the two wavelengths produce qualitatively similar excitatory responses, except that repeated stimulation with 456 nm reduces the cell's discharge level, which might point to inhibitory mechanisms responding to shorter wavelengths. This inhibitory mechanism was revealed only when the test spot diameter was reduced to 0.2° (right column, below), centred over the cell's receptive field. Apparently the red sensitive cones in the cell's surround dominate the responses so strongly throughout the visible spectrum, that responses of the inhibiting green cones can be revealed only when spatially isolated.

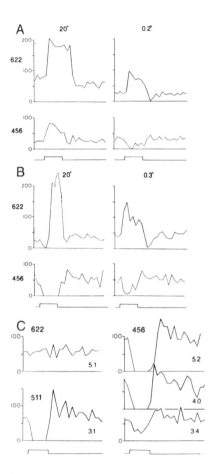

FIG. 1   Response profiles (spike frequency against time) of red/green antagonistic colour-opponent ganglion cells in Rhesus monkey retina. Monochromatic stimuli ($\sim$ 10,000 quanta sec^{-1} μm^{-2}) of 200 msec duration, with wavelength as indicated next to each graph were delivered every 1.5 sec.

(A)   Cell *dominated* by the red-sensitive cone mechanism in the surround of the receptive field; a weak inhibition from the green-sensitive cones is seen only with short wavelengths when the field size is reduced from 20° to 0.2° visual angle; white steady background of 30,000 td (5500 K).

(B)   Same experiment in a cell with *balanced* input from red- and green-sensitive cones.

(C)   Test for differentiation between blue- and green-sensitive cones acting on a ganglion cell. Monochromatic test stimuli with test light irradiance (quanta sec^{-1} μm^{-2}) as indicated in logarithmic values at the end of each trace. Red steady background (Corning filter No. 2408) of 300,000 td.

Interestingly, the majority of colour-opponent cells were clearly dominated by one of the cone mechanisms. Only a minority (14%) showed an overt cone antagonism, as illustrated in Fig. 1B. Under conditions identical to those in Fig. 1A this cell is clearly excited by 622 nm and inhibited by 456 nm. The cell's receptive field centre is apparently small since a 456-nm test spot of 0.3 degree still evokes some inhibition from the surround; the cell shows a *balanced* input from centre cones and surround cones over a large range of stimulus diameters.

To differentiate between input from blue- and green-sensitive cones the sensitivity of each cell to 456- and 511-nm test stimuli was determined in the presence of red adapting light, which can isolate either the green- or the blue-sensitive cones (see Zrenner and Gouras, 1981). This procedure is shown in Fig. 1C for the cell presented in Fig. 1B. Owing to the suppression of the red-sensitive cone the cell is unresponsive to 622-nm test lights even of high irradiance ($10^{5.1}$ quanta sec^{-1} μm^{-2}), whereas 456 nm of comparable irradiance evokes a strong inhibitory response. To produce an equally large response with 511 nm, the test light irradiance had to be decreased by more than two log units ($10^{3.1}$ quanta sec^{-1} μm^{-2}), as shown in the lower left of Fig. 1C. The 456-nm test lights of comparable irradiance evoked a much smaller inhibitory response (lower right). Since the blue cone's sensitivity drops rapidly from 456 to 511 nm while the green sensitive cone's sensitivity increases (see Zrenner and Gouras, 1981, Fig. 1), this test supports our hypothesis that the green sensitive cones and not the blue sensitive cones mediate the inhibition in the cell shown in Figs 1B and C.

Application of the test shown in Fig. 1 to more than 180 colour-opponent cells revealed that red/green colour-opponent cells do not form a spectrally homogeneous group; there is a considerable variation in the action spectra of these cells, even under identical spatial and temporal conditions; the two cone mechanisms involved in antagonistic interactions are not equally strong in each cell, one of them usually dominates. This is demonstrated best if a threshold response criterion is used to derive an action spectrum for a cell as shown in Fig. 2. Eight colour-opponent cells, recorded in four different monkeys under identical conditions, exhibit quite different spectral sensitivity functions. The green-sensitive cone mechanism (filled symbols) strongly dominates in the uppermost cell's action spectrum; the strengths of the green- and red-sensitive mechanisms (open symbols) are about balanced in the cell's action spectrum shown in the centre of the figure; by contrast, in the lowermost spectrum, the red-sensitive cone mechanism strongly dominates. In the latter cell, as in many others, the antagonistic green-sensitive mechanism could only be detected when the cones of the dominating red-sensitive mechanism were bleached with strong chromatic (long-wavelength) adapting light, as will be shown in Fig. 3. This picture strikingly shows that there is an almost continuous gradation in the weight of the opponent mechanisms involved, so that in red/green-opponent

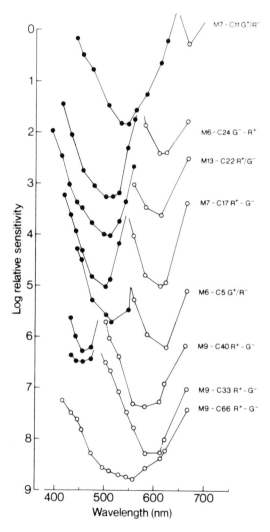

FIG. 2 Action spectra of 8 red/green colour-opponent cells, recorded under identical conditions (white background, 20,000 td, Ganzfeld stimuli of 200 msec duration) based on a constant response threshold criterion. Note the shift of the neutral point from 480 nm to 630 nm. In this figure, the action of R-cones is indicated by open symbols, that of G-cones by closed symbols. Action spectra are shifted arbitrarily along the X-axis (relative sensitivity) for comparison.

cells, under identical conditions, the neutral point can vary from 630 nm to 480 nm.

In order to investigate these fluctuations more systematically a scale of cone dominance was introduced with values ranging from 1 to 7. This classification is clarified in the action spectra of Fig. 3. In the presence of a neutral, white

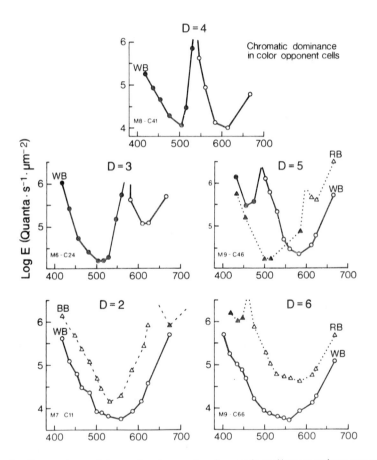

FIG. 3   Illustrations of the scale of cone dominance in red/green colour-opponent cells as revealed by action spectra based on a constant response threshold. D = 4 indicates balance of both opposing mechanisms in the presence of the white background, WB, (5500 K, 20,000–30,000 td, thick lines). D = 3 and D = 5 indicate dominance of the green- and red-sensitive mechanism, respectively. D = 2 and D = 6 indicate extremely strong dominance of either the green or red mechanism. Application of chromatic backgrounds (300,000 td) in an individual cell (red, RB and blue, BB, dotted and broken lines, Corning filter No. 2408 and No. 5543, respectively) clearly reveals the dominating mechanism. Open symbols indicate excitatory signals, closed symbols inhibitory ones.

background of 30,000 td the red/green antagonistic cell on the top shows balanced inputs. Such cells exhibit a maximum of excitatory responses (open symbols) near 600 nm, and a maximum of inhibitory responses near 500 nm, both occurring at about the same threshold. For such cells a dominance value (D) of 4 was chosen, indicating that the strength of both cone mechanisms is about equal in the cell.

Only 14% of our tonic cells showed such balanced opponency; the majority of the tonic cells when studied on a white background (WB, solid lines in Fig. 3) were dominated either by the red (centre row, right) or the green-sensitive cone mechanism (centre row, left), with the neutral point shifting accordingly. In these cells a chromatic background (here red background RB, triangles connected by dotted lines) can suppress the activity of the dominant cones, so that the weaker antagonistic response (filled symbols) becomes the dominant one, shifting the neutral point more than 100 nm. One might have tentatively identified this very short-wave band of inhibition (dots, maximum near 440 nm), seen in the presence of white backgrounds, as being mediated by the blue-sensitive cones. However, the red background revealed that green-sensitive cones (filled triangles) were responsible for producing the short-wavelength part of the spectrum, as has been described also by Zrenner and Gouras (1981). Such cells which showed clear opponency already in the presence of white backgrounds but exhibited clear dominance of one of the cone mechanisms were rated by a dominance value of 3, if green-sensitive cones were dominant, and by a dominance value of 5, if red-sensitive cones were dominant.

There is still a number of cells left (about 13%), which on a white background do not show colour-opponency at all (lower-most row of Fig. 3). Even chromatic backgrounds (RB, dotted line, lower right) can only slightly weaken this extremely dominating long-wavelength mechanism, so that a rudimentary short-wavelength inhibition at the left end of the spectrum can be seen. The red-sensitive mechanism is so extremely dominant, that even a strong red background cannot suppress it. A dominance value of 6 was given to such cells, where the red cone input was so strong, that green-sensitive antagonistic cones could be detected only by chromatic adaptation with long-wavelength light.

Its extremely green cone dominated counterpart is shown on the lower left. Even on a blue background (BB, hatched line), which usually weakens the green-sensitive cones considerably, these cones dominate the cell to such a degree, that opponency is barely traceable at 666 nm, with a neutral point near 650 nm. In the case of the 666-nm test the inhibition became visible only near the cell's response threshold, since with high test light intensities the excitatory G-cones would still have been stimulated. Following the scale introduced above, a value of D = 2 expresses this *extreme* dominance of green-sensitive cones.

There was another group of tonic cells left (about 20%), which did not show colour-opponency at all, in spite of careful searching for it with all test lights and all backgrounds available. These cells showed either excitatory or inhibitory tonic responses throughout the whole spectrum. Apparently in these cells one cone mechanism becomes so extremely predominant, that the antagonizing cone mechanism, usually present in tonic ganglion cells, cannot be detected anymore at all. Assuming that these cells represent extremes in the above scale of dominance values they were assigned a D-value of 7 if they resembled the action spectrum of red-sensitive cones or a D-value of 1 if they followed the green-sensitive cone's action spectra. Each of the 182 tonic ganglion cells was then assigned to one of these seven groups.

When we examine the incidence of each of the groups (in terms of number of cells) at different *retinal eccentricities*, an interesting picture of the distribution of cone opponency emerges: as shown in Fig. 4, even in the foveolar region (0–1°, dots), all varieties of dominance values (abscissa, 1 to 7) are seen, but the largest fraction of cells had values of 4, which indicates balanced opponency.

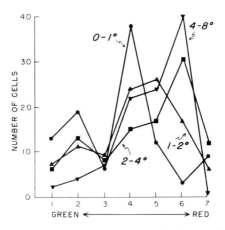

FIG. 4   Incidence of the several degrees of cone dominance (abscissa) in various regions of the central retina: foveolar region (0–1 degree, dots), 1–2 degrees (triangles base down), 2–4 degrees (squares) and 4–8 degrees (triangles, base up) retinal eccentricity.

Notice that in all areas of the central retina (0–8°) representatives of each dominance value are seen. However, there is a systematic difference. As one moves away from the fovea, the proportion of cells dominated by the red sensitive cone mechanism increases progressively as indicated by a large number of cells with dominance values of 5, located between 1° and 2° retinal eccentricity (triangles, base down) and those with D-values of 6, located between 2° and 4° eccentricity (squares). Cells beyond 4° (triangles, base up) do not shift further in their dominance value; however, the proportion of cells with large dominance values still increases indicating a further shift to red cone dominance, even beyond 4° retinal eccentricity.

There is another interesting correlation, shown in Fig. 5, concerning the sign of the centre, i.e., whether stimulation of the centre of the receptive field produces excitatory (+) or inhibitory (−) responses. In most of the cells an excitatory mechanism dominates in the centre of the receptive field (solid line in Fig. 6). Strongly red cone dominated cells (D > 4) are usually excited

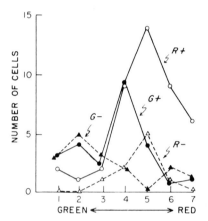

FIG. 5   Distribution of cone dominance (see Fig. 3), grouped according to the sign and spectral sensitivity of the centre mechanism; either excitatory (+ , solid lines) or inhibitory (− , broken lines) responses are mediated by red-sensitive (R) or green-sensitive (G) cones.

(open circles), less often inhibited (open triangles) through their dominant mechanism located in the centre. Very rarely the dominant mechanism is located in the surround (closed symbols at D-values 5, 6 and 7). Balanced cells (D = 4) are commonly and equally often excited by green as by red cones in their centre (circles, at D = 4); less commonly they are inhibited through the centre mechanism (triangles at D = 4). Green cone dominated cells (D < 4) are about equally often inhibited and excited through their dominating mechanism in the centre (closed symbols at D = 1, 2 and 3). Rarely the dominating mechanism is located in the surround (open symbols at D = 1, 2 and 3).

Interestingly, on-centre cells (circles) are most often balanced (D = 4) or almost balanced (D = 3 and D = 5) and thereby provide strong mutual opponency, while off-centre cells (triangles) are very often dominated by one cone mechanism, so that opponency can only play a minor role.

Cells that receive input from blue-sensitive cones form only a small sample of tonic cells (8%) and are very different, as described by Gouras and Zrenner (1979b), Zrenner and Gouras (1981): their spectral sensitivity functions are strikingly similar in shape and absolute sensitivity; all but one of the cells were *excited* by blue-sensitive cones. The one inhibited blue-sensitive cell was very near to the foveola. In the presence of a strong yellow background the sensitivity in the short-wavelength region was 1 to 1.5 log units higher than that of any other cell on any photopically equivalent background light (see also Gouras and Zrenner, this volume).

Discussion

While the blue/yellow-opponent system forms a spectrally homogeneous group of tonic ganglion cells, the red/green-opponent system is heterogeneous. There appears to be a continuum of red/green-opponent cells, ranging from strongly colour-opponent to non-colour-opponent ones. This gradation of colour-opponency exists in each area of the central retina. With increasing eccentricity, however, red cone dominated cells become more and more frequent. The psychophysical experiments of Connors and Kinney (1962) support this view; they report that beyond 10° eccentricity the sensitivity to a red light becomes much higher than that to a green one; such a shift is in agreement with the findings in ganglion cells described here, as well as with those of Krüger and Gouras (1980), who found a relatively strong effect of red light in driving cortical cells whenever their stimulating slits were relatively long. The most logical hypothesis suggested by our data is that there are more red-sensitive cones than green-sensitive ones, with their proportion increasing towards the retinal periphery, except in the foveola, where the two cone types are numerically about even.

Almost exclusively the response of the centre mechanism has shorter latencies (20 to 30 msec) than the surround (40 to 60 msec); thus, latency can serve as an additional indicator for defining the centre or surround mechanism in colour-opponent cells (Zrenner and Gouras, 1978; Gouras and Zrenner, 1979a). If this criterion is applied to the remaining cells which were not spatially mapped it turns out that in the overwhelming majority of the cells the spectrally dominating cone mechanism forms the *centre* of the receptive field.

In cells that receive input from blue-sensitive cones, strength of colour-opponency does not vary to the same extent. The spectral sensitivity functions of all ganglion cells having input from blue-sensitive cones are strikingly similar in shape and absolute sensitivity, despite their different retinal locations (Zrenner and Gouras, 1980, 1981).

We would like to propose that the heterogeneity of red/green colour-opponent cells provides a greater range of responsiveness to different chromatic borders within each area of the retina as outlined in the following. If we call the boundary between two areas of different spectral composition a chromatic border, then many chromatic borders can be imagined which, when moved through the receptive field of a specific colour-opponent ganglion cell, would not produce a noticeable response gradient; there are many colours which have quantitatively the same effect on such a cell, in either an excitatory *or* inhibitory manner. However, there is always a small fraction of cells of which the neutral point lies *between* the spectral loci of the two colours forming the chromatic border. These cells and only these cells can respond maximally by changing from excitation to inhibition or vice versa, thus signalling optimally a chromatic border moved through the cell's receptive field (for a more detailed discussion see Zrenner, 1983). For instance, two colours with very close spectral loci (e.g., 530 nm and 540 nm) would have almost no effect on a cell of type 6 or 2 in Fig. 3; another cell (type 4), however, has its neutral point in between the two spectral loci and would respond with a reversal of polarity; if both wavelengths are presented successively to its receptive field, this cell can signal the small difference in wavelength composition very strongly. This applies not only to wavelengths, but also to chromaticity differences in general. Since the neutral points of the various types of R/G-cells are spread continuously throughout the visible spectrum, there is always a cell that is reversed in polarity by successive colour-contrast even when the differences in spectral composition are small.

Therefore, the gradation in the red/green antagonistic ganglion cell's cone opponency can enhance the visual system's capability of responding optimally to a large variety of chromatic borders within each part of the visual field, but particularly in the fovea, where cone dominance values are most evenly distributed (Fig. 5). It is not surprising then that colour discrimination in human observers improves as the stimulated area increases (Brown, 1952), since a larger number of spectrally *different* ganglion cells becomes involved. It is also not surprising then that colour discrimination (Δ_λ against λ) is best in the midspectral region, since *most* of the red/green colour-opponent cells have their neutral point located there.

The systematic variation in colour-opponency described above might be caused by a gradual decrease of the cone antagonism towards the retinal periphery which causes the more numerous red-sensitive cones to dominate the spectral sensitivity. In lower vertebrates there is evidence of gradation in neutral points of C-type horizontal cells (Burkhart, 1979) and dominance of red-sensitive cones in L-units (Fuortes and Simon, 1974). Variations in horizontal cell cone input and feedback could provide an important source of graded cone opponency in the primate retina as described above.

Acknowledgement

We are very grateful to Professor Dr E. Dodt for continuous support of this project and Mrs Granz and Mrs Breitenfelder for technical assistance. This work was supported by a Fogarty Fellowship award to E.Z. and a National Institutes of Health Research Grant (EY 02591) to P.G.

References

Brown, W. R. J. (1952). The effect of field size and chromatic surroundings on colour discrimination. *J. opt. Soc. Am.* **42**, 837–844.

Burkhardt, D. (1979). Spectral response curves of C-type horizontal cells predicted from measured cone action spectra. *Invest. Ophthalmol. Visual Sci.* (ARVO-Suppl.) **18**, 76.

Connors, M. M. and Kinney, J. A. S. (1962). Relative red–green sensitivity as a function of retinal position. *J. opt. Soc. Am.* **52**, 81–84.

Creutzfeld, O. D., Lee, B. B. and Elepfandt, A. (1979). A quantitative study of chromatic organization and receptive fields of cells in the lateral geniculate body of the rhesus monkey. *Exp. Brain Res.* **35**, 527–545.

De Monasterio, F. M. and Gouras, P. (1975). Functional properties of ganglion cells of the rhesus monkey retina. *J. Physiol., Lond.* **251**, 167–195.

DeMonasterio, F. M., Gouras, P. and Tolhurst, D. A. (1975). Concealed colour-opponency in ganglion cells of the rhesus monkey retina. *J. Physiol., Lond.* **251**, 217–229.

De Valois, R. L. (1972). Processing intensity and wavelength information by the visual system. *Invest. Ophthalmol.* **11**, 417–427.

De Valois, R. L. and De Valois, K. K. (1975). Neural coding of color. In *Handbook of Perception*, Vol. V *Seeing* (eds Carterette, E. and Friedman, M. P.), pp. 117–166. London and New York, Academic Press.

Fuortes, M. G. F. and Simon, E. J. (1974). Interactions leading to horizontal cell responses in the turtle retina. *J. Physiol., Lond.* **240**, 177–198.

Gielen, C. C. A. M. (1980). Spatio-temporal and chromatic properties of visual neurones in the rhesus monkey geniculate nucleus. Thesis, Katholieke Universiteit te Nijmwegen.

Gouras, P. (1968). Identification of cone mechanisms in monkey ganglion cells. *J. Physiol., Lond.* **199**, 533–547.

Gouras, P. and Zrenner, E. (1979a). Enhancement of luminance flicker by color-opponent mechanisms. *Science* **205**, 587–589.

Gouras, P. and Zrenner, E. (1979b). The blue sensitive cone system. *Excerpta Medica Int. Congr. Ser.* **450/1**, 379–384.

Krüger, J. and Gouras, P. (1980). Spectral selectivity of cells and its dependence on slit length in monkey visual cortex. *J. Neurophysiol.* **43**, 1055–1069.

Marc, R. E. and Sperling, H. G. (1977). Chromatic organization of primate cones. *Science* **196**, 454–456.

Wiesel, T.N. and Hubel, D. H. (1966). Spatial and chromatic interactions in the lateral geniculate body of the rhesus monkey. *J. Neurophysiol.* **29**, 1115–1156.

Zrenner, E. (1983). Neurophysiological aspects of color vision in primates. Comparative studies on simian retinal ganglion cells and the human visual system. Monograph. *Studies of Brain Function*, Vol. 9 (eds Braitenberg, V., Barlow, H. B., Bullock, T. H., Florey, E., Grüsser, O.-J. and Peters, A.). Berlin/Heidelberg/New York, Springer.

Zrenner, E. and Gouras, P. (1978). Retinal ganglion cells lose color opponency at high flicker rates. *Invest. Ophthalmol. Visual Sci.* (ARVO-Suppl.) **17**, 130.

Zrenner, E. and Gouras, P. (1979). Cone opponency in tonic ganglion cells and its variation with eccentricity in rhesus monkey retina. *Invest. Ophthalmol. Visual Sci.* (ARVO-Suppl.) **18**, 77.

Zrenner, E. and Gouras, P. (1980). The blue sensitive mechanism in ganglion cells of macaque retina. *Invest. Ophthalmol. Visual Sci.* (ARVO-Suppl.) **19**, 7.

Zrenner, E. and Gouras, P. (1981). Characteristics of the blue sensitive cone mechanism in primate retinal ganglion cells. *Vision Res.* **21**, 1605–1609.

The Interaction of Opponent Cone Mechanisms in Cells of the Macaque Lateral Geniculate Nucleus

B. B. LEE and V. VIRSU

Introduction

A distinctive feature of the visual pathway of the monkey is the presence of many cells whose visual responses display wavelength selectivity, in the sense that the spectral sensitivity function for a cell deviates substantially from the photopic sensitivity function for the whole animal. This wavelength selectivity may be pronounced, so that some wavelengths cause an increase in cell firing rate and others a decrease, or less pronounced in that the cell's spectral response function consists of either an increase or a decrease in firing at all wavelengths. For nearly all wavelength-selective cells, it is necessary to postulate an excitatory input from one or more cone mechanisms and an antagonistic, inhibitory cone input from other(s). For many cells opponent cone inputs can be identified by measuring action spectra after differential adaptation (de Monasterio and Gouras, 1975).

The way opponent cone mechanisms interact when suprathreshold stimuli are presented is not yet clear. A linear interaction between cone mechanisms was used by Creutzfeldt *et al.* (1979) to derive the spectral responsiveness of parvocellular layer (PCL) cells of macaque lateral geniculate nucleus (LGN). We show here further evidence that a linear interaction between opponent cone mechanisms can account quite well for intensity−response functions of neurones from the parvocellular layers, and even apparently nonlinear effects occurring when different wavelengths are presented simultaneously can be explained on the basis of linear interaction.

COLOUR VISION
ISBN 0 12 000000 0

Intensity-Response Functions at Different Wavelengths

We recorded from cells in the PCL of the LGN of the anaesthetised macaque and measured intensity-response functions at different wavelengths. Stimuli used were flashed on or moved slowly over a cell's receptive field, and were large in comparison with receptive field size. A dim white background (5 cd m^{-2}) was present to minimize rod influences. The sustained response component was measured. Functions were similar irrespective of the method of stimulus presentation.

Typical sets of intensity-response functions for two different cells are shown in Figs 1A and B. The cell in Fig. 1A gives an excitatory response to a Wide band of Short wavelengths (WS: Creutzfeldt *et al.*, 1979), as seen in curves for wavelengths from 400 to 600 nm. At 650 nm the function is nonmonotonic; weaker stimuli evoke a decrease in maintained firing rate but with stronger stimuli the curve turns upward. With longer wavelengths a suppression of firing occurs. The cell in Fig. 1B gives an excitatory response to a Narrow band of Short wavelengths (NS). At 400 and 450 nm excitatory responses are evoked by weaker stimuli, but at least at 450 nm stronger stimuli evoke less vigorous responses; 500 nm stimuli scarcely evoke a response, while at longer wavelengths suppression of maintained firing is present. These functions for inhibitory wavelengths can of course only be followed over a limited range until maintained activity has decreased to zero.

The nonmonotonic functions in Figs 1A and B clearly indicate the interaction of opponent cone mechanisms with different thresholds. For the description of light responses of individual cones, the most commonly used relation is the modified saturating hyperbolic function first introduced by Naka and Rushton (1966) to describe the behaviour of S-potentials in the fish retina. This has the form

$$R = \frac{R_{\text{max}} I^n}{\sigma^n + I^n} \tag{1}$$

where R is the response evoked by a stimulus of intensity I, with R_{max} the maximal response obtainable and σ and n as constants. A value of one for n was used by Naka and Rushton (1966) but other workers have found other values necessary for receptors or post-receptoral cells (Boynton and Whitten, 1970; Werblin, 1974; Hemila, 1977).

If each opponent mechanism obeys this function and they interact linearly, then the cell response (R) may be related to stimulus intensity (I) by

$$R = \frac{E_{\text{max}} (\alpha I)^{n_e}}{\sigma_e^{n_e} + (\alpha I)^{n_e}} - \frac{S_{\text{max}} (\beta I)^{n_s}}{\sigma_s^{n_s} + (\beta I)^{n_s}} \tag{2}$$

where E_{max} and S_{max} are the saturation levels of each mechanism in impulses per second, σ_e, n_e, σ_s and n_s are constants, and α and β are the sensitivities of each cone mechanism at the wavelength tested.

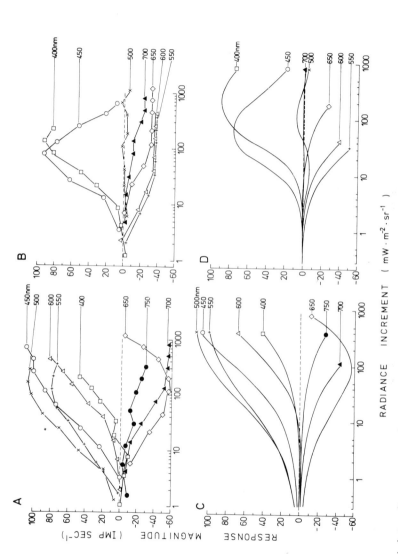

FIG. 1 (A, B) Intensity–response functions for a WS and a NS cell at various wavelengths. A series of bars (0.5 × 10°) of increasing intensities was moved (2 deg sec⁻¹) across the receptive field. Maintained firing rate was subtracted from each 200 msec peak to give net response. (C, D) Sets of curves for the cells of A and B fitted (least squares) using the model described in the text. For cone pigment sensitivities the values of Smith and Pokorny quoted in Boynton (1979) were convolved with the transmission curves of the filters used. Constants for the WS cell in A were: E_{max} 532, S_{max} 418 impulses sec⁻¹; σ_e 11.4, σ_s 22.1; n_e 0.70, n_s 0.70. Constants for the NS cell in B were: E_{max} 99, S_{max} 109 impulses sec⁻¹; σ_e 0.28, σ_s 16.8; n_e 1.86; n_s 1.16.

If, for the WS cell, the spectral sensitivity of the excitatory mechanism is taken to be that of the middle-wavelength (M-) cone, and the suppressive mechanism that of the long-wavelength (L-) cone, and if then values of the constants are adjusted so as to optimally fit the data, the set of curves shown in Fig. 1C is obtained. Correspondence between the data and the simulated curves is good; relative positions of the functions at different wavelengths are reproduced, as is the nonmonotonic curve at 650 nm.

A set of fitted curves for the NS cell is shown in Fig. 1D; the sensitivities of the short-wavelength (S-) cone and the M-cone were assumed for the excitatory and suppressive mechanisms respectively. Again, a good fit is achieved at most wavelengths, with a nonmonotonic function at 450 nm. Values for the constants for these two cells for the fitted curves are given in the legend to Fig. 1.

With cells giving excitatory responses to long wavelengths (WL and NL), it is difficult to achieve a good fit to sets of intensity–response functions by simply assuming an excitatory input from the L-cone and an inhibitory one from the M-cone, a fact noted by Abramov (1977), who postulated a two-stage interaction of M- and L-cones. However, if the suppressive mechanism receives input from an inhibitory pool of M- and L-cones, intensity–response functions for these long-wavelength cells can be better described.

As far as the values of constants found in these and other cells are concerned, saturation levels of the excitatory and suppressive mechanisms were of the order of a few hundred impulses per second. Since these levels of firing were reached during initial transients with flashed stimuli, such values of E_{max} and S_{max} can be considered feasible. Values of half-saturation constants must be divided by the cone sensitivities to give half-saturation values for a particular wavelength. Values of exponents were always between 0.7 and 2.0 and usually did not exceed 1.5. Such a range of values exists in the literature. However, exact values of these parameters were not critical, since, within limits, disturbance of one parameter from its optimum could be compensated for by adjustment of the others.

Any model containing six free parameters obviously has considerable flexibility, yet the ability to fit intensity–response functions at such a range of wavelengths is impressive. However, Equation (2) has several other properties which may be observed in cell responses themselves. One of these is the nonadditivity that may be observed when two wavelengths are presented simultaneously.

Responses to Combinations of Wavelengths

Figure 2 shows sets of intensity–response functions for the cell of Fig. 1A for different wavelengths alone and in combination. Radiance increments have been normalized so that responses evoked by each wavelength separately and together are represented by points lying above one another.

If two stimuli near the short-wavelength end of the spectrum (450 and 500 nm) are presented together the response is larger than when either is presented alone (Fig. 2A). However, if one wavelength is near the cross-over point, its response tends to occlude more vigorous responses to a wavelength near the spectral extreme, as is seen in Fig. 2B. The response to 600 nm is less than to 500 nm, but the addition of the 500 nm to the 600 nm stimulus scarcely increases the response. A similar nonadditivity of responses is present if 500 nm and 650 nm stimuli are combined (Fig. 2C). This non-additivity is best seen with the maximal intensity tested. At 650 nm there is a very small response (12 impulses sec^{-1}), and the response to 500 nm is much larger (73 impulses sec^{-1}) but when both stimuli are presented together the response is much less (33 impulses sec^{-1}) than to 500 nm alone.

If the model of Equation (2) is used to predict the responses to these wavelength combinations, employing the parameters derived for Fig. 1C, the theoretical curves of Figs 2 D to F are obtained. The model parameters, derived from responses when individual wavelengths are presented, are obviously quite successful in predicting the result of presenting wavelength mixtures.

Discussion

Nonadditivity with combined stimuli is a consequence of Equation (2) due to the compressive nonlinearity inherent in Equation (1). In the examples of Fig. 2, the two short wavelengths which mainly activate the excitatory mechanism evoke vigorous responses. They evoke a larger response together than separately, though linear addition of responses will not take place because of the compressive nonlinearity. With a mid-spectral wavelength both opponent mechanisms are strongly activated, since the visual pigments absorb optimally in this region, and thus both are driven some way up their input−output functions. The linear difference between the mechanisms may be small however, and only a small response may result. If a short-wavelength stimulus is added to the mid-spectral stimulus, it is not able to drive the excitatory mechanism much further up its input−output function because of the compressive nature of the function. Response magnitude is therefore only marginally increased. The non-additivity of responses thus finds a ready explanation which does not involve the postulation of nonlinear interaction between opponent mechanisms.

Nonadditivity of cell responses does not contradict the Laws of Colour Additivity, which appear to be based on the linear absorption of light by the visual pigments. Out of a set of wavelength combinations that evoke a given response from a cell, only for that subset of combinations for which absorption by the cone pigments is identical will the laws of additivity hold for the cell. For other pairs of wavelength combinations, addition of a further stimulus will evoke differing changes in firing rate. Of course, a cell that receives input from only two cone mechanisms will be dichromatic in its colour matches.

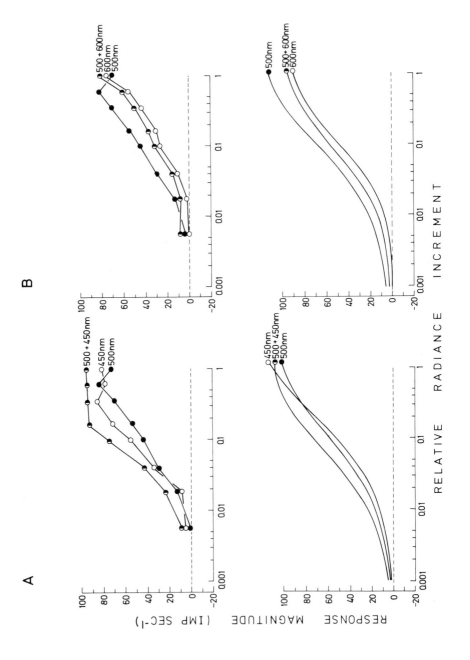

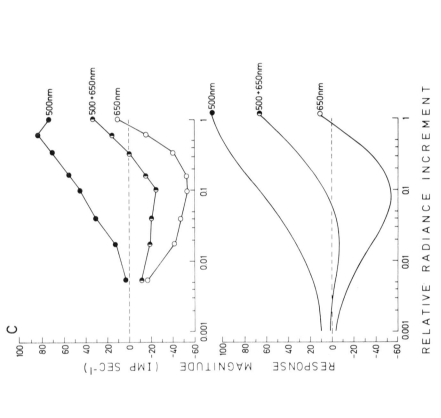

FIG. 2 Summation of various wavelengths by the WS cell of Fig. 1. Maximal radiances for different wavelengths were 450 nm/665, 500 nm/250, 600 nm/1634, 650 nm/1180 mW sr^{-1} m^{-2}. Below are sets of curves predicted from the model, using parameters derived for Fig. 1.

The formulation of Equation (2) need not be unique; other saturating functions with compressive nonlinearity could also be used. Furthermore, Equation (2) can scarcely be other than an oversimplification considering the synaptic complexity within the retina itself, and any additional interactions which might occur within the lateral geniculate nucleus. The fact that a linear interaction of opponent mechanisms, as in Equation (2), goes some way toward accounting for cell responses may suggest that opponent cone mechanism interaction occurs at a very early stage before any nonlinear inhibitory processes occur.

Although Equation (2) is in principle simple, in practice a complex dependence of responses on stimulus and background wavelength composition and intensity can result. If a steady white background is interrupted by stimuli of different wavelength compositions and intensities, it is possible for the opponent cone mechanisms to act synergistically to produce vigorous responses (see Valberg *et al.*, this volume).

Secondly, since responses are related to a difference term deriving from two mechanisms with different spectral sensitivities, responses will be very sensitive to small changes in one or both of them, and responses are affected by quite small changes in the wavelength composition of broad-band colours (Northdurft and Lee, 1982).

Lastly, complex effects are a consequence of Equation (1) when adapting backgrounds are used. Depending on its wavelength composition, an adapting background will drive each mechanism some way up its input–output curve. The response evoked by a stimulus superimposed on this background will be affected by compressive nonlinearity in each mechanism. It is also possible that each mechanism will show adaptive changes *per se*, that is the half-saturation constants (σ_e and σ_s) may change as a result of the background.

Large changes in the half-saturation constants of individual cones have been reported in lower vertebrates (Normann and Perlman, 1979) but in primates what little evidence is available suggests that such changes are not so marked unless bleaching occurs (Boynton and Whitten, 1970). The ganglion cells of lower mammals show a remarkable ability to adapt to changing light level by shifting their intensity–response functions as if the cone half-saturation constants were changing (Sakmann and Creutzfeldt, 1969; Green and Powers, 1982). In the primate lateral geniculate nucleus, however, we have found that such shifts of intensity–response functions as do occur when illumination level changes are not adequate to maintain the same cell sensitivity over a large range of light levels (Virsu and Lee, in preparation), and certainly the adaptive capacity of primate visual cells is inferior to that of the cat. In any event, differential changes in σ_e and σ_s in Equation (2), together with the compressive nonlinearity of the functions, will additionally complicate the quantitative behaviour of the cell, and the use of adapting backgrounds is thus a procedure whose apparent simplicity masks a number of complex effects.

Acknowledgement

V.V. was supported during part of this work by the Alexander von Humboldt Foundation.

References

Abramov, I. (1977). Interactions among chromatic mechanisms. In *Spatial Contrast* (eds Spekreijse, H. and van der Tweel, L. H.). Amsterdam: North Holland.

Boynton, R. M. (1979). *Human Color Vision*. New York, Holt, Rinehart and Wilson.

Boynton, R. M. and Whitten, D. N. (1970). Visual adaptation in monkey cones: recordings of late receptor potentials. *Science* **170**, 1423–1426.

Creutzfeldt, O. D., Lee, B. B. and Elepfandt, A. (1979). A quantitative study of chromatic organisation and receptive fields of cells in the lateral geniculate body of the rhesus monkey. *Expl. Brain Res.* **35**, 527–545.

de Monasterio, F. M. and Gouras, P. (1975). Functional properties of ganglion cells of the rhesus monkey retina. *J. Physiol., Lond.* **251**, 167–195.

Green, D. G. and Powers, M. K. (1982). Mechanisms of light adaptation in rat retina. *Vision Res.* **22**, 209–216.

Hemila, S. (1977). Background adaptation in the rods of the frog's retina. *J. Physiol., Lond.* **265**, 721–741.

Naka, K. I. and Rushton, W. A. H. (1966). S-potentials from luminosity units in the retina of fish. *J. Physiol., Lond.* **185**, 587–599.

Normann, R. A. and Perlman, I. (1979). The effects of background illumination on the photoresponses of red and green cones. *J. Physiol., Lond.* **286**, 491–507.

Nothdurft, H.-C. and Lee, B. B. (1982). Responses to coloured patterns in the macaque lateral geniculate nucleus, Pattern processing in single neurones. *Exp. Brain Res.* **48**, 43–54.

Sakmann, B. and Creutzfeldt, O. D. (1969). Scotopic and mesopic light adaptation in the cat's retina. *Pflugers Arch.* **313**, 168–185.

Virsu, V. and Lee, B. B. Light adaptation in cells of the macaque lateral geniculate nucleus and its relation to human light adaptation. *J. Neurophysiol.*, in press.

Werblin, F. S. (1974). Control of retinal sensitivity II. Lateral interactions at the outer plexiform layer. *J. gen. Physiol.* **63**, 62–87.

Luminance Ratio and the Spectral Responsiveness of Cells in the Macaque Lateral Geniculate Nucleus

A. VALBERG, B. B. LEE, O. D. CREUTZFELDT and D. A. TIGWELL

Introduction

The spectral responsiveness of wavelength-selective cells in the primate visual system is usually determined experimentally by testing with monochromatic lights either on a dark (or dim) background or with some kind of adapting field. This is, of course, far from the stimulus conditions in which the visual system usually operates. Naturally-occurring stimuli consist of broad-band wavelength compositions of different saturations which may be brighter or dimmer than the mean adaptation level. Simultaneous and successive contrast effects are both present under normal conditions.

There have been few attempts (DeValois and Marrocco, 1973) to evaluate quantitatively the behaviour of cells under these conditions. In the experiments reported here the responses of cells in the parvocellular layers (PCL) of the macaque lateral geniculate nucleus were studied when stimuli of various wavelength compositions (narrow- and broad-band filters) were alternated with a white adapting background. White stimuli, when presented on a dark background, may increase or decrease maintained firing rate, depending on cell type; wide-band cells' (WL and WS) firing rates are increased and narrow-band cells' (NL and NS) firing rates decreased (Creutzfeldt, Lee and Elepfandt, 1979). For PCL cells suprathreshold responsiveness to various wavelengths and to white can be accounted for neurophysiologically by opponent models

COLOUR VISION
ISBN 0 12 000000 0

(Creutzfeldt *et al.*, 1979; Lee and Virsu, this volume; Lee, Virsu and Elepfandt, 1983), that can be related to the opponent coordinates used to describe sensory colour and lightness differences (Seim and Valberg, 1982).

In our stimulus situation, responses to chromatic and achromatic stimuli will be a function of the luminance ratio of stimulus to background. The various spectrally-tuned neuronal channels respond differentially to achromatic stimuli under these conditions, suggesting a role for such cells in the perception of achromatic colours. From the results below it appears that luminance ratio is a meaningful parameter for description of cell responses to chromatic stimuli with this stimulus paradigm, implying a role for these cells in coding for saturation (Valberg, 1974).

Intensity–Response Functions for Stimuli Alternated with a White Field

For generation of intensity-response curves, stimuli were centered over the receptive fields of cells in the PCL of the anaesthetized macaque, *M. fascicularis*. Receptive fields were 8–10° parafoveal. Stimuli were alternated with a white field (120 cd m^{-2}); both stimuli and field were about 4° × 5° in size. Stimuli were presented for 300 msec every 1.5 sec, thus the white field was the main determinant of the adaptive state of the cell. Mean firing rate in the 200 msec sustained component following the initial transient was measured, the maintained firing rate was subtracted, and the resulting net response plotted against the luminance ratio (Y) of stimulus to field ($Y = L/L_0$ where L and L_0 are the luminances of stimulus and white field respectively). Luminances (CIE 10° supplementary observer) were computed from the relative spectral power distribution of the light source and the spectral transmission of the interference filters (Schott NAL; half bandwidth at half maximum 25 nm). The CIE $y_{10}(\lambda)$ function was used as the spectral luminosity function, because of the large stimulus size and the eccentricity of receptive fields. This choice was also based on the finding of de Monasterio and Schein (1980) that this function matches the spectral sensitivity of parafoveal phasic cells.

Figure 1 shows sets of intensity–response curves for PCL cells classified according to Creutzfeldt *et al.* (1979). Figures 1A and B contain curves for wide-band cells. If the luminance ratio (Y) of stimulus to white field was very low, a decrease in firing rate was observed independent of stimulus wavelength. This is a weak off-suppression consequent upon removal of the white field, white stimuli being excitatory for wide-band cells. As stimulus intensity increases, chromatic thresholds for the different spectral stimuli are seen to be at luminance ratios between 0.01 and 0.1, that is with luminances for the chromatic stimuli 2 to 1 log units below that of the adapting field. For excitatory stimuli, with increasing intensity the response magnitude increases rapidly to a maximum, giving the cell a 1 to 1.5 log unit dynamic range.

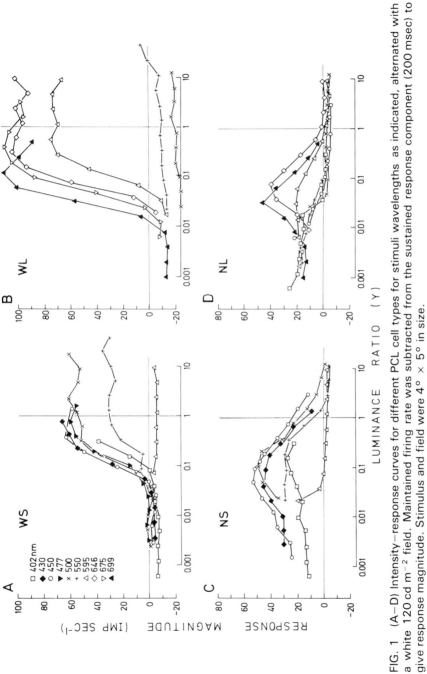

FIG. 1 (A–D) Intensity–response curves for different PCL cell types for stimuli wavelengths as indicated, alternated with a white 120 cd m^{-2} field. Maintained firing rate was subtracted from the sustained response component (200 msec) to give response magnitude. Stimulus and field were 4° × 5° in size.

Normally, further increases in intensity did not much affect responses, although in a few cases a subsequent decrease in response magnitude occurred. For inhibitory stimuli the function cannot be followed beyond the point at which firing rate falls to zero, though sometimes such stimuli evoked an excitatory response when luminance was more than 1 log unit above that of the white field.

Intensity–response curves for an NS and an NL cell are shown in Figs 1C and D. At very low luminance ratios a weak excitatory response occurs owing to removal of the white field; white stimuli suppress the firing rate of narrow-band cells. Chromatic threshold appears to be about 2 to 2.5 log units below that of the adapting field. For excitatory stimuli increasing intensity is accompanied by an increase in response until a luminance ratio of 0.03 to 0.1, a value scarcely above threshold for wide-band cells. A further increase in intensity results in a decrease in response magnitude. In the examples shown, with a luminance ratio of one almost no response is present. With some other narrow-band cells somewhat higher luminance ratios were required to abolish excitatory responses.

Curves for light-inhibited cells encountered resembled responses of narrow-band cells to inhibitory stimuli with a low chromatic threshold and suppression of activity at all wavelengths. In some cases, however, the adapting effect of the white field was sufficient to reveal concealed excitatory inputs (Padmos and Norren, 1975).

The sets of curves in Fig. 1 were typical for the cells recorded so far with the luminance ratios at threshold and response maxima being fairly consistent from cell to cell within the same class, although the actual magnitude of the maximal response was variable. Thus typical behaviour for narrow-band cells was lower chromatic threshold and response saturation at lower luminance ratios than for wide-band cells, and then a decrease in response magnitude. Wide-band cells tended to maintain a high response level at the higher luminance ratios used here.

The intensity–response curves in Fig. 1 may be compared with intensity–response curves for stimuli projected upon a dim background (Lee and Virsu, this volume). The spectral responsiveness of the various cell types is similar, but the dynamic range of cells was smaller with the stimulus paradigm used here.

Luminance Ratio and Response Normalization

If white stimuli were used, with a luminance ratio of one no response was evoked. For white stimuli brighter than the white adapting field wide-band cell firing rates were increased and narrow-band cell firing rates diminished; the effects were reversed for stimuli dimmer than the white field. The luminance ratio between the stimulus and adapting field and not absolute luminance thus determined the response.

In each of the cells of Fig. 1, the curves appear to fall into two groups, one for excitatory and one for inhibitory spectral stimuli, with a scatter within each group of about 0.3 log unit on the abscissa. Plotting responses on a relative radiance basis, the curves were spread out over about two log units. This apparent normalization to luminance ratio is illustrated for an NL cell in Fig. 2. In Fig. 2A responses are plotted as a function of luminance ratio and in Fig. 2B as a function of radiance ratio of the stimulus to the white adapting field. The sets of curves appear to fall together in Fig. 2A, but the scatter is large in Fig. 2B.

The NL cell of Fig. 2 was studied extensively and gave reproducible responses. For the 529 and 550 spectral stimuli increasing intensity results first in a decrease and then an increase in response. This may be attributed to stronger activation of long-wavelength (L-) cones while the middle-wavelength cones are saturated at higher stimulus intensities. A similar curve was found for 571 but here stronger stimuli resulted in a further decrease in response. Such complex curves were atypical, and indicate interaction of at least three mechanisms.

We also measured intensity–response curves to stimuli with different amounts of white added, i.e. with differing degrees of saturation but equal luminance. Similar results were reported by DeValois and Marrocco (1973). The results, with those of Fig. 1, permit a multidimensional analysis of unit responses, and provide some neurophysiological justification for a psychophysical representation of colours by opponent purity, the difference of cone absorptions divided by luminance (Valberg, 1981).

The Effect of White Surrounds

Projection of a white surround around a colour stimulus has a most dramatic effect on its appearance, especially when the surround is of higher luminance than the centre. The surround adds "black" to the central stimulus by simultaneous contrast (induction). Thus, for example, white turns grey, orange turns brown and yellow becomes olive (the "related" colours of Ostwald).

We recorded intensity–response curves of the different PCL types with and without a steady 120 cd m^{-2} white surround ($20° \times 30°$) around the stimulus and white field. Luminance of the white adapting field and the surround were the same.

A typical set of curves for an NL cell are shown in Fig. 3. Compared with Figs 1D and 2A, all curves are shifted to the right, with maximum response occurring near a luminance ratio of one. A similar shift of response curves of 0.5 to 1.0 log units was seen for other cell types. This effect could not be duplicated by addition of reasonable amounts of stray light to the stimulus.

This is a surprising result, since adaptation level outside a cell's receptive field is not considered a determinant of its responses. If remote adaptational

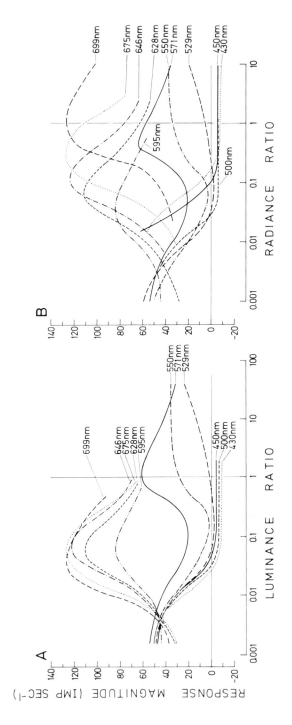

FIG. 2   Intensity–response curves for an NL cell plotted as a function of luminance ratio (A) or radiance ratio (B) of stimulus to a white adapting field.

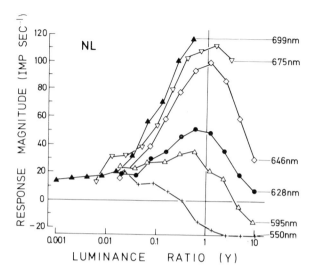

FIG. 3 Intensity−response curves for an NL cell in the presence of a 120 cd m⁻², 20° × 30° surround. Curves are shifted to the right in comparison with the NL cells of Figs 1 and 2.

effects play an important role in adjusting cell responsiveness, quantitative descriptions of responses of wavelength-selective cells must take this into account.

Discussion

The behaviour of PCL cells described here is compatible with and complements the classification of Creutzfeldt *et al.* (1979), in that narrow-band and wide-band cells give optimal responses at different luminance ratios. On the other hand, using our stimulus paradigm, in which a chromatic stimulus alternated with a white adapting field, a classification based solely on responsiveness with respect to wavelength, or spectral neutral points, would be ambiguous. For instance, narrow-band cells' activity is always suppressed when the luminance ratio is high enough. However, varieties within each type were not uncommon; one example of an atypical NL cell is shown in Fig. 2, and Gouras and Zrenner (1981) have pointed out there may be a range of degrees of opponency between L- and M-cones.

Intensity−response curves with stimuli presented on a dim background can be approximated by the linear interaction of saturating hyperbolic functions (Lee and Virsu, this volume; Lee *et al.*, this volume). Each function relates relative cone absorption to the output of a cone mechanism. Although the parameters of such a function may not be those best suited to describe cone signals themselves, the spectral sensitivity of each function is that of one of the cone types. We also tested an inhibitory mechanism with the spectral sensitivity of the photopic luminosity function.

The same model may be used to simulate the responses shown in Fig. 1. We used the spectral sensitivities of Estévez (1979), which come very close to the spectral sensitivities derived from the microspectrophotometric measurements of cones of *M. fascicularis* by Bowmaker, Dartnall and Mollon (1980).

Since in these experiments the independent variable is luminance ratio and not radiance increment, we first computed absorption values $(\bar{A}_{ij})$ for each cone mechanism (i) and filter (j), when the filters have the same luminance as the white field (120 cd m^{-2}). Then

$$A_{ij} = Y\bar{A}_{ij} \tag{1}$$

where A_{ij} is the absorption of a cone mechanism for a particular filter relative to $\bar{A}_{ij}$ and Y is luminance ratio.

The linear interaction between cone mechanisms then becomes

$$R_j = \frac{E_{max}\,(A_{ij})^{n_e}}{\sigma_e^{n_e} + (A_{ij})^{n_e}} - \frac{S_{max}\,(A_{i'j})^{n_s}}{\sigma_s^{n_s} + (A_{i'j})^{n_s}} - C \tag{2}$$

where R_j is the cell response, E_{max} and S_{max} are the saturation levels for each of the cone mechanisms and σ_e and σ_s, and n_e and n_s are constants. i and i' refer to the excitatory and suppressive cone mechanisms respectively. C is the contribution of the removal of the white background to the response, and is also directly derived from Equation (2) by inserting values of A_{ij} appropriate for the white field. This assumes that the discharge rate of the cell to the white field has adapted back to the maintained level.

Such a treatment applied to the NL cell in Fig. 1 suggests an excitatory input from the L-cone mechanism and an inhibitory input from the M-cone mechanism. If the output of a mechanism corresponding to the CIE y_{10} (λ) function (which is essentially a sum of L- and M-cone sensitivities) is subtracted from that of the L-cone mechanism a good account of the results may also be obtained.

The results presented here demonstrate that luminance contrast relative to a white adapting field can be treated as a better determinant of the responsiveness of the PCL wavelength-selective cells than radiance ratio. This might be due to similarity between the luminosity function and the sum of spectral sensitivities of L- and M-cones. It is generally true that a difference of cone outputs divided by their sum leads to normalization similar to that shown in Fig. 2A. However, these cells might also use the luminosity function or a similar broadband spectral function in their coding of spectral information.

Acknowledgement

This work was supported by a twinning grant from the European Science Foundation.

References

Bowmaker, J. K., Dartnall, H. J. A. and Mollon, J. D. (1980). Microspectrophoto-metric demonstration of four classes of photoreceptors in an Old World primate, *Macaca fascicularis. J. Physiol., Lond.* **298**, 131–143.

Creutzfeldt, O. D., Lee, B. B. and Elepfandt, O. D. (1979). A quantitative study of chromatic organisation and receptive fields of cells in the lateral geniculate body of the rhesus monkey. *Exp. Brain. Res.* **35**, 527–545.

de Monasterio, F. M. and Schein, S. J. (1980). Protan-like spectral sensitivity of foveal Y ganglion cells of the retina of macaque monkeys. *J. Physiol., Lond.* **299**, 385–396.

DeValois, R. L. and Marrocco, R. T. (1973). Single cell analysis of saturation discrimination in the macaque. *Vision Res.* **13**, 701–711.

Estévez, O. (1979). *On the fundamental data-base of normal and dichromatic colour vision.* Thesis, University of Amsterdam.

Gouras, P. and Zrenner, E. (1981). Color vision: a review from a neurophysiological perspective. *Prog. Sens. Physiol.* **1**, 139–179.

Lee, B. B., Virsu, V. and Elepfandt, A. (1983). Strength of cell responses in macaque lateral geniculate nucleus as a function of intensity and wavelength. Submitted for publication.

Padmos, P. and Norren, D. V. (1975). Cone systems interaction in single neurons of the lateral geniculate nucleus of the macaque. *Vision Res.* **15**, 617–619.

Seim, T. and Valberg, A. (1982). Uniformity of lightness and colour: a new formula to describe the Munsell system. Submitted for publication.

Valberg, A. (1974). Lateral interaction between large retinal stimuli and symmetric receptive fields. *Physica Norvegica* **7**, 227–235.

Valberg, A. (1981). Advantages of an opponent colour metric and the opponent purity concept. *Die Farbe* **29**, 127–144.

Chromatic Response Properties of Parvocellular Neurons in the Macaque LGN

A. DERRINGTON, P. LENNIE and J. KRAUSKOPF

DeValois, Abramov and Jacobs (1966) showed that LGN cells in macaque fell into three broad groups identified by their responses to monochromatic lights as "red–green" and "yellow–blue" chromatically opponent units and chromatically "non-opponent" units. Recent psychophysical evidence (Krauskopf, Williams and Heeley, 1982) complements this work but suggests an even more compact distribution of signalling channels. These channels comprise a luminance mechanism insensitive to chromatic change and two chromatic mechanisms insensitive to luminance change. One of these chromatic mechanisms is insensitive to variation along a tritanopic confusion line, and the other to variations along a line of constant blue cone stimulation.

Consider the structure of receptive fields that might underlie the two chromatic channels. A cell that received opposed inputs from long- (R) and middle-wavelength (G) sensitive cones would be blind to changes in chromaticity along a tritanopic confusion line, since by definition stimulation of both R and G cones is constant along such a line. An increase in luminance will excite one cone mechanism but inhibit the other, and will elicit no response from the cell if the sensitivities of these mechanisms are equal. Similarly, an ideal cell which receives input from B cones opposed to R plus G cones will not respond to changes in chromaticity along a line of constant B cone stimulation. As before, an increase in luminance will elicit no response if the sensitivities of these mechanisms are equal.

COLOUR VISION
ISBN 0 12 000000 0

This is a preliminary report of experiments, one important aim of which was to determine more precisely the relation between the psychophysical evidence and the properties of macaque LGN cells. We believed that responses to stimuli modulated in different directions through a fixed point in color space would allow us to characterize the cells more precisely. To permit the description of such manipulations we adopted MacLeod and Boynton's (1979) chromaticity diagram as a basis of our color space, adding to it a luminance axis orthogonal to their "tritanopic" and "constant blue" axes. For any cell that responds to the linear sum of its cone inputs there will be a single direction for which the response will be maximal and an orthogonal plane in which there is no response. For the "ideal" cells discussed above the best directions will be either the tritanopic confusion or the "constant blue" axis. Thus we can characterize completely the response of a cell by its best direction (or its null plane) and its sensitivity. It is important to note, as we shall see, that the best direction may vary with the spatial and temporal frequency of the stimulus.

This analysis led us to measure the responses to stimuli modulated in different directions in color space about a fixed point. We used a color television system designed by W. J. Kropfl of Bell Laboratories. It allowed us to produce moving grating patterns whose spatial and temporal modulation was variable along any direction in our color space. In the experiments described here we used uniform fields, or gratings, that were modulated at 3.75 or 15 Hz.

We find it convenient to discuss modulations in terms of their polar coordinates in our color space. The first coordinate specifies the direction in the isoluminant plane, such that a change toward red in the "constant blue" direction is assigned 0 degrees, and a change toward yellow along a tritanopic confusion line is assigned 90 degrees. The second coordinate is the luminance angle, specified as 0 degrees in the isoluminant plane, $+90$ degree for pure increments in luminance and -90 degrees for pure decrements in luminance.

The locations of the television primaries are plotted on a CIE chromaticity diagram in Fig. 1. Also plotted are the white point (the point about which all stimuli were modulated) and, passing through it, the tritanopic confusion line and the line of constant blue cone stimulation.

Results

All the observations described here were made on parvocellular neurons in the LGNd of anaesthetized and paralyzed macaques (fascicularis or mulatta).

First let us consider results for uniform fields. Peristimulus time histograms of the responses to modulations in eight uniformly spaced directions in the isoluminant plane are plotted in Fig. 2. Each histogram shows the variation in discharge rate in response to 3 cycles of stimulus modulation. The cell responds best to modulation along the tritanopic confusion line (90 degrees)

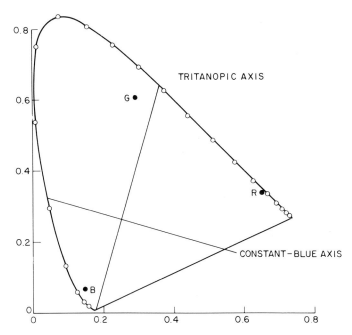

FIG. 1   C. I. E. chromaticity diagram showing loci of television primaries, tritanopic confusion line, and line of constant blue cone stimulation. The lines intersect at the white point used in the experiments.

and not at all to modulation along the line of constant blue excitation. In common parlance this is a "yellow–blue" cell, and close to "ideal" in that it responds hardly at all to luminance modulation.

The amplitude of the response (the magnitude of the Fourier component at the frequency of stimulus modulation) is plotted in Fig. 3 for two cells. The first row shows responses to modulations in the isoluminance plane, the left-hand panel for the cell of Fig. 2 and the right-hand panel for a representative cell of the other chromatic class, whose response is maximal for modulations close to 0 degrees (the "constant blue" line).

Figure 4 shows, for 98 cells studied in 4 monkeys, the distribution of the null directions in the isoluminant plane. There are two tight clusters, group 1 centered close to the "constant blue" axis, and group 2 close to the tritanopic axis. To characterize a cell completely we need to know the effects of luminance modulation. As we rotate the direction of modulation vertically out of the isoluminant plane we introduce progressively greater modulation of luminance. The effect of this change, for stimuli in the plane passing through the constant blue axis, is depicted in the middle row of Fig. 3 for one cell of each class. The left-hand plot shows how poorly the "blue–yellow" cell responds to luminance

DIRECTION OF MODULATION IN ISOLUMINANT PLANE

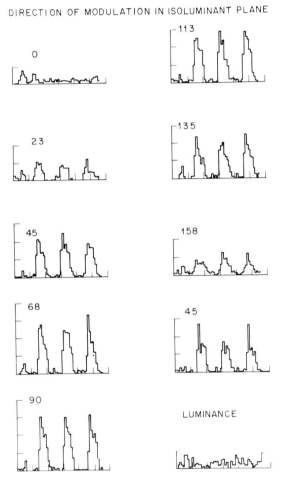

FIG. 2   Peristimulus time histograms of responses to modulation in eight different directions in the isoluminance plane and to pure luminance modulation. The 45 degree modulation was repeated in order to give an impression of the reliability of the recordings. The scale divisions are 25 impulses per second in the vertical direction and 100 msec in the horizontal direction.

modulation in the plane that passes through its null axis. The right-hand plot shows how a "red–green" cell responds quite well to luminance modulation around its preferred axis; indeed its best response is elicited by stimulus modulation somewhat outside the isoluminant plane.

The bottom row of Fig. 3 shows the effects of varying the amount of luminance modulation in the vertical plane passing through the tritanopic confusion axis. The cell depicted on the left behaves ideally: The response is largest

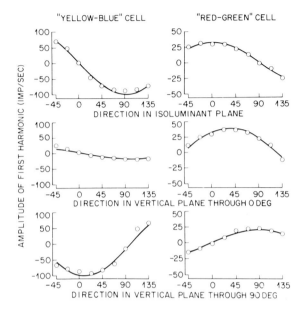

FIG. 3   Responses of two cells to modulation in three planes of our color space. Left-hand column: a cell which responds best to modulation near the tritanopic confusion line. Right-hand column: a cell which responds best to modulation near the line of constant blue cone stimulation. First row: modulation within the isoluminant plane. Second row: vertical slice through the line of constant blue cone stimulation. Third row: vertical slice through the tritanopic confusion line.

in the isoluminant plane and falls off as the luminance component increases. The cell depicted on the right would not have responded at all if it were an ideal unit with its best response in the constant blue axis.

The smooth curves drawn through these points are generated by a model in which the outputs of linearly responding spectrally selective mechanisms are summed algebraically. The good fit of these theoretical curves testifies to the adequacy of the assumptions. The linearity assumption is further directly supported by separate measurements of the variation of response amplitude with contrast.

So far, we have considered only the effects of uniform fields. However, many chromatically opponent units in the LGNd have center-surround organized receptive fields (Wiesel and Hubel, 1966). For such units an increase in the spatial frequency of the pattern will favor the center mechanism, and will cause the direction of the best response to be rotated away from the isoluminant plane. This is what we found for many cells of the "red–green" class, but not for the smaller group of "blue–yellow" units; cells in the latter group appear not to have center-surround organized receptive fields (Wiesel and Hubel, 1966).

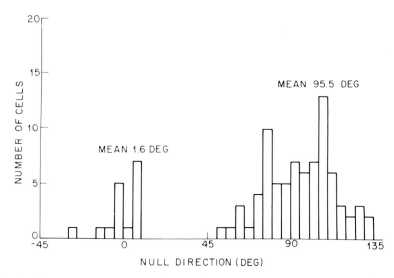

FIG. 4 Frequency distribution of the null directions in the isoluminant plane for 98 cells from 4 monkeys. The mean directions for the two groups of cells are 1.6 and 95.5 degrees with standard deviations of 6.4 and 18.4 degrees respectively.

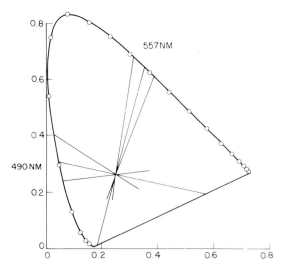

FIG. 5 C.I.E. chromaticity diagram showing loci plus and minus one standard deviation for the null axes of our two groups of cells.

Our results may be compared to those of DeValois *et al.* (1966) by transforming the directions of best response in the isoluminant plane into the C. I. E. coordinate system and determining the wavelength at which these lines intersect the spectrum locus. The results of this analysis is shown in Fig. 5. The mean intersection points are 490 nm and 557 nm. The standard deviations of the intersection points are 3 and 5 nm, respectively.

References

DeValois, R. L., Abramov, I. and Jacobs, G. H. (1966). Analysis of response patterns of LGN cells. *J. opt. Soc. Am.* **56**, 966–977.

Krauskopf, J., Williams, D. R. and Heeley, D. W. (1982). Cardinal directions of color space. *Vis. Res.* **22**, 1123–1131.

MacLeod, D. I. A. and Boynton, R. M. (1979). Chromaticity diagram showing cone excitation by stimuli of equal luminance. *J. opt. Soc. Am.* **69**, 1183–1186.

Wiesel, T. N. and Hubel, D. H. (1966). Spatial and chromatic interactions in the lateral geniculate body of the rhesus monkey. *J. Neurophysiol.* **29**, 1115–1156.

Development of Color Vision Mechanisms in the Ground Squirrel

GERALD H. JACOBS, MARK E. McCOURT and JAY NEITZ

Introduction

Questions about the ontogeny of mammalian color vision remain for the most part unanswered. Results obtained from humans tested at about two months of age indicate that although some color vision capacity is present during early postnatal life, infants lack some (as yet incompletely understood) features of adult color vision (Pulos, Teller and Buck, 1980; Hamer, Alexander and Teller, 1982). On the other hand, macaque monkeys tested at two months of age already seem to possess fully the trichromatic color vision characteristic of that species (Boothe, Teller and Sackett, 1975).

Behavioral studies of the development of color vision are inherently difficult because they require that exacting psychophysical measurements be made on subjects who are hard to test and whose capacities may be changing rapidly over the test period. An alternative approach to the problem is to investigate the development of the biological mechanisms known to underlie color vision. This course at least could define the possibilities for the development of color vision. It is the approach we have taken. We have examined the development of the response properties of neural elements in the ground squirrel visual system which are known to transmit the information needed to yield color vision. We describe here some ontogenetic changes in these mechanisms and the effects of variations in photic environment.

COLOUR VISION
ISBN 0 12 000000 0

The Ground Squirrel

The California ground squirrel (*Spermophilus beecheyi*) is a highly diurnal rodent whose vision and visual system have been studied in our laboratory for several years. In this section we outline the essential facts about vision in this species.

Like other ground squirrels, the California ground squirrel has a heavily cone-dominated retina with fewer than 10% of all photoreceptors identified as rods (Jacobs, Fisher, Anderson and Silverman, 1976). This animal has dichromatic color vision with a well defined neutral point located at about 505 nm (Anderson and Jacobs, 1972). Behavioral and electrophysiological studies indicate that this dichromacy is based on the operation of two classes of cone photopigments whose absorbance peaks are at about 525 and 440 nm (Jacobs and Tootell, 1981).

In a large-scale investigation of the response properties of single fibers in the optic nerve of the California ground squirrel it was found that under photopic conditions about 70% of all fibers received inputs solely from those photoreceptors containing the 525 nm photopigment (Jacobs and Tootell, 1981). These fibers can be further subdivided along other response dimensions: directional selectivity, transient versus sustained response patterns, receptive field organization, etc. The remaining fibers receive inputs from both the 440- and 525-nm mechanisms and most show spectrally opponent responses. Direct tests of color discrimination indicate that the spectrally opponent fibers transmit information adequate to account for the color vision of the California ground squirrel (Jacobs, Blakeslee and Tootell, 1981).

Methods

Details of the rearing conditions employed and the procedures used for recording from optic nerve fibers in the California ground squirrel are given elsewhere (McCourt and Jacobs, 1983). In brief, pregnant ground squirrels were housed in individual cages designed to provide one of three lighting regimens: complete darkness, cyclic white light (12 h light/dark alternation), or cyclic red light. The spectral characteristics of the red light were such that it would be expected to be about 1000 times more effective in activating the 525-nm cones than the 440-nm cones. The idea was that this environment would provide relatively normal inputs to those units having connections solely from the 525-nm cones, but grossly abnormal inputs to those units having connections to both the 440-nm and the 525-nm cones. Squirrel pups were born in one of these three environments where they remained until they were removed for study.

Single units were recorded from the optic nerves of anesthetized ground squirrels at a location just anterior to the optic chiasm. Each unit was categorized according to whether its input was solely from the 525 nm mechanism or whether it was driven by both the 440- and 525-nm mechanisms. Other details of the unit's response were also examined, but these are not considered here.

The development of the electroretinogram (ERG) of the California ground squirrel was also studied. ERGs were recorded conventionally from anesthetized animals using a tungsten electrode which was inserted into the posterior chamber. Stimuli were 400-msec flashes of monochromatic light presented in Maxwellian view. A two-channel optical system made it possible to examine the responses to these stimuli in combination with various adapting fields.

Results

General Aspects of Development

California ground squirrels are normally born in nest burrows. Their early visual development is relatively slow. In the eight litters we examined, lid opening occurred between 30 and 33 days of age. Following lid opening the young squirrels grow rapidly, and by about 70 days of age their weights are comparable to those of wild-trapped adult animals. There was no difference in growth rate for animals reared in the three different photic environments.

The Electroretinogram

To assess the functional status of the distal retina in young squirrels we examined several features of the ERG. The intent was to establish the ages at which signals originating in both the 440- and 525-nm mechanisms achieved their adult status. All observations were from animals reared in cyclic white light.

At dark-adapted threshold and on achromatic adapting backgrounds the photopic b-wave (bl) of the ground squirrel can be completely accounted for on the basis of the operation of cones containing the 525-nm pigment (Jacobs and Tootell, 1979). Ontogenetic changes in the contribution made by the 525-nm mechanism to the ERG could thus be assessed by examining bl thresholds in squirrels who were tested at various times after lid opening.

The top panel of Fig. 1 shows the thresholds for the bl component of the ERG for young squirrels tested at various ages, and for adult animals comparably tested. Two days after lid opening the bl component of the squirrel ERG is of low amplitude, is relatively insensitive, and is easily fatiguable. However, five days after lid opening, in this case at 38 days of age, bl threshold has dropped about two log units, and does not differ from thresholds of adult squirrels. From that point onwards there are no further changes in the threshold of the bl component. Measurements of the amplitude of bl to very intense flashes of light yielded a similar picture. Both these features indicate that the 525-nm cones provide full and adultlike input to the ERG within several days following lid opening, at least by 40 days of age.

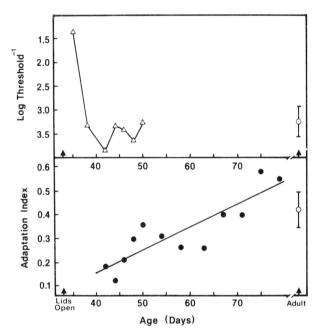

FIG. 1   Ontogenetic changes in the ERG of the California ground squirrel. Each data point shows the results from a single animal. The top panel shows thresholds (5 μV criterion) of the photopic (bl) component of the ERG recorded from animals tested at various ages. This component indexes the contribution of the 525 nm mechanism. The values to the right (mean ± 1 SD) were obtained from eleven adult animals equivalently tested. The bottom panel plots the magnitude of chromatic adaptation of the bl component as a function of age. As explained in the text, this measure indexes the contribution of the 440-nm mechanism to the ERG. Values to the right (mean ± 1 SD) are the results from similar tests run on seven adult animals. The time of lid opening is indicated at the left (small arrow).

The 440-nm cones can be shown to contribute to the bl response when the ground squirrel ERG is recorded under conditions of intense chromatic adaptation (Jacobs and Tootell, 1977). To quantify this contribution, we measured bl thresholds for two test lights, 470 and 595 nm, under conditions where the eye was first steadily adapted with a 595-nm light and then later with a 470-nm light. If the response to the test lights reflects only the operation of a single cone mechanism, then the threshold relationship for the two will remain the same under both conditions of adaptation. Conversely, the extent to which the threshold relationship changes under the two conditions can be used to gauge the magnitude of differential chromatic adaptation. The magnitude of differential adaptation for this combination of adapting and test lights is shown for several adult ground squirrels to the right in the bottom panel of Fig. 1.

This index averages about 0.44 log unit. To the left in that panel are the adaptation indices obtained from young animals. Some differential chromatic adaptation could be seen as early as five days after lid opening, but it could not be measured accurately until the animals were 42 days of age. From that point the index increased slowly and achieved the adult value at about 70 days of age. This experiment indicates that (a) the contribution of the 440-nm mechanism to the ERG, as revealed by chromatic adaptation, achieves adult status approximately six weeks after lid opening, and (b) the time required for the 440-nm mechanism to reach its adult status (as indexed by the ERG) is much longer than the time required by the 525-nm mechanism.

Optic Nerve Responses

Single unit recording experiments were initiated when the squirrels reached about 55 days of age. Units were recorded from 37 animals divided among the three experimental groups. A total of 2697 optic nerve fibers were categorized according to whether they received inputs from one or both cone classes.

There were three principal findings in this experiment: first, the proportion of optic nerve fibers receiving inputs from both cone mechanisms is much lower in the young squirrel than it is in the adult animal; second, such units increase in proportion as the animal ages until they finally achieve the adult level; and third, the time required for these units to achieve the adult standard depends on the photic environment in which the young animal has been reared.

These results are illustrated in Fig. 2, which plots for each animal tested the percentage of optic nerve fibers found to receive inputs from both cone mechanisms. In the youngest animals examined (*ca.* 50–55 days old) the proportion of such units was under 15%, a value significantly lower than that for adult animals. This initial value was not different for animals reared in the three different photic conditions. Beyond 55 days the proportion of units receiving inputs from both cone classes increased, but at different rates for the three groups. Least-squares fits to the data points show that animals reared in white light reach the adult level at about 79 days of age, while those reared in total darkness reach the same point somewhat later, at about 100 days of age. The animals reared in red light required very much longer than either of these groups to achieve adult status, perhaps about 400 days.

Discussion

These experiments reveal a number of interesting features of the development of the mechanisms for color vision in the ground squirrel. As judged by its contribution to the ERG, the 525-nm mechanism is fully developed within a week following lid opening. At this age, however, signals originating from the 440-nm mechanism still contribute only feebly to the ERG. The 440-nm

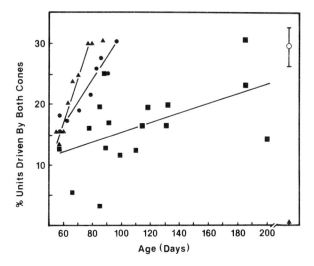

FIG. 2 The developmental change in the proportions of optic nerve fibers found to receive inputs from both cone mechanisms in ground squirrels reared in cyclic white light (▲), complete darkness (●), and cyclic red light (■). Each point is the result for one animal. The average number of units categorized for each animal was 73. The regression lines drawn through the data points were fitted by the method of least squares. The open circle to the right shows the mean percentage of units in the optic nerve of the adult ground squirrel receiving inputs from both cone mechanisms. The error bar encloses the 95% confidence interval for this proportion. These latter values were obtained from experiments performed on over 200 ground squirrels.

mechanism required much longer to achieve its adult status. ERG measurements cannot, of course, differentiate between the development of photoreceptor signals *per se*, and the establishment of those neural pathways by which these signals contribute to bl. Nevertheless, they imply that the development of the short-wavelength mechanism is slower than the corresponding development of the 525-nm mechanism. These experiments also indicate that the outputs from both these mechanisms are fully adultlike about six weeks after lid opening; that is, at about 70 days of age.

Given that it requires about 70 days before both cone mechanisms are adultlike, it is perhaps not surprising that up to this time the proportion of optic nerve fibers receiving inputs from both mechanisms is still very low. Indeed, at 55 days of age, the proportion of such units encountered in the nerve is only half of what it is in the adult. For animals reared in the white light environment it takes nearly 80 days before the proportion of optic nerve fibers receiving inputs from both cone mechanisms reaches the adult level.

Although the age-related increase in the proportion of optic nerve fibers receiving inputs from both mechanisms shown in Fig. 2 is clear, its basis is not.

One possibility suggested by the ERG experiments is that the short-wavelength mechanism matures rather slowly. Another is that this outcome is due to differing efficacies of the recording procedures for young and adult animals. A number of controls were employed to eliminate obvious sources of such bias (McCourt and Jacobs, 1983), but we cannot discount the possibility that the slow increase in the proportion of fibers seen to receive inputs from both mechanisms might simply reflect the fact that these fibers in particular achieve a recordable size (degree of myelination?) at a later stage than do the other fibers. We are currently examining the anatomical development of the optic nerve in the ground squirrel to assess this possibility. Whatever the reasons for this low proportion of units, it is clear that prior to about 80 days of age the full range of information needed to support color vision in the ground squirrel is not transmitted to the central visual system. The strong implication is that the "normal" color vision in this species develops rather gradually during postnatal life.

Not only does it appear that the neural substrates for color vision develop postnatally in the ground squirrel, but also that the time required for their organization to become fully adult-like can be strongly influenced by the nature of the photic environment in which the developing animal is reared. Especially impressive was the effect of the red light condition. In that case, many months were required before the nerve appeared normal. Although this spectrally-biased environment appears not to prevent the eventual attainment of a normal retinal output, the analogy of this result to the effects of various environmental rearrangements on the development of the ocular dominance properties of cortical neurons is nevertheless obvious. In both cases changing the balance of inputs to the system has a more powerful effect on development than a complete absence of stimulation, but whereas the ocular dominance change involves synaptic interactions in the cortex, the chromatic effect is exerted somewhere in the retina. Since the red light environment would be expected to provide a highly biased input to the sites of spectrally opponent interactions, it seems reasonable to suppose that it is at those retinal locations where this aberrant photic environment may have its effect. The ERG experiment suggests that these sites are in the outer retina.

Acknowledgement

This research was supported by a grant from the National Eye Institute (EY-00105).

References

Anderson, D. H. and Jacobs, G. H. (1972). Color vision and visual sensitivity in the California ground squirrel (*Citellus beecheyi*). *Vision Res.* **12**, 1995–2004.

Boothe, R., Teller, D. Y. and Sackett, G. P. (1975). Trichromacy in normally reared and light deprived infant monkeys (*Macaca nemestrina*). *Vision Res.* **15**, 1187–1191.

Hamer, R. D., Alexander, K. R. and Teller, D. Y. (1982). Rayleigh discriminations in young human infants. *Vision Res.* **22**, 575–588.

Jacobs, G. H., Blakeslee, B. and Tootell, R. B. H. (1981). Color discrimination tests on fibers in the ground squirrel optic nerve. *J. Neurophysiol.* **45**, 903–914.

Jacobs, G. H., Fisher, S. K., Anderson, D. H. and Silverman, M. S. (1976). Scotopic and photopic vision in the California ground squirrel: Physiological and anatomical evidence. *J. comp. Neurol.* **165**, 209–227.

Jacobs, G. H. and Tootell, R. B. H. (1977). Spectral mechanisms in the retina of the Arctic ground squirrel. *Canad. J. Zool.* **55**, 1454–1460.

Jacobs, G. H. and Tootell, R. B. H. (1979). Spectral components in the b-wave of the ground squirrel electroretinogram. *Vision Res.* **19**, 1243–1247.

Jacobs, G. H. and Tootell, R. B. H. (1981). Spectral-response properties of optic-nerve fibers in the ground squirrel. *J. Neurophysiol.* **45**, 891–902.

McCourt, M. E. and Jacobs, G. H. (1983). Effects of photic environment on the development of spectral response properties of optic nerve fibers in the ground squirrel. *Exptl. Br. Res.* (In press).

Pulos, E., Teller, D. Y. and Buck, S. L. (1980). Infant color vision: A search for short-wavelength-sensitive mechanisms by chromatic adaptation. *Vision Res.* **20**, 485–493.

Human Pattern Evoked Potentials and Colour Coding

O. ESTÉVEZ and T. DIJKHUIS

Introduction

In animal preparations colour coding processes can be directly followed from receptor level up to higher centres. In humans we are, in general, restricted to the use of indirect methods such as the cortical evoked potentials (EPs for short). Visual Evoked Potentials, themselves a subject of considerable interest, have proved their usefulness as a means of analysing the signal transport that takes place from retina to cortex (Regan, 1972; Spekreijse, Estévez and Reits, 1977). Among the many attributes of the image that may affect – and perhaps be encoded in the VEPs – are spatial contrast and colour.

The literature on contrast or Pattern EPs (see e.g. Regan, 1972; Spekreijse *et al.*, 1977) suggests that several of the "spatial" attributes of the visual stimulus do indeed influence the Pattern EPs in specific ways. Some, like border sharpness, can clearly be said to be "encoded" to some extent in the responses.

The case for "colour" coding in the EPs is less strong. While a number of studies have been conducted using colour as the main experimental variable (see References), results have been contradictory and open to serious criticism (Spekreijse *et al.*, 1977).

We feel that, in colour studies, one can achieve a better control of the visual stimulus either by expressing the stimuli in terms of "cone fundamentals" or, better, by explicitly attempting to modulate each cone class input separately and in a controlled degree using silent substitution (Estévez and Spekreijse, 1982).

COLOUR VISION
ISBN 0 12 000000 0

The questions we asked in this study were:

a) Do different cone systems contribute differently to the PEPs?

and,

b) When two cone systems are simultaneously modulated, is the attribute "colour" encoded in the responses?

Methods

A partial answer to the first question is known: the "blue" cones, although capable of eliciting a PEP if given the right stimulus (Estévez, Spekreijse, van den Berg and Cavonius, 1975) probably do not participate on the same footing as the two long-wavelength systems "red" and "green" (see also Tansley *et al.*, this volume). This fact, plus several technical constraints, made us restrict our study to the "red" and "green" cone systems and their interactions. (Note: We shall, in what follows, refer to these systems as the Long – or L – and Middle – or M – systems.)

The stimulus and recording technique used have been fully described in Estévez *et al.* (1975), but a brief account here will help understand the present results.

The subjects sit, with silver-chloride electrodes attached on the occipital part of the scalp, in a screened cage and their electro-encephalogram (EEG) is fed to a conventional EEG amplifying machine.

The visual stimulus is formed by means of two modulated lamps and a mirror where the pattern is etched. The pattern used was a checkerboard with a set of transmitting and a set of reflecting squares. The patterned mirror is placed at 45° to the observer such that the light of one lamp is seen through the transmitting squares and the other on the reflecting squares. When the intensity of the two lamps is equated, only a homogeneous blank field is seen. When the lamps are modulated in counter phase, the etched pattern can be seen with a contrast that follows the light modulation.

The stimulus time course and frequency can be varied at will, but, for this experiment, it was usually a squarewave at 2 Hz. Responses were obtained for patterns ranging from 6 to 60 arc-minutes and contrasts between 3% and 50%, depending on the type of experiment.

For the purpose of this experiment, each of the lamps forming one set of checks actually consisted of two coloured lights, a red and a green, that could be modulated independently. This allowed us to form either a "yellow" pattern, when the red and green lights were modulated in phase, or a coloured pattern, when the red and green lights were in counter phase. However, the counter phase modulation was chosen based on silent substitution calculations: the aim was to present a pattern that would be "seen" by only one cone system at a pre-specified contrast; furthermore, once the silent substitution stimuli were known, they could be combined in any time-course and proportion desired before feeding the lamps.

The first part of the experiment consisted of validating the silent substitution values chosen, essentially reproducing the experiment and results of Estévez *et al.* (1975). As estimates of cone "fundamentals" an average of the subject's own measured sensitivities was used. Although pi-mechanism sensitivities appear to represent quite well the measured functions, it turns out that silent substitution values computed using any reasonable set of fundamentals (Vos and Walraven, 1971; Smith and Pokorny, 1975; Estévez, 1979) are all very similar when colours with a broad spectral distribution are used, as was our case.

Results and Discussion

The results of presenting a pattern with 20-min checks and 15% contrast to both the L and M systems are shown in Fig. 1; the left column shows the result of presenting a so-called "reversal" pattern, i.e. one where dark and bright checks interchange places; the right column shows the responses to a pattern that appears for 240 msec and then disappears leaving a blank field of the same average intensity for another 240 msec. These stimuli are presented 200 times and the EPs recorded are averaged to improve the signal to noise ratio.

In the first row, responses to presentation of these patterns simultaneously to the M and L systems (i.e. a yellow pattern) are shown; in the second and third row, those to presentation to each apart.

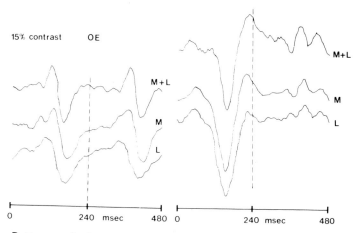

FIG. 1   Pattern evoked responses to combined L and M cone inputs (upper row) and isolated inputs (lower rows).

The responses of the upper row, to a yellow stimulus (M + L), are typical of those usually obtained with a white stimulus. These responses can be taken to represent the activity evoked by the repetitive presentation of an achromatic spatial contrast. The responses obtained by stimulating either the M or L cone systems alone are in all respects comparable with each other and to those of the first row. Remarkable, in these results, is that responses to a pattern "seen" by both L and M simultaneously do not appear larger than those to a pattern "seen" by only one.

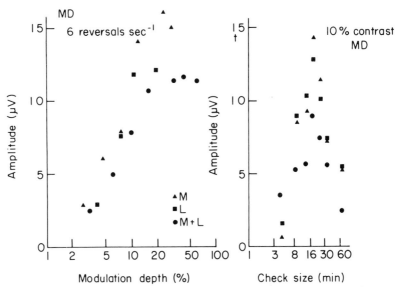

FIG. 2   Pattern evoked responses peak to peak amplitudes as function of (a) contrast modulation and (b) check size.

In Fig. 2, some of the results of subject MD, who was studied extensively, are shown. In the left panel, the peak-peak amplitude of the responses to a pattern "reversal" (6 Hz, 18 min checks) are plotted as a function of per cent stimulus contrast. We see that, for the isolated M and L inputs (triangles and squares), the amplitude increases with contrast up to the highest value attainable (about 20% for the L and 25% for the M inputs; please note that the maximum effective "isolated" contrast can never be 100% − as with an achromatic stimulus − because of the silent substitution technique; see for details Estévez and Spekreijse, 1974 and 1982). For the combined input M + L (circles), the responses also increase in amplitude, but seem to reach a "plateau" at contrasts larger than 20%.

On the right of Fig. 2, the contrast was held constant at 10%, and the amplitudes are plotted as a function of check size. Here we see that, in all three conditions, the largest amplitudes are obtained with checks about 18 min subtense.

Once again, it is remarkable in both results that the responses to the M + L input are never larger than those to M or L alone. In fact, the M + L responses may even be smaller for both the optimum check size (Fig. 2, right) and for large contrasts (Fig. 2, left). These types of results have been reproduced with all combinations of contrast, frequency and check size in several subjects.

Three conclusions can be drawn at this point:

First, because whenever isolated L and M systems are presented with a similar stimulus they evoke a similar response, we conclude that the neural pathways leading from either system to the point at which the responses are generated are in all respects equivalent.

Second, because the responses to simultaneous L and M inputs are never larger than to either one alone we infer that there cannot be separate generators for the two systems; if there were, one would obtain a response twice as large for L + M as for L or M stimuli. A corollary of this conclusion is that there is only one generating site receiving contrast inputs from either L or M (and possibly, if the stimulus is right, from short-wavelength cones and even rods; see Estévez *et al.*, 1975).

Third, from these results it is clear that signals from L and M cones can, and do, interact: these signals appear to compete for input to the EP generator site because responses to both inputs simultaneously are often smaller than to one alone. However, the interactions we find are certainly not opponency in a chromatic sense, since the use of fully "achromatic" patterns (yellow or white), or chromatic ones (when either L or M are stimulated alone) yield similar responses. We suggest that spatial contrast, not colour, is the only relevant attribute of the stimuli.

To clarify this point, in Fig. 3 we present the results of an experiment aimed at bringing out the L and M interactions. In this figure we plot the responses of two subjects (the authors) to a 10 per cent contrast pattern, first presented to each of the M or the L systems alone – while the other was silenced (upper two rows) – and after when the two images were alternated, i.e. one cone type "saw" the pattern appear at the moment the other "saw" it disappear (lower row; the drawings next to the responses represent schematically the stimulus as "seen" by the M and L systems).

The responses to stimulation of M or L alone are large, resemble each other and, as stated above, also resemble those to white light stimulation. However, if the L and M patterns are alternated, i.e. a pattern is seen by L while M sees a blank and vice versa (as shown in the lowest row), then the generated response is much smaller than either one alone. In fact, this response is comparable to that obtained by presenting a white reversing pattern of a similar contrast (Spekreijse *et al.*, 1977).

Now, the interesting aspect of this type of stimulus is that we can also search for specific effects of modulating colour, as distinct from modulating only spatial contrast. This is because the alternating L and M images can be arranged

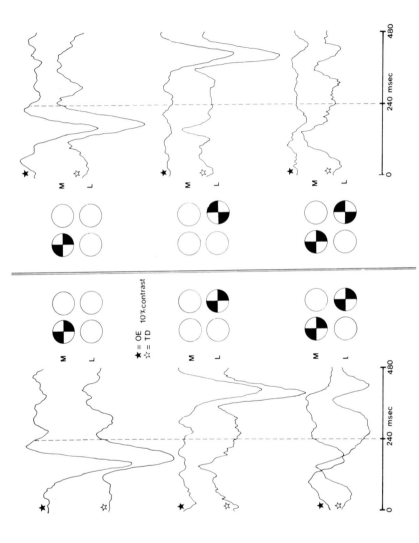

FIG. 3   Responses to isolated pattern modulation of L or M cone inputs (upper row) and to alternation of the L and M inputs (lower row) in two ways: maximum ''colour modulation'' (left column) or maximum ''contrast modulation'' (right column).

★ = OE   10%contrast
☆ = TD

in two ways. In the first way, "bright" and "dark" fields from the L image are substituted by corresponding "bright" and "dark" fields from the M image; this represents no change in the spatial contrast, but it gives maximum "colour" modulation since a bright green field turns into a bright red one and vice versa; there is "colour reversal". In the second way, the "bright" fields of the L image are replaced by the "dark" fields of the M image, this exchanges the intensity of adjacent fields (which means spatial "contrast reversal"), but preserves the colour: a square is seen as a green going from dark to light and the adjacent one as a red going from bright to dark.

The results of the two forms of presenting the patterns are shown side by side in Fig. 3. For the two subjects studied, the "colour reversal" stimulus (left column) yields a similar response to that of the "contrast reversal" (right column) one.

This supports our suggestion that the interactions observed in these evoked potentials between signals from L and M systems reflect only competition for input to the generating site and not colour interactions.

Conclusions

Our findings on the interactions between L and M inputs at, or before, the Pattern EP site provide further support to similar results of Regan and Spekreijse (1974), Estévez (1977), and Spekreijse *et al.* (1977). In these papers, as well as in a review paper by Regan (1975), it was suggested that only a single Pattern EP generator must be available to both the L and M systems.

What our work further clarifies is that the PEP generator reacts specifically to spatial contrast signals from either of the cone mechanisms, whether the stimulus involves colour modulation or not. Furthermore, from these and other results not shown in this paper (Dijkhuis, Master Thesis, University of Amsterdam), we have clearly established that modulation of either the L or M system with the same parameters produces responses indistinguishable from each other; a finding that strongly suggests that, up to the site where the PEP signals are generated, the neural pathways of the L and M systems are fully equivalent.

That "chromatic" modulation does not contribute to these responses does not, of course, rule out that colour could be "coded" in some other, as yet unidentified, way. Caution, however, is recommended in judging evoked potential studies purporting to show that colour is the coded variable. Although modulating "colour" at constant luminance can result in different forms of EP responses, these changes in the EPs cannot automatically be taken as evidence of "chromatic" coding. What we have shown in our study, through a controlled manipulation of independent cone inputs, is that not all interactions between cone systems are necessarily colour interactions.

References

Ciganek, L. and Ingvar, D. H. (1969). Colour specific features of visual cortical responses in man evoked by monochromatic flashes. *Acta Physiol. Scand.* **76**, 82–92.

Ciganek, L. and Shipley, T. (1970). Color evoked brain responses in man. *Vision Res.* **10**, 917–919.

Clynes, M. and Kohn, M. (1964). Specific responses of the brain to colour stimuli. Proc. 17th Ann. Conf. Eng. Med. and Biol.

Estévez, O. (1977). EP's to contrast modulation. In *Spatial Contrast* (eds Spekreijse, H. and van der Tweel, H.). Amsterdam, North Holland Publishing House.

Estévez, O. (1979). On the fundamental data-base of normal and dichromatic color vision. Thesis, University of Amsterdam, Kripps Repro, Meppel.

Estévez, O. and Spekreijse, H. (1974). A spectral compensation method for determining the flicker characteristics of the human colour mechanisms. *Vision Res.* **14**, 823–830.

Estévez, O. and Spekreijse, H. (1982). The "silent substitution" method in visual research. *Vision Res.* **22**, 681–691.

Estévez, O., Spekreijse, H., van den Berg, T. J. T. P. and Cavonius, C. R. (1975). The spectral sensitivities of isolated human color mechanisms determined from contrast evoked potential measurements. *Vision Res.* **15**, 1205–1212.

Krauskopf, J. (1973). Contributions of the primary chromatic mechanisms to the generation of visual evoked potentials. *Vision Res.* **13**, 2289–2298.

Regan, D. (1972). *Evoked Potentials in Psychology, Sensory Physiology and Clinical Medicine.* London, Chapman and Hall.

Regan, D. (1975). Recent advances in electrical recording from the human brain. *Nature* **253**, 401–406.

Regan, D. and Spekreijse, H. (1974). Evoked potential indications of colour blindness. *Vision Res.* **14**, 89–95.

Shipley, T., Jones, R. W. and Fry, A. (1965). Evoked visual potentials and human color vision. *Science* **150**, 1162–1164.

Smith, V. C. and Pokorny, J. (1975). Spectral sensitivity of the foveal cone photopigments between 400 and 500 nm. *Vision Res.* **15**, 161–171.

Spekreijse, H., Estévez, O. and Reits, D. (1977). Visual evoked potential and the analysis of visual processes in man. In *Visual Evoked Potentials in Man: New Developments* (ed. Desmedt, J. E.). Oxford, Clarendon Press.

Vos, J. J. and Walraven, P. L. (1971). On the derivation of the foveal receptor primaries. *Vision Res.* **11**, 799–818.

White, T. N., Kataoka, R. W. and Martin, J. I. (1976). Colour-evoked potentials; development of a methodology for the analysis of the processes involved in colour vision. In *Visual Evoked Potentials in Man: New Developments* (ed. Desmedt, J. E.). Oxford, Clarendon Press.

Spectral Tuning and Contour Representation in Area 17 of the Awake Monkey

M. TANAKA, B. B. LEE and O. D. CREUTZFELDT

Introduction

A number of studies have reported on the responses of neurones in area 17 of the monkey to chromatic and nonchromatic visual stimuli (Hubel and Wiesel, 1968; Dow and Gouras, 1973; Gouras, 1974; Schiller, Finlay and Volman, 1976; Michael, 1978a–c; Gouras and Krüger, 1979). In all these studies results were obtained from anaesthetized animals.

There is general agreement that signals from spectrally-selective afferents reach area 17, but, as well as spectrally-selective neurones with various properties, cells have been described which respond only to luminance borders irrespective of the spectral composition of the stimulus. Further, special attention has been drawn to cells with double-opponent centre-surround organization from green (M-) and red (L-) cones (Michael, 1978a, b), but a similar organization in which the blue cones participate has not yet been found.

We report here results from recordings from the awake, trained macaque, the Barbary ape (*Macaca sylvanus*). The results confirm and extend earlier observations obtained from acute experiments.

Recording of Cell Responses

Monkeys were trained to fixate on a small spot of light. When the spot dimmed, they were required to release a lever in order to obtain fruit juice; the animal's fixation could be prolonged up to 9 sec. A frame for head fixation and a recording chamber over area 17 were implanted. The animal's eye position was monitored by an infrared sensor. If the animal failed to maintain fixation, data were discarded. We have recorded from about 250 cells in one animal over a seven month period, using glass-coated platinum iridium electrodes inserted through the dura.

Stimuli consisted of moving squares and bars of different sizes and wavelength compositions. Stimulus luminance was usually 20 cd m^{-2} on a 5 cd m^{-2} background. In addition to stimuli presented on this background, chromatic stimuli were presented inset into a white field so that a chromatic but not a luminance difference was present. Stimulus presentation could be binocular or monocular. Stimulus speed was usually 4 deg sec^{-1} but sometimes faster and slower speeds were used, as well as flashed stimuli.

Responses to Moving Stimuli

About 40% of visually responsive neurones were wavelength-selective in that such cells were sensitive to the spectral composition of stimuli of the same luminance. Other neurones responded to luminance or chromatic borders. In single electrode penetrations perpendicular to the cortical surface, usually cells of the same response type were found, i.e. cells were either wavelength-selective or non-spectrally sensitive contour detectors. This suggests a clustering of cells of the same response type (Michael, 1981; Krüger and Fischer, this volume), but uncertainty as to the exact course of the electrode in our experiments made it impossible to say if groupings were columnar. Wavelength-selective cells of differing spectral responsiveness were mixed within a particular penetration.

In many penetrations, it proved difficult to evoke visual responses even in the awake monkey. Such unresponsive neurones were often found at the beginning of a penetration, in superficial layers. Although we cannot rule out the possibility that damage may have been caused by the electrode, many such cells responded well to novel stimuli, but their responses adapted rapidly. This suggests that such effects are not unique to the anaesthetized preparations.

Wavelength-Selective Cells

Many wavelength-selective cells gave very sustained responses to moving stimuli, and such cells could be classified in a similar way to cells in the parvocellular layers of the lateral geniculate nucleus (Creutzfeldt *et al.*, 1979). All types of parvocellular wavelength-selective cells were found in area 17: examples are shown in Fig. 1. The "NS" (Narrow-band, Short-wavelength) cell gave an excitatory response to stimuli below 500 nm and its maintained activity was suppressed by white stimuli. The "WS" (Wide-band, Short-wavelength) and "WL" (Wide-band, Long-wavelength) cells gave excitatory responses to wavelengths below 600 nm and above 500 nm respectively, and gave an excitatory response to white stimuli. The "NL" cell gave an excitatory

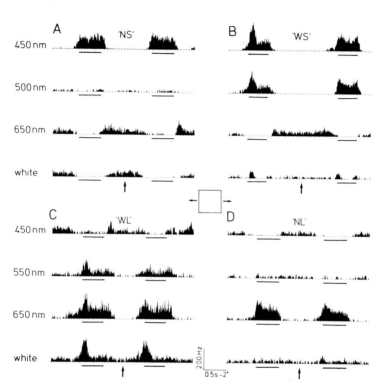

FIG. 1   Response histograms for four tonically-responding, wavelength-selective, area 17 cells to 2° × 2° moving squares of different wavelength composition, as indicated. Forward and backward directions of movement are shown; the arrows indicate the stimulus turn-around points. The stimulus markers under the histograms indicate the time during which the stimulus was over the cell's receptive field, as monitored by a photometer.

response above 600 nm and a small response at the border of the white stimulus in one movement direction. "NL" cells often gave responses to dark moving targets (see Fig. 3), but as in the lateral geniculate nucleus and retina (Gouras and Zrenner, 1981), cells giving excitatory responses to long wavelengths may show variability in the strength of excitatory cone input. Some cells were found for which the maintained activity was tonically suppressed by stimuli of all wavelengths, but they gave a tonic response to dark squares, in the same way as LI cells in the geniculate.

The responses shown in Fig. 1 are very similar to those found with similar stimuli in the lateral geniculate nucleus, and suggest that these cell types may receive direct afferent input.

Most wavelength-selective cells were also tested in a colour contrast situation, with stimuli inset in a white or chromatic surround either equalized for luminance or with different luminance ratios. Such stimuli often enhanced responsiveness, as can be the case in the lateral geniculate nucleus (Valberg, Lee, Creutzfeldt and Tigwell, this volume).

The stimulus paradigm used here was not very suitable for demonstration of double opponency (Michael, 1978a–c), although some histograms resembling responses shown by Michael (1978b) were found. On the other hand, some cells responded to moving stimuli in a wavelength-selective manner, but sustained responses occurred at only some wavelengths. Thus such a cell might give a sustained response to a 650-nm stimulus, but at other wavelengths a burst of firing occurred only at the leading and/or trailing edges of the square. Such effects are weak in the geniculate and must be due to spatial filtering within the cortex.

Contour-Sensitive Cells

Many neurones responded vigorously to borders, no matter whether the border consisted of a luminance or chromatic difference. Contrast or colour reversal did not affect the response significantly. Such cells have also been found in anaesthetized monkeys and have been extensively investigated by Gouras and Krüger (1979).

An example of such a cell is shown in Fig. 2. Responses to different wavelengths and to white and black squares are shown in Fig. 2A, and in Fig. 2B are shown responses to different wavelengths inset into an equal-luminance white background. A narrow tongue stimulus evokes very similar responses (Fig. 2C).

It is remarkable that the border response is always located at the same place independent of the nature of the border: the location of the response does not shift to either side of the border dependent on the stimulus conditions. This is most striking in the case of contrast reversal of a black–white stimulus border: the discharge locus occurs at the same point in space irrespective of contrast direction. A similar property is found in complex cells of the cat visual cortex and has been attributed to convergence of on- and off-centre afferents (Heggelund, 1981). Convergence onto contour-sensitive cells is also necessary to account for their responses. Such convergence must include wavelength-selective PCL cells, since MCL cell responses to equal-luminance, chromatic changes are weak (Hicks *et al.*, 1983).

Binocularity and Orientation Sensitivity

Of 50 cells for which visual responses to the different eyes were compared, a high proportion (88%) were binocular though varying degrees of binocularity were found. This percentage is substantially in excess of many of those reported in the literature. Binocular cells invariably showed similar response properties

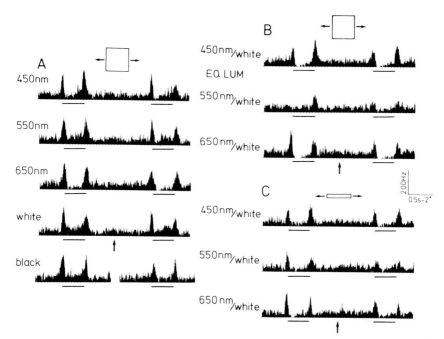

FIG. 2   Response histograms for a contour-sensitive, area 17 cell. (A) Responses to various square stimuli of different wavelength on a dim background and to a black square in a 20 cd m⁻² white surround. (B) Responses to the same stimuli inset into a white surround. (C) Responses to a narrow tongue, as shown; stimuli were set in a white surround. Other details as in Fig. 1.

through the two eyes. An example of a tonically responding, wavelength-selective cell is shown in Fig. 3. The similar spectral responsiveness in both eyes is apparent for the cell in Fig. 3. Differing degrees of summation were found with binocular stimulation: binocular responses were sometimes smaller, but usually equal or greater than monocular responses. Binocular responses were, however, always smaller than the sum of monocular responses.

Both wavelength-selective as well as contour-sensitive cells showed various degrees of direction and orientation selectivity, though we were struck by the small number of strongly orientationally selective cells. Most cells only displayed orientation bias, and our results are in agreement with those of De Valois *et al.* (1982) in this respect.

Discussion

We have found in area 17 of the awake, behaving monkey that patterns of cell responses are qualitatively very similar to those reported in the anaesthetized

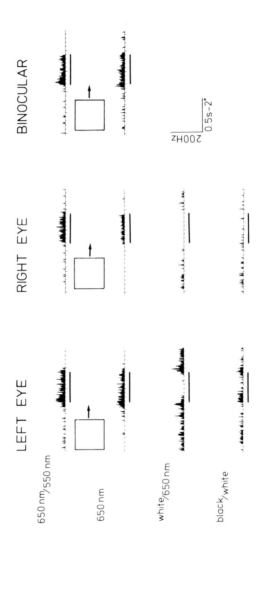

FIG. 3 Response histograms for a "NL" wavelength-selective cell to moving 650 nm, white and black squares, and a 650 nm square in a luminance-matched 550 nm surround, with monocular presentation through either eye and binocular presentation; the latter series was not complete.

preparation. However, cell responses were generally vigorous and often sustained and it is possible that this higher responsivity led, on the one hand, to a high proportion of cells which could be driven from both eyes and, on the other, to a broadening of orientation tuning.

In the primate's area 17 there appear to be two populations of neurones, which to some extent are concerned with different properties of the visual stimulus. Cells for which responsiveness was mainly determined by the wavelength composition of the stimulus, and cells which respond to borders appear to be clustered in a somewhat "columnar" fashion, although the spatial organizations of these columns remains uncertain (Michael, 1981, and this volume; Krüger and Fischer, this volume).

Cells with tonic, wavelength-selective responses appear to have similar properties to cells in the parvocellular layers of the lateral geniculate nucleus, insofar as the same types of spectral response classes could be found in both thalamus and cortex. However, in the LGN, the wavelength composition of a stimulus tends to be the main determinant of cell responsiveness, with spatial factors being of minor importance. In area 17, we found some wavelength-selective cells that gave tonic responses only to stimuli of particular shapes or particular orientations, indicating some dependence of the degree of wavelength selectivity on spatial factors.

Contour-sensitive cells are remarkable in that a given neurone signals a luminance and/or colour border passing across its receptive field without information as to the direction of this change. Representation of the visual environment by this system is comparable to a line-drawing of a visual scene as proposed by Jung (1973) for the cat's cortical neurones, or to the zero-crossing detectors postulated by Marr and Hildreth (1980).

It is uncertain to what degree afferents from the magnocellular layers of the lateral geniculate nucleus are responsible for properties of contour-sensitive cells. Since magnocellular cells are on- and off-centre, their responses are not directly comparable to those of contour-sensitive cells, which respond at an identical locus to both light and dark edges. Convergence of on- and off-centre cells on single cortical units must therefore be assumed.

Monocular visual responses are qualitatively identical with each other and with the binocular response. Binocular responses may, of course, vary with stereoscopic depth (Poggio and Talbot, 1981), but we did not test for such effects. The fact that single cortical neurones receive, directly or indirectly, the same input, or combinations of inputs, from the two eyes indicates a very high specificity of matching binocular inputs at a single cell level.

From the psychophysical viewpoint, the identical monocular chromatic properties of single cortical cells may account for the ability to dichoptically fuse chromatic fields to form a coloured field of similar hue to that of the monochromatic mixture, at least as long as the two chromatic fields are not too far apart in wavelength.

Acknowledgement

We thank Sigrid Knocke for her patience in training monkeys.

References

Creutzfeldt, O. D., Lee, B. B. and Elepfandt, A. (1979). A quantitative study of chromatic organization and receptive fields of cells in the lateral geniculate body of the rhesus monkey. *Exp. Brain Res.* **35**, 527−545.

DeValois, R. L., Yund, E. W. and Hepler, N. (1982). The orientation and direction selectivity of cells in macaque visual cortex. *Vision Res.* **22**, 531−544.

Dow, B. M. and Gouras, P. (1973). Color and spatial specificity of single units in rhesus monkey foveal striate cortex. *J. Neurophysiol.* **36**, 79−100.

Gouras, P. (1974). Opponent-colour cells in different layers of foveal striate cortex. *J. Physiol., Lond.* **238**, 583−602.

Gouras, P. and Krüger, J. (1979). Responses of cells in foveal visual cortex of the monkey to pure color contrast. *J. Neurophysiol.* **42**, 850−860.

Gouras, P. and Zrenner, E. (1981). Color coding in primate retina. *Vision Res.* **21**, 1591−1598.

Heggelund, P. (1981). Receptive field organisation of complex cells in cat striate cortex. *Exp. Brain Res.* **42**, 99−107.

Hicks, T. P., Lee, B. B. and Vidyasagar, T. R. (1983). Responses of cells in macaque lateral geniculate nucleus to sinusoidal gratings. *J. Physiol.* (In press).

Hubel, D. H. and Wiesel, T. N. (1968). Receptive fields and functional architecture of monkey striate cortex. *J. Physiol., Lond.* **195**, 215−243.

Jung, R. (1973). Visual perception and neurophysiology. In *Handbook of Sensory Physiology*, Vol. VII/3: Central processing of visual information. A: Integrative functions and comparative data (ed. Jung, R.), pp. 1−153. Berlin, Springer-Verlag.

Marr, D. and Hildreth, E. (1980). Theory of edge detection. *Proc. roy. Soc. B* **207**, 187−217.

Michael, C. R. (1978a). Color vision mechanisms in monkey striate cortex: dual opponent cells with concentric receptive fields. *J. Neurophysiol.* **41**, 572−588.

Michael, C. R. (1978b). Color vision mechanisms in monkey striate cortex: simple cells with dual opponent-color receptive fields *J. Neurophysiol.* **41**, 1233−1249.

Michael, C. R. (1978c). Color-sensitive complex cells in monkey striate cortex. *J. Neurophysiol.* **41**, 1250−1266.

Michael, C. R. (1981). Columnar organisation of color cells in monkey's striate cortex. *J. Neurophysiol.* **46**, 587−604.

Poggio, G. F. and Talbot, W. H. (1981). Mechanisms of static and dynamic stereopsis in foveal cortex of rhesus monkey. *J. Physiol., Lond.* **315**, 469−492.

Schiller, P. H., Finlay, B. L. and Volman, S. F. (1976). Quantitative studies of single cell properties in monkey striate cortex. I. Spatiotemporal organisation of receptive fields. *J. Neurophysiol.* **39**, 1288−1319.

Color Processing in Primate Striate Cortex

CHARLES R. MICHAEL

The retinas of Old World monkeys contain three types of cones, each with a different visual pigment. It is generally believed that these three cone pigments are the basis for the trichromatic nature of normal color vision. The main problem for the neurophysiologist is to determine how information from the three cone classes is processed in the retina, in the lateral geniculate nucleus and, ultimately, in the visual cortex. Microelectrode studies at various levels in the rhesus monkey's visual pathway have shown that wavelength information is integrated through opponent color mechanisms. In both the retina and the lateral geniculate most color-coded cells have receptive fields consisting of an "on" or "off" circular center connected with one cone type and an annular surround of the opposite sign connected with a different class of cone. These neurons are capable of responding to both color and contrast information because they possess both opponent color and opponent spatial mechanisms.

In my recent studies of the monkey's striate visual cortex (Michael, 1978a–c; 1979; 1981) I have found four classes of cells that also process both color and spatial aspects of the visual image. Based on their response properties and their receptive field organization, these cells were classified as concentric, simple, complex and hypercomplex. However, they were a distinctly separate population from the simple, complex and hypercomplex cells studied previously by others (Hubel and Wiesel, 1962; 1965; 1968). They shared the common property that they generally responded only to color stimuli and not at all to white light in any form. All of them appeared to be connected to red- and to green-sensitive cones but not to blue cones or to rods.

COLOUR VISION
ISBN 0 12 000000 0

Receptive Fields and Spectral Sensitivities

The first class of cells had concentric receptive fields with one red–green opponent color system in the circular field center and the opposite opponent-color organization in the annular surround (Michael, 1978a). A concentric cell's field consisted of a red on, green off center and a green on, red off surround or of the reverse arrangement. Cells with blue/yellow combinations were not seen. These dual opponent cells were most sensitive to the simultaneous presentation of two different colors, one covering the field center and the other illuminating the surround. In other words, a red on, green off center cell gave a maximum on response to a red spot surrounded by a green annulus. As one might expect, these cells were not influenced by large red or green spots which covered the entire receptive field.

The spectral sensitivity of the field center of a concentric cell is illustrated in Fig. 1. The data points collected in the light adapted state are connected by solid lines. There are two curves, a red-sensitive one (crosses) associated with the on response and a green-sensitive one (triangles) related to the off discharge. By introducing a monochromatic background light (620 or 460 nm), it was possible to adapt selectively one cone system and to study the spectral sensitivity of the other in relative isolation. Under these circumstances the two curves were much broader, overlapped considerably and had peaks at about 540 and 580 nm, respectively. Except for the reversal of the response signs, the spectral sensitivity curves for the surround were very similar to those illustrated.

The second group, the simple cells, were also dual opponent color units (Michael, 1978b). Their response properties and their spectral sensitivities were essentially the same as those of the concentric cells. However, their receptive fields were rectangular, not circular. In most cases the fields consisted of a central oblong region containing one red–green opponent color system flanked on either side by parallel antagonistic areas with the opposite opponent color organization. Sometimes the field contained only two subdivisions which lay adjacent to one another. Because the different regions of the fields were separated by straight-line boundaries, the simple cells were most responsive to colored bar or edge stimuli.

Spectral sensitivity curves obtained on white and on monochromatic backgrounds are illustrated for a simple cell in Fig. 2. This particular unit received an on input from red-sensitive cones and an off input from green-sensitive cones in the field center. Although not illustrated, the two flanks had exactly the opposite inputs. Consequently, these cells, like the concentric units, were most sensitive to the simultaneous presentation of two complementary colors which illuminated oppositely organized parts of the receptive field.

Simple cells were highly sensitive to the axis orientation of line stimuli. Studies with monochromatic backgrounds revealed that their orientation

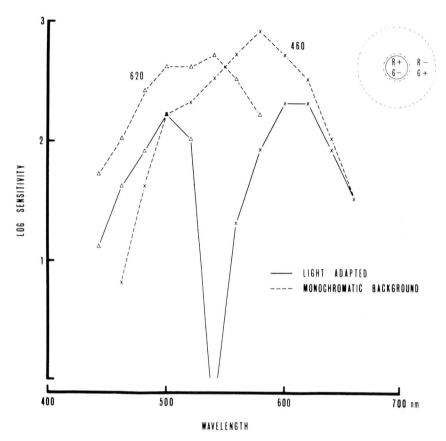

FIG. 1 Spectral sensitivity of the red-on, green-off center of a concentric cell. The receptive field and the stimulus are diagrammed in the upper right-hand corner of the illustration. Crosses designate on responses; triangles, off responses. In the light-adapted state (1.0 $\log_{10}$ cd m^{-2} background) long wavelengths caused on discharges while short ones evoked off responses. There was no response at 540 nm. With either red (620 nm) or blue (460 nm) adapting spots covering only the field center, the responses were either all on or all off at all wavelengths. The spectral sensitivities under the conditions of chromatic adaptation were similar to the absorption spectra of the red- and the green-sensitive cones (Bowmaker *et al.*, 1978) (Fig. 3, Michael, 1978a).

sensitivity was not due to opponent color influences between cones with different absorption spectra. Rather it was mediated by the antagonistic interaction between cones with the same spectral properties but with different spatial locations in the receptive field.

Color-sensitive complex cells were the third class of neurones (Michael, 1978c). They had square or rectangular receptive fields which could not be

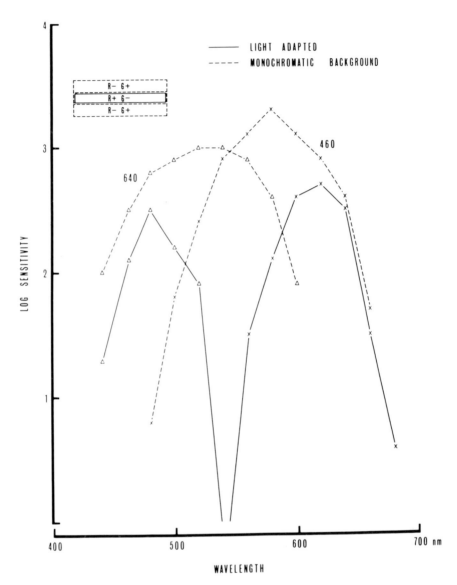

FIG. 2   Spectral sensitivity of the red-on, green-off central field component of a simple cell. The organization of the receptive field and the stimulus utilized are shown in the upper left-hand corner of the illustration. White background, $1.0 \log_{10}$ cd m^{-2}. Other conventions and experimental procedures are the same as employed in Fig. 1 (Fig. 4, Michael, 1978b).

mapped with stationary stimuli; the fields did not have excitatory or inhibitory subdivisions. These cells responded only to moving monochromatic bars or edges of the proper orientation. Some were excited only by two-color edge stimuli. Spectral sensitivity curves obtained on a white background were narrow and had a single peak. Those obtained with appropriate monochromatic backgrounds were broader and similar to the absorption spectra of either the green- or the red-sensitive cones (Bowmaker, Dartnall, Lythgoe and Mollon, 1978). Figure 3 illustrates a pair of such curves. In the light

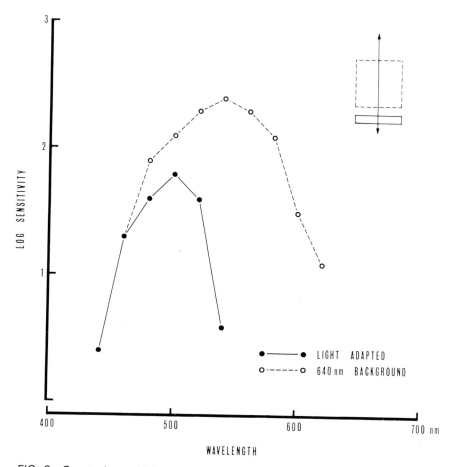

FIG. 3 Spectral sensitivity curve of a color-sensitive complex cell. Moving stimulus bar and receptive field are shown at the upper right. Points connected by solid lines were obtained in the light-adapted state with a white background (1.2 $\log_{10}$ cd m^{-2}). Points connected by interrupted lines were obtained from the same cell with the white background plus a monochromatic background (640 nm) superimposed on it (Fig. 5, Michael, 1978c).

adapted situation the relatively narrow curve peaked at 500 nm while with the red adapting background (640 nm) the much broader curve had a peak which was shifted to about 540 nm. The shape of the curve obtained with the mono- chromatic background was similar to the absorption spectrum of the monkey's green-sensitive cones (Bowmaker *et al.*, 1978). Thus, this cell seemed to have an antagonistic input from red-sensitive cones which was suppressed in the presence of the colored background. The complex cells received excitatory con- nections from either the red or the green cones and "silent" antagonistic inputs from the other class. In essence, they had an opponent color input but only the on excitatory component manifested itself in the responses of the cell.

The fourth and final class was the hypercomplex neuron (Michael, 1979). These cells were excited only by movement of a specifically oriented mono- chromatic edge or bar of light which had to be limited in its length at both ends. Their receptive fields consisted of an orientation-sensitive central activating area flanked on opposite sides by orientation-sensitive "silent" antagonistic areas. Line stimuli moving through the activating area of the receptive field excited the cell; stimuli moving simultaneously across all three regions did not evoke a response. Both the activating and antagonistic regions were highly sensitive to stimulus orientation and, for any given cell, had the same axis orientation.

Figure 4 shows the spectral sensitivity curves for the central activating area of a hypercomplex cell under light-adapted conditions and in the presence of a blue background. The curves appear to be very similar to those shown in Fig. 3 for a complex unit. The cell was excited by monochromatic bars of long wavelength and had a peak sensitivity at 620 nm, indicating an input from red- sensitive cones. It apparently was inhibited by green-sensitive cones, as revealed by the blue adapting background. Although not shown, the spectral sensitivity of each antagonistic flank was the same as the light-adapted curve illustrated. The activating area and the two flanks of a hypercomplex cell always had the same spectral sensitivity.

Columnar Organization

There is considerable evidence that cortical neurons with common physio- logical properties are confined in vertical columns. The two best documented types are the orientation and the ocular dominance columns (Hubel and Wiesel, 1962; 1965; 1968). All of the cells in an orientation column have the same axis requirements for line stimuli, regardless of their receptive-field organization. Cells confined to an ocular dominance column respond preferentially or ex- clusively to the same eye.

The color cells are also restricted to vertical columnar regions which extend from the cortical surface to the white matter (Michael, 1981). By definition, all of the cells within a column respond only to monochromatic stimuli.

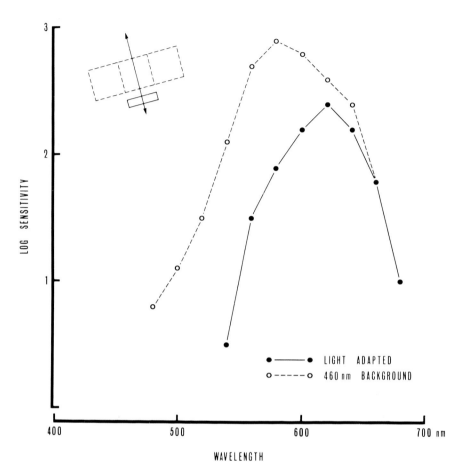

FIG. 4   Spectral sensitivity curve of the central activating area of a color-sensitive hypercomplex cell measured with a white background (1.4 $\log_{10}$ cd m^{-2}) and with a blue (460 nm) background. Receptive field and moving stimulus indicated at upper left. Conventions as in Fig. 3 (Fig. 6, Michael, 1979).

Otherwise they may vary in their receptive-field organization, axis orientation or eye preference. Colour columns are 100 to 250 μm wide and sometimes may extend in length over several millimeters. The boundaries of the columns appear to be unrelated to those of the orientation or the eye-preference columns.

Figure 5 is a reconstruction of an electrode track which traversed all of the cortical layers at an angle slightly offset from perpendicular. All nineteen cells responded exclusively to color stimuli and, thus, all were members of a single color column. Complex and hypercomplex cells were found at the top and the bottom of the track while concentric and simple neurons occupied the middle.

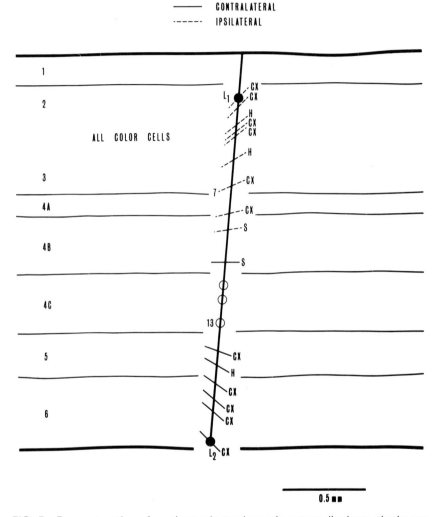

FIG. 5   Reconstruction of an electrode track nearly perpendicular to the layers of the cortex. All units encountered were responsive only to color stimuli. Circles represent concentric cells; S, simple, CX, complex; H, hypercomplex (Fig. 3, Michael, 1981).

The axis orientations of successive cells changed in an orderly sequential fashion, rotating clockwise from an initial angle of 45° to a final one of 135°. The first nine cells were in an ocular dominance column controlled by the ipsilateral eye while the remaining units in the track were under the influence of the contralateral eye.

The three concentric and the two simple cells in Fig. 5 were red on, green off center double opponent units. The remaining fourteen complex and hyper-complex cells had single spectral sensitivity curves which peaked at the red end of the spectrum. Their curves were similar to those for the red on component of the concentric and simple cells. None corresponded to those for the green off system. It appears, then, that this penetration passed across parts of two eye columns and across numerous axis orientation columns but stayed within a single color column dominated by a long wavelength preference.

At oblique track angles an electrode did not stay in a single color column for a long distance. Instead it passed through parts of successive columns which were revealed as clusters of color cells. In multiple oblique penetrations made in the same plane color clusters in one track were found directly above or below similar groups in the other tracks. These chromatically related clusters presumably represented corresponding portions of individual color columns.

Figure 6 is a reconstruction of three oblique electrode tracks which were made in the same plane and were parallel to one another. There were a total of five clusters each in tracks 1 and 2 and four clusters in penetration 3. The cells within these vertically aligned groups had related spectral sensitivity curves, indicating that they probably represented several segments of single color columns. As an example, consider the last cluster in each of the three tracks. The three units in layer 4A in track 3 were all simple cells with a red on, green off central component (610, 510 nm peaks). In the last cluster in track 2 the first cell was simple and the second was concentric (layer 4C). Both were red on, green off center (also 610, 510 nm peaks). The next two units in the cluster were in layer 5 and were complex cells with peaks in the red (*ca.* 610 nm). Finally, in track 1 the last cluster, which was in layer 6, consisted of one complex and two hypercomplex cells, all of which were also red-sensitive. Apparently these three groups of cells were part of a single red-dominated color column.

Figure 7 is another illustration of three oblique electrode tracks made from posterior to anterior through the visual cortex. However, this figure differs from the last one in several respects. Unlike the case in Fig. 6, these tracks were in three different, parallel planes with track 1 being most medial and number 3 being most lateral; they have been projected onto the plane of the cortical surface and viewed from above. Color cells are marked with the letter C and the boundaries of the areas containing color cells are indicated by the dotted lines. The regions containing color cells were clearly slabs or sheets rather than cylinders. The units contained within a slab had closely related spectral sensitivities. All of the complex and hypercomplex cells in a slab had peaks in a narrow portion of the spectrum. Any concentric or simple cells in the same slab had opponent field centers with the on component peaking at about the same place as the curves for the complex and hypercomplex cells. For example, the third set down from the top consisted of seven color units.

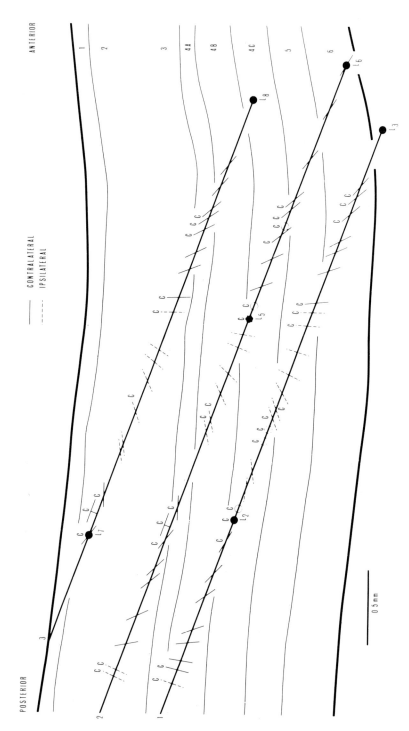

FIG. 6   Reconstruction of three parallel oblique (70°) electrode tracks made in a single plane. Clusters of color cells in one track were located directly above or below color groups in other penetrations. Portions of four neighboring color columns were seen in all three tracks, with one additional column found at the beginning of tracks 1 and 2 (Fig. 7, Michael, 1981).

Three complex neurons in track 1 were located in layers 2 and 3. The pair of cells in track 2 were simple while the remaining pair in penetration 3 were complex. All of the complex cells had peak spectral sensitivities at about 490–500 nm. The simple cells had green on, red off field centers (peaks at 490 and 620 nm, respectively). This correspondence of spectral sensitivities was seen within each of the seven slabs of color cells shown in this figure.

From the surface reconstructions it became clear that there was an alternating pattern of short- and long-wavelength peak sensitivity from one column to the next. For instance, in Fig. 7 the sequence started at the top with two cells that responded best to 490 nm, followed by a group which preferred 610 nm stimuli. The sequence ended at the bottom with a collection of neurons that were most responsive to short wavelengths.

The monocular geniculate axons entering the striate cortex terminate primarily in layer IV (IVA and IVC). One would expect that the cells with the least complicated receptive-field organization or ocular influences would be found in the immediate vicinity of these fibers. Concentric and simple cells, which are presumably early stages in cortical color integration, were confined to lamina IVA and IVC and were driven by only one eye. Nearly all of the wavelength-sensitive complex and hypercomplex cells were found above or below layer IV and most were driven by both eyes. The implication is that these more specialized neurons received their afferents from cells within the cortex itself.

The receptive-field organization of these color cells, their ocular preference, their laminar location and the results of multiple-unit recordings, which were considered elsewhere (Michael, 1978a–c; 1979), suggest that the synaptic organization within a column may be serial: geniculate fibers to concentric to simple to hypercomplex cells. Within a column the concentric and simple cells always had the same double opponent-color organization, e.g. all red on, green off center or all the reverse. The complex and hypercomplex cells in the same column always had single spectral sensitivity curves, which peaked at about the same point as the on component of the concentric and simple cells' field centers. It appears, then, that in a column the early stages were double opponents while the later ones had single spectral sensitivity curves. Nevertheless, there appeared to be no narrowing of the spectral sensitivity at higher stages. A hypercomplex cell had about the same bandwidth as the on center component of a concentric cell.

Acknowledgement

This work was generously supported by NIH Grant EY 00568.

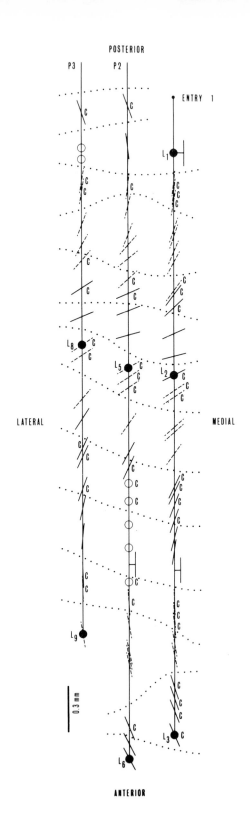

References

Bowmaker, J. K., Dartnall, H. J. A., Lythgoe, J. N., Mollon, J. D. (1978). The visual pigments of rods and cones in the rhesus monkey, *Macaca mulatta. J. Physiol., Lond.* **274**, 329–348.

Hubel, D. H. and Wiesel, T. N. (1962). Receptive fields, binocular interaction and functional architecture in the cat's visual cortex. *J. Physiol., Lond.* **160**, 106–154.

Hubel, D. H. and Wiesel, T. N. (1965). Receptive fields and functional architecture in two non-striate visual areas (18 and 19) of the cat. *J. Neurophysiol.* **28**, 229–289.

Hubel, D. H. and Wiesel, T. N. (1968). Receptive fields and functional architecture of monkey striate cortex. *J. Physiol., Lond.* **195**, 215–243.

Michael, C. R. (1978a). Color vision mechanisms in monkey striate cortex: dual-opponent cells with concentric receptive fields. *J. Neurophysiol.* **41**, 572–588.

Michael, C. R. (1978b). Color vision mechanisms in monkey striate cortex: simple cells with dual opponent-color receptive fields. *J. Neurophysiol.* **41**, 1233–1249.

Michael, C. R. (1978c). Color-sensitive complex cells in monkey striate cortex. *J. Neurophysiol.* **41**, 1250–1266.

Michael, C. R. (1979). Color-sensitive hypercomplex cells in monkey striate cortex. *J. Neurophysiol.* **42**, 726–744.

Michael, C. R. (1981). Columnar organization of color cells in monkey's striate cortex. *J. Neurophysiol.* **46**, 587–604.

FIG. 7 (opposite)   Reconstruction of three electrode tracks made in three parallel planes about 300 μm apart. They were projected onto the plane of the cortical surface and viewed from above. Color cells are marked by the letter C; areas containing only color cells are bounded by dotted lines. The color columns appear to be sheets or slabs (Fig. 9 from Michael, 1981).

Colour Coiumns and Colour Areas

J. KRÜGER and B. FISCHER

It has been known for a long time that the cerebral cortex can be subdivided into anatomically distinct areas. Investigations during the last 20 years have shown that within such areas smaller subunits, often termed columns, can be found in many species. It is a major research goal to relate physiological functions to areas and to columns. In the monkey, Zeki (1973, 1977) identified a prestriate area (or complex of areas) where colour sensitivity was concentrated and Michael (1981) found a system of colour columns in the striate cortex.

In two separate studies we have examined colour responses in a prestriate area belonging to Zeki's V4 complex (Fischer with R. Boch) and in striate cortex (Krüger with M. Bach).

In the first study rhesus monkeys were trained to fixate a small red spot for randomly varying periods of time while other stimuli of different size and colour were switched on and off in the near periphery (0.5° – 10°). Electrode penetrations were made through the intact dura perpendicular to the surface of the skull in a region indicated by the dashed line of Fig. 1. We explored single cells in the anterior half of the prelunate gyrus above the tip of the inferior occipital sulcus and in the lateral part of the posterior bank of the superior temporal sulcus. Some 90% of the over 300 cells tested responded well to the onset of white small (½° × ½°) stimuli in the receptive field. Typically, the total field size was 5 to 20 times larger than the optimal stimulus size. Introducing broad-band red, green, yellow or blue colour filters usually did not change the cells' responses by apreciable amounts. In particular, cells that did not respond to white stimuli (about 10%) remained unresponsive when we used these colour filters. Less than 7% of the cells preferred one or the other of the

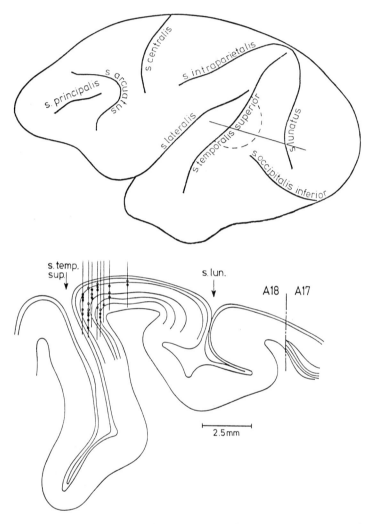

FIG. 1   Above: Drawing of the left hemisphere of a rhesus monkey brain. Penetrations were made into the region indicated by the broken line. Below: Camera lucida drawing of a brain section (perpendicular to the surface and parallel to the straight line above) with reconstructed electrode tracks and cell sites indicated by the circles.

4 colours, i.e. they responded strongly to one colour but weakly to the others and to white. Among the cells that responded differentially to colours the majority preferred small red stimuli similar to the fixation target which the monkey had seen for many weeks of daily training.

Using this simple method of colour stimulation we failed to demonstrate the existence of a great preponderance of colour coded cells. It turned out instead that the prelunate cortex receives a strong input from extraretinal sources: (1) prelunate cells have an enhanced on-response to stimuli that were simultaneously selected as a target for a saccade (Fischer and Boch, 1981a); (2) they may be activated prior to saccades to constantly illuminated targets in the receptive field (Fischer and Boch, 1981b); (3) this presaccadic activation can be modified by continuous daily training of the animal (Fischer and Boch, 1982). These observations and the low percentage of cells that really need colour to be activated make it very unlikely that this part of the visual association cortex or a subdivision of it is exclusively devoted to colour vision (see also Schein, Marrocco and De Monasterio, 1982; Krüger and Gouras, 1980). The present investigation rather suggests that the function of this cortical area is related to the behavioural relevance of the properties of visual stimuli: Among these colour may become a determinant for certain animals under certain circumstances. Recording from approximately the same cortical areas, Zeki (1973, 1977) has found up to 87% colour-coded cells. Since his animals were both anaesthetized and paralysed, the extra-retinal inputs to the prelunate cortex (e.g. those that precede saccades to a stimulus lying in the receptive field) would be reduced or eliminated and the whole state of control of the excitability of this cortical area might be different, leaving the cells with their pure afferent sensory inputs that originate from the retina. Under these conditions more cells may appear to be colour biased. On the other hand our results seem to agree well with the small percentages of colour coded cells reported in the superior temporal sulcus by Van Essen, Maunsell and Bixby (1981) and in area V4 by Schein *et al.* (1982).

In the second study, an array of 30 parallel microelectrodes covering an area of 0.8 mm ×0.64 mm (Krüger and Bach, 1981) was vertically lowered into area 17 of N_2O-anaesthetized, paralysed vervet monkeys. The aim was a thorough investigation of a small cortical volume, comprising the determination of specificities to a variety of stimulus parameters and analyses of spatial response patterns and of activity interrelations. Among other stimuli, large field red, green and white lights turned on and off were applied. In three monkeys, recordings at four to six depth levels between layers II/III and VI were highly successful: Nearly all of the electrodes yielded neuronal activity, and at about half of them a single spike could be isolated.

Inspection of the arrays of PST-histograms immediately revealed that in any layer

1) the relative strengths of the responses to red, green and white lights differed from electrode to electrode,
2) responses to white were very clear for the great majority of electrodes.

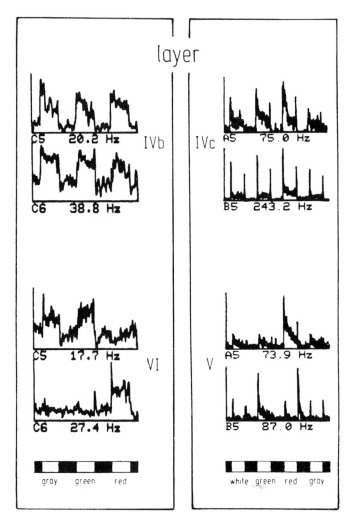

FIG. 2   Multi-microelectrode recordings from area 17 of vervet monkeys: PST-histograms of responses to large coloured fields. Adjacent histograms show activity from
two neighbouring electrodes out of the total of 30 electrodes (C5/C6 resp. A5/B5;
separation 160 μm). For each histogram, the maximum firing rate is given below.

   Left frame: Colour-nonselective responses with strong responses to white found
in layer IVb vertically above colour-selective responses in layer VI. Binocular stimulation.

   Right frame: Colour non-selective responses in layer IVc found above colour-
selective ones in layer V. Stimulation of right eye only.

   Activity was from well-isolated spikes (right frame, and C6 top left), and from essentially one spike which could not be isolated with full certainty (C5, C6 bottom left,
C5 top left). On- and off-phases each lasted 2000 msec. Red and green (colour-foil
filtered) lights appeared about equally bright to human observers, and also as bright
as "gray" (200 cd m^{-2}) at bottom left. "White" and "gray" at bottom right differed
by about 0.4 log units, the former appeared brighter, the latter darker than the colours.

A very precise histological reconstruction (Krüger and Bach, 1982) was performed in order to relate colour preferences to recording site positions. Although sites with similar preferences were often found above one another there were so many examples of very strong discrepancies that as a whole the idea of colour columns was found to be unconvincing. Figure 2 (left) shows responses from two neighbouring electrodes C5 and C6 (separation 160 μm). In layer IVb, essentially no colour preference is seen whereas vertically below in layer VI strong colour preferences (with clear colour opponent response components) can be seen. Similarly, in the right half of the figure, again two neighbouring sites in layer IVc, showing no signs of colour preference, are located above two colour-sensitive sites in layer V.

The following sources of discrepancies with the findings of Michael (1981) can be considered:

1) Instead of colour columns encompassing the whole cortical thickness, independent columnar systems might exist for the infra- and supra-granular layers. This would be analogous to the columnar system of orientation preference (Krüger and Bach, 1982; Bauer *et al.*, 1980). It would also be in better agreement with the spotlike deoxyglucose distribution reported by Tootell *et al.* (1980).
2) There might be a difference in columnar organization between vervet and rhesus monkeys.

Often more than one neurone contributed to the response in the present study. This cannot explain the discrepancy: A strong colour selective response cannot be produced by several colour-nonselective neurones, and a strong response to white cannot stem from several colour selective neurones each being unresponsive to white.

A great problem is common to both studies contained in the present communication: by what criteria should a cell be qualified as a "colour cell"? There are three obvious qualitative definitions, namely the presence of (1) responses to coloured but not to white stimuli, (2) a large difference in strength of response to two colours irrespective of other stimulus parameters, and (3) a large difference in strength of response to two colours for at least one out of several stimulus configurations. For example, the neurones whose "non-colour" responses are shown in the upper half of Fig. 2, if it turned out that they gave differential responses to colours with moving slits, would then have to be considered as colour cells according to the third but not according to the first two definitions. In addition, and most importantly, limits for magnitude and time course differences of responses would have to be specified.

Schein *et al.* (1982) and Van Essen *et al.* (1981) found low proportions of colour cells in area V4; and Hubel and Wiesel reported a low proportion in the striate cortex. We have found it difficult to define the neuronal quality of colour sensitivity in a way which we felt certain that all researchers would agree upon. Therefore it is possible that the discrepancy between the findings of Zeki and Michael on the one hand, and the above-mentioned and our groups on the other hand, is merely an apparent one, stemming from a communication deficiency. In such a case it would be helpful if the essence of a positive finding were communicated via depicted raw responses instead of abstracted notions.

References

Bauer, R., Dow, B. M. and Vautin, R. G. (1980). Laminar distribution of preferred orientations in foveal striate cortex of the monkey. *Exp. Brain Res.* **41**, 54–60.

Fischer, B. and Boch, R. (1981a). Enhanced activation of neurons in prelunate cortex before visually guided saccades of trained rhesus monkeys. *Exp. Brain Res.* **44**, 129–137.

Fischer, B. and Boch, R. (1981b). Selection of visual targets activates prelunate cortical cells in trained rhesus monkeys. *Exp. Brain Res.* **41**, 431–433.

Fischer, B. and Boch, R. (1982). Modifications of presaccadic activation of neurons in the extrastriate cortex during prolonged training of rhesus monkeys in a visuo-oculomotor task. *Neurosci. Lett.* **30**, 127–131.

Hubel, D. H. and Wiesel, T. N. (1968). Receptive fields and functional architecture of monkey striate cortex. *J. Physiol., Lond.* **195**, 215–243.

Krüger, J. and Gouras, P. (1980). Spectral selectivity of cells and its dependence on slit length in monkey visual cortex. *J. Neurophysiol.* **43**, 1055–1069.

Krüger, J. and Bach, M. (1981). Simultaneous recording with 30 microelectrodes in monkey visual cortex. *Exp. Brain Res.* **41**, 191–194.

Krüger, J. and Bach, M. (1982). Independent systems of orientation columns in upper and lower layers of monkey visual cortex. *Neurosci. Lett.* **31**, 225–230.

Michael, C. R. (1981). Columnar organization of color cells in monkey's striate cortex. *J. Neurophysiol.* **46**, 587–604.

Schein, S. J., Marrocco, R. T. and DeMonasterio, F. M. (1982). Is there a high concentration of color-selective cells in area V4 of monkey visual cortex? *J. Neurophysiol.* **47**, 193–213.

Tootell, R. B., Silverman, M. S. and DeValois, R. L. (1980). Color-Dependent Deoxyglucose Patterns within Macaque Cortex. *Investig. Ophthalmol. vis. Sci.* **19**, *Suppl.*, p. 226.

Van Essen, D. C., Maunsell, J. H. R. and Bixby, J. L. (1981). The middle temporal visual area in the macaque: myeloarchitecture, connections, functional properties and topographic organization. *J. comp. Neurol.* **199**, 293–326.

Zeki, S. M. (1973). Colour coding in rhesus monkey prestriate cortex. *Brain Res.* **53**, 422–427.

Zeki, S. M. (1977). Colour coding in the superior temporal sulcus of the rhesus monkey visual cortex. *Proc. roy. Soc. Lond. B* **197**, 195–223.

Colour Processing in Prestriate Cortex of Vervet Monkey

V. O. ANDERSEN, C. GULD and O. SJÖ

During the past decade Zeki (1978, 1980) has made an extensive anatomical study of the partitioning of prestriate cortex into subareas. He is of the opinion that each of these subareas is devoted to the analysis of only one attribute, or only a few attributes, of the visual stimulus, such as colour or direction of movement. He found that colour processing is heavily represented in the visual area V4, which stretches from the lateral part of the anterior bank of the lunate sulcus over the prelunate gyrus to the lateral part of the posterior bank of the superior temporal sulcus. Except for a small representation of colour-coded cells in V2 (posterior bank of lunate sulcus) he concluded that colour does not seem to be represented in other subareas of prestriate cortex.

Several recent reports (Fischer, Boch and Bach, 1981; Krüger and Gouras, 1980; Schein, Marrocco and de Monasterio, 1980) partly disagree with Zeki's view on the importance of V4 in the processing of colour. We think that the controversy may originate from the varying definitions of colour-coded cells. At peripheral levels in the visual pathway, colour cells are those that give opponent responses to monochromatic stimuli, i.e. on-responses to signals from one type of cone and off-responses to signals from another. Zeki (1978) reports only a few cells that give on–off opponent responses. Nevertheless, in his terminology cells are classified as opponent-colour cells if they respond to one set of wavelengths and not to another, and if they do not respond to white. In a report on colour columns in the striate cortex, Michael (1981) defines colour cells as those cells responding to monochromatic stimuli but not to white, thus rejecting those narrowband cells that also respond to white.

COLOUR VISION
ISBN 0 12 000000 0

In view of the dispute on the extent to which cells in prestriate subareas are selectively devoted to colour, we are investigating spectral responses and receptive field properties of cells in V2, V3, and that part of V4 lying in the lateral part of the anterior bank of the lunate sulcus. Flashing monochromatic and white stimuli are added to monochromatic or white adapting backgrounds via a Maxwellian-view stimulator. CIE photopic luminances were used, so that, at the different luminances chosen for stimulus and background, flashes looked equally bright on equally bright backgrounds. For details of the methods, see Bertulis, Guld and Lennox-Buchthal (1977).

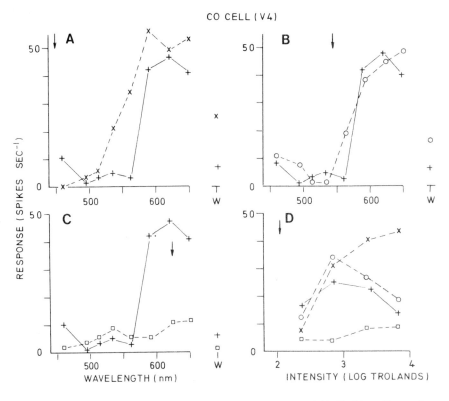

CO CELL (V4)

FIG. 1   The effect of an adapting background on spectral (A, B, C) and intensity (D) responses from a cell in the lateral part of the anterior bank of lunate sulcus (V4). Responses were evoked by flashing light (8 narrow-band wavelengths or white (W) adjusted to equal photopic luminances) through a slit with size and orientation adjusted to best response in the receptive field. Each point of a spectral curve is the sum of the response for four intensities (3.82, 3.55, 2.84 and 2.37 log Trolands) and each point of an intensity curve is the sum of the response from the eight colours and white. The spectral response with a white background (solid line) is compared with that at a chromatic background (broken line) of the wavelength indicated by the arrow in A, B and C. All adapting backgrounds had intensity 2.05 log Trolands (arrow in D).

Responses from a colour-coded cell in V4 are shown in Fig. 1. On a white background (solid line, panels A–C) it responds only to flashes of long wavelength and the response to a white flash (+ at W) is small. This type of response was described by Zeki. We have found that chromatic backgrounds profoundly influence the responses (broken lines). On a blue background (A) the response to middle and long wavelengths increases as does the response to white. On a green background (B) the responses are somewhat reduced. A red background (C) abolishes the response of the cell at long wavelengths. Similar V4 cells that did not respond to white on a white background, always did so to a limited band of wavelengths. They could for example respond to short wavelengths but not to middle and long wavelengths, or they could respond to both middle and long wavelengths but not to short wavelengths. Also encountered were cells sensitive to purples, i.e. cells activated by both long and short wavelengths but not by the middle range. The spectral response of most cells was influenced strongly by different chromatic backgrounds. Some cells responded neither to white nor to colour on a white background, but, surprisingly, they did respond briskly on a monochromatic background to monochromatic stimuli of wavelengths near that of the background and to white flashes. Without a chromatic background such cells would hardly be detected.

Cells in V4 that did respond to white on a white background usually also responded briskly to all wavelengths. In most of these cells the effect of the background was weak, although some of them gave no response at a range of wavelengths with some backgrounds. Most commonly the zero response occurred when the flash was at the same wavelength as the background.

A summary of the properties of the cells recorded in V4 is shown in Fig. 2. A small response to white (low white index) is always related to a small response at some colour (low value of the colour index). It is suggested that these cells are colour-opponent (CO in Fig. 2C). Cells that respond moderately to white may be colour-biased (CB), and the remaining cells are probably not colour-coded (NC). This classification is supported by the fact that all cells have a lower response to some colour than to white, i.e. we have not hitherto recorded from a cell that plots below the stippled line in the colour index diagram (Fig. 2A).

All cells examined in this way in visual area V3 were of the NC type, as the cell marked V3 in Fig. 2A. The majority of cells in V2 were of the same type; however, in V2 a few cells were colour-biased or colour-opponent, with properties similar to those found in V4.

For most cells in the prestriate cortex the response varied with stimulus intensity in the way shown in Fig. 1D. At some suprathreshold intensity the response saturated and often the response became weaker with further increase in the intensity. The effect of stimulus intensity has implications for the investigation of wavelength specificity. A few cells in V4 that were systematically

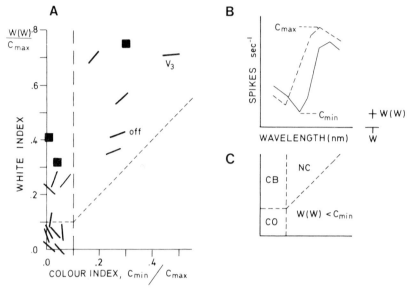

FIG. 2   Colour coding and orientation selectivity for 17 cells in the lateral part of the anterior bank of the lunate sulcus.

(A) A white index and a colour index are calculated from spectral responses such as those in Fig. 1 (see B). An orientationally selective cell is indicated by a slit showing the orientation in the receptive field that gave best response. A square shows that the cell was non-oriented. The cell marked "off" gave only off-responses. All other cells gave on-responses. V3 is a cell from visual area V3.

(B) W(W) is the response to a white flash on a white background. C_{max} is the largest response and C_{min} is the smallest response to a monochromatic flash obtained on a monochromatic or on a white background. White index is $W(W)/C_{max}$ and colour index is C_{min}/C_{max}.

(C) A classification of the cells as colour-opponent (CO), colour-biased (CB) and not colour-coded (NC) is suggested.

investigated in this respect gave a nearly flat spectral response at suprathreshold luminances; whereas when flash and background had nearly the same luminance the response was zero except for a high peak at one or a small number of wavelengths.

Most cells in prestriate cortex required a long narrow slit to give best response. The response could disappear when the width of the slit was doubled. Usually, the slit had to be precisely oriented, as half response was at ± 10° from the optimum orientation. Figure 2A shows that most cells in V4 were orientationally selective (the bars in the figure indicate the orientation in the receptive fields that gave best response). Only two CB cells and one NC cell gave best responses to a square. Receptive fields were within a 7° semicircle in the lower left quadrant of the visual field and their sizes were limited, though larger in V3 and V4 (3–5°) than in V2 (1–2°).

It may be argued that all cells in the visual pathway that respond to light stimuli of photopic luminances probably get inputs from different cone mechanisms. Indeed it may be so, since the cells we classified as not colour-coded gave different spectral responses on different chromatic backgrounds. Therefore their colour index in Fig. 2 was in the range 0.2 to 0.5. It is, however, a fact that when examined for colour properties with the same method most cells in V4 and some cells in V2 are orders of magnitude more sensitive to colour than the cells in V3. Therefore we conclude that in most aspects our observations on colour processing in prestriate cortex are in good agreement with those described by Zeki.

Acknowledgement

This work was supported by the Danish Medical Research Council.

References

Bertulis, A., Guld, C. and Lennox-Buchthal, M. (1977). Spectral and orientation specificity of single cells in foveal striate cortex of the vervet monkey, *Cercopithecus aethiops. J. Physiol., Lond.* **268**, 1–20.

Fischer, B., Boch, R. and Bach, M. (1981). Stimulus versus eye movements: Comparison of neural activity in the striate and prelunate visual cortex (A17 and A19) of trained rhesus monkey. *Exp. Brain Res.* **43**, 69–77.

Krüger, J. and Gouras, P. (1980). Spectral selectivity of cells and its dependence on slit length in monkey visual cortex. *J. Neurophysiol.* **43**, 1055–1069.

Michael, C. R. (1981). Columnar organization of color cells in monkey's striate cortex. *J. Neurophysiol.* **46**, 587–604.

Schein, S. J., Marrocco, R. T. and de Monasterio, F. M. (1980). Spectral properties of cells in the prestriate cortex of monkey. *Soc. Neurosci. Abstr.* **6**, 580.

Zeki, S. M. (1978). Uniformity and diversity of structure and function in rhesus monkey prestriate visual cortex. *J. Physiol., Lond.* **277**, 273–290.

Zeki, S. M. (1980). The representation of colours in the cerebral cortex. *Nature* **284**, 412–418.

Initial Analysis of Opponent-Colour Interactions Revealed in Sharpened Field Spectral Sensitivities

DAVID H. FOSTER and ROSEMARY S. SNELGAR

Field spectral sensitivities of the long- and medium-wavelength sensitive colour mechanisms of the human eye, when derived in the presence of a small, mono-chromatic (or white) auxiliary conditioning field, spatially coincident with the test field, are found (Foster, 1979, 1981) to be narrower and sharper than the corresponding Stiles Π mechanisms (Stiles, 1978). The peak of the long-wavelength sensitive mechanism shifts from about 570 nm to about 610 nm, and the peak of the medium-wavelength sensitive mechanism shifts from about 540 nm to about 530 nm. A shoulder or subsidiary lobe is also present on the short-wavelength side of the field spectral sensitivity (FSS) curve of the long-wavelength sensitive mechanism and a complementary though smaller shoulder is present on the long-wavelength side of the medium-wavelength sensitive mechanism. The short-wavelength sensitive mechanism shows no sharpening of its FSS curve with introduction of the coincident auxiliary field (at least for medium-to-high intensities of the field) (Foster, 1981). Evidence has been offered elsewhere that spectral sharpening of the long- and medium-wavelength sensitive mechanisms is the result of a shift from detection mediated by the non-opponent system to detection mediated by the opponent-colour system (Foster, 1981). It was hypothesized that the auxiliary field produces high spatial-frequency masking at the boundaries of the test and auxiliary fields; the spatial transient that would normally be responded to by the non-opponent system is suppressed.

COLOUR VISION
ISBN 0 12 000000 0

A fundamental question relating to the notion that opponent-colour inter-actions underlie spectral sharpening is this: can sharpened FSSs be represented as a simple difference of sensitivities of long- and medium-wavelength sensitive receptor mechanisms? To answer this question, we obtained data on spectral sharpening of FSSs of long- and medium-wavelength sensitive mechanisms over a range of intensities of a (monochromatic) auxiliary conditioning field, spatially coincident with the test field. To provide a set of fundamental mechanism sensitivities, we obtained (for the same subjects) unsharpened FSSs for the long-, medium-, and short-wavelength sensitive mechanisms, Stiles's mechanisms Π_5, Π_4, and Π_3 (or Π_1). A computer-based interactive modelling technique was then used to explore possible combinations of variously transformed sensitivities of long-, medium-, and short-wavelength sensitive fundamental mechanisms.

Methods

Measurements were made using apparatus and methods described by Foster (1981), where details are given in full.

Field Spectral Sensitivity Measurements

The test flash was monochromatic, disc-shaped, dia. 1.05° and of duration 200 msec. It was presented on a concentric disc-shaped, variable-intensity, monochromatic, main conditioning field, dia. 10.0°. The monochromatic auxiliary conditioning field, when present, was also disc-shaped and spatially coincident with the test field. A 3° square fixation array of four tiny lights was used to assist central fixation. Field spectral sensitivities were obtained by a direct field-adjustment method (Foster, 1981). The test flash of wavelength appropriate to the mechanism of interest was set 0.3 log units above increment (or absolute) threshold; the 10.0° main conditioning field was introduced, and its intensity adjusted by the subject to return the test flash to threshold. The efficiency and accuracy of this technique have been discussed elsewhere (Foster, 1981). Test-flash wavelengths were set at 664, 516, and 421 nm for the long-, medium-, and short-wavelength sensitive mechanisms respectively. For measurements of unsharpened FSSs, the coincident auxiliary field was removed. For the short-wavelength sensitive mechanism, however, a 10.0° 576-nm auxiliary field, intensity 9.31 log quanta sec^{-1} deg^{-2}, was introduced to improve isolation of the mechanism (Stiles, 1978). To control for macular-pigment absorption on measured spectral sensitivities, the unsharpened FSS of the medium-wavelength sensitive mechanism was redetermined at 8° eccentricity. For measurements of sharpened FSSs, the coincident auxiliary field was set at 531 and 619 nm for the long- and medium-wavelength sensitive mechanisms respectively. Intensities of the auxiliary field were varied from 7.5 to 9.5 log quanta sec^{-1} deg^{-2}.

Data presented here were obtained for subject JT, who was male, aged 20 years, had normal colour vision, and was unaware of the purpose of the experiment. Similar data were obtained from two other subjects.

Analysis

Data on FSSs were analysed by means of a computer-based generalized linear interactive modelling technique GLIM (Baker and Nelder, 1978), with normal error and identity link. For completeness, a contribution from the short-wavelength sensitive fundamental mechanism was also included. Modelling was performed at two levels: immediately before and immediately after $\log_{10}$ compression of mechanism (quantum) sensitivity (compare Sperling and Harwerth, 1971; Ingling and Tsou, 1977; King-Smith and Kranda, 1981). The family of models thus under consideration at each level was as follows:

$$L'_I(\lambda) = a_{I, L', L}L(\lambda) + a_{I, L', M}M(\lambda) + a_{I, L', S}S(\lambda)$$
$$M'_I(\lambda) = a_{I, M', L}L(\lambda) + a_{I, M', M}M(\lambda) + a_{I, M', S}S(\lambda)$$

(1)

where:

L, M, and S are the FSSs of the fundamental long-, medium-, and short-wavelength sensitive mechanisms,
L'_I and M'_I are the sharpened forms of L and M at auxiliary-field intensity I,
λ is main-field wavelength,
$a_{I, j, k}$ are the coefficients weighting the L, M, and S terms.

Note that for each auxiliary-field intensity I and sharpened FSS the number of freely adjustable parameters was at most three. (A single additive constant relating absolute vertical positions of experimental and theoretical FSSs was subsumed.)

Smoothed versions of the fundamental functions L and M were used in Equations (1). This was not critical to the analysis and the smoothed and unsmoothed versions of the two fundamental functions did not differ by more than 0.027 log units RMSE over the affected portion of the wavelength range.

For each sharpened FSS L'_I and M'_I and auxiliary-field intensity I, maximum-likelihood estimators for the coefficients $a_{I, j, k}$ were computed by GLIM under various constraints, which included setting some coefficients to unity or zero.

Goodness of fit was evaluated generally by the unit-independent quantity $(w^2)'$, the proportion of variance *not* accounted for by the model (i.e., the ratio of variance about the predicted values to variance about the grand mean). For log-transformed spectral sensitivities, goodness of fit was also evaluated by RMSE, in log units.

Results

In Fig. 1, unsharpened field spectral sensitivities for the long-, medium-, and short-wavelength sensitive mechanisms are shown by points indicated by open squares, circles, and diamonds, respectively. For ease of comparison, data for the short-wavelength sensitive mechanism have been displaced upwards by 1.0 log unit, and those for the medium-wavelength sensitive mechanism downwards by 0.2 log unit. The smooth curves joining the experimental points are cubic splines, and have no theoretical significance here.

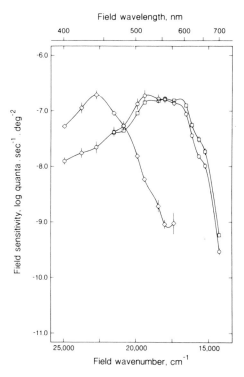

FIG. 1   Field spectral sensitivities of long-, medium-, and short-wavelength sensitive mechanisms (points indicated by open squares, circles, and diamonds respectively) determined without an auxiliary field coincident with the test field. The reciprocal of the intensity of a 10.0° main conditioning field necessary to raise test-flash threshold by 0.3 log units is plotted against the wavenumber of the main field. Data for the short-wavelength sensitive mechanism have been displaced upwards by 1.0 log unit and those for the medium-wavelength sensitive mechanism downwards by 0.2 log unit. For test-flash wavelengths, see text. Each point is the mean of either six or 12 readings and the vertical bars show ± 1 SEM where this is sufficiently large. Subject JT. (Smoothed versions of these data were used as fundamentals to generate the computer-fitted sharpened field spectral sensitivities shown in Figs 2a and b.)

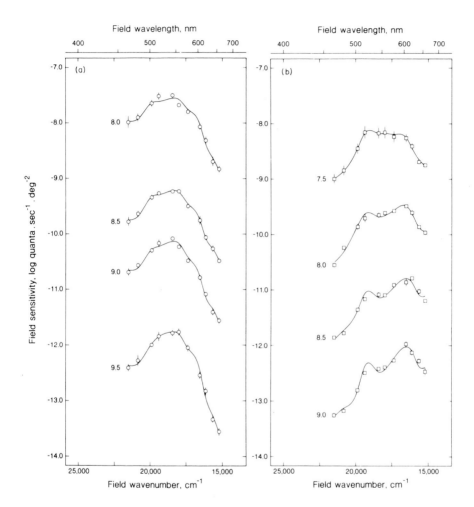

FIG. 2 (a) Field spectral sensitivities of the medium-wavelength sensitive mechanism determined with an auxiliary conditioning field, wavelength 619 nm, coincident with the test field. The reciprocal of the intensity of a 10.0° main conditioning field necessary to raise test-flash increment threshold by 0.3 log unit is plotted against main-field wavenumber. The intensity, in log quanta sec^{-1} deg^{-2}, of the coincident auxiliary field is shown against each set of data. The top set of data is in the correct position. Each successive set has been displaced downwards by 1.0-log-unit increments. Each point is the mean of either six or 12 readings and the vertical bars indicate ± 1 SEM where this is sufficiently large. Subject JT. The smooth curves result from the best-fitting model (see text).

(b) Field spectral sensitivities of the long-wavelength sensitive mechanism determined with an auxiliary conditioning field, wavelength 531 nm, coincident with the test field. Other details as for Fig. 2a.

The open symbols in Figs 2a and 2b show FSSs for (2a) the medium-wavelength sensitive mechanism and (2b) the long-wavelength sensitive mechanism when obtained with an auxiliary field coincident with the test field. The intensity of the auxiliary field, in log quanta $\sec^{-1} \deg^{-2}$, is indicated against each set of data. The top FSS in each figure is in the correct position; for clarity successive FSSs have been displaced downwards by 1.0-log-unit increments. The smooth curves in each figure result from the best-fitting model (see below).

Table 1 summarizes the results of the modelling. The quantity tabulated is $(w^2)'$, the proportion (per cent) of variance not accounted for by each model in fitting the sharpened FSSs of the long- and medium-wavelength

TABLE 1   Fits to the sharpened FSS data of Figs 2a and b (open symbols) of the two best-fitting models at pre-and post-log compression levels. "$L + M$" denotes the model $a_{l,j,L}L + a_{l,j,M}M$, and "$L + M + S$" the model $a_{l,j,L}L + a_{l,j,M}M + a_{l,j,S}S, j = L', M'$, see Equations (1). The proportion (per cent) of variance not accounted for $(w^2)'$ is shown for each of the models, levels, and auxiliary-field intensities. Significant reductions in $(w^2)'$ resulting from inclusion of short-wavelength component S are indicated by * ($P < 0.001$).

		Sharpened FSS, medium-wavelength sensitive mechanism				Sharpened FSS, long-wavelength sensitive mechanism			
		Auxiliary-field intensity (log quanta $\sec^{-1}$ $\deg^{-2}$)				Auxiliary-field intensity (log quanta $\sec^{-1}$ $\deg^{-2}$)			
		8.0	8.5	9.0	9.5	7.5	8.0	8.5	9.0
pre-log level	"$L + M$"	7.5	2.8	5.5	3.3	2.9	5.2	11.0	10.4
	"$L + M + S$"	6.9	1.5	4.3	1.7	0.8*	5.2	10.2	9.7
post-log level	"$L + M$"	2.2	2.1	2.1	1.1	3.2	2.1	4.5	5.3
	"$L + M + S$"	1.8	0.3*	1.0	0.9	0.6*	1.8	3.4	2.4

sensitive mechanisms, at four different intensities of the auxiliary fields. Data are given for the two possible interaction levels (before and after log compression of mechanism sensitivity), and for the two most successful combinations of FSSs in each case (weighted combinations of FSSs of long- and medium-wavelength sensitive fundamental mechanisms, and of long-, medium-, and short-wavelength sensitive fundamental mechanisms).

Two points are evident. First, independent of the number of FSSs involved in the linear combinations, the fits at the post-log-compression level are uniformly better than at the pre-log-compression level. The total proportion of variance unaccounted for at the post-log level is $0.30-0.44$ times smaller than at the pre-log level. In the case of the combination of three signals, this reduction in variance unaccounted for is significant ($t_{14} = 2.56$, $P < 0.05$). Second, although there is the expected reduction in $(w^2)'$ with introduction of the short-wavelength sensitive mechanism (a consequence of an increase in the number of free coefficients in the model), the improvement in fit reaches significance only occasionally.

Table 2 lists for the sharpened FSSs of the long- and medium-wavelength sensitive mechanisms at the four auxiliary-field intensities the coefficients for

TABLE 2   Weighting coefficients (SEMs in parentheses) for the three-component log-transform model and RMSEs of each fit (without adjustment for individual degrees of freedom) to the experimental data of Figs 2a and b.

		Auxiliary-field intensity (log quanta sec^{-1} deg^{-2})			
		8.0	8.5	9.0	9.5
Sharpened FSS, medium-wavelength sensitive mechanism	$a_{l,M',L}$	−1.44(0.75)	−2.10(0.24)	−2.56(0.59)	−2.24(0.68)
	$a_{l,M',M}$	2.07(0.55)	2.51(0.17)	3.00(0.44)	3.05(0.52)
	$a_{l,M',S}$	−0.21(0.06)	−0.52(0.10)	−0.48(0.11)	−0.25(0.12)
RMSE (log units)		0.057	0.024	0.048	0.055

		Auxiliary-field intensity (log quanta sec^{-1} deg^{-2})			
		7.5	8.0	8.5	9.0
Sharpened FSS, long-wavelength sensitive mechanism	$a_{l,L',L}$	0.60(0.30)	2.33(0.42)	3.05(0.78)	3.92(0.79)
	$a_{l,L',M}$	0.04(0.22)	−1.47(0.31)	−2.21(0.57)	−2.88(0.58)
	$a_{l,L',S}$	−0.29(0.02)	−0.14(0.15)	0.09(0.11)	0.35(0.10)
RMSE (log units)		0.023	0.041	0.061	0.061

the best-fitting model (three FSSs combined at the post-log-compression level). The quantities tabulated are the coefficients $a_{l,j,k}$ of Equations (1), along with their SEMs, and the RMSE, in log units, for each fit. There is a systematic increase in magnitude of the L and M coefficients with increase in auxiliary-field intensity I.

The smooth curves in Figs 2a and b respectively show, after spline interpolation, the results of the best-fitting model in relation to the sharpened FSSs of the medium- and long-wavelength sensitive mechanisms. Notice the systematic increase in magnitude of the lobe on the short-wavelength side of the long-wavelength sensitive mechanism as auxiliary-field intensity increases.

Adequacy of the Model

How good is the fit of the three-component log-transform model specified in Table 2 to the experimental data? The total RMSE for the sharpened FSSs of the long- and medium-wavelength sensitive mechanisms over all auxiliary-field intensities is 0.048 log units; this rises to 0.067 log units when the number of degrees of freedom is taken into account. The latter RMSE may be compared with the experimentally measured SEM associated with individual data points of 0.060 log units. The difference is not significant ($F_{46,110} = 1.26$, $P > 0.1$).

Discussion

The principal outcome of this analysis is that a simple weighted difference of sensitivities of long- and medium-wavelength sensitive fundamental mechanisms describes well the sharpened field spectral sensitivities of the long- and medium-wavelength sensitive mechanisms obtained when an auxiliary field is made coincident with the test field. For all the models specified in Table 1, the proportion of variance accounted for (the complement of $(w^2)'$) fell within the range 94.4–98.6 per cent. The fit was significantly better when carried out at the post-log-compression level than at the pre-log-compression level. The introduction of the short-wavelength sensitive mechanism led to a small, but not significant overall ($\chi^2_{64} \leq 12.6$, $P > 0.5$), improvement in fit.

An important qualitative attribute of the computed spectral sensitivities, mentioned earlier and illustrated in Figs 2a and b, is that there is an obvious lobe on the short-wavelength side of the sharpened FSSs for the long-wavelength sensitive mechanism, and a rather smaller effect for the medium-wavelength sensitive mechanism. This property of experimentally determined sharpened FSSs has been confirmed elsewhere (Foster and Snelgar, in prep).

The fact that model fitting was best at the post-log-compression level may have relevance to the observation that the SEMs associated with observed mean field sensitivities are essentially constant when measured in log quanta sec^{-1} deg^{-2}.

Two caveats should be expressed concerning the representation here of sharpened FSSs of long- and medium-wavelength sensitive mechanisms as a simple weighted difference of fundamental spectral sensitivities evaluated after logarithmic compression. First, the operational FSSs of Fig. 2 are unlikely to represent solely the sensitivities of individual opponent-colour channels. For the adapting field probably acts to reduce sensitivity both at the receptors and at a later opponent site, and the relative strengths of these effects will vary with the wavelength of the main field. No attempt has been made in this initial analysis to disconfound these effects. Second, the compression of sensitivity by log transformation may be operationally indistinguishable from compression by some other plausible power-law functions.

Acknowledgements

RSS was supported by an award from the Medical Research Council.

References

Baker, R. J. and Nelder, J. A. (1978). *The GLIM System*. Algorithms Group, Oxford.

Foster, D. H. (1979). Effect of a small blue adapting field on the spectral sensitivity of the red-sensitive colour mechanism of the human eye. *Optica Acta* **26**, 293–296.

Foster, D. H. (1981). Changes in field spectral sensitivities of red-, green- and blue-sensitive colour mechanisms obtained on small background fields. *Vision Res.* **21**, 1433–1455.

Ingling, C. R., Jr and Tsou, B. H.-P. (1977). Orthogonal combinations of the three visual channels. *Vision Res.* **17**, 1075–1082.

King-Smith, P. E. and Kranda, K. (1981). Photopic adaptation in the red–green spectral range. *Vision Res.* **21**, 565–572.

Sperling, H. G. and Harwerth, R. S. (1971). Red–green cone interactions in the increment-threshold spectral sensitivity of primates. *Science* **172**, 180–184.

Stiles, W. S. (1978). *Mechanisms of Colour Vision*. London, Academic Press.

Adaptive Mechanisms Controlling Sensitivity to Red − Green Chromatic Flashes

C. F. STROMEYER III, R. E. KRONAUER and G. R. COLE

Introduction

In Stiles' (1939) classical study on the two-color increment threshold, a mono-chromatic test flash is detected on a uniform chromatic adapting field. Stiles (1978) isolated various chromatic π-mechanisms which were thought to adapt independently. The threshold of each mechanism was presumably raised as more light was added to the adapting field. However, recent observations have shown that when a flash is detected against a field of similar color, the threshold may actually be lowered by the addition of an adapting field of rather different color. This increased sensitivity due to the second, added field we shall call *chromatic facilitation*. The present experiments examine the adaptive mechanisms that are responsible for chromatic facilitation for stimuli detected with the middle (M) and long wave (L) cones. First, however, we shall consider chromatic facilitation for the short wave (S) cone pathway where separable adaptive mechanisms have been clearly demonstrated.

With suitable stimulus conditions, a violet test flash is detected with the S cones (Stiles, 1953). Pugh and Mollon (1979) propose that adaptation of the S cone pathway occurs at two serial sites. The first site of adaptation is the S cones; increasing the field intensity reduces sensitivity by direct stimulation of these cones. Signals from the S cones then pass through a second or opponent site, whose sensitivity is maximal when the spectral composition of the adapting field is "neutral" and thus produces a balance between the

COLOUR VISION
ISBN 0 12 000000 0

adapting signals from the S cones and the M and L cones. The role of the second site can be dramatically demonstrated by first elevating the threshold of the violet test flash with a short wave field that is intense enough to produce response saturation. Adding steady (Mollon and Polden, 1977a) or flashed yellow light (Stromeyer, Kronauer and Madsen, 1979) to the entire adapting field can relieve this saturation and considerably lower the threshold. The yellow light acts through the M and L cones and reduces the polarization of the second site. The spectral sensitivity of the S cones is so different from the M and L cones that one can independently manipulate the two adaptational sites. The chromatic facilitation produced by the yellow field is due to the second site, since the yellow light has a negligible direct effect on the S cones.

Chromatic facilitation has also been demonstrated with light of long wavelength (*ca.* > 540 nm) that strongly stimulates only the M and L cones. Adding green light to an intense red adapting field may lower the threshold for a red test stimulus that contains considerable energy at low spatial and temporal frequencies (Sternheim, Stromeyer and Spillmann, 1978; Sternheim, Stromeyer and Khoo, 1979; Wandell and Pugh, 1980; Stromeyer and Sternheim, 1981). Since the spectral sensitivity of the M and L cones overlap considerably, the green and red fields adapt both classes of cones and change the sensitivity of any opponent sites, if they exist. The method presented below shows how the two adapting sites may be segregated.

Figure 1a schematically shows the quantal catches of the M and L cones for various adapting fields and test stimuli. For the purposes of illustration, both cone types have the same peak absorbance. The lower dashed line shows that deep-red light produces many more quantal catches in L cones than M cones, while the upper dashed line shows that green light has a strong effect on both cone classes. The adapting field is represented by a point between these lines, and the test flash is a vector originating from this point. Incremental flashes ranging from green to deep-red form a fan of vectors whose extremes lie parallel to the dashed lines. A test vector of any angle can be obtained with a composite consisting of simultaneous, incremental and decremental red and green flashes. For example, vector 2 produces an increment only in the L cones, for the positive red and negative green flash components produce no net stimulation of the M cones, while vector 1 produces an increment only in the M cones.

Presumably much of the adaptation to a steady field occurs within the cones, as shown by recordings from turtle cones which adapt following Weber's law (Normann and Perlman, 1979). Figure 1b takes this adaptation into account, for the axes are the Weber fractions $\Delta M/M$ and $\Delta L/L$.

Vector 3 represents a simple luminance increment − a reddish flash on an *intense* reddish field of the same chromaticity. Figure 1a indicates that the flash produces considerably more quantal catches in the L cones. However, in the normalized coordinates the flash is represented by a + 45° vector and has equal

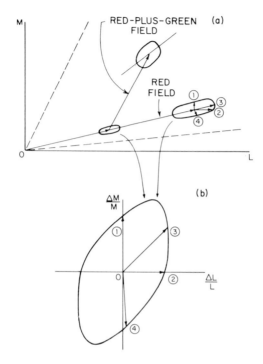

FIG. 1   (a) The quantal catches in the M and L cones produced by a test flash on an adapting field. The upper and lower dashed lines represent the effect of a green and deep-red field, respectively. A given adapting field is represented by a vector extending from the origin; two intensities of a red field are shown, as well as a red-plus-green mixed field. The contour at the end of each field vector represents thresholds for different combinations of simultaneous positive and negative red and green flashes. The two contours for the red field collapse into the same contour (b) when the test increments are normalized by the effect of the field. The numbered test vectors are described in the text.

effects on the M and L cones. In Stiles' (1959) model such a flash equally stimulates the π_4 and π_5 mechanisms. Since the flash has the same chromaticity as the field, it may be quite ineffective in stimulating mechanisms that are sensitive to chromatic changes. Adding green light to the red field may increase the visibility of the red test flash, since the green added field rotates the normalized $+45°$ vector toward the horizontal, and the flash can better stimulate a chromatic detection mechanism (Stromeyer and Sternheim, 1981). The observer's task changes from that of detecting a red flash on a red field to detecting a red flash on a yellowish field. The reason the vector rotates is that the red field alone adapts the L cones much more than the M cones and when the green field is added it will have a much stronger adapting effect on the less adapted M cones. The rotation of the vector is due solely to the first site (i.e. cone) adaptation. Thus chromatic facilitation measured with the red flash might be caused by first site adaptation.

To determine whether second site adaptation also influences sensitivity, we can examine the behavior of the vertical and horizontal vectors, which represent unique stimulation of the M and L cones, respectively. These vectors do not rotate when the green addend is superimposed on the red field. By plotting thresholds in normalized coordinates, we take into account the adaptive effect of the green field on the cones per se. We measured a wide range of test vectors on a red field and a red-plus-green mixed field. A shortening of the horizontal and vertical vectors due to the green addend field provides evidence for second site adaptation. The Smith and Pokorny fundamentals (1975; tabulated in Boynton, 1979), converted to a quantal basis, were used to represent the results.

Methods

Stimuli

Figure 2 shows a profile of the stimulus, which consists of a central 1.2° diameter test area surrounded by identical, contiguous annuli of 7.2° diameter. The components were superimposed on intense uniform red and green adapting fields. The field appeared uniform. Positive and negative flashes were produced by modulating the light in the central test area above or below the level of the annuli. All green and red components were 541 or 638 nm with a full bandwidth at 50% of $\simeq 8-10$ nm. Fixation was guided by a 3° diamond array of four tiny black points or by two black points horizontally separated by 3° and centered on the test flash.

The test flash had either sharp edges in space and time (1.2° dia and 200 msec) or very diffuse edges (the 1.2° flash was defocussed by 10 diopters and turned on and off with a 1-sec Gaussian envelope, SD = 250 msec, discretized into 17 steps of 59 msec). Defocussing increased the visual size of the flash, viewed alone, to about 2.2° but did not reduce the peak intensity.

The figures and figure legends list the metamer of the adapting field, calculated from the color matching functions of the 1931 CIE Standard Observer as modified by Judd (Wyszecki and Stiles, 1967). The Smith and Pokorny fundamentals are a linear transformation of these functions.

Apparatus

A 6-channel Maxwellian view was used. The main fields were derived from a xenon arc, while the green test and annulus and red test and annulus were derived from diffuse light emitting diodes, LEDs (Stanley ESBG5531 and

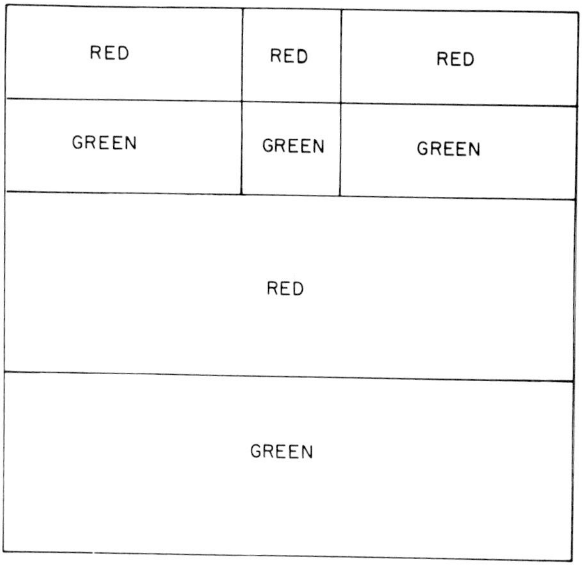

FIG. 2   Spatial profile of stimuli for sharp flashes. The central 1.2°-diameter area is surrounded by identical 7.2° annuli, and these components are superposed on uniform adapting fields. Negative test flashes are produced by electronically reducing the light in the central test area below the level of the annulus. Spectral components are 541 and 638 nm.

General Instrument MV5753). Pairs of matched interference filters were used with the latter stimuli. Light for the main adapting fields passed through a grating monochromator or interference filters. The test and annuli were formed with a photometric cube — a beam splitter cube whose face was aluminized except for a central elliptical hole, the test area, that appeared circular to the observer.

The Maxwellian lens focussed the beams on a 2.3 mm artificial pupil and achromatizing lens, and a pair of matched relay lens formed an image of the artificial pupil in the observer's pupil (Buss *et al.*, 1982). The observer bit on a bite bar held in an x-y-z translator. To produce the diffuse test flash, the final lens was moved inward so that the test was defocussed 10 diopters beyond optical infinity; the observer thus could not bring the test area into better focus. The fixation marks and outer edge of the field were in sharp focus.

The test LEDs were modulated with a current amplifier driven by a 12 bit D-A computer output. A computer look-up table was constructed so that the light was a linear function of the modulating signal. The test LEDs were always operated at a constant mean voltage. To construct the tables, each test LED, with interference filter in place, was flashed at 256 levels around the mean, covering the range. Each flash lasted 205 msec, and 64 readings were averaged during the last 5 msec with a radiometer and analog input to the computer. The linearity was checked periodically by measuring the symmetry of positive versus negative flashes.

For each session, the annuli and adapting fields were calibrated radiometrically (Stromeyer *et al.*, 1979), and the test area was visually matched to its corresponding annulus by adjusting a neutral density wedge in the test channel.

Procedure

The observers have normal color discrimination as tested with the Farnsworth-Munsell 100-Hue-Test. C.F.S. was the author and H.C. was naive.

A run was preceded by 3 min adaptation to the field, followed by presentation of a constant ratio of simultaneous, red and green positive and negative flashes. The length of the test vector was measured with a two temporal-alternative forced-choice staircase which estimates the 71% correct point on the psychometric function (Wetherill, 1963). The intensity changed in 0.10 log unit steps. The staircase was lowered a step when the observer was correct twice and was raised a step when he was incorrect. The last 8 or 12 staircase reversals were averaged. Each threshold estimate is based on 4–8 runs. For each figure, the conditions were approximately randomized.

Results

Increased Chromatic Facilitation with Diffuse Test Flashes

Wandell and Pugh (1980) have made the most extensive measurements of chromatic facilitation using a 667 nm foveal test flash of 1° and 200 msec and a forced-choice staircase. We repeated their experiment with the *same* stimuli and a signal detection method (Stromeyer *et al.*, 1977). Stimuli were produced with light from the xenon arc. The adapting field was 650 nm and 10.9 log quanta deg^{-2} sec^{-1} (5800 trolands) used alone or with a green addend field of 540 nm and 9.5 log quanta deg^{-2} sec^{-1} (2400 trolands). The two field conditions are designated R and R + G in Table 1, which list the thresholds. The third column shows the threshold difference, Δ, for the two field conditions. The threshold is only about 0.1 log unit lower on the mixed field. We choose a value of $d' = 1.0$ as threshold; Δ was only trivially different if derived from other d'-values. Wandell and Pugh (1980) obtained a much larger Δ of 0.6 log units for observer B.W. with the same conditions; their second observer showed a reduced effect of 0.3 log units, using somewhat weaker fields. Using similar conditions, Wandell, Welsh and Maloney (1982b) measured an effect of 0.1–0.4 log units with various observers, although two observers

TABLE 1   Threshold in log quanta deg^{-2} sec^{-1} for 667 nm flash

| *Sharp Flash* | | | |
Observer	Field: R	R + G	Δ
C.F.S.	9.37	9.26	0.11
H.C.	9.45	9.36	0.09
G.C.	9.45	9.40	0.05
Diffuse Flash			
Observer	Field: R	R + G	Δ
C.F.S.	9.96	9.50	0.46
H.C.	9.92	9.58	0.34

showed no effect. Thus the effect may be rather small, in agreement with our results.

To obtain a larger Δ, the test flash was defocussed by 10 diopters and turned gradually on and off with a raised cosine envelope of 1.0 and 2.2 sec duration for observers H.C. and C.F.S., respectively. The bottom half of Table 1 shows that this change raised the threshold much more for the R than the R + G field condition, thus considerably increasing Δ. The diffuse test flash is relatively harder to detect on a field of similar color. Thus, making the flash diffuse appears to selectively elevate the luminance threshold. The following experiments with composite flashes confirm this result.

Diffuse Composite Red and Green Flashes

Thresholds for diffuse composite flashes were measured on a red field and a red-plus-green field. The test was a 1.2° spot, defocussed by 10 diopters (visual size *ca.* 2.2°) and presented with a 1 sec Gaussian envelope (SD = 250 msec). Red and green stimulus components were 638 and 541 nm.

Results for the mixed field are shown in Fig. 3 for C.F.S. The troland values of the red and green field components were 3402 and 1066 (10.41 and 9.13 log quanta deg^{-2} sec^{-1}) and were chosen on the basis of the results of Wandell and Pugh (1980) which showed that a similar green addend field increased the visibility of a red flash on a similar red field. The adapting field was metameric with 610 nm (Methods). Each ray represents a fixed ratio of positive and negative red and green flashes. The filled circles on the rays are thresholds from separate staircase runs, and crosses are the means of the runs. These plotted values correspond to the peak of the spatially and temporally varying flash. The rightward pointing horizontal ray represents an incremental flash that stimulates only L cones; the downward pointing vertical ray represents a

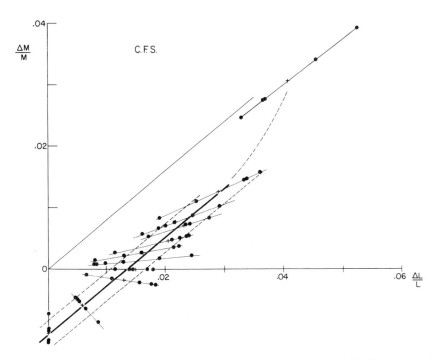

FIG. 3   Thresholds for the diffuse flash on a red-plus-green field. The red and green field components were 3402 and 1066 trolands. The field was metameric with 610 nm. The test flash was a 1.2°-diameter spot defocussed by 10 diopters (visual size *ca.* 2.2°) and turned on and off with a Gaussian waveform (SD = 250 msec). Each ray represents a fixed ratio of red and green flashes. The filled circles on the rays represent separate staircase runs, while the crosses represent the mean of these runs. The axes specify the peak quantal catch change that the flash produces in the M and L cones, normalized by the quantal catches due to the field. The heavy solid line fitted to the crosses shows that detection is proportional to a linear difference of M and L cone signals produced by the test flash. The parallel dashed lines specify the interquartile range.

decrement that stimulates only M cones. The straight portion of the solid line fitted to the crosses suggests that there is a single detection mechanism that linearly combines $\Delta M/M$ and $\Delta L/L$. Since the slope of the line is 0.80, the detection parameter is proportional to $0.8\Delta L/L - \Delta M/M$. The chromatic detection mechanism thus responds to the difference of the M and L cone signals elicited by the test flash. Test flashes along the solid line appeared reddish when slightly suprathreshold. The upper right cross shows that a second, luminance detection mechanism appears to intrude for tests of $(\Delta M/M)/(\Delta L/L) \cong 0.8$. Certain flashes could not be used owing to insufficient light (e.g. flashes along the + 45° diagonal).

The inner contour in the left panel of Fig. 4 shows the same results (Fig. 3), while the outer contour shows thresholds measured on the red field alone (green adapting light of 66 td was also present to achieve negative green flashes). Most of the points for the red field are fitted with a slightly curved line. The straight portion of the line has a slope of 0.97. Flashes along this straight part of the curve appeared reddish near or slightly above threshold; the flashes often appeared redder than the adapting field. The line bends continuously in the region where the luminance mechanism intervenes. The threshold for such a flash is represented by the upper right cross designated R. As weak negative green flashes of increasing strength are added to the positive red flash, the ray rotates toward the horizontal, where the flash stimulates *only* L cones. The threshold drops considerably with this rotation. The simple incremental red flash stimulates both the M and L cones with an increment, and this flash is particularly ineffective for the more sensitive chromatic mechanism.

The results in the left panel show that the thresholds are lower on the mixed field. However, for vectors with slopes of about + 15° to + 35°, the thresholds are quite similar for the two field conditions. For these vectors, detection is controlled largely by the difference of the M and L cone signals elicted by the test flash. The contours are highly elongated along the + 45° luminance axis, and thus a rotation of the vector away from this axis will strongly increase detection. A simple incremental red flash is designated by the letter R on both detection contours; the angle of the two vectors is + 42.4° and 23.5° respectively. The green field produces this vector rotation according to the Weber prediction for independent cone adaptation. Thus differential cone adaptation and the consequent rotation of the test vector strongly controls chromatic facilitation with the diffuse test flash.

The right panel of Fig. 4 shows similar results for observer H.C. The red and green field components were 3437 and 2088 trolands (88 trolands of green light was present for the red field condition). The green field component is about twice the value used for C.F.S. The mixed fields for H.C. and C.F.S. are metameric with 610 and 600 nm respectively.

Most of the data points for H.C. are fitted with straight lines, which presumably represent the threshold for a red chromatic mechanism. According to the Weber prediction, the green field differentially adapts the cones and rotates the + 45° vector on the red field to + 19° on the red-plus-green. A simple incremental red flash was *not* actually used; however, the position of the vectors for this flash for the two fields are designated by the letter R and squares (+ 41.6° and + 17.4°).

The threshold contour for the mixed field again lies inside the contour for the red field. For vectors in quadrant 4 (lower right), which represent flashes that produce M cone decrements, *part* of the shortening of the vectors on the mixed field may result from the M cone adaptation being less complete than the Weber prediction. For H.C., the red-plus-green field produces 3.8 times as

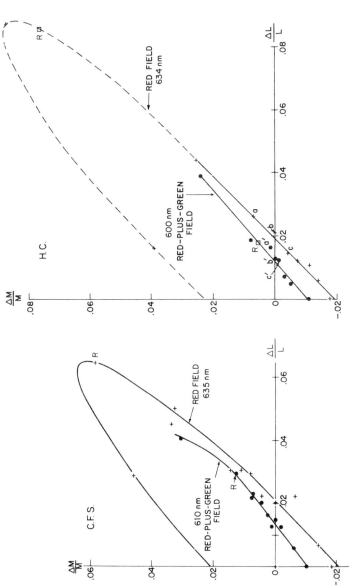

FIG. 4 Thresholds for the diffuse flash on a red field and a red-plus-green field. The red field component was 3402 and 3437 trolands for observers C.F.S. and H.C. respectively, while the green component was 1066 and 2088 respectively. (A weak green component was also present with the red field to produce negative green flashes.) The metamer of the adapting field is given in this and the remaining figures. Straight lines fit most of the data over a considerable range, suggesting that for both field conditions, a "red" chromatic mechanism is responsible for detection. The lettered vectors are discussed in the text. The letter R designates a simple incremental red flash.

many quantal catches in the M cones than does the red field condition, and Weber's law may not hold precisely over this range. This is consistent with the reduced slope for the mixed field condition (0.83 and 0.80 for H.C. and C.F.S.) versus the red field condition (1.00 and 0.97). However, for the L cones, the red-plus-green field used with H.C. produces only 1.36 times as many quantal catches as does the red field condition, and Weber's law may hold well over such a small range. Thus the shortening of the horizontal vector for the mixed field may be caused by second site adaptation.

To further assess second site adaptation, we can examine the absolute thresholds for vectors around the horizontal direction, where the L cones are uniquely stimulated. The vectors labelled a and a' in Fig. 4 represent *identical* physical test conditions: in the normalized coordinates a' is closer to the horizontal because the green addend field more strongly adapts the M cones. Vectors b and b' and c and c' also represent identical pairs. The absolute red light component of these pairs of vectors was not significantly different for the two field conditions, as determined by a t-test. However, in the normalized coordinates where the sensitivity of the L cones is reduced by the green addend field the $\Delta L/L$ component of the vector is significantly smaller for vectors a' and b' but not c'.

Sharp Composite Red and Green Flashes

Detection contours were also measured for sharp flashes (1.2°, 200 msec) on a red and a red-plus-green field. The red field component was 3086 and 3143 trolands for C.F.S. and H.C. respectively, while the green component was 1044 trolands. (A green component of 44 trolands was also present with the red field.) The red and mixed fields were metameric with 636 and 609 nm respectively.

The results are shown in Fig. 5. The curves were fitted by eye to symmetrized data representing the average of pairs of data points symmetrically disposed about the origin. The curves thus do not have a simple mathematical form. The fitted curves were then transposed onto Fig. 5. These symmetrized curves emphasize asymmetries in the data. For example, for C.F.S. thresholds on the mixed field are systematically smaller for red shifts, plotted below the +45° axis, than for green shifts plotted above the axis.

For the red field, heavy straight lines are each fitted to three data points. These lines are approximately vertical, indicating that a considerable change in the variable $\Delta M/M$ has rather little effect on threshold in this region. Thus, for example, adding a negative green flash to a positive red flash has rather little effect as the green flash is varied over a fair range. This suggests that a sharp incremental, or decremental, red flash on a red field is detected predominantly with L cone signals.

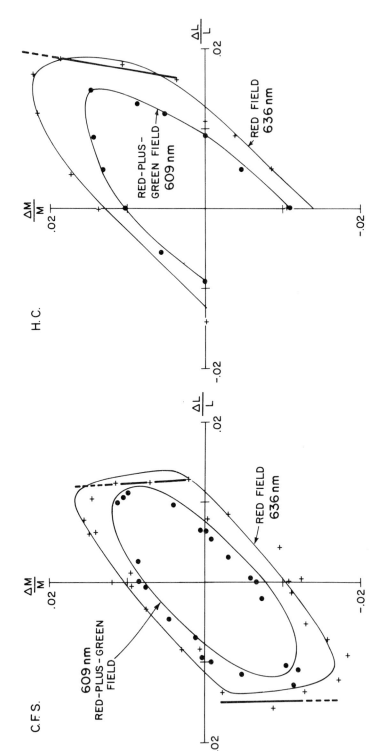

FIG. 5 Thresholds for the sharp test flash (1.2°, 200 msec) on a red field and a red-plus-green field. The red field component was 3086 and 3143 trolands for C.F.S. and H.C. respectively, while the green component was 1044 trolands. The curves were fitted to symmetrized data points as described in the text. The heavy straight lines are approximately vertical, indicating that for the red field considerable variation of the M cone test signal has little effect in this region.

Second Site Adaptation

The results for the sharp flashes in Fig. 5 again show that thresholds are lower on the mixed field, suggesting that second site adaptation affects sensitivity. Second site adaptation was examined further with sharp flashes near the horizontal axis, where the flash uniquely stimulates the L cones. Three field conditions were employed: a red field R, a mixed red-plus-green field R + G, and a yellow field Y. The fields are metameric with 636, 599, and 581.6 nm. The troland values of the fields are described in the legend of Fig. 6. The yellow field is approximately neutral for the red−green system. The Y and the R fields produce equal quantal catches in the L cones and thus the two fields equally adapt the L cones.

Figure 6 shows thresholds obtained with the three fields. Vectors with the same letter represent physically identical test conditions, where only the adapting field has been changed. The curves fitted to the right-most data in each panel have the same shape as the curves fitted to the red field results in Fig. 5. However, the thresholds for the red field conditions are somewhat higher in Fig. 6, especially for C.F.S. (several months separated the measurements). The vectors for H.C. in Fig. 6 become significantly shorter as the field is made more yellow. The same holds for C.F.S., although there is not a significant difference between vectors b' and b''. The large difference between vectors b and b'' is particularly interesting, for the test flash only stimulates L cones and the red and yellow fields equally adapt these cones. The chromaticity of the field strongly affects detection independently of the differential effect of the *test* flash on the L and M cones.

The color-matching functions were used to calculate the precision of wavelength discrimination represented by the b'' vectors on the Y field. A value of 0.005 on the $\Delta L/L$ axis corresponds to a wavelength shift of 0.24 nm. Thus the wavelength difference limen is about 0.25 and 0.18 nm for H.C. and C.F.S.

Figure 7 provides further evidence for second site adaptation. It shows the threshold ($\Delta L/L$) from previous figures for a test flash that stimulates only the L cones (horizontal vectors) as a function of the metamer of the adapting field. The thresholds were read off from the fitted curves. The threshold decreases systematically over a considerable range as the field becomes more yellow. Logarithmic curves fit the data for sharp flashes ($r^2 = 0.98$).

Discussion

Chromatic Detection

By making the test flash diffuse, we selectively elevate the luminance threshold. This is supported by two results. First, Table 1 shows that there is a selective elevation for a diffuse red flash on a similar red field. The flash is presumably detected by a luminance change, since there is little chromatic difference

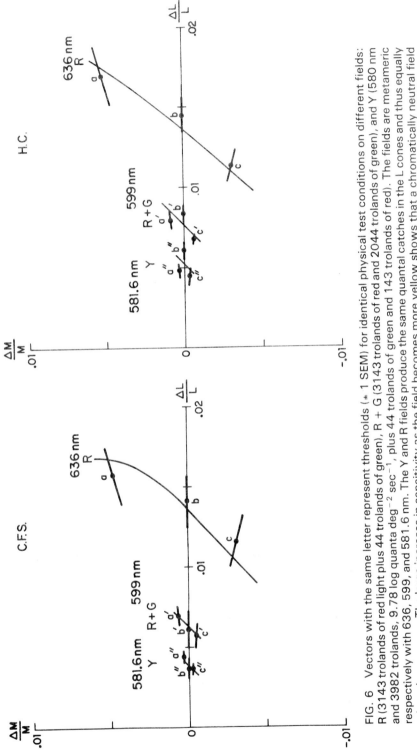

FIG. 6 Vectors with the same letter represent thresholds (± 1 SEM) for identical physical test conditions on different fields: R (3143 trolands of red light plus 44 trolands of green), R + G (3143 trolands of red and 2044 trolands of green), and Y (580 nm and 3982 trolands, 9.78 log quanta deg^{-2} sec^{-1}, plus 44 trolands of green and 143 trolands of red). The fields are metameric respectively with 636, 599, and 581.6 nm. The Y and R fields produce the same quantal catches in the L cones and thus equally adapt these cones. The large increase in sensitivity as the field becomes more yellow shows that a chromatically neutral field improves sensitivity independently of the differential cone adaptation and consequent rotation of the test vectors that it produces.

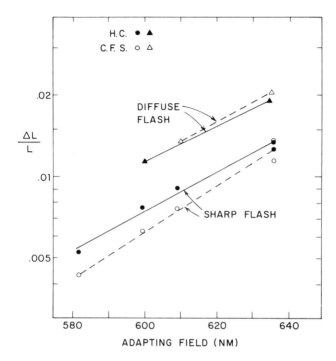

FIG. 7 Thresholds (ΔL/L) for test flashes that uniquely stimulate the L cones (horizontal vectors) as a function of the metamer of the adapting field. Data are read from fitted curves in previous figures.

between the test flash and field. Second, the detection contours for the diffuse flash (Fig. 4) are highly elongated along the luminance axis (+ 45° diagonal). These results agree with the observations of Thornton and Pugh (1981) who measured the threshold for a diffuse flash as a function of its wavelength (test spectral sensitivity functions) on intense fields of 560–600 nm. The threshold was most elevated at the point where the test and field wavelengths precisely matched. This selective elevation was considerably reduced for sharp flashes (1°, 200 msec). The chromatic mechanisms are most sensitive at low spatial and temporal frequencies (King-Smith and Carden, 1976; Kelly and van Norren, 1977; Stromeyer *et al.*, 1978; Noorlander, Heuts and Koenderink, 1981).

The diffuse flash selectively elevates the luminance threshold, and thus the detection contours reveal chromatic mechanisms over a large region of the vector space (Fig. 4). The straight lines fitted to many of the points show that a chromatic mechanism responds to a linear difference of M and L cone signals elicited by the test flash on both the red and red-plus-green fields. A simple incremental diffuse red flash on the red field stimulates both the M and L cones and is thus particularly ineffective for the chromatic differencing mechanism.

The detection contours for the sharp flashes (Fig. 5) are much less elongated along the + 45° luminance axis. The results suggest that the sharp red flash on the *red* field may be detected predominately with L cone signals, for adding a considerable range of negative green flashes to an incremental red flash (heavy straight lines in Fig. 5), and similarly adding a considerable range of positive green flashes to a decremental red flash, has little effect. This means that the luminance detection of a red flash on a similar red field may be mediated largely by L cone signals. Wandell, Sanchez and Quinn (1982a) argued on the basis of experiments on test spectral sensitivity, test mixture thresholds, and chromatic discrimination of threshold flashes that a sharp incremental red flash (1.1°, 300 msec) on an intense red field is detected largely by L cone signals. The flash produces predominantly a luminance change. In contrast, Eisner and MacLeod (1981) argue that luminance flicker detection, of even deep-red light, may be largely mediated by the M cones when an intense red adapting field is employed. We intend to further test the hypotheses using our method and test flashes with different temporal parameters, such as rapid flicker.

Chromatic Facilitation and Adaptive Mechanisms

The threshold contours for the diffuse test flashes are highly elongated along the + 45° luminance axis. The green addend field increases the visibility of a diffuse incremental red flash on a red field in part by rotating the test vector away from the luminance axis. The rotation occurs because the green field more rapidly adapts the M cones than the L cones. As the vector is rotated away from + 45° there is an increase in the difference of the M and L cone signals elicited by the flash and this facilitates chromatic detection. This facilitation due to vector rotation is reduced for the sharp flash (Fig. 5) because the contours are less elongated along the + 45° axis. Also, for the red field, test flashes in the region from + 45° to fairly near the horizontal axis (i.e. in the region of the heavy straight lines) may be detected predominantly by the L cones. If so, then the simple incremental red flashes on the red field do not produce strong M cone signals for the green addend field to attenuate.

The rotation of the vectors by the green addend field is ascribed to first site, differential cone adaptation. The present results provide clear evidence that chromatic facilitation is not caused solely by this mechanism. Wandell *et al.* (1982b) also provide evidence that supports this view. The present results show that for a test flash that uniquely stimulates the L cones, the threshold ($\Delta L/L$) descends considerably as the adapting field is changed from red to yellow. The results are quantitatively similar for sharp and diffuse flashes. This effect is presumably caused by second-site adaptation, and the chromatic detection system is most sensitive when adapted to chromatically neutral light. Boynton and Kambe (1980) similarly observed that equiluminance (120 trolands) red–green discrimination in a bipartite field became more sensitive as the mean wavelength of the field was varied from 620 to 580 nm. LeGrand (1949) concluded from an analysis of the MacAdam ellipses that equiluminous, chromatic discrimination mediated by the red- and green-sensitive cones was best when the test field was in red–green balance, and discrimination was reduced when the field was shifted in the red or green direction.

Evidence for a second adaptation site in the red–green pathways is also provided by adaptation to temporally modulated chromatic fields (Guth, Benzschawel and Friedman, 1976; Mollon and Polden, 1977b; Jameson, Hurvich and Varner, 1979; Reeves, 1981, 1982), and adaptation to small chromatic pedestal fields (Foster, 1981). The present results demonstrate second site adaptation when the adapting field is intense, uniform and steady.

Acknowledgement

This research was supported by Grant EY01808 from the National Eye Institute.

References

Boynton, R. M. (1979). *Human Color Vision*. New York, Holt, Rinehart, and Winston.
Boynton, R. M. and Kambe, N. (1980). Chromatic difference steps of moderate size measured along theoretically critical axes. *Color: Res. and Appl.* 5, 13–23.
Buss, C. M., Hayhoe, M. M. and Stromeyer, C. F. III (1982). Lateral interactions in the control of visual sensitivity. *Vision Res.* 22, 693–709.
Eisner, A. and MacLeod, D. I. A. (1981). Flicker photometric study of chromatic adaptation: Selective suppression of cone inputs by colored backgrounds. *J. opt. Soc. Am.* 71, 705–718.
Foster, D. H. (1981). Changes in field spectral sensitivities of red-, green- and blue-sensitive colour mechanisms obtained on small background fields. *Vision Res.* 21, 1433–1455.
Guth, S. L., Benzschawel, T. and Friedman, A. (1976). Post-receptor chromatic adaptation. *J. opt. Soc. Am.* 66, 1103A.
Jameson, D., Hurvich, L. M. and Varner, F. Dent (1979). Receptoral and post-receptoral visual processes in recovery from chromatic adaptation. *Proc. natl. Acad. Sci. USA* 76, 3034–3038.
Kelly, D. H. and van Norren, D. (1977). Two-band model of heterochromatic flicker. *J. opt. Soc. Am.* 67, 1081–1091.
King-Smith, P. E. and Carden, D. (1976). Luminance and opponent-color contributions to visual detection and adaptation and to temporal and spatial integration. *J. opt. Soc. Am.* 66, 709–717.
LeGrand, Y. (1949). Les seuils différentiels de couleurs dans la théorie de Young. *Revue Opt. théor. instrum.* 28, 261–278.
Mollon, J. D. and Polden, P. G. (1977a). Further anomalies of the blue mechanism. *Invest. Ophthal. Vis. Sci. Suppl.* 17, 140.

Mollon, J. D. and Polden, P. G. (1977b). An anomaly in the response of the eye to light of short wavelengths. *Phil. Trans. roy. Soc. Lond.* **B 278**, 207–240.

Normann, R. A. and Perlman, I. (1979). The effects of background illumination on the photoresponses of red and green cones. *J. Physiol., Lond.* **286**, 491–507.

Noorlander, C., Heuts, M. J. G. and Koenderink, J. J. (1981). Sensitivity to spatio-temporal combined luminance and chromaticity contrast. *J. opt. Soc. Am.* **71**, 453–459.

Pugh, E. N., Jr and Mollon, J. D. (1979). A theory of the π_1 and π_3 color mechanisms of Stiles. *Vision Res.* **19**, 293–312.

Reeves, A. (1981). Transient desensitization of a red–green opponent site. *Vision Res.* **21**, 1267–1277.

Reeves, A. (1982). Exchange thresholds for green tests. *Vision Res.* **22**, 961–966.

Smith, V. C. and Pokorny, J. (1975). Spectral sensitivity of the foveal cone photopigments between 400 and 500 nm. *Vision Res.* **15**, 161–171.

Sternheim, C. E., Stromeyer, C. F. III and Khoo, M. C. K. (1979). Visibility of chromatic flicker upon spectrally mixed adapting fields. *Vision Res.* **19**, 175–183.

Sternheim, C. E., Stromeyer, C. F. III and Spillmann, L. (1978). Increment thresholds: Sensitization produced by hue differences. In *Visual Psychophysics and Physiology* (eds Armington, J. C., Krauskopf, J. and Wooten, B. R.). New York, Academic Press.

Stiles, W. S. (1939). The directional sensitivity of the retina and the spectral sensitivities of the rods and cones. *Proc. roy. Soc. Lond.* **B 127**, 64–105.

Stiles, W. S. (1953). Further studies of visual mechanisms by the two-colour threshold method. In *Coloquio sobre Problemas Opticos de la Vision*, Vol. 1, pp. 65–103. Madrid, Union Internationale de Physique pure et appliquée.

Stiles, W. S. (1959). Color vision: The approach through increment–threshold sensitivity. *Proc. natn. Acad. Sci. USA* **45**, 100–114.

Stiles, W. S. (1978). *Mechanisms of Colour Vision*. New York, Academic Press.

Stromeyer, C. F. III, Klein, S. and Sternheim, C. E. (1977). Is spatial adaptation caused by prolonged inhibition? *Vision Res.* **17**, 603–606.

Stromeyer, C. F. III, Khoo, M. C. K., Muggeridge, D. and Young, R. A. (1978). Detection of red and green flashes: evidence for cancellation and facilitation. *Sensory Processes* **2**, 248–271.

Stromeyer, C. F. III, Kronauer, R. E. and Madsen, J. C. (1979). Response saturation of short-wavelength cone pathways controlled by color-opponent mechanisms. *Vision Res.* **19**, 1025–1040.

Stromeyer, C. F. III and Sternheim, C. E. (1981). Visibility of red and green spatial patterns upon spectrally mixed adapting fields. *Vision Res.* **21**, 397–407.

Thornton, J. and Pugh, E. N. Jr (1981). Low frequency test spectral sensitivity. *Invest. Ophthal. Vis. Sci. Suppl.* **20**, 61.

Wandell, B. A. and Pugh, E. N. Jr (1980). Detection of long-duration, long-wavelength incremental flashes by a chromatically coded pathway. *Vision Res.* **20**, 625–636.

Wandell, B. A., Sanchez, J. and Quinn, B. (1982a). Detection/discrimination in the long-wavelength pathways. *Vision Res.* **22**, 1061–1069.

Wandell, B. A., Welsh, D. and Maloney, L. (1982b). Adaptation in the long-wavelength pathways. *Vision Res.* **22**, 1071–1074.

Wetherill, G. B. (1963). Sequential estimation of quantal response curves. *J. roy. statist. Soc.* **B 25**, 1–48.

Wyszecki, G. and Stiles, W. S. (1967). *Color Science: Concepts and Methods, Quantitative Data and Formulas*. New York, Wiley.

Sensitivity of the Red – Green Hue Channel in Light and Dark Adaptation

ADAM REEVES

Introduction

Thresholds for the detection of a 200-msec, 3-deg foveal red test flash rise slightly just after turning off a *dim* red or green adapting background, while falling after turning off a yellow background of any intensity (Reeves, 1981). This result, an example of "dynamic dyschromatopsia" (see review by Mollon, 1982), suggests that thresholds for such tests are mediated through a red–green hue channel: specifically, a neural pathway with an opponently-coded site which is desensitized by the offset of a "polarizing" (red or green, but not yellow) background. However, thresholds always fall after turning off somewhat more intense red or green backgrounds, and it is not obvious why a hypothetical red–green opponent site should not also be desensitized in this case. Mollon and Polden (1977) suggested that after turning off moderate or intense backgrounds, thresholds for long-wavelength tests could be mediated by a nonopponent pathway whose sensitivity recovered at the start of dark adaptation (DA). If this is so, extinction of a bright polarizing background might desensitize the red–green opponent site, but this would not be revealed by changes in the threshold for detection. The purpose of the present research, therefore, was to develop a special test to isolate the response of the red–green pathway.

For the long-wavelength one deg tests, it was assumed that the only possible detection pathways were the red–green opponent pathway and the (non-opponent) luminance channel defined operationally by flicker photometry. On this assumption, the sensitivity of the opponent pathway may be measured

COLOUR VISION
ISBN 0 12 000000 0

with a test which alternates between luminance-equated fields of different wavelengths. Any reportable flicker in such a test must be mediated by the opponent pathway, if the luminance match is precise enough to silence the response of the luminance channel.

This paper reports full DA curves for such flicker thresholds to characterize the temporal response of the red–green opponent channel. Reeves (1983) measured flicker thresholds at a fixed brief interval in the dark, to characterize the intensity response. The largest opponent site effect was at -3.0 log ergs deg^{-2} sec^{-1} for a 626-nm background; similar intensities were used here.

Methods

Observers

The author (AR), aged 34, and a paid assistant (AW), aged 26, served as trained observers here and in Reeves (1983). (Present findings may be age dependent: e.g., Sturr *et al.*, 1982). Both observers have normal color vision; AR is myopic and was corrected by spectacle lenses.

Stimuli and Apparatus

The foveal, 1-deg test was 520 msec in duration and alternated every 125 or 82 msec between luminance-equated red (641 nm) and yellow (580 nm) fields (half-bandwidth 9 nm). The fundamental alternation rates of the square-wave flicker, 4 Hz and 6.1 Hz, were near the optimum for hue channels (e.g., Regan and Tyler, 1971). The test-field wavelengths were far enough apart to generate visible flicker near the threshold for detection, even when the fields were luminance equated. Shorter test wavelengths were not used, to avoid possible rod or blue cone intrusions.

Tests and backgrounds were presented by a five-channel Maxwellian-view system. Channels 1 and 2 provided one-deg 580-nm and 641-nm test fields, and channels 3 and 4 provided the 8-deg background. Channel 5 provided two tiny deep red (651 nm) fixation dots, one deg above and below the edge of the test, for use in the dark (in the light, these dots were invisible, but fixation was guided by a tiny black dot mounted in the center of the background). All five channels were adjusted to be concentric before each experimental run. The source was a 1000 W Osram high pressure Xenon arc lamp, driven by a current stabilized power supply. Five beams were collected from the source and passed through at least 6-mm thick heat-absorbing glass. Grating monochromators (Jobin-Yvon) with entrance and exit slits of 2.5 mm provided light of 580 nm in channel 1 and 496 nm, 536 nm, 570 nm, 626 nm, or 655 nm in channel 3 (spectral side-bands were carefully eliminated by masking the light beam prior to the entrance slits). A Schott type DAL interference filter provided 641-nm light in channel 2. Bandwidths at half-maximum were less than 9 nm for the monochromators and 16 nm for the DAL filter. Channel 4 provided unfiltered white light in light-adaptation and was shut off in dark adaptation. Test duration (520 msec) was controlled by a Vincent Uniblitz shutter placed at a filament image located in the test beam after channels 1 and 2 had been combined. The test was alternated in square-wave fashion between channels 1 and 2 by moving balsa wood vanes in tandem across nodal points in the beams, so that either one or the other was open. The vanes were driven by independently-amplified mechanically-stabilized loudspeaker coils, adjusted so that ripple was less than 0.02 log units between alternation rates of 0.1 Hz and 30 Hz when light in the two channels was identical. The background channels could also be alternated in square-wave fashion, by moving a single metal strip across physically adjacent nodal points in the two channels: holes were drilled in the strip to admit light through either but not both channels. In passing from one beam to the other, ripple was less than 0.05 log units. Measured rise and fall times for test and background were less than 2 msec. The absolute intensities of all channels were controlled by neutral-density (ND) wedges in each beam, and in the common beams after combination. The relative intensities of the two test beams were controlled by rotating a circular polaroid sheet in the common test beam: the two separate test beams were cross-polarized before combination. All wedges were set by hand, except that the ND wedge controlling overall test intensity (placed in the common beam) was set by a hand-held multi-turn pot whose position gave no clue as to actual test intensity. Observers viewed these stimuli with their right eyes; their left eyes were patched. The final images of the five channels were 2 mm at the pupil. Head movements were restrained with a plastic dental impression mounted to the optical rail. Correct placement of the images on the pupil was checked before each run, and the observer made the final small adjustments necessary to ensure that the fields were exactly superimposed: such adjustments were critical for channels 1 and 2, as slight misalignments made the test move in the visual field and give rise to a spurious impression of flicker. Calibration of radiance was undertaken with an E.G. & G. type 55-2 multiprobe detector, whose signal was amplified by a chopped, stabilized amplifier with a known response to a weak, calibrated current source. The detector was placed near the focal point of the final lens of the apparatus, in the position of the observer's eye. (Photometric measurements made with the same device agreed within 0.1 log units.) The peak wavelength passed through each spectral filter was checked against a calibrated monochromator and was correct within 2 nm.

Procedure

Thresholds were measured on an unchanging adaptation background (the "steady" condition), and by *tracking* and *extinction* procedures in light and dark adaptation (LA and DA).

To *track* the course of adaptation, the observer adjusted test intensity until the test was just visible (the "detection threshold"), or until the test could be just seen to flicker (the "flicker threshold"), in different trials. (The observer was not required to discriminate between impressions of hue flicker and luminance flicker.) The test alternated at 4 Hz, or, in control conditions, at 12 Hz, and was presented for 1.2 sec, once every 5 sec. Adjustments of both test energy (to one or other threshold) and the relative intensities of the two fields had to be made concurrently, since the luminance match between the 641-nm and 580-nm test fields varied with the adaptive state of the eye. Luminance matches were performed by a form of flicker photometry, in which the test fields were alternated at 15 Hz, and the relative intensities were varied until flicker was minimized. To locate both the threshold and luminance match, a boot-strapping procedure was used. The observer made an initial luminance match in the steady condition, and then adjusted overall test intensity to the threshold for just-visible flicker (at 4 Hz) throughout LA or DA. An assistant then made the test clearly visible by setting overall test energy to about 0.8 log units above the flicker threshold,[1] and the observer made the fine adjustments necessary to match luminance. Next, the assistant duplicated the observer's matches, and the observer concurrently set overall test energy to flicker threshold. After luminance matches and flicker thresholds had stabilized, data were collected from 4 to 6 more trials, in which the luminance matches were adjusted by the assistant to the average of the observer's previous few settings.

An *extinction* procedure (Reeves, 1981) was used to measure thresholds at the start of DA. Test duration was 520 msec, and the test alternated at 6.1 Hz to ensure that three cycles of alternation were presented. The test was turned on T msec after the background was turned off (160 msec $< T <$ 2 sec). The background remained off for one sec, if $T <$ 600 msec, and for 2.4 sec, if $T >$ 600 msec, before being turned back on to maintain adaptation. Observers then readapted to the background for at least 4 secs between trials for T < 600 msec, and at least 10 sec for $T >$ 600 msec.

Results

Dark Adaptation (DA)

Thresholds for the 641/580 nm alternating test are plotted against sec in DA (on a logarithmic scale) in Figs 1 to 5 for observer AR. Background wavelength, μ, is given in each figure. Background intensities were chosen so that steady

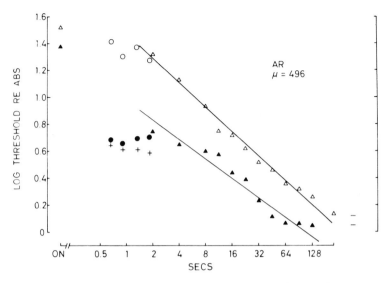

FIG. 1   Log detection (▲,●) and flicker (△,○) thresholds, for a one deg, 641/580 nm alternating test flash, plotted relative to absolute threshold against seconds from the offset of the adapting field to half-way through the test flash (log scale). Background 496 nm, −2.4 log ergs deg^{-2} sec^{-1}. *Tracking method:* thresholds (△,▲) with alternation at 4 Hz. Tests were shown for 1.2 sec, once every 5 sec. Thresholds after 3 min are shown by dashes (−) on the right. *Extinction method:* thresholds (○,●) with alternation at 6.1 Hz: test duration 520 msec. That tracking and extinction thresholds meet at 2 sec shows that the differences between the procedures did not upset the results. Log detection thresholds for a normal 641 nm, 1 deg, flash (+) are shown for comparison; fortunately they are very similar to the detection thresholds for the alternating test. *Steady thresholds* are plotted at far left (marked ON on the abscissa); detection thresholds (▲) for the 641 nm and 641/580 nm tests superimposed. Observer: AR.

thresholds for detection (▲, marked ON) were about 1.4 log units above absolute threshold for detection (and were closely proportional to $\Pi_5 \mu$ Wyszecki and Stiles, 1967). Open symbols show thresholds for just-visible flicker, and closed symbols show thresholds for detection (see legend for details). Both sets of thresholds course downwards as DA continues.

Recovery of log threshold may be described as linear with a power of time (t), for $t > 2$ sec, as shown by the best-fitting straight lines in these figures. For example, the line fitting the detection thresholds (×) in Fig. 3 has a slope (against $\log_2 t$) of 0.14 and intercepts $t = 1$ sec at 0.98 log units. In linear units, threshold $= 9.33\, t^{-0.50}$. Alternatively, assuming threshold recovery is exponential (e.g., Rushton and Henry, 1968), log threshold $= 0.79\, e^{-0.04 t}$. These two equations differ by less than 0.03 log units for $3 < t < 100$ sec, but for $t < 3$ sec, the exponential predicts thresholds between 0.73 and 0.79 and perhaps is to be preferred.

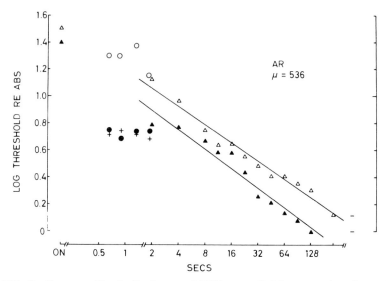

FIG. 2   Same as Fig. 1. Background 536 nm, -2.9 log ergs deg^{-2} sec^{-1}.

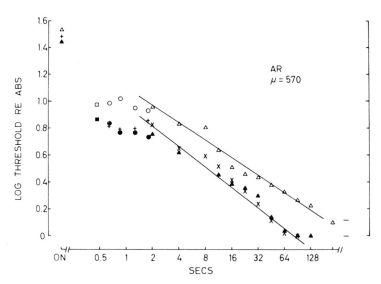

FIG. 3   Same as Fig. 1. Background 570 nm, -3.0 log ergs deg^{-2} sec^{-1}.
Squares show extinction thresholds from Reeves (1983) for the same conditions.

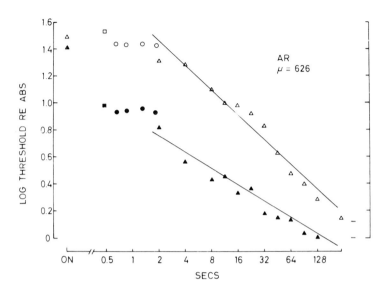

FIG. 4   Same as Fig. 3. Background 626 nm. -2.7 log ergs deg^{-2} sec^{-1}.

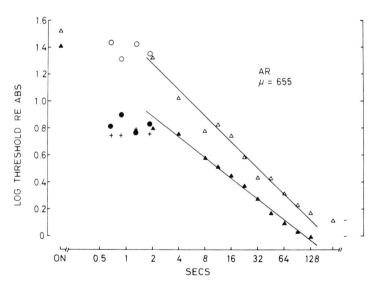

FIG. 5   Same as Fig. 1. Background 655 nm, -2.1 log ergs deg^{-2} sec^{-1}.

As expected from earlier results, the detection thresholds do not vary systematically with background wavelength. However, the flicker thresholds do vary. With a yellow background (Fig. 3), flicker thresholds both in the steady and DA conditions lie only about 0.15 log units above the detection thresholds. However, with blue−green (Fig. 1) or red (Figs 4 and 5) backgrounds, flicker thresholds stay well above detection thresholds over almost the full course of DA. Similar results can be seen in the condensed format of Fig. 6 for AW.

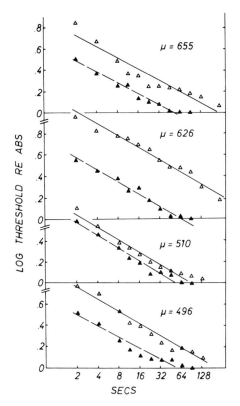

FIG. 6   Same backgrounds as Figs 1 to 5, as marked. The extinction procedure was not run. Observer: AW.

Control data obtained with 626-nm and 496-nm backgrounds for both observers (not plotted) showed that upsetting the nominal luminance matches by 0.1 log units did not materially alter the flicker thresholds. However, upsets of 0.2 or 0.3 log units began to lower (never raise) the flicker thresholds. Thus, even if the nominal matches were imperfect, any residual luminance flicker had no real influence.

To verify that the opponent channel mediated the flicker thresholds just reported, the same luminance-matched test fields were alternated at 12 rather than at 4 or 6.1 Hz. Flicker thresholds in the dark were 1.2 log units, or more, higher at 12 Hz than at the slower rates. If both sets of flicker thresholds had been mediated by the luminance channel, they would have been within about 0.3 log units of each other (as shown by Reeves, 1983).

Early Dark Adaptation (DA)

Thresholds in early DA, as measured with the extinction procedure, were quite flat in Figs 1 to 6. This was unexpected, since at least for white light tests, thresholds drop fast in the first few seconds (Baker, Doran and Miller, 1959). To discover whether this curious result would hold up at higher background intensities, both observers were run with background intensities sufficient to raise test thresholds by 1.8 and 2.8 log units above absolute threshold.

Results from the extinction method are shown at the highest background intensity for observer AR in Fig. 7 (time is now linear). Results for AW and for the other background intensity were similar. The lowest points connected by the dotted line show the detection thresholds, which cluster together for

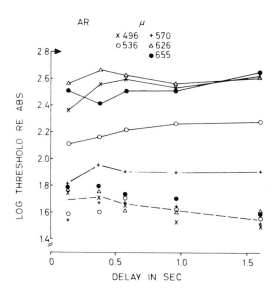

FIG. 7 Log detection thresholds (lower points, connected by dotted line) and flicker thresholds (upper points, solid lines) in early dark adaptation (linear time scale), for the 641/580 nm alternating test. Background wavelengths μ as marked: Intensities were 1.4 log units higher than those in Figs 1 to 5. Steady threshold marked by an arrow (at 2.8) on the far left. Observer: AR (data for AW were also quite flat).

the various background wavelengths. The upper points show flicker thresholds: those for the yellow background (+) are the lowest, and those for the red (●,△) and blue−green (×) are the highest, as is to be expected from the opponent site effect. Clearly, none of the thresholds vary much between 0.16 and 1.6 sec, whether elevated by opponent site desensitization (flicker thresholds for μ = 496, 626, and 655 nm) or not (the rest).

Light Adaptation (LA)

In LA conditions, the monochromatic adaptation background was substituted for by a white background whose intensity had been adjusted so that detection thresholds would be the same on it as on the monochromatic background. Luminance matches were obtained by flicker photometry with the same bootstrapping procedure as before. Flicker thresholds (tracking method) were found to rise after the substitution by 0.2−0.3 log units, and then take roughly one min to recover to baseline. This is illustrated in Fig. 8, which shows flicker (●) and detection (○) thresholds after a 496-nm background was made white (at t = 0), and in Fig. 9, where a 626-nm background was made white.

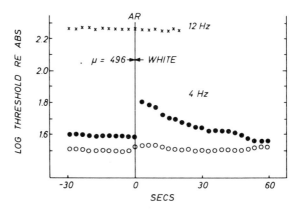

FIG. 8   Log detection (○) and flicker (●) thresholds for the 641/580 nm, 4 Hz alternating test, before and after the substitution (at t = 0) of a white field for the 496 nm, −2.4 log ergs deg^{-2} sec^{-1} adaptation field. Control flicker thresholds (×) at 12 Hz were 0.5 log units higher, or more, showing that the luminance channel probably did not mediate the 4 Hz flicker thresholds. Observer: AR (AW's data, not shown, were similar).

Reeves (1981, 1983) found that 626-nm backgrounds flickered (i.e., turned off and on) at 2 Hz throughout the period of adaptation did not desensitize the opponent site at the start of DA. This result was essentially replicated here: flicker thresholds (tracking method) were within 0.2 log units of detection

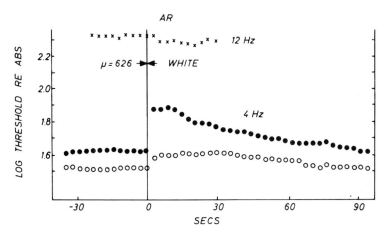

FIG. 9 Same as Fig. 8. Adaptation background 626 nm, -2.7 log ergs deg^{-2} sec^{-1}. Observer: AR (AW's data were again similar).

thresholds throughout DA, after adaptation to flickered (2 Hz) 626-nm and 496-nm backgrounds of the mean intensities used in Figs 1 and 4. In LA, after adaptation to a background which flickered at 2 Hz between 496 nm and 626 nm, flicker thresholds did not change when a white background was substituted (intensities were chosen so that detection thresholds were the same on all three backgrounds).

Conclusions

We may interpret DA curves as revealing two effects: the recovery of a "first site" prior to the stage of opponent combination, and the initial desensitization followed by eventual recovery of an opponently-coded "second site". (This interpretation was advanced by Pugh and Mollon (1979) for the case of transient tritanopia.) On the assumption that the presence or absence of yellow fields has no effect on the sensitivity of the red–green opponent site itself, recovery of thresholds following extinction of a yellow background reveals the recovery of the first site alone. Hence, the *differences* between flicker thresholds occurring after extinction of polarizing (non-yellow) and yellow backgrounds should show the effect of the opponent site alone.

In the case of LA, first-site sensitivity is probably unaltered because the change from red or green to white backgrounds of about the same brightness has little effect on the states of adaptation of middle- and long-wavelength cones. It seems reasonable to assume that the rise in flicker threshold in the light adaptation condition was produced almost exclusively by the opponent site.

The results show, however, that although the time course of the assumed opponent site effects in DA and LA were similar, the effect was slightly larger at the start of DA (0.4−0.5 log units) than at substitution in LA (0.2−0.3 log units), for equally intense 496 nm and 626 nm backgrounds. The significance of this discrepancy is not yet clear.

The conclusion drawn here, that substitution or extinction of a polarizing field can desensitize a red−green opponent channel, depends on a sharp distinction between that channel and the luminance channel, which, if it is desensitized, tends to recover rapidly (e.g., Reeves, 1982; Sharpe and Mollon, 1982). Middle- and long-wavelength tests may in principle be detected by either channel, and it is the greater sensitivity of the luminance channel in most DA conditions that has prevented the sluggish recovery of the hue channel from being previously observed.

Acknowledgement

I thank Dieter Bauer, who built the Maxwellian-view system used in these experiments.

Note

1.   A complication is that the influence of the background is an important factor. If test energy is very high, flicker minimization is easy, but the background is too dim (relatively) to influence the equation. If test energy is low, so that the test is near its detection threshold, widely different luminances can be accepted as a match. After considerable practice, observers were able to make reasonably consistent matches when the test was 0.8 log units above detection threshold, and this (rather arbitrary) figure was used throughout the experiments reported here. The arbitrariness introduced here, however, made it important to conduct the control experiments with test stimuli whose nominal luminance matches were slightly upset.

References

Baker, H. D., Doran, M. D. and Miller, K. E. (1959). Early dark adaptation to dim luminances. *J. opt. Soc. Am.* **49**, 1065−1070.

Mollon, J. D. (1982). Color Vision. *Ann. Rev. Psychol.* **33**, 41−85.

Mollon, J. D. and Polden, P. G. (1977). An anomaly in the response of the eye to light of short wavelengths. *Phil. Trans. roy. Soc. B.* **278**, 207−240.

Pugh, E. N. and Mollon, J. D. (1979). A theory of the π_1 and π_3 color mechanisms of Stiles. *Vision Res.* **19**, 293−312.

Reeves, A. (1981). Transient desensitization of a red−green opponent site. *Vision Res.* **21**, 1267−1277.

Reeves, A. (1983). Distinguishing opponent and nonopponent detection pathways in early dark-adaptation. *Vision Res.* **23**, in press.

Reeves, A. (1982). Exchange thresholds for long-wavelength incremental flashes. *J. opt. Soc. Am.* **72**, 565−570.

Regan, D. and Tyler, C. W. (1971). Temporal summation and its limits for wavelength changes: an analog of Bloch's law for color vision. *J. opt. Soc. Am.* **61**, 1414–1421.

Rushton, W. A. H. and Henry, G. H. (1968). Bleaching and regeneration of cone pigments in man. *Vision Res.* **8**, 617–631.

Sharpe, L. T. and Mollon, J. D. (1982). Dynamic changes in sensitivity to long-wavelength incremental flashes. *Doc. Ophthal. Proc. Series* **33**, 53–60.

Sturr, J. F., Kelly, S. A., Kobus, D. A. and Taub, D. A. (1982). Age-dependent magnitude and time course of early light adaptation. *Percept. Psychophys.* **31**, 402–404.

Wyszecki, G. and Stiles, W. S. (1967). *Color Science.* New York, Wiley.

Nonlinear Nature of the Yellow Chromatic Valence

MITSUO IKEDA and MIYOSHI AYAMA

The notion of opponent-colour processes has been well accepted among visual scientists and we often see in the literature the chromatic valence curves of the red-versus-green and yellow-versus-blue processes. It is important now to investigate the properties inherent in these curves before we apply them in various fields related to colour.

We will investigate here (1) the additivity of chromatic valence by asking whether linear addition occurs between, say, the yellow chromatic valences at two wavelengths; (2) the curve shape of the chromatic valence functions, by asking whether the curves are smooth as required if they are linear transformations of colour matching functions (Judd, 1949; Jameson and Hurvich, 1955; Boynton, 1960; Romeskie, 1978); and (3) chromatic valence in a colour defective subject, by asking whether the shape and additivity of his functions are the same as for normal subjects.

1. Additivity

The summation index method (Ikeda, 1963; Boynton, Ikeda and Stiles, 1964) was applied to investigate the additivity of chromatic valence between two different stimuli. To study the yellow chromatic valence, for example, a unique blue reference light of a fixed retinal illuminance, 100 td, and of a field size $2°$ arc, was presented at the centre of a white surrounding field of 5400 K, 100 td and $7°$ arc. Upon the reference light a stimulus λ_1 was superposed and its radiance N_{10} was adjusted to produce an equilibrium between yellow and blue perceptions. A similar experiment was done for another stimulus λ_2, and N_{20} was obtained. Then λ_1 and λ_2 were mixed together with a certain ratio of N_{20}/N_{10} and a third equilibrium was established, giving radiances N_{1m} and N_{2m} of λ_1 and λ_2, respectively. The summation index σ is defined by:

$$\sigma = 0.30 - \log(\varrho_1 + \varrho_2),$$

where $\varrho_1 = N_{1m}/N_{10}$ and $\varrho_2 = N_{2m}/N_{20}$. If the yellow valences of the two stimuli add linearly with each other, then σ will equal 0.30 regardless of the value of the ratio ϱ_2/ϱ_1.

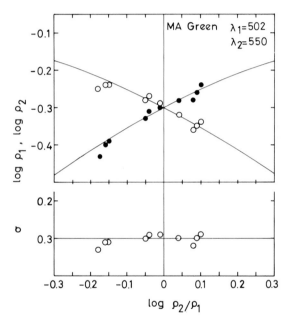

FIG. 1 $\varrho_1 - \varrho_2$ plots (upper) and σ plots (lower) as a function of the ratio ϱ_2/ϱ_1 for the green chromatic valence. Open circles in the upper figure denote $\log \varrho_1$ and filled circles $\log \varrho_2$. Solid curves, including horizontal line in the lower figure, are theoretical curves for linear summation. Subject: MA, $\lambda_1 = 502$ nm, $\lambda_2 = 550$ nm.

An example of measurement with $\lambda_1 = 502$ nm and $\lambda_2 = 550$ nm is presented in Fig. 1, taken from Ikeda and Ayama (1980). The figure shows $\log \varrho_1$ and $\log \varrho_2$ curves (upper) and σ (lower) for the green chromatic valence. The solid curves in both panels indicate linear summation ($\varrho_1 + \varrho_2 = 1$ or $\sigma = 0.30$). The results fit these theoretical curves very well and imply that the valence is made up from only one type of cone or by linear combination of the responses of more than one cone type. Similar linear summation was found for all wavelength combinations when red, green and blue valences were investigated.

Nonadditive results were often found, however, for yellow valence, one example being shown in Fig. 2, where $\lambda_1 = 530$ nm and $\lambda_2 = 630$ nm.

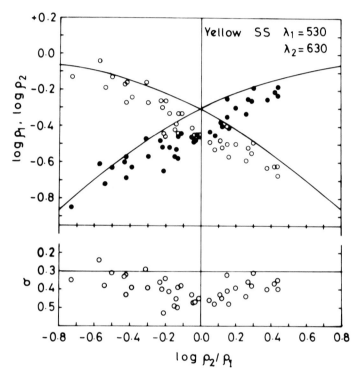

FIG. 2   Similar plots as in Fig. 1 but for the yellow chromatic valence. Subject: SS, $\lambda_1 = 530$ nm, $\lambda_2 = 630$ nm.

The solid curves indicate theoretical curves of linear summation and the experimental points clearly deviate from them, showing an additivity failure of the enhancement type (superadditivity). A similar additivity failure in the yellow chromatic valence was always observed whenever a short and a long wavelength stimulus were combined. We may conclude, therefore, that the yellow chromatic valence is constructed from at least two cone outputs and that these two outputs are combined in a nonlinear manner. This result is in agreement with the findings of Larimer, Krantz and Cicerone (1975) and Werner and Wooten (1979).

2. Chromatic Valence Curve

Chromatic valence curves were measured for red, yellow, green and blue by the cancellation method of Jameson and Hurvich (1955). A test stimulus of wavelength λ was equated in brightness to the surrounding white of 100 td and a reference light of unique colour opponency to the colour under investigation was superposed upon the test stimulus. An equilibrium point was reached by adjusting the radiance of the reference light N_λ. From such measurements the chromatic valences for an equal-energy spectrum can be calculated.

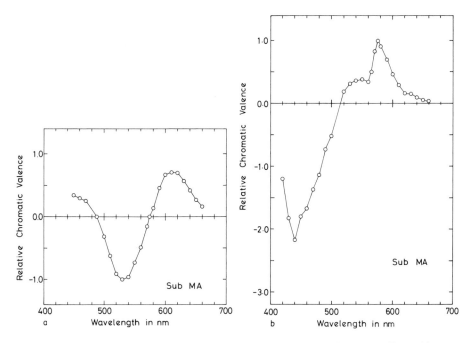

FIG. 3 Chromatic valence curves of red−green process (a) and yellow−blue process (b). Values are normalized relative to peaks of green and yellow curves. Subject: MA.

Results are shown for one subject in Fig. 3. As can be seen in Fig. 3a the red-versus-green chromatic valence curve has a smooth and simple shape. The curve can be represented by a linear combination of the colour matching functions, $\bar{x}(\lambda)$, $\bar{y}(\lambda)$ and $\bar{z}(\lambda)$, and consequently of the spectral sensitivity functions of three cone types, such as those proposed by Vos (1978). This result is consistent with the linear additivity found in the summation index experiment.

Quite different results were obtained for the yellow-versus-blue chromatic valence curve (Fig. 3b). Apart from the large values of the blue chromatic valence curve, the yellow chromatic valence curve appears to be double peaked with a dip near 560 nm, a wavelength fairly close to the unique yellow wavelength of this subject (577 nm). This complex curve cannot be represented by a linear combination of the colour-matching functions. Some complicated (nonlinear) combination of cone responses is needed to construct the yellow valence function.

Double peaked yellow valence curves were observed for all four normal subjects that we studied, though details differed between subjects. Similar irregularity is visible in Werner and Wooten's curves (1979), and in retrospect a dip can also be seen even in the yellow chromatic valence curve of Jameson and Hurvich's (1955) subject H, even though they represent his data with a smooth and simple curve. Thus the irregularity we found in the yellow chromatic valence curves is not unusual but is regularly observed.

3. Defective Colour Vision Observer

The additivity experiment and the measurement of the yellow-versus-blue chromatic valence curve were repeated for a male protanope. Measurements of the red and green chromatic valences were not possible for this subject.

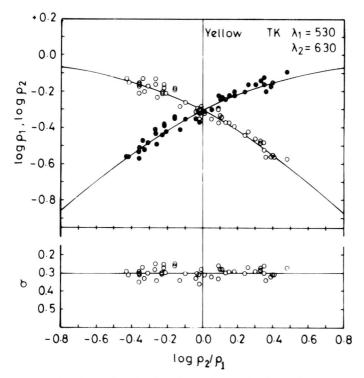

FIG. 4 $\varrho_1 - \varrho_2$ plots (upper) and σ plots (lower) as in Fig. 2, but for a protanope, TK.

Figure 4 shows results of a summation experiment for a wavelength combination of 530 nm and 630 nm, for which wavelengths an additivity failure of the enhancement type was observed in normal subjects. For the protanope additivity holds exactly, as experimental points fall on the solid curves that represent linear summation. The protanope's chromatic valence curve is shown in Fig. 5. Its yellow part is quite smooth and simple, and can be fitted satisfactorily with a linear combination of the colour-matching functions, $\bar{x}(\lambda)$, $\bar{y}(\lambda)$ and $\bar{z}(\lambda)$. The blue part of the curve can similarly be well fitted.

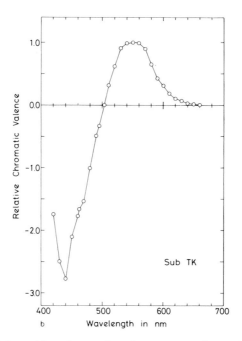

FIG. 5   Yellow−blue chromatic valence curve of a protanope, TK.

These results for the protanope are interpreted by assuming he lacks red cones and consequently the red-versus-green opponent process. Thus his yellow chromatic valence may be constructed from the green cone output alone.

References

Boynton, R. M. (1960). Theory of color vision. *J. opt. Soc. Am.* **50**, 929−944.

Boynton, R. M., Ikeda, M. and Stiles, W. S. (1964). Interactions among chromatic mechanisms as inferred from positive and negative increment thesholds. *Vision Res.* **4**, 87−117.

Ikeda, M. (1963). Study of interrelations between mechanisms at threshold. *J. opt. Soc. Am.* **53**, 1305−1313.

Ikeda, M. and Ayama, M. (1980). Additivity of opponent chromatic valence. *Vision Res.* **20**, 995.

Jameson, D. and Hurvich, L. M. (1955). Some quantitative aspects of an opponent-colors theory. I. Chromatic responses and spectral saturation. *J. opt. Soc. Am.* **45**, 546–552.

Judd, D. B. (1949). Response functions for types of vision according to the Müller theory. *J. Res. Nat. Bur. Stud.* **42**, 1.

Larimer, J., Krantz, D. H. and Cicerone, C. M. (1975). Opponent process additivity – II. Yellow/blue equilibria and nonlinear models. *Vision Res.* **15**, 723–731.

Romeskie, M. (1978). Chromatic opponent-response functions of anomalous trichromats. *Vision Res.* **18**, 1521–1532.

Vos, J. J. (1978). Colorimetric and photometric properties of a 2° fundamental observer. *Color Res. Appl.* **3**, 125–128.

Werner, J. S. and Wooten, B. R. (1979). Opponent chromatic mechanisms: relation to photopigments and hue naming. *J. opt. Soc. Am.* **69**, 422–434.

Contribution of Opponent-Colour Channels to Brightness

HIROHISA YAGUCHI and MITSUO IKEDA

Introduction

A saturated colour is perceived as brighter than a desaturated colour when the two are equated in luminance. This effect is well known as the Helmholtz-Kohlrausch effect, and can be demonstrated in spectral colours by the difference observed between the luminous efficiency function measured by flicker photometry and that obtained by heterochromatic brightness matching: the difference between the two functions resembles the saturation function (Wagner and Boynton, 1972; Comerford and Kaiser, 1975; Ikeda, Yaguchi, Yoshimatsu and Ohmi, 1982). In the case of nonspectral colours, obtained by mixing spectral colours, the Helmholtz-Kohlrausch effect is observed in the form of a failure of brightness additivity (Yaguchi and Ikeda, 1980). The theoretical explanation of this effect has been discussed by many investigators (Guth and Lodge, 1973; Ingling and Tsou, 1977; Bauer and Röhler, 1977; Yaguchi and Ikeda, 1982) and they agree in assuming that luminance is determined only by the achromatic channel, whereas brightness is determined by both the achromatic channel and the two opponent-colour channels.

In the present paper, we first reconfirm the contribution of opponent-colour channels to brightness by investigating the relationship between the shape of the luminous efficiency curve for brightness and the additivity failure of the reduction type that occurs when two wavelengths are mixed. Secondly, we analyse the additivity property in each subject and obtain a nonlinear model that describes the additivity failure.

COLOUR VISION
ISBN 0 12 000000 0

Method

Heterochromatic brightness matching was used both in measuring the luminous efficiency functions and in testing the additivity law for brightness. A 4-channel Maxwellian-view optical system was used to provide a bipartite field subtending 2 deg of arc, and an adapting field of 5 deg 50 min arc. Two monochromatic lights provided by two channels were presented in the left half of the bipartite field. Two other channels provided white light (of the same CIE chromaticity coordinates: $x = 0.32$, $y = 0.33$, and the same retinal illuminance). One of the latter channels provided the reference light presented in the right half of the bipartite field and the other the adapting field. The bipartite field and the adapting field were alternated every four seconds.

Three males, HY (28 years old), SR (25 years) and KK (24 years), and one female MA (23 years) with normal colour vision served as subjects. Measurements of the luminous efficiency functions and the additivity test with a 100-td reference light were carried out for the subjects SR and MA. For the other two subjects, HY and KK, three levels of reference light, 10, 100 and 1000 td, were investigated.

Additivity was tested for the bichromatic mixture of wavelengths λ_1 and λ_2. Let the radiances of monochromatic lights whose wavelengths are λ_1 and λ_2 be $L_{e,01}$ and $L_{e,02}$ when they are separately matched in brightness to a white reference light. Next, let the radiances of λ_1 and λ_2 be $L_{e, m1}$ and $L_{e, m2}$ when, presented as a mixture, they are matched in brightness to the same white reference light. If we define ϱ_1 and ϱ_2 as follows:

$$\varrho_1 = L_{e, m1}/L_{e,01}$$
$$\varrho_2 = L_{e, m2}/L_{e, 02}$$

then the additivity property can be evaluated by the value $\varrho_1 + \varrho_2$. If $\varrho_1 + \varrho_2 = 1$, additivity holds; if $\varrho_1 + \varrho_2 > 1$, there is a failure of the reduction type ("subadditivity"); and if $\varrho_1 + \varrho_2 < 1$, there is a failure of the enhancement type ("superadditivity").

In the present experiment, in order to avoid a change of colour in the mixture, the ratio of ϱ_1 to ϱ_2 was fixed while the subject made his adjustment of brightness. The values of λ_1 and λ_2 were 500 nm (510 nm for subject KK) and 660 nm respectively. Eleven ratios of ϱ_1 to ϱ_2 were chosen.

Results and Discussion

Relationship Between the Luminous Efficiency Function and the Additivity Property

Luminous efficiency functions for heterochromatic brightness matching are shown for four subjects in Fig. 1. The curves are normalized at 570 nm. We see no significant difference between the luminous efficiency functions in the

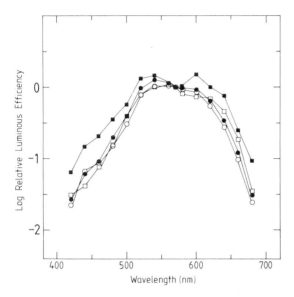

FIG. 1   Luminous efficiency functions at 100 td for four subjects, KK (filled squares), MA (open squares), HY (filled circles), and SR (open circles).

region 420–600 nm except for subject KK, who shows a rather broad luminous efficiency function. In the long-wavelength region, however, there are clearer differences between subjects.

$\varrho_1 - \varrho_2$ plots are shown in Fig. 2 for the mixtures of 500-nm green (510 nm for KK) and 660-nm red for four subjects. A straight line connecting points (0,1) and (1,0) represents linear additivity, that is $\varrho_1 + \varrho_2 = 1$. Any points beyond this line to the upper right indicate an additivity failure of the reduction type, and points in the lower left region indicate an additivity failure of the enhancement type. The results of Fig. 2 show clear subadditivity for all subjects. Deviation from the straight line is not symmetrical: all subjects show the maximum additivity failure in a region toward the ϱ_1 axis. There is also a remarkable difference among subjects. The $\varrho_1 - \varrho_2$ plots of the subject KK are the farthest from the additivity line, indicating the largest reduction in brightness. From Figs 1 and 2 it may be said that the additivity failure of the reduction type is particularly marked for the subject whose luminous efficiency curve is broadest.

This relationship was reflected in other experimental results. Figure 3 shows for subject KK the luminous efficiency curves at three different retinal illuminances, 10, 100 and 1000 td. As retinal illuminance increases, the luminous efficiency curve broadens. Correspondingly, as shown in Fig. 4, the $\varrho_1 - \varrho_2$ curves of KK increasingly depart from the additivity line with increasing retinal

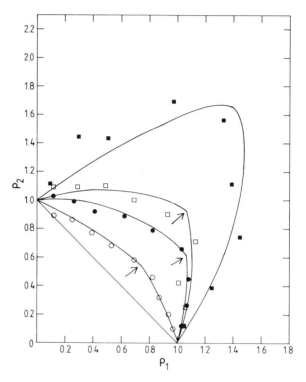

FIG. 2 $\varrho_1 - \varrho_2$ plots for 500–660 nm pair (510–660 nm for KK) for four subjects, KK (filled squares), MA (open squares), HY (filled circles), and SR (open
circles). Arrows indicate the perceived red–green equilibrium for each subject.
Solid curves are the theoretical $\varrho_1 - \varrho_2$ curves.

illuminance. For another subject HY, in contrast, the luminous efficiency curve
did not significantly differ at different retinal illuminances; and similarly the
$\varrho_1 - \varrho_2$ plots did not vary for this subject.

These experimental results are compatible with the hypothesis that both the
broadening of the luminous efficiency curves and the subadditivity of
brightness are caused by contributions of opponent-colour channels to
brightness.

Theoretical Analysis of Asymmetrical Additivity Failure

The contribution of the opponent-colour channels to brightness is confirmed
by the asymmetry of the $\varrho_1 - \varrho_2$ plots. The asymmetrical nature of additivity
failure was observed by Tessier and Blottiau (1951) and Yaguchi and Ikeda
(1982) in heterochromatic brightness matching, and by Boynton, Ikeda and
Stiles (1964) and Kranda and King-Smith (1979) in detection of increments.

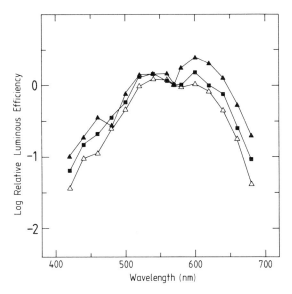

FIG. 3 Luminous efficiency functions at three levels of retinal illuminance,
10 td (open triangles), 100 td (filled squares), and 1000 td (filled triangles) for
subject KK.

Yaguchi and Ikeda (1982) suggested that the hue cancellation in the
red−green opponent-colour channel caused the brightness reduction: they
showed that the maximum brightness reduction point in $\varrho_1 - \varrho_2$ plots coin-
cided with the red−green equilibrium for each subject. They proposed a
nonlinear model to explain the asymmetry. In this model, a unit brightness
of a monochromatic light of wavelength λ_i is defined as:

$$A_i^2 + (|C_{1i}|^p)^2 + (|C_{2i}|^q)^2 = 1,$$

where A_i, C_{1i} and C_{2i} are the responses of the achromatic channel, the red−
green opponent-colour channel, and yellow−blue opponent-colour channel,
respectively. For a mixture of two monochromatic lights of wavelengths λ_1
and λ_2, this expression becomes

$$(\varrho_1 A_1 + \varrho_2 A_2)^2 + (|\varrho_1 C_{11} + \varrho_2 C_{12}|^p)^2 + (|\varrho_1 C_{21} + \varrho_2 C_{22}|^q)^2 = 1.$$

The nonlinearity of the red−green opponent-colour channel with an exponent
p and that of the yellow−blue opponent-colour channel with an exponent q
are assumed to explain the asymmetry found in $\varrho_1 - \varrho_2$ curves. The vector
model proposed by Guth and Lodge (1973) equated p and q to unity, but it
then cannot explain the asymmetrical $\varrho_1 - \varrho_2$ curve.

Exponents $p = 0.64$ and $q = 0.36$ were determined by numerous $\varrho_1 - \varrho_2$

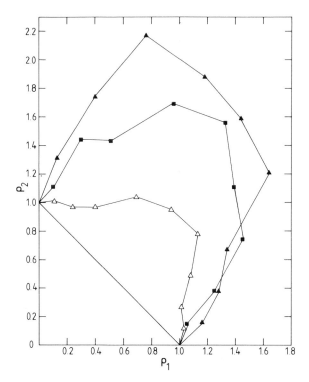

FIG. 4 $\varrho_1 - \varrho_2$ for 510–660 nm pair at three levels of retinal illuminance, 10 td (open triangles), 100 td (filled squares), and 1000 td (open triangles) for subject KK.

plots of various $\lambda_1 - \lambda_2$ pairs for the subject HY and then applied to the other subjects. The coefficients A_i, C_{1i} and C_{2i} were determined for each subject as follows. At the red–green equilibrium, the response of the red–green opponent-colour channel in the mixture of 500 nm and 660 nm should become zero. The ratios of C_{11} to C_{12} were chosen so that the value of $\varrho_1 C_{11} + \varrho_2 C_{12}$ became equal to zero at the red–green equilibrium point (obtained by colour naming) for each subject except for subject KK. Since KK did not carry out colour naming, the farthest point in his $\varrho_1 - \varrho_2$ plots was assumed to be his red–green equilibrium. Because the contribution of the yellow–blue opponent-colour channel to brightness seems to be negligible for the combination of 500 nm and 660 nm, values of $C_{21} = 0.0$ for 500 nm and $C_{22} = 0.002$ for 660 nm were adopted for all subjects.

The coefficients A_i, C_{1i}, and C_{2i} are presented for each subject in Table 1. The continuous solid curves in Fig. 2 are the theoretical $\varrho_1 - \varrho_2$ curves based on these coefficients; the arrows correspond to the red–green equilibrium for each subject. Each cusp appearing in the theoretical $\varrho_1 - \varrho_2$ curve corresponds

TABLE 1   The coefficients A_i, C_{1i} and C_{2i} of the theoretical $\varrho_1 - \varrho_2$ curves.

Subject	500 nm*			600 nm		
	A_1	C_{11}	C_{21}	A_2	C_{12}	C_{22}
SR	0.83	-0.41	0.00	0.72	0.55	0.002
HY	0.75	-0.52	0.00	0.33	0.91	0.002
MA	0.56	-0.75	0.00	0.43	0.84	0.002
KK	0.11	-0.99	0.00	0.50	0.79	0.002

* 510 nm was used for the subject KK.

to the zero response of the red–green opponent-colour channel, that is, the red–green equilibrium.

The theoretical $\varrho_1 - \varrho_2$ curves fit the experimental $\varrho_1 - \varrho_2$ plots very well for all subjects. The subject who has the broadest luminous efficiency curve is expected to show a large contribution of the red–green opponent-colour channel to brightness. When this contribution is expressed as C_{11} for 500 nm it increases in the order: KK, MA, HY, and SR; but the contribution expressed as C_{12} for 660 nm does not vary systematically for the four subjects, as shown in Table 1. This unexpected problem might be caused by an inadequate choice of p and q.

We conclude that the contribution of the opponent-colour channels to brightness causes the broadening of the luminous efficiency curve as well as the additivity failure of the reduction type. Furthermore, the asymmetry of $\varrho_1 - \varrho_2$ plots for individual subjects can be explained by the nonlinear contribution of the opponent-colour channels to brightness.

Acknowledgement

We are very grateful to Drs J. D. Mollon and L. T. Sharpe who have commented on earlier drafts of this manuscript.

References

Bauer, H. D. and Röhler, R. (1977). Brightness generation in the human visual system. Colour-brightness: a contribution of cortical colour channels to brightness sensation. *Vision Res.* **17**, 1211–1216.

Boynton, R. M., Ikeda, M. and Stiles, W. S. (1964). Interactions among chromatic mechanisms as inferred from positive and negative increment thresholds. *Vision Res.* **4**, 87–117.

Comerford, J. P. and Kaiser, P. K. (1975). Luminous–efficiency functions determined by heterochromatic brightness matching. *J. opt. Soc. Am.* **65**, 466–468.

Guth, S. L. and Lodge, H. R. (1973). Heterochromatic additivity, foveal spectral sensitivity, and a new color model. *J. opt. Soc. Am.* **63**, 450–462.

Ikeda, M., Yaguchi, H., Yoshimatsu, K. and Ohmi, M. (1982). Luminous-efficiency functions for point sources. *J. opt. Soc. Am.* **72**, 68–74.

Ingling, C. R. and Tsou, B. H. (1977). Orthogonal combination of the three visual channels. *Vision Res.* **17**, 1075–1082.

Kranda, K. and King-Smith, P. E. (1979). Detection of coloured stimuli by independent linear systems. *Vision Res.* **21**, 733–745.

Tessier, M. and Blottiau, F. (1951). Variations des caractéristiques photométriques de l'oeil aux luminances photopiques. *Revue d'Optique.* **30**, 309–322.

Wagner, G. and Boynton, R. M. (1972). Comparison of four methods of heterochromatic photometry. *J. opt. Soc. Am.* **62**, 1508–1515.

Yaguchi, H. and Ikeda, M. (1980). Helmholtz-Kohlrausch effect investigated by the brightness additivity. *J. Illum. Inst. Japan.* **64**, 566–570.

Yaguchi, H. and Ikeda, M. (1982). Nonlinear nature of the opponent-color channels. *Color Res. Appl.* **7**, 187–190.

Relationship of Opponent-Colours Cancellation Measures to Cone-Antagonistic Signals Deduced from Increment Threshold Data

J. E. THORNTON and E. N. PUGH, Jr

This paper is concerned with the psychophysical isolation of pathways that code spectral information. "Isolation", as we shall use the term here, means that an experimental measurement (e.g., a threshold) *depends exclusively on the activity of a single visual pathway*. A "pathway" is a model of information flow from a specified class or classes of photoreceptors to higher visual centers, which accounts for a set of lawful empirical properties on the basis of physical, chemical, physiological and purely formal theory. The paradigmatic example of psychophysical isolation is the isolation of the rod pathway, exemplified in the classic investigation of Aguilar and Stiles (1954).

The concept of isolation must be distinguished from the notion of physiological separability or "insulation". The isolation of "rods" from "cones" neither depends on nor implies that the neurons transmitting signals from the two classes of end organs are anatomically or physiologically insulated from one another at all levels of the visual system. Rod isolation is possible under some conditions in spite of the rod/cone interaction which is observed under other conditions. Thus, effective isolation of a pathway is an empirical question. Validation of a claim that a specific operation yields isolation is enhanced when other, converging operations give consistent and more refined characterization of the pathway.

COLOUR VISION
ISBN 0 12 000000 0

By analogy with the isolation of rods from cones, an important goal of color research is the *isolation* of visual pathways involved in coding spectral information. The first systematic attempt to isolate component pathways of photopic vision was that of Stiles (1939). Stiles's two-color increment threshold technique and his component branch or π-mechanism analysis provides an operationally rigorous and experimentally reliable isolation procedure. Although by 1953 it was certain from the very existence of $5-7$ π-mechanisms that each one could not be determined by a distinct foveal cone class, the belief persisted that in isolating a π-mechanism one had indeed isolated some genuine functional entity. Stiles's experiments (which operationally define the π-mechanisms) employed only monochromatic fields (with the exception of the use of auxiliary fields, which were not varied), and thus were all executed on the "surface" of color space. The property of Field Additivity, were it obeyed, would further characterize an isolated π-mechanism, and lead to a natural extension of the π-mechanism model to the interior of color space (Wyszecki and Stiles, 1967, p. 578). Field mixture experiments, in which thresholds for an isolated π-mechanism are measured upon monochromatic fields and bichromatic mixtures of these fields, test whether or not an isolated mechanism obeys Field Additivity.

Figure 1 shows foveal data collected this summer with the field-mixture paradigm. The test wavelength for these measurements was 430 nm. The background wavelength for the data on the left was 470 nm; the data on the right are the thresholds measured upon 578 nm alone and various mixtures of 470-nm and 578-nm fields. The conditions employed were approximately those used by Stiles to isolate the π_1 component branch. Here, as reported previously (Mollon and Polden, 1977; Pugh and Mollon, 1979; Polden and Mollon, 1980; Pugh and Larimer, 1980), Field Additivity indisputably fails for the π_1 mechanism. We do not believe that this failure requires that one give up the intuition that a component branch in Stiles's two-color threshold paradigm isolates something. Rather, what these and other field-mixture data (e.g., Wandell and Pugh, 1980) clearly tell us is that the theoretical interpretation of an isolated π-mechanism as an insulated information channel is inadequate. Whatever is isolated when one isolates a π-mechanism cannot be thought of in the simple manner that one (perhaps naively) thinks of the scotopic visual system when it is isolated from the photopic. For the chief fact about scotopic vision is that under true scotopic isolation, all action spectra are governed by one spectral sensitivity, and that sensitivity is proportional to the absorption spectrum of the rod's pigment, rhodopsin. On the other hand, the invariance of the test spectral sensitivity under π_1 and π_3 isolation conditions persistently suggested that all the facts about these two π-mechanisms might admit a common explanation.

A specific theoretical proposal about what Stiles had isolated when he isolated the π_1 branch was made when the first field-mixture study on π_1 was

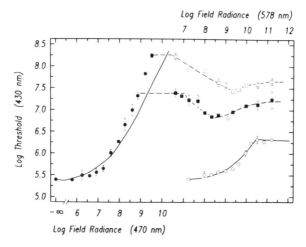

FIG. 1   A field-mixture experiment measuring threshold for a 430-nm test upon
monochromatic backgrounds and bichromatic mixtures of 470 nm and 578 nm.
All units are quanta sec^{-1} deg^{-2} (the test is measured at its peak in space and
time). On the left (●) are tvr data measured on the 470-nm field alone; the solid
curve through the data is Stiles' template (Wyszecki and Stiles, 1967). The tvr
data on the lower right (○) was measured on the 578-nm field alone; again the
Stiles template was fit to the data. The dashed curves show threshold measured
on bichromatic field mixtures of variable 578-nm components (shown by scale
on top) and two fixed 470-nm components: $10^{8.86}$ (■) and $10^{9.52}$ (□) quanta
sec^{-1} deg^{-2}. The (◇) represents the threshold measured in another experiment
(Fig. 4; $n = 7$) on the mixture field judged to be in yellow–blue equilibrium.
Observer: TE.

reported (Pugh, 1976), and was elaborated (Augenstein and Pugh, 1977) as
clear evidence was obtained that cone-antagonistic signals were involved in
setting the gain or sensitivity of whatever was being isolated. Particularly
important in clarifying the matter and in making the connection with π_3 data
was the demonstration of Mollon and Polden (1977) and Polden and Mollon
(1980) of the "sensitization" or "field cancellation" effect seen on the right side
of Fig. 1. The results of these and other studies were consolidated, and a com-
prehensive theory of what was isolated when one isolated the π_1 or π_3 component branches was proposed (Pugh and Mollon, 1979). To explain the obedience
of the short-wave spectral region to the Test Displacement Law under π_1 and
π_3 isolation conditions, the theory hypothesized that the threshold signal
detected did start in one class of photoreceptors, the α-cones, and did undergo
some (first site) gain control there. The signal next travelled through a "second
site" with a cone antagonistic gain control in which signals from the α-cones opposed signals from the β- and γ-cones (notation: $\alpha/(\beta,\gamma)$; see Note 1). If either
of the antagonistic inputs dominated the other, the second site was "polarized",

i.e. desensitized. Features of the data in Fig. 1 which can be explained by the two-site model are these. (1) The 470 nm tvr curve rises at a rate steeper than Weber's Law because it represents adaptation occurring at both first and second sites simultaneously. (2) The long-wave secondary mode of the π_1 field sensitivity is caused by adaptation resulting from second site polarization due to signals from β- and γ-cones; this adaptation plateaus (Stiles's "limited conditioning effect") when the signal from those cones asymptotes due to bleaching. (3) The addition of 578-nm light to a bright, fixed 470-nm adapting field causes threshold to drop because it restores a balance between the antagonistic inputs to the second site.

The notion that cones send opposite signed signals to neurons proximal to the cones did not originate with field-mixture studies. The idea is implicit in Hering's Opponent Process Color Theory, and has been developed (Hurvich and Jameson, 1957; Jameson and Hurvich, 1968) to explain data of a very different sort: the existence and intensity invariance of hue equilibria. A fundamental tenet of Opponent Colors Theory is a belief that one can *isolate* an opponent channel by introspection: one can say whether or not a given opponent channel is active, and what sign its activity has. Although this belief cannot be rationalized with the logic that supports threshold experiments (Teller and Pugh, this volume), it nonetheless has led to a successful experimental paradigm, the hue cancellation experiment (Jameson and Hurvich, 1955; Krantz, 1975; Larimer, Krantz and Cicerone, 1974, 1975) which has provided color vision with a rich, quantitative data base.

Since the π_1 field cancellation effect was attributed to $\alpha/(\beta, \gamma)$ cone antagonism in the gain control at the hypothesized second site, it was natural to inquire whether this antagonism could be the same as that postulated by Opponent Color Theory for the summing point of its yellow–blue channel. Pugh and Larimer (1980) tested the prediction that fields in yellow–blue equilibrium would not elevate threshold by second-site polarization. Their experimental results were consistent with this hypothesis. In addition, their use of the yellow–blue cancellation paradigm with intense steady-state fields revealed a new phenomenon consistent with the Pugh/Mollon theoretical explanation of π_3: an apparently "bleaching-limited yellow signal" in the color cancellation experiment. The apparent convergence of these two very different types of experiments was encouraging. Yet one could argue that the Pugh/Larimer experiment was simply not powerful enough to reject the hypothesis they tested, since the sensitization troughs in the field-mixture experiments are quite broad. (Note the $\diamond$ in Fig. 1 which was measured on the background judged to be yellow–blue equilibrium in a separate experiment.) Furthermore, an attempt by Polden and Mollon (1980) to make the same comparison did not support the hypothesis.

The goal of the experiments to be described here was to apply another converging operation to provide a stronger test of the identity of the pathways of the blue−yellow opponent judgments and of the π_1/π_3 data. In a sense our idea was a generalized version of the Stilesian principle that the test and field sensitivity of a "mechanism" ought to be the same. If signals from β- and γ-cones do oppose those from α-cones at the input to a second site, then under appropriate conditions transient threshold signals from the β- and γ-cones should propagate through the second site and be detected, just like the α-cone signal. The idea of a "yellow" threshold signal is at least an interesting logical possibility predicted by the two-site theory (as well as by Opponent Colors Theory), but it was by no means obvious what the "appropriate conditions" were. Little direct evidence could be found for it in the detection literature (however, see Stiles, 1967, Fig. 7). Our search began with an informative detour through the more travelled territory of β/γ cone-antagonism in detection experiments, a brief detour we make here.

Threshold evidence for the existence of β/γ cone antagonism has been of two types: (1) the subadditivity of threshold mixtures of mid-wave and long-wavelength lights (Ikeda, 1963; Boynton, Ikeda and Stiles, 1964; Guth, 1965; Kranda and King-Smith, 1979); and (2) the appearance of a "Sloan" notch near 580 nm in spectral sensitivity data, i.e., a notch separating two sensitivity peaks or shoulders clearly improperly positioned and too peaked to be due to the β- or γ-cones (Sloan, 1928; Sperling and Harwerth, 1971; King-Smith and Carden, 1976). Both types of evidence are usually attributed to detection through a cone-antagonistic pathway. In hope of improving the isolation of this pathway at detection threshold, we developed a spatio-temporal "low frequency" test stimulus (Thornton, 1981). Its temporal profile is one period (trough-to-trough) of a 2 Hz sine wave and its spatial profile is Gaussian, about 3 degrees across at half-height. Selection of these temporal and spatial parameters was based on the belief that in this case the problem of isolation was one of improving the sensitivity of a low-band-pass chromatic channel relative to the high-frequency-sensitive luminance channel. Eliminating from the stimulus any temporal or spatial edges, which introduce energy at high frequencies, was expected to favor detection by chromatic channels. All the data in this paper were collected using this low frequency stimulus, with the exception of Fig. 5A.

Isolation of chromatic signals is also aided by the use of two-alternative forced-choice trials (2AFC). Although 2AFC trials are somewhat slower than yes−no or method of adjustment procedures, they are much less susceptible to "criterion content" biases. To give an introspective example, it seems that the "luminance criterion" is easier for an observer to use − it is a more salient change near threshold. This salience encourages observers to adopt a conservative, "luminance" criterion even though a chromatic criterion would permit a lower threshold. 2AFC trials minimize this problem; college students usually give reasonable data in less than 30 minutes of training. In all the threshold data reported here, 2AFC trials were used in a staircase procedure in which stimulus intensity was decreased 0.04 log units after each correct response and increased 0.16 log units after each error. Threshold was estimated by the average of the 25 stimulus intensities following the third staircase reversal. In the graphs, plotted points are means of between two and eight such staircases (error bars show ± 1.0 SEM).

Figure 2 shows both threshold versus wavelength (tv λ) data and test mixture data providing evidence for β/γ antagonism at threshold. All thresholds were measured on a white, xenon 10° background of 6000 trolands. As Sperling

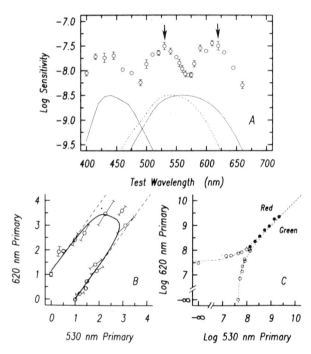

FIG. 2   (A) Spectral sensitivity for detection of low frequency test measured on a 6000 td xenon background. Units on ordinate are inverse quanta sec^{-1} deg^{-2}. Curves below data show estimates of cone spectral sensitivities from Vos (1978). Arrows mark wavelengths (530 and 620 nm) used in test mixture experiment displayed in B and C. (B) Test mixture experiment plotted on a linear scale with the unit of each axis taken to be the threshold quantity of that primary. The solid curve is the fit of a multimechanism model similar to that used by Kranda and King-Smith (1979). The present model differs in that a single opponent pathway may signal detection based either on a response increment or decrement. The resulting "thresholds" for that pathway are shown by the dotted lines. (C) The threshold data from B plotted on a logarithmic scale in units of quanta sec^{-1} deg^{-2}. The dotted lines from B are shown extrapolated to higher intensities. The supra-threshold data (●) show the results of red−green hue equilibrium staircases at a number of fixed 530 nm intensities. Observer: DK.

and Harwerth (1971) have argued, tvλ data like those shown in Fig. 2A support β/γ antagonism because the spectral location of the long- and mid-wave peaks, their bandwidth, and the depth of the cleft between them cannot be accounted for by a positive combination of the receptor sensitivities (drawn at bottom in Fig. 2A).

Direct evidence for β/γ cone antagonism can also be obtained in a test mixture experiment measuring threshold for bichromatic mixtures of the two wavelengths shown by arrows in Fig. 2A (530 and 620 nm). To determine a single threshold, the intensity ratio of the primaries was held constant and their joint intensity varied via a 2AFC staircase. This procedure was repeated at a number of mixture ratios and for each primary alone. The data are plotted in Fig. 2B in linear units scaled so that threshold for each primary alone is set to 1.0 on that axis. Here β/γ cone-antagonism is evident where the test mixture increases the amounts of both primaries (and the quantum catches of the cones) but decreases detectability. The data has been fit with a multi-mechanism model similar to the one used by Kranda and King-Smith (1979). In this model, sensitivity is pooled across mechanisms by probability summation. Within a mechanism, sensitivity to a bichromatic mixture is given by a linear combination of the mechanism's sensitivities to the two primaries. Therefore, in linear units, the threshold for an individual mechanism is a straight line. In Fig. 2B, the linear sides of the threshold contour indicate substantial isolation, for apparently no other detection mechanism intrudes until the mixture exceeds 3 times the threshold amount of each primary. When a single mechanism is isolated over some portion of the threshold contour, the slope of that segment gives the relative sensitivity of that mechanism to the two primaries. The parallelism of the linear sides of the threshold contour argues that the same mechanism is governing detection on both sides. This would seem to require that detection be based on the signals of a fairly homogeneous population of chromatically coded neurones.

Finally, Fig. 2C shows the agreement between the opponency at threshold and the opponency evident in supra-threshold hue judgement. In this figure, the open symbols are the data from Fig. 2B plotted on a log axis so that more of the mixture space can be displayed. The filled symbols show the results of red–green hue cancellation staircases which determined the amounts of 620-nm primary needed to cancel fixed amounts of the 530-nm primary leaving mixtures in red–green equilibrium. The dotted lines show the extension of the parallel portions of the threshold contour to suprathreshold levels. The graph shows that the incremental greenness and redness curves converge at higher intensities to the red–green equilibrium locus.[2] It appears that the β/γ balance point in the pathway isolated at threshold is the same as that postulated by Opponent Colors Theory to explain suprathreshold red–green equilibrium. Other results comparing the long-wave/mid-wave threshold inhibitory effect and red–green equilibria under various states of chromatic adaptation have been presented elsewhere (Thornton and Pugh, 1981). The general finding was that the wavelength of unique yellow and the wavelength of the minimum of the sensitivity trough in a tvλ curve agreed closely with the wavelength of the field for backgrounds in the spectral range tested (560–600 nm). Because of this agreement, we feel justified in replacing the term β/γ antagonism with the term red–green opponency, and in calling the pathway isolated the red–green pathway.

We now had the information necessary to search rationally for a perturbation signal mediated by the (β, γ) side of the $\alpha/(\beta, \gamma)$ cone-antagonistic π_1 pathway. The primary reason for expecting such a signal to exist was the manifest requirement for $\alpha/(\beta, \gamma)$ antagonism in the gain control at the second site. Since previous data showed that gain at the second site was reduced when the $\alpha/(\beta, \gamma)$ signals were not balanced (Pugh and Larimer, 1980), we chose as the adaptation condition a 470-nm and 578-nm bichromatic field judged to be in yellow–blue equilibrium. The intensity of the 470 nm component was the same, $10^{8.86}$ quanta sec^{-1} deg^{-2}, as that in the lower field-mixture curve in Fig. 1. The intensity of the 578 nm component was $10^{9.13}$ quanta sec^{-1} deg^{-2}.

Figure 3 shows tvλ data with three sensitivity peaks similar to those in Fig. 2A. Under these near neutral conditions in the mid- and long-wave spectral regions the low frequency stimulus is largely detected by the red–green pathway. To isolate a perturbation signal originating in the (β, γ) cones which is not detected by the red–green pathway, the wavelength of the stimulus must be carefully selected to be near the red–green crossover point. This

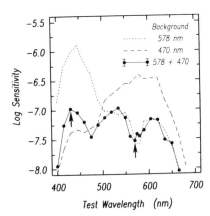

FIG. 3   Low frequency test spectral sensitivity data measured on three backgrounds: 578 and 470 nm ($10^{9.13}$ and $10^{8.86}$ quanta sec^{-1} deg^{-2}) and the bichromatic mixture of these two fields, which was judged to be in yellow–blue equilibrium. Arrows show wavelengths (430 and 570 nm) used in test mixture experiment in Fig. 4. Error bars in symbol key show the mean size averaged across all three fields (mean size of 1.0 SEM was 0.059 log units). Observer: TE.

wavelength, found to be about 570 nm under these adaptation conditions, was then used as one primary in a test mixture experiment in which the other primary, 430 nm, was from the short-wave peak (see arrows).

The results of that mixture experiment are shown in Fig. 4A in linear units. Test stimuli of these wavelengths clearly do inhibit detection of one another, although the effect is not as pronounced as the red–green inhibition effect seen in Fig. 2B. The isolation in this threshold contour is not sufficient to decide whether the sides are parallel. However, we have collected data on more intense, xenon backgrounds demonstrating that parallelism can be obtained when the isolation is better. In any case, parallelism is not rejected in these data as shown by the fit of a model in which parallel sides were required. For mid-wave primaries only 15 nm away from the minimum of the sensitivity trough, detection is not inhibited at all by addition of a fractional 430-nm component to the mixture (Thornton and Pugh, 1982). Furthermore, test mixture experiments performed on the above 578-nm field component alone also failed to show any threshold inhibition between 430 nm and mid-wavelength primaries.

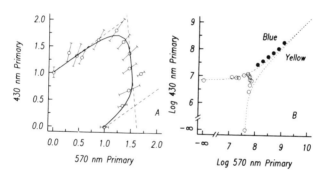

FIG. 4 (A) Thresholds for bichromatic mixtures of 570 and 430 nm measured on the 578 + 470 nm mixture background from Fig. 3. Data are plotted on a linear scale in "threshold" units. Parallel dotted lines show "iso-response" curves (one for just detectable increments, one for decrements) within the opponent pathway. (B) Same data and dotted lines replotted on logarithmic scale in units of quanta sec^{-1} deg^{-2}. Suprathreshold data (●) show yellow–blue hue equilibria. Observer: TE.

Figure 4B shows the relationship between the threshold data (open symbols) and suprathreshold yellow–blue hue equilibria (filled symbols) obtained using a staircase to find the 430-nm intensities necessary to equilibrate several fixed 570-nm lights. The division of the space into bluish and yellowish halves is consistent with the threshold data and justifies the application of the adjective yellow–blue to the π_1/π_3 pathway.

Recent work by L. J. Friedman in our laboratory (Friedman, Thornton,

Knoblauch and Pugh, 1982) has extended the π_1/π_3 pathway model to protanopic and deuteranopic observers. Since such dichromats are usually conceived as retaining the yellow–blue chromatic system more-or-less intact, they should display all of the field- and test-mixture evidence for α/β or α/γ cone-antagonism presented above. Figure 5A shows a field mixture experiment for a protanope. The left panel shows tvr data on a 470-nm background, the right shows tvr data on a 590-nm background and on mixture fields formed by various amounts of 590-nm light added to fixed amounts of 470-nm light. The "field cancellation" or "sensitization" effect which is diagnostic of

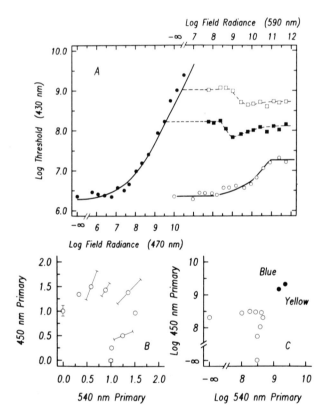

FIG. 5 (A) Field mixture experiment in a protanope using backgrounds of 470 and 590 nm and a 430-nm, 200 msec, 1° test. All units are quanta sec^{-1} deg^{-2}. Solid curves are Stiles template, dashed curves are drawn through thresholds measured on mixture backgrounds with fixed 470-nm components of $10^{9.52}$ and $10^{10.16}$ quanta sec^{-1} deg^{-2}. (B) Thresholds for bichromatic mixtures of 540 and 450 nm measured on a 6000 td xenon background. (C) Data from B (o) plotted on a logarithmic scale with units of quanta sec^{-1} deg^{-2}. Suprathreshold yellow–blue hue equilibria (•) on the same background. Observer: KK.

cone-antagonism in trichromats is also clearly observable in dichromats. Figure 5B shows a low frequency test mixture experiment on a white, xenon background using primaries of 450 and 540 nm. Threshold inhibition is observed, although the magnitude of the inhibition effect from this and other dichromatic observers is definitely not as large as we have observed in trichromats using the same background. Apparently, the sensitivity of the yellow−blue opponent system is reduced relative to the luminance system in dichromats. In an observer who is believed to retain a single opponent, chromatic system, there is little question about how these cone antagonistic effects should be associated with suprathreshold color appearance. Figure 5C shows that suprathreshold yellow−blue hue equilibria agree well with the inhibition seen in the test mixture experiment.

We conclude that the two-site yellow−blue pathway can provide a coherent account for a large body of threshold and suprathreshold data. In particular, it explains the bulk of psychophysical data concerning signals from the α-cones. But there are at least two empirical observations concerning the α-cone signals that are not accommodated by the model. First, within the two-color increment threshold paradigm itself there is the elusive π_2 mechanism (Stiles, 1953). π_2 has the same test spectral sensitivity as π_1 and thus apparently represents a pathway originating in the α-cones. The field sensitivity of this tvr component has a striking notch near unique yellow, suggesting that the π_2 adaptation governed by long-wave fields might occur at a $\beta/(\gamma,\alpha)$ color opponent site. Unfortunately our efforts to study π_2 have been frustrated by the fact that it seems to disappear in observers trained with the 2AFC procedure − apparently the π_1 branch has an intrinsically greater sensitivity with that procedure. Second, classic Opponent Colors Theory (Hurvich and Jameson, 1957; Larimer *et al.*, 1975) postulates an α-cone input into the red−green channel in order to account for the redness in short-wavelength lights. Although we have collected test mixture data which can be interpreted as indicating summation of the redness in short-wavelength and long-wavelength lights (Thornton and Pugh, 1982), the pattern of summation and inhibition is complex and not yet well understood, but further experiments and theoretical investigations are underway. We feel that the refinement of procedures for isolating pathways, and the development of convergent operations for characterizing these pathways are basic to deeper understanding of the processes of photopic vision through psychophysics.

Acknowledgement

Special thanks are due to the observers involved in these experiments: Tom Eppright and David Kurland. This work was supported by NSF grant BNS 79-24163.

Notes

1. In an effort to keep the identity of the three foveal cone classes distinct from perceptual color qualities associated with certain regions of the spectrum, we use the symbols α, β, γ to refer to the short-wave-sensitive (SWS, $\lambda_{max} = 420$ nm), the mid-wave-sensitive (MWS, $\lambda_{max} = 530$ nm), and long-wave-sensitive (LWS, $\lambda_{max} = 555$ nm), respectively. To refer to the convergence with opposite signs of signals from different cone classes into a specific pathway, we use the term "cone-antagonism" – e.g., "β/γ cone-antagonism" and "$\alpha/(\beta, \gamma)$ cone-antagonism".
2. When a family of curves parallel in linear units is replotted in logarithmic units, all members converge asymptotically to that member of the family passing through the origin in the linear space.

References

Aguilar, M. and Stiles, W. S. (1954). Saturation of the rod mechanism of the retina at high levels of stimulation. *Opt. Acta* **1**, 59–65.

Augenstein, E. J. and Pugh, E. N. Jr (1977). The dynamics of the π_1 colour mechanism: further evidence for two sites of adaptation. *J. Physiol.* **272**, 247–281.

Boynton, R. M., Ikeda, M. and Stiles, W. S. (1964). Interactions among chromatic mechanisms as inferred from positive and negative increment thresholds. *Vision Res.* **4**, 87–117.

Friedman, L. J., Thornton, J. E., Knoblauch, K. and Pugh, E. N. Jr (1982). Cone antagonism in red–green dichromats. *Invest. Ophthal. Vis. Sci.* **22** (Suppl.), 120.

Guth, S. L. (1965). Luminance addition: general considerations and some results at foveal threshold. *J. opt. Soc. Am.* **55**, 718–722.

Hurvich, L. M. and Jameson, D. (1957). An opponent-process theory of color vision. *Psych. Rev.* **64**, 384–404.

Ikeda, M. (1963). Study of interrelations between mechanisms at threshold. *J. opt. Soc. Am.* **53**, 1305–1313.

Jameson, D. and Hurvich, L. M. (1955). Some quantitative aspects of an opponent-colors theory I: Chromatic responses and spectral saturation. *J. opt. Soc. Am.* **45**, 546–552.

Jameson, D. and Hurvich, L. M. (1968). Opponent-response functions related to measured cone photopigments. *J. opt. Soc. Am.* **58**, 429–430.

King-Smith, P. E. and Carden, D. (1976). Luminance and opponent-color contributions to visual detection and adaptation and to temporal and spatial integration. *J. opt. Soc. Am.* **66**, 709–711.

Kranda, K. and King-Smith, P. E. (1979). Detection of coloured stimuli by independent linear systems. *Vision Res.* **19**, 733–745.

Krantz, D. H. (1975). Color measurement and color theory: II. Opponent-colors theory. *J. Math. Psych.* **12**, 304–327.

Larimer, J., Krantz, D. H. and Cicerone, C. M. (1974). Opponent-process additivity. I: Red/Green equilibria. *Vision Res.* **14**, 1127–1140.

Larimer, J., Krantz, D. H. and Cicerone, C. M. (1975). Opponent process additivity. II: Yellow/Blue equilibria and nonlinear models. *Vision Res.* **15**, 723–731.

Mollon, J. D. and Polden, P. G. (1977). An anomaly of light adaptation. *Invest. Ophthal. Vis. Sci.* **16** (Suppl.), 177.

Polden, P. G. and Mollon, J. D. (1980). Reversed effect of adapting stimuli on visual sensitivity. *Proc. Roy. Soc.* **B210**, 235–272.

Pugh, E. N. Jr (1976). The nature of the π_1 mechanism of W. S. Stiles. *J. Physiol.* **257**, 713–747.

Pugh, E. N. Jr and Larimer, J. (1980). Test of the identity of the site of blue/yellow hue cancellation and the site of chromatic antagonism in the π_1 pathway. *Vision Res.* **20**, 779–788.

Pugh, E. N. Jr and Mollon, J. D. (1979). A theory of the π_1 and π_3 color mechanisms of Stiles. *Vision Res.* **19**, 293–312.

Sloan, L. L. (1928). The effect of intensity of light, state of adaptation of the eye, and size of photometric field on the visibility curve. *Psych. Monog.* **38**, No. 1, 1–87.

Sperling, H. G. and Harwerth, R. S. (1971). Red–green cone interactions in the increment-threshold spectral sensitivity of primates. *Science* **172**, 180–184.

Stiles, W. S. (1939). The directional sensitivity of the retina and the spectral sensitivities of the rods and cones. *Proc. roy. Soc.* **B127**, 64–105.

Stiles, W. S. (1953). Further studies of visual mechanisms by the two-colour threshold technique. *Coloq. Probl. Opt. Vis. (U.I.P.A.P., Madrid)* **1**, 65–103.

Stiles, W. S. (1967). Mechanism concepts in colour theory. *Newton Lecture, J. Colour Group, No. 11*, 106–123.

Thornton, J. E. (1981). Relating chromatic antagonism in π_5 to red/green hue cancellation. PhD Thesis, University of Michigan, University Microfilms, Ann Arbor.

Thornton, J. E. and Pugh, E. N. Jr (1981). Low frequency test spectral sensitivity. *Invest. Ophthal. Vis. Sci.* **20** (Suppl.), 61.

Thornton, J. E. and Pugh, E. N. Jr (1982). Threshold inhibition within the yellow/blue pathway. *Invest. Ophthal. Vis. Sci.* **22** (Suppl.), 18.

Vos, J. J. (1978). Colorimetric and photometric properties of a 2° fundamental observer. *Color Res. and Appl.* **3**, 125–128.

Wandell, B. A. and Pugh, E. N. Jr (1980). Detection of long-duration, long-wavelength incremental flashes by a chromatically coded pathway. *Vision Res.* **20**, 625–636.

Wyszecki, G. and Stiles, W. S. (1967). *Color Science: Concepts and Methods, Quantitative Data and Formulas.* New York, Wiley.

Yellow – Blue Cancellation on Yellow Fields: Its Relevance to the Two-Process Theory

JAMES NICK and JAMES LARIMER

Introduction

Recent experiments (Walraven, 1976; Werner and Walraven, 1982; Shevell, 1977; Larimer, 1981) have generated a controversy as to the nature of the effect of a continuously present chromatic adapting field on color appearance. The issue underlying the controversy is whether or not the von Kries coefficient law is valid for all stimulus conditions. Studies have shown that the law is incorrect because of the failure of the proportionality rule which is a corollary of this theory. The nature of the failure suggests that a second process must be operating in addition to the multiplicative sensitivity changes that are expected by the coefficient law.

Hurvich and Jameson (1958) hypothesized that the second process is an additive signal arising from the adapting field. This signal is most effective in altering the appearance of dim lights superimposed on the field and is ineffective otherwise. Thus for dim lights the proportionality rule fails, but not for bright ones (Shevell, 1977; Larimer, 1981). Walraven (1976) argues from his data that the second process completely discounts the field by linearly removing signals from the adapting field that are in common with transient signals from lights superimposed upon the field. By this view only transient signals are processed. Thus he finds no failures of the proportionality rule.

The experiments which we report here were intended to explore this controversy using the yellow–blue equilibrium colors.

COLOUR VISION
ISBN 0 12 000000 0

Experiment 1

In this experiment an admixture of 460 nm blue light (denoted ΔB) plus 579 nm yellow light (denoted ΔY) of 1.86° visual angle was flashed for 1 sec on a concentric 579 nm yellow adapting field which subtended a visual angle of 3.58°. For each condition the intensity of the adapting field and ΔY were fixed. A double random staircase was used to determine the intensity of the ΔB that yielded a yellow–blue equilibrium mixture on the field. On each trial the observer was instructed to indicate whether the mixture appeared yellowish or bluish. The equilibrium locus was the estimated blue intensity that would equally often elicit yellow and blue responses. The data from this experiment are given in Fig. 1.

The figure contains data for five field conditions: no field, open circle; and for increasing field intensities given in the figure key in $\log_{10}$ quanta^{-1} sec^{-1} deg^{-2}. On the abscissa is the intensity of the yellow addend, ΔY, and on the

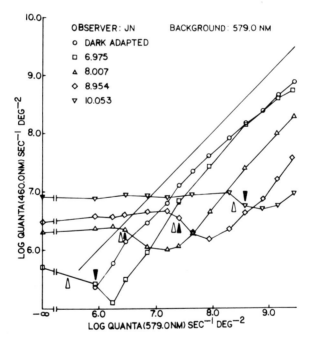

FIG. 1   The intensity of ΔB (460 nm, plotted on the ordinate in $\log_{10}$ quanta sec^{-1} deg^{-2}) as a function of ΔY (579 nm, plotted on the abscissa) required to cancel ΔY on various adapting fields. The field intensities are given in the symbol key in $\log_{10}$ quanta sec^{-1} deg^{-2}. The solid arrows are the intensities of ΔY for which observers first reported seeing a clear yellow incremental flash on the field. The open arrows are the intensities of ΔY that were independently determined to be at threshold in a 2AFC task on the corresponding fields.

ordinate the intensity of the blue variable, ΔB. Each set of points is a yellow—blue equilibrium locus. The proportionality rule which would have each locus plotted as a slope one line is grossly violated in these data. There are three features of these data that need to be considered.

For the dark adapted condition and all fields for which the ΔY is sufficiently intense, the loci lie along unit slope lines. This region in each data set is called the von Kries region and here the data obey the proportionality law. It is generally agreed that such regions exist and these data are not controversial.

On each of the nonzero field conditions it was possible to measure a ΔB intensity that satisfied the staircase criterion when no ΔY was present. These points are plotted on the ordinate and they position the horizontal plateau region of each equilibrium loci. In these regions the observers subjectively reported that they responded blue when they saw the flash and yellow otherwise. One could argue that the staircase procedure in this condition is similar to a yes—no threshold task. In that case the horizontal plateau could represent the threshold for ΔB on the field when ΔY is either not present or subthreshold. To support this contention the solid arrows are the intensities for ΔY for which observers first reported seeing a clear yellow incremental flash on the field. The open arrows are the increment thresholds for ΔY alone on these fields determined in a separate two-alternative forced-choice threshold experiment under identical adaptation conditions. In every case, the arrows locate the rightmost end of the plateau region of the equilibrium loci.

There is a little controversy in this interpretation of the horizontal plateau. If the field is completely discounted, then the transition from the plateau to the von Kries region should be abrupt. If on the other hand the field generates a signal that adds with the signal generated by the flashed mixture, then the transition should be smooth and gradually increasing to the von Kries region. Neither of these predictions are borne out in Fig. 1.

The transition from the horizontal plateau to the von Kries region is a shallow dipping region for each field intensity condition. We have attributed this dip elsewhere (Nick and Larimer, 1981) to an edge or gap effect similar to that reported by Boynton, Hayhoe and MacLeod, 1977. The downward portion moving to the right is due to the increased effectiveness of ΔB when ΔY is at or slightly superthreshold. The edge formed by ΔY could serve to delineate a smaller integration pool for the signal generated by ΔB. This, in effect, increases ΔB's spatial flux density thereby making it more effective. The gradual upperward sloping region is consistent with an additive signal from the yellow field.

Experiment 2

Two procedures were used in this experiment: a standard two-alternative forced-choice detection procedure to generate baseline tvi functions over a wide range of yellow background intensities and a cancellation procedure to determine yellow–blue equilibrium loci, over the same range. The stimulus configuration in both phases of this experiment was the same as before except that no ΔY was present in the flash.

The results for observer JN are shown in Fig. 2. The results from the threshold procedure are plotted with circles; the results from the cancellation experiment are plotted with triangles. The curves are the increment threshold function of Stiles computer fitted through the data points.

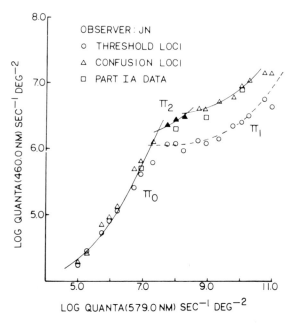

FIG. 2   The intensity of ΔB (460 nm, plotted on the ordinate in $\log_{10}$ quanta sec^{-1} deg^{-2}) at threshold (plotted as circles) as a function of the intensity of a yellow adapting field (579 nm, plotted on the abscissa). The intensity of ΔB determined by a cancellation procedure (plotted as triangles) that is equally often called yellow or blue (we refer to this as a confusion locus) as a function of the intensity of a yellow adapting field. The squares are the corresponding data points from the ordinate in Fig. 1.

The results of the threshold experiment clearly show the presence of two distinct branches of the tvi function and the beginning of a third branch, probably π_3, which will be disregarded for this discussion.

While it can be seen in this figure that there is little or no difference between the results of the two procedures along the lower branch, the cancellation procedure causes both a 0.5 log unit parallel shift upward for the upper branch and the isolation of yet another mechanism.

The lower branch has been identified as π_0 or rods through an ancillary experiment in which we determined the test spectral sensitivity function for the mechanism. The resulting test sensitivities obtained from this experiment are very well accounted for by the scotopic spectral sensitivity function.

The upper branch in Fig. 2 was identified as π_1 by first comparing the test and field spectral sensitivities obtained from a computer fit of Stiles' template to the data with tabled values for Stiles' "average observer" and secondly, by the excellent fit of the test-spectral sensitivity function to Stiles' π_1 color mechanism. The middle branch was identified as π_2 by comparing the obtained field sensitivity with the tabled value.

It is important to note here that the cancellation procedure was used in the test-spectral sensitivity experiments and that the results yielded data consistent with Stiles' Displacement Laws even though the observer used a subjective yellow–blue decision strategy rather than the usual threshold detection strategy.

Overall, the results of this experiment appear consistent with the hypothesis that the vertical position of the plateaus is determined by the threshold of ΔB on Y. The open squares are the data points on the ordinate from Fig. 1. It is important that the cancellation procedure used to determine the confusion loci yields tvi curves that are composed of the same identifiable branches found using standard threshold determination techniques only shifted upwards along the π_1 branch. The most parsimonious explanation for this small displacement and the isolation of an underlying segment of π_2 may simply be the criterion changes implicit in the two different measurement techniques. Two-alternative forced-choice procedures optimize detectability and generally put the observer at a lower point on the psychometric function than yes–no procedures. When the yellow addend is absent or subthreshold, the cancellation procedure is similar to a yes–no procedure. The π_2 mechanism is revealed with the cancellation procedure most likely because the psychometric function for π_2 is steeper than the corresponding π_1 psychometric function under these stimulus conditions.

Experiment 3

The experiments in this part of the investigation were carried out to directly show the effects of increasing the intensity of the yellow adapting field. The cancellation procedure used in Experiment 2 was used in these experiments. The only difference was that, for each experiment, a specific intensity of ΔY was selected and held constant while the intensity of the yellow background was increased.

Figure 3 shows the results for observer JN for a constant ΔY of various intensities ($\log_{10}$ quanta sec^{-1} deg^{-2}) given in the figure key. In addition to the data points and the solid lines fit through them, the tvi curves obtained from the cancellation experiment in Fig. 2 where ΔY was absent have been plotted as dashed curves for comparison.

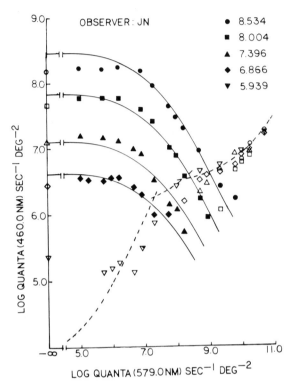

FIG. 3   The intensity of ΔB (460 nm, plotted on the ordinate in $\log_{10}$ quanta sec^{-1} deg^{-2}) that cancels a fixed yellow addend, ΔY, as a function of the intensity of a yellow adapting field (579 nm, plotted on the abscissa). The different symbols indicate different intensities of the yellow addend given in the key in $\log_{10}$ quanta sec^{-1} deg^{-2}. The inverted template was fitted to the solid points.

It is evident that the results obtained from this experiment are again composed of two distinct parts. First consider the data plotted with the filled circles. The solid, concave, downward curve computer fitted through these points is an inverted Stiles template. The good fit of the inverted template to the data points and its field point suggest that a gain change occurring in the yellow pathway is largely responsible for the observed reduction in ΔB through this background range. That is, as the gain of the yellow pathway decreases with increasing background intensities, the efficacy of the constant ΔY component decreases and is tracked by a corresponding decrease in ΔB. Note that this decrease in ΔB occurs through a background range where the gain of the blue pathway (π_1) is mostly unaltered. In addition, a simultaneous, least-squares fit of the inverted template to all the data obtained in this background region for all constant ΔYs shows that the adapting field intensity which causes a

1.0 log unit decrease in ΔB is in good agreement with the tabled field points for Stiles' long-wavelength mechanisms, π_4 and π_5, for a 579 nm adapting field. Both Shevell (1982) and Larimer (1981) have argued that the field is discounted about 80% under similar stimulus conditions. If the degree of discounting depended upon the field intensity, then the roll off in ΔB would not be expected to follow the Weber-Fechner line. Since the data clearly do follow the Weber-Fechner line, this supports the constant-proportion-discounted hypothesis and explains why little additive field effect is seen on dim fields.

Continued increases in the background intensity cause ΔB to drop below the $\Delta Y = 0$ locus before abruptly returning to generally follow along the π_1 gain function as shown by the dashed, concave, upward curve. It was found that ΔB reliably returned to the $\Delta Y = 0$ locus at the point where ΔY drops below threshold. The dip below the $\Delta Y = 0$ locus is again attributable to the "Gap Effect" which allows ΔB to be perceived as blue below the point where it would otherwise drop below threshold.

Experiment 4

This last series of experiments were designed to investigate the effect of changing the size of the adapting field. The procedure for these experiments used precisely the same wavelengths, the same intensities of ΔY, and of adapting backgrounds, and the same protocols as in the first experiment. The only difference was that three adapting field sizes were used in addition to the 3.58° field used in the first experiment.

The results of one of these experiments for observer JN is shown in Fig. 4. For this experiment, the background intensity was fixed at 8.007 $\log_{10}$ quanta $\sec^{-1} \deg^{-2}$ for all four background sizes. The most obvious feature of this figure is the systematic stratification of the plateaus which could be interpreted as being consistent with the hypothesis that a background-size-dependent restoring force is present which acts to contribute an increasingly larger blue signal in the test area as size is increased.

Another interesting aspect of these data is the difference found between the shape of the curves obtained with 1.86° adapting field (i.e., those that were the same size as the test field) and those that were larger. The curve for the 1.86° background in Fig. 4 conforms closely to the expected shape of Shevell's two-process template. The curves for the larger backgrounds exhibit the dip and the gradual transition to the von Kries region. This observation is supported by the excellent fit of the two-process template when the increments and the field are of the same size. This result, combined with the finding that an estimate of the magnitude of the additive signal from the background yielded a value of 7.9 $\log_{10}$ quanta $\sec^{-1} \deg^{-2}$, is consistent with the notion that when the test and adapting fields share a common perimeter, the

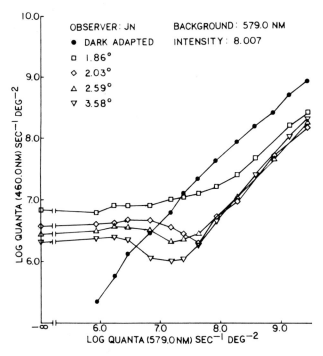

FIG. 4   The intensity of ΔB (460 nm, plotted on the ordinate in $\log_{10}$ quanta sec^{-1} deg^{-2}) as a function of ΔY (579 nm, plotted on the abscissa) required to cancel ΔY on different sized adapting fields all of the same intensity, 8.007 $\log_{10}$ quanta sec^{-1} deg^{-2}. The adapting field sizes are given in degrees of visual angle in the figure key. The solid circles are the equilibria determined in the dark without an adapting field.

background signal will add to the signal elicited by ΔY – i.e., little or no discounting. A similar calculation for the other field sizes show that as the field size increases so does the degree of discounting – perhaps to a limit of roughly 80%.

Conclusion

The results of these experiments suggest that the presence of an edge may be the crucial factor in determining whether the visual system will integrate color information arising from an adapting field along with that from a superimposed test field. Because the wavelength used by Shevell in his experiments strongly activated the edge encoding beta (middle-wavelength sensitive) and gamma (long-wavelength sensitive) cones, crisp, well-defined edges were always formed between his test field and the background. These edges, in turn, may have acted to interrupt the process by which the visual system apparently extracts color information from an edge and integrates it over a homogeneous field in order to fill in its center. Thus, color information extracted from the edge around the test field included redness from the background as well as from the red and green transients. In the present experiments, however, the blue test light alone, which evokes little or no activity in the beta and gamma cones, is not sufficient to form the necessary edges when superimposed on larger yellow backgrounds. Consequently, the integration process is not interrupted and the background remains "discounted". It is only when edges are formed either by a luminance step created by superthreshold amounts of ΔY or by the physical perimeter of the adapting field that a portion of the yellow from the background becomes integrated with the test-field. Apparently, as Gilchrist (1979) has noted "when one speaks of mixing colors, one should actually speak of mixing edges (changes in the light) rather than of mixing light itself".

References

Boynton, R. M., Hayhoe, M. M. and MacLeod, D. I. A. (1977). The gap effect: chromatic and achromatic visual discrimination as affected by field separation. *Optica Acta* **24**, 159–177.

Gilchrist, A. L. (1979). The perception of surface blacks and whites. *Scient. Am.* **240**, 112–124.

Hurvich, L. M. and Jameson, D. (1958). Further development of a quantified opponent-colors theory. In *Visual Problems of Colour II*. London, HMSO, pp. 691–723.

Larimer, J. (1981). Red/green opponent colors equilibria measured on chromatic adapting fields: Evidence for gain changes and restoring forces. *Vision Res.* **21**, 501–512.

Nick, J. and Larimer, J. (1981). Adding yellow makes blue more effective. *Invest. Ophthalmol. Vis. Sci.* **20**, 206.

Pugh, E. N. Jr and Larimer, J. (1980). Test of the identity of the site of blue/yellow hue cancellation and the site of chromatic antagonism in the π_1 pathway. *Vision Res.* **20**, 779–788.

Shevell, S. K. (1978). The dual role of chromatic backgrounds in color perception. *Vision Res.* **18**, 1649–1661.

Shevell, S. K. (1982). Color perception under chromatic adaptation: equilibrium yellow and long-wavelength adaptation. *Vision Res.* **22**, 279–292.

Walraven, J. (1976). Discounting the background – the missing link in the explanation of chromatic induction. *Vision Res.* **16**, 289–295.

Werner, J. S. and Walraven, J. (1982). Effect of chromatic adaptation on the achromatic locus: the role of contrast, luminance and background color. *Vision Res.* **22**, 929–943.

A Case for the Revision of Textbook Models of Color Vision: The Detection and Appearance of Small Brief Lights

DONALD C. HOOD and MARCIA A. FINKELSTEIN

Introduction

Most secondary textbooks would lead one to believe that the major problems in relating visual physiology to psychophysics have been solved. In general, three classes of models are either implicitly or explicitly assumed: a standard psychophysical model that explains color perception in terms of the activity elicited in chromatic and achromatic channels; a physiological model that includes four classes of opponent cells and two classes of nonopponent cells; and a psychophysiological model that assumes a one-to-one correspondence between the physiological cell types and the psychophysical channels.

The psychophysical, physiological, and psychophysiological models were originally formulated to explain the detection and appearances of lights presented under a specific set of conditions. Those conditions included large, long-duration stimuli presented under specified states of adaptation. We refer to those models as "textbook" models because many secondary texts either explicitly or implicitly assume they apply to all situations. However it is well, but not widely, known that psychophysical and physiological data contradict a number of the assumptions of these models. Many people in the field have pointed out these problems, but the more appealing misconceptions and over-simplifications continue to find their way into both the primary and secondary literature.

In the following sections, we use the detection and appearance of small,

COLOUR VISION
ISBN 0 12 000000 0

brief lights as a case study of some of the problems confronting the textbook view of the photopic system. In the process, we try to make the various kinds of assumptions as clear as possible.

Textbook Psychophysical Model

The basic assumptions of the textbook psychophysical model are listed in Fig. 1. There are two chromatic channels and one achromatic channel, each defined according to a set of *sensitivity assumptions* and *signalling assumptions*. The former specify the relation between the input to a channel and its sensitivity. The latter relate the channel's output to behavior. We will be concerned in this chapter with two types of signalling assumptions which we refer to as *appearance* and *detection assumptions.*

Consider first the sensitivity assumptions. Each channel has a unique spectral sensitivity function which is assumed to be fixed, based on the adapting conditions. The two chromatic channels, the "red–green" and "yellow–blue", are spectrally opponent; they are excited by lights of some wavelengths and inhibited by others. Each has a relative spectral sensitivity that corresponds to some fixed weighted difference of receptor absorption spectra. The graphs in Fig. 1 show the spectral sensitivity for the excitatory (solid curve) and inhibitory (dashed curve) responses of the red–green channels. The achromatic channel, on the other hand, is nonopponent and responds with the same polarity to lights of all wavelengths. Its relative spectral sensitivity is described by a weighted sum of cone absorption spectra and is generally assumed to match the photopic luminosity function.

The opponent–nonopponent distinction has consequences for the appearance assumptions. The chromatic system is assumed to signal hue information with the overall polarity (positive or negative) of the red–green and yellow–blue channels coding the hues for which they are named. In contrast, the achromatic system signals a single (achromatic) percept independent of stimulus wavelength.

The model also includes detection assumptions. These relate the outputs of the chromatic and achromatic channels to the overall sensitivity of the observer in the light-adapted state. A number of different detection assumptions are found in the psychophysical literature (see Fig. 1 for specific examples).

Models like that in Fig. 1 have been remarkably successful in describing the detection and appearance of lights under a variety of conditions (cf. Hurvich and Jameson, 1957; King-Smith and Carden, 1976; Ingling and Tsou, 1977; Guth, Massof and Benzschawel, 1980). We will see below, however, that the textbook implication that these models describe photopic activity under all conditions is refuted by psychophysical data.

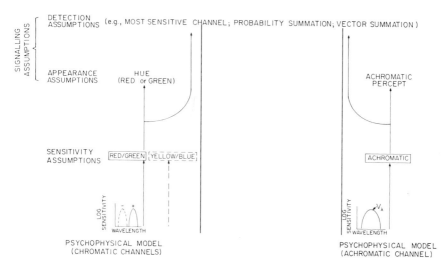

FIG. 1   The textbook psychophysical model of color vision. The appearances and relative detectabilities of lights are due to activity in two chromatic channels and one achromatic channel. The spectrally opponent nature of the chromatic channel is indicated by the minus and plus signs above the sample red–green spectral sensitivity; negative and positive labels are assigned arbitrarily. The relative spectral sensitivity of the achromatic channel has the same polarity at all wavelengths and is assumed to match the photopic luminosity function, V_λ. See text for details.

Detection Data: Test Sensitivities

Figure 2 contains the results of two detection experiments. In one (Finkelstein and Hood, unpublished) the observer's task was to detect a large (49′), long-duration (500 msec) light and in the other (Finkelstein and Hood, 1982a) a small (10′), brief (40 msec) light. Both lights were presented to the fovea on a 4.0 log td "white" (unfiltered tungsten) adapting background. The large-spot data (open circles) can be fitted by the spectral sensitivities of the chromatic channels. The solid and dashed curves through these data are the relative spectral sensitivities of the red–green and yellow–blue channels respectively (from Ingling and Tsou, 1977 for the light-adapted eye). The data are well fit by an envelope of the opponent sensitivities. Applications of the textbook psychophysical model to data like these lead to the conclusion that detection occurs mainly via the opponent channels (e.g. Sperling and Harwerth, 1971; King-Smith and Carden, 1976; Ingling and Tsou, 1977; Guth *et al.*, 1980).

The small-spot data (filled circles) are not so easily explained. The solid curve through these data is the relative spectral sensitivity of the achromatic system (i.e. the photopic luminosity function). While the photopic luminosity

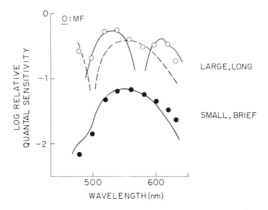

FIG. 2   Test sensitivities for foveal lights 49' in diameter and 500 msec in duration (open circles labelled large, long) or 10' in diameter and 40 msec in duration (filled circles labelled small, brief). Stimuli were presented in the center of a 4.0 log td "white" (unfiltered tungsten) adapting background. The solid and dashed curves fit to the large-spot data are estimates of the relative spectral sensitivities of the red−green and yellow−blue channels respectively (from Ingling and Tsou, 1977). The curve through the small-spot data is the photopic luminosity function and is assumed to represent the relative spectral sensitivity of the achromatic system.

function describes the data fairly well, there are deviations towards the ends of the spectrum. The test sensitivities fall below the achromatic curve in the short wavelengths and lie above it in the long. Nonetheless, this curve certainly provides a better fit than either of the opponent spectral sensitivities.

If we accept the textbook model, then these data suggest that large spots are detected by the chromatic system and small spots are detected primarily by the achromatic system. However, we will see in the following two sections that an achromatic detection hypothesis is contradicted by a variety of other data. Further, no version of the textbook model that maintains an invariant set of spectral sensitivities can handle the small-spot data. Any viable interpretation of the data requires revision of the sensitivity and appearance assumptions.

Detection Data: Field Sensitivities

The simplest hypothesis to explain the small-spot spectral sensitivities in Fig. 2 is that the lights are detected by the achromatic system (e.g. King-Smith and Carden, 1976). However, the field sensitivity data presented below contradict the simple hypothesis. They reveal a considerable opponent influence on sensitivity that requires revising the psychophysical model of Fig. 1.

First let us briefly review the methodology and logic of the field sensitivity procedure. The procedure is best introduced by contrasting it with the test sensitivity approach of the preceding section. Test sensitivities involve measuring detection thresholds for a range of test wavelengths. Plots of the data generally show, as in Fig. 2, relative sensitivity (i.e. the reciprocal of the number of quanta required for detection) as a function of test wavelength. Field sensitivity experiments, on the other hand, begin with a suprathreshold test of fixed wavelength and intensity. The test is presented upon mono-chromatic fields. The observer's task is to adjust the intensity of the field to bring the test to threshold. Thus the independent variable is field wavelength, not test wavelength. The result is a spectral sensitivity for desensitization of the test, a measure of the relative abilities of fields of different wavelengths at reducing sensitivity to the test. The procedure thus taps all the mechanisms that influence test sensitivity, whether they actually comprise the detection pathways or only interact with the detection pathways to desensitize them.

Figure 3 (from Finkelstein and Hood, 1982a) shows field sensitivities obtained for flashed fields with a small, brief 580 nm test (see figure for details).

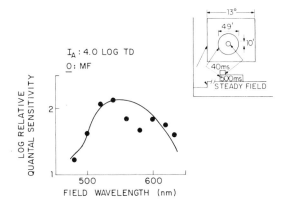

FIG. 3   Field sensitivity data obtained for flashed fields of monochromatic light. The test was 580 nm and 0.3 log unit above threshold intensity. The plot shows the log reciprocal flash intensity required to bring the test to threshold. The flashed fields were 49′ in diameter and 500 msec in duration, the test 10′ in diameter and 40 msec in duration. Test and flash were presented in the center of a 4.0 log td unfiltered tungsten adapting background (see inset). The solid curve is the photopic luminosity function (see text and Finkelstein and Hood, 1982a for details).

The axes plot the log reciprocal number of quanta needed as a function of the flashed-field wavelength. The solid curve is the achromatic system spectral sensitivity positioned to coincide with the data at 560 nm. The fit is very poor. The field sensitivities, like the *large*-test sensitivities of Fig. 2, show a dip in sensitivity at 580 nm and narrow peaks on either side. The shape of the data indicates that sensitivity to small, brief lights is influenced by a red−green opponent mechanism. (For further evidence of the involvement of a red–green mechanism see Finkelstein and Hood, 1982a). Small spots are not detected by an independent achromatic channel.

Wavelength Discrimination

Thus far it is clear that chromatic mechanisms can affect sensitivity to small, brief lights. However, we cannot conclude that the chromatic mechanisms actually comprise the small-spot detection pathways. Chromatic mechanisms may merely interact with the (achromatic) detection pathways to desensitize them. However, studies examining the discriminability and appearances of these lights implicate chromatic pathways in detection.

The textbook model assumes that the achromatic system signals an achromatic percept regardless of stimulus wavelength. Two lights detected by the system should therefore be identical at threshold. The discrimination threshold is reached only after intensities are sufficient to differentially stimulate a second system. We measured discrimination and detection thresholds for pairs of lights. Even the lights in the middle portion of the spectrum could be discriminated near threshold. Specifically, small 541 nm and 580 nm tests are discriminated within 0.06 log unit of their detection thresholds (Finkelstein and Hood, 1982b). That discrimination and detection performance were nearly equal implicates chromatic pathways in the detection of small, brief lights.

It could be argued that discrimination of the 541 nm and 580 nm lights is based on some nonchromatic cue, for example temporal information. However, this is not the case. We measured the appearance of the small, brief tests and found that these lights elicit different hue names near threshold. The 580 nm light is most often seen as white. The other wavelengths also appear desaturated and in general appear reddish above 580 nm and greenish or bluish–green below 580 nm. These results are in agreement with those of published studies (cf. Hill, 1947; Weitzman and Kinney, 1967; Ingling, Scheibner and Boynton, 1970; Krauskopf, 1978).

Taken together, the test sensitivities, field sensitivities, and wavelength discrimination data create serious problems for the textbook model of color vision. The test sensitivities look like the spectral sensitivity of the achromatic system. However, the field sensitivities show a huge opponent influence on detection, and the discrimination data suggest that chromatic mechanisms actually comprise the detection pathways. How do we account for the lack of an obvious opponent contribution to detection in the test sensitivity data? One possible solution is considered in the next section.

Alternative Psychophysical Model: Variable Tuning

The differences between the large- and small-spot data suggest that the relative spectral sensitivities of the opponent chromatic pathways become progressively broader as test size decreases. What we will call the "variable tuning hypothesis" states that small, brief lights are detected by chromatic pathways that change their spectral tuning with changes in stimulus parameters (cf. Massof and Bird, 1978; Wandell and Pugh, 1980; Finkelstein and Hood, 1982a). The hypothesis discards the notion of discrete red−green and yellow−blue pathways that represent some fixed weighted difference of receptor absorption spectra. Instead the tuning to the relevant dimension, wavelength, is drastically changed by presumably irrelevant dimensions, size and duration.

One way to broaden the spectral sensitivity function of a chromatic channel is to change the relative weights of the cone inputs. The result is a function that is broader at one end of the spectrum and narrower at the other. However, the model requires a more drastic revision to explain the data. A broadened red and/or yellow portion of a channel could be made to fit the test sensitivity data. However, it would not be sufficient to explain why the tests can be discriminated and, more problematical, why lights below 580 nm appear green. To solve these problems, more than one red−green (or yellow−blue) channel is needed.

An hypothesis that includes multiple red−green channels with variable tuning can account for both the small-spot detection and the discrimination data. The test sensitivities can be explained as an envelope of the underlying channel spectral sensitivities. Recall that the test sensitivities of Fig. 2 were not identical to the spectral sensitivity of the achromatic system. Test sensitivities both narrower and broader than the achromatic curve can be produced with different combinations of relatively narrow-band spectral sensitivities.

The traditional appearance assumptions also must be modified. The model of Fig. 1 assumes that hue is coded in the overall polarity of response in the red−green and yellow−blue channels. For example, a positive output from the red−green channel may signal a red percept, while in the yellow−blue channel, it might signal yellow. However, an implication of the variable tuning assumption is that under some conditions (e.g. when small, brief tests are used), these channels give a positive response to a wide range of wavelengths.

To understand the problem this creates, assume for a moment that there are two red−green channels, a R + /G − and a G + /R −. Two channels are assumed for purposes of discussion since many readers will be familiar with the R + /G − and G + /R − cells hypothesized by some physiologists. However, just as the evidence for only two cell types is weak (see below), there is no reason why more than two red−green channels may not exist. In any event, one consequence of broadening their spectral tuning functions is that small spots will produce positive responses in both channels for a range of stimulus wavelengths. The result, according to the traditional appearance assumption, is a greenish–reddish percept. However, small spots do not violate the opponent nature of color appearance. They do not appear both green and red at the same time.

One solution is to discard the assumption of a fixed link between positive and negative responses in a given channel and a given pair of hues. That is, instead of assuming a one-to-one correspondence between the output of a channel and a unique hue, a positive response in the R + /G− channel need not mean there will be red in the percept. To account for the appearances of lights, we will need to hypothesize more complicated relationships between the pattern of activity across channels and appearance. As an example of a more complicated hypothesis, suppose that an achromatic percept is signalled by equal activity across all channels. The 541 nm and 580 nm tests appear more achromatic than large lights because they elicit more similar responses from different channels. However, a sufficient number of channels give sufficiently different responses to the two tests to render them discriminable (i.e. different hues) at threshold.

To summarize, the small-spot data lead us to discard the assumptions of fixed spectral sensitivity functions, two chromatic mechanisms, and the simple link of channel to appearance. Some may feel we have gone too far. However, the physiological data to be discussed suggest the same course.

Physiological Model

Thus far discussion has dealt exclusively with *psychophysical* models. These models explain photopic vision in terms of the activity elicited in a hypothesized set of psychophysical channels. Another approach to understanding psychophysical data is to relate them to an hypothesized underlying physiology. Not all psychophysicists are concerned with the physiological bases of behavioral data, feeling that the psychophysical models can stand on their own. However, if the psychophysicist does invoke physiology − either indirectly by using the terminology of the physiologist, or directly by applying the physiological literature to his own data − then he must be careful to make his assumptions clear. This means specifying what he assumes to be the underlying physiology (i.e. a physiological model) and what he assumes to be the link between physiology and behavior (a psychophysiological model). In this section we present, and critically examine, a textbook physiological model and offer an alternative conceptualization. The next section examines alternative psychophysiological models.

The physiological model derives primarily from the work of DeValois, Abramov, and Jacobs (1966). Two general categories of cells, color-opponent and nonopponent, are assumed. These are further divided into four types of opponent cells and two types of nonopponent cells. The R + /G− and Y + /B− opponent cells are excited by long-wavelength lights and inhibited by short wavelengths; the crossover points fall around 590 nm and 500 nm respectively. The G + /R− and B + /Y− cells are excited by short wavelengths and inhibited by long, again with crossover points near 590 nm and 500 nm respectively. The two classes of nonopponent cells are referred to as excitators (excited by lights of all wavelengths) and inhibitors (inhibited by all wavelengths). The R + /G− and G + /R− spectral sensitivities (like those of the Y + /B− and B + /Y− cells) are mirror images. The excitator and inhibitor sensitivity functions are also mirror images and are similar in shape to the photopic luminosity function.

Textbook Physiological Model Refuted: Alternative Physiology

The textbook physiological model is contradicted in several important ways by the physiological data. First, published data provide little support for the assumption of mutually exclusive and exhaustive classes of cells. Certainly they do not imply just four classes of opponent cells. By whatever criterion these cells are classified − wavelength of peak sensitivity, crossover point, "wiring" of cone inputs − the evidence thus far points to more than four cell types (e.g. de Monasterio, Gouras, and Tolhurst, 1975b; see also discussion in Hood, 1981 for other problems).

Even were we to accept the categorization into discrete classes of opponent cells, the sensitivity assumptions are refuted by small-spot data. Specifically, the relative spectral sensitivities of opponent cells are not invariant but depend on the size of the test. The variable tuning of these cells is illustrated by the data of Fig. 4 (from Wiesel and Hubel, 1966). The figure shows spectral sensitivities measured for a single LGN cell under three sets of conditions. The lower solid curve traces the spectral sensitivity obtained with a large test flash under light-adapted conditions; the cell is spectrally opponent, showing a neutral point around 540 nm. When, however, a small test spot is used, the cell responds with increased activity to all wavelengths (lower dashed curve).

This cell is typical of numerous cells reported in the literature. Opponent cells can become nonopponent with changes in the spatial and temporal aspects of stimulation (e.g. de Monasterio, Gouras, and Tolhurst, 1975a; Gouras and Zrenner, 1979; see Finkelstein and Hood, 1982a for additional references and discussion). As we will see in the next section, the variability in spectral tuning has implications for physiological explanations of psychophysical data.

Psychophysiological Model

We come now to the problem of the relation between psychophysics and physiology. Psychophysiological connections are made in either of two ways. One involves adding assumptions about the relationship of behavior to the

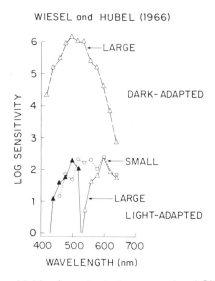

FIG. 4   Spectral sensitivities for a single rhesus monkey LGN cell measured under three sets of conditions: dark-adapted, large test (upper dashed curve); light-adapted (1 cd m^{-2}), large test (solid curve) or small test (small-dashed curve). Open symbols signify that the cell showed increased firing at stimulus onset (''on'' responses). Filled symbols signify that the cell showed either decreased firing at stimulus onset or increased firing at the offset (''off'' responses). In the dark, all responses are on-responses. In the light-adapted state, the same large test elicits on-responses when the wavelength is above 540 nm and off-responses below 540 nm; the cell does not respond to 540 nm light. Decreasing the test size produces on-responses at all wavelengths, with near-maximum activity at 540 nm. Modified from Wiesel and Hubel (1966).

physiological model. These *linking assumptions* are analogous to the psychophysical signalling assumptions. The second approach is to make *psychophysiological assumptions* which equate classes of cells with psychophysical channels. The textbook versions of the two models are shown in Fig. 5. The solid arrows give the appearance-linking assumptions. Nonopponent cells are associated with an achromatic percept and opponent cells with the perception of hue. Excitation and inhibition in a particular opponent cell code a particular pair of hues, with a single cell coding either redness and greenness or yellowness and blueness. The textbook psychophysiological assumptions are indicated by the dashed arrows. Nonopponent cells comprise the achromatic channel, while opponent cells comprise the chromatic channels.

   The textbook version of either approach to relating psychophysics to physiology will, of course, suffer from the same weaknesses as the textbook psychophysical model. The variable spectral tuning suggested by the small-spot psychophysical data and demonstrated physiologically is inconsistent with

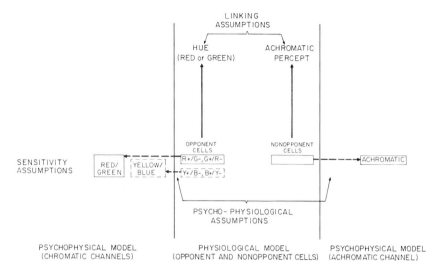

FIG. 5   The textbook psychophysiological models of the cone system. Physiology is related to behavior via either of two classes of assumptions. Linking assumptions (solid arrows) specify direct connections between activity in particular types of cells and particular behaviors. Psychophysiological assumptions (dashed arrows) make connections between cell types and psychophysical channels. See text for details.

traditional appearance and linking assumptions. In the case of the physiology, this is nicely illustrated by the data of Fig. 4. According to the linking assumptions, excitation of this typical "red−green" (R + /G−) cell signals a red percept, inhibition green. What does this imply about the percepts elicited by small, brief lights? Since the cell is excited by small spots of all wavelengths, the textbook model would predict that all these lights contain some redness. Furthermore, since small spots also excite G + /R−, Y + /B−, and B + /Y− cells, they should all contain in addition some greenness, yellowness and blueness. They do not. Finally, the top curve shows the spectral sensitivity of the cell in the dark. The curve resembles the scotopic luminosity function since the cell is rod-driven under dark-adapted conditions. All responses are excitatory, but lights in the dark do not appear red.

We first saw these data discussed in relation to problems of color coding in a 1970 chapter by Hurvich and Jameson. Only recently have psychophysicists begun revising textbook psychophysiological models to account for the small-spot psychophysical and physiological data. The revisions involve changes in linking assumptions and psychophysiological assumptions. For example, Ingling (1978) adds an achromatic channel made up of opponent cells and allows these cells to signal an achromatic percept.

Our approach is to propose a different set of assumptions from Ingling's. We propose a revised pattern code for hue equivalent to the psychophysical pattern hypothesis. Again, as an example, suppose that when all cell types have equal activity the percept is achromatic. High activity in a R + /G− cell like that in Fig. 4 does not necessarily mean "red" in the percept. The activity may even be linked to an achromatic or pure yellow appearance depending on the concurrent activity in Y/B cells.

Although the pattern code resembles quality codes proposed for other senses and may seem at first a minor revision of the textbook assumptions, it is actually a rather drastic change. We have lost the simple cellular explanation of why a light can not appear both red and green at the same time. Further now increased activity in a cell no longer tells us anything definite about the perceptual response. In fact, to maintain a linking assumption in which under some conditions a cell's firing is linked to a red percept and under other conditions it is not probably requires a process somewhat akin to Helmholtz's unconscious inference (Hochberg, 1982).

In contrast to Ingling's model, our strategy does not require that opponent cells comprise an achromatic channel. Keep in mind, however, that the opponent cell-chromatic channel connection is maintained only by allowing the chromatic channels (and opponent cells) to signal an achromatic percept. Also bear in mind that we believe the physiological evidence is sufficiently weak to raise serious concerns about the existence of mutually exclusive and exhaustive classes of cells.

Final Comments

Throughout this chapter we have been careful to make explicit the classes of assumptions underlying different models. This is necessary if we are to avoid the confused way in which physiological terms are often used in the literature. Psychophysicists differ greatly in the ways they use physiological data. Some ignore the data, believing that they are at best misleading; others select data and appeal to the selected subset the way some appeal to the Bible they have never read. Some seek physiological data as sources of ideas but carefully exclude physiological terms from their models; others build rigorous hypotheses by specifying appropriate assumptions. It is often not easy to decide how a physiological term is being used. For example, the term "red−green cell" can imply a linking assumption; a sensitivity assumption; a physiological assumption about the number of classes of cells or the cone inputs to these cells; or, in the hands of some, a hypothetical construct that need not have any relationship to physiological data. If physiological terms are to be used in models of behavior then the assumptions underlying their use must be made clear. The specific terminology adopted is not important. What is important is that the terminology provide a means for understanding what is being assumed. In this way each class of assumptions can be evaluated individually in the context of available psychophysical and physiological data.

Acknowledgements

We thank Bruce Goldstein, Norma Graham, and Dean Yager for their helpful comments. We are particularly grateful to Norma Graham for numerous discussions over the years. Many of the concepts and some of the terminology evolved during these discussions. For a similar approach to the spatial frequency literature, see her soon-to-be published book.

References

De Valois, R. L., Abramov, I. and Jacobs, G. H. (1966). Analysis of response patterns of LGN cells. *J. opt. Soc. Am.* **56**, 966–977.

Finkelstein, M. A. and Hood, D. C. (1982a). Opponent-color cells can influence detection of small, brief lights. *Vision Res.* **22**, 89–95.

Finkelstein, M. A. and Hood, D. C. (1982b). Detection and discrimination of small, brief lights: variable tuning of opponent channels. Manuscript under review.

Gouras, P. and Zrenner, E. (1979). Enhancement of luminance flicker by color-opponent mechanisms. *Science* **205**, 587–589.

Guth, S. L., Massof, R. W. and Benzschawel, T. (1980). Vector model for normal and dichromatic color vision. *J. opt. Soc. Am.* **70**, 197–212.

Hill, N. E. G. (1947). The measurement of the chromatic and achromatic thresholds of coloured point sources against a white background. *Proc. Phys. Soc.* **59**, 574–585.

Hochberg, J. (1982). Perception. In *Handbook of Physiology*, Vol. 3: *The Nervous System* (ed. Darien-Smith, J.). In press.

Hood, D. C. (1981). Comments on linking the psychophysics of color vision to current physiology. In *Relating physiology to psychophysics: current problems and approaches.* Twelfth symposium, Center for Visual Science.

Hurvich, L. M. and Jameson, D. (1957). An opponent-process theory of color vision. *Psychol. Rev.* **64**, 384–404.

Hurvich, L. M. and Jameson, D. (1970). Color vision and color coding. In *Perception and its Disorders, Res. Publ. A.R.N.M.D.* **48**, 12–25.

Ingling, C. R. Jr (1978). Luminance and opponent color contributions to visual detection and to temporal and spatial integration: Comment. *J. opt. soc. Am.* **68**, 1143–1146.

Ingling, C. R., Scheibner, H. M. D. and Boynton, R. M. (1970). Color naming of small foveal fields. *Vision Res.* **10**, 501–511.

Ingling, C. R. Jr and Tsou, B. H.-P. (1977). Orthogonal combination of the three visual channels. *Vision Res.* **17**, 1075–1082.

King-Smith, P. E. and Carden, D. (1976). Luminance and opponent-color contributions to visual detection and adaptation and to temporal and spatial integration. *J. opt. Soc. Am.* **66**, 709–717.

Krauskopf, J. (1978). On identifying detectors. In *Visual Psychophysics and Physiology* (eds Armington, J. C., Krauskopf, J. and Wooten, B. R.). New York, Academic Press.

Massof, R. W. and Bird, J. F. (1978). A general zone theory of color and brightness vision. I. Basic formulation. *J. opt. Soc. Am.* **68**, 1465–1471.

de Monasterio, F. M., Gouras, P. and Tolhurst, D. J. (1975a). Trichromatic colour opponency in ganglion cells of the rhesus monkey retina. *J. Physiol., Lond.* **251**, 197–216.

de Monasterio, F. M., Gouras, P. and Tolhurst, D. J. (1975b). Concealed colour opponency in ganglion cells of the rhesus monkey retina. *J. Physiol., Lond.* **251**, 217–229.

Sperling, H. G. and Harwerth, R. S. (1971). Red–green cone interactions in the increment-threshold spectral sensitivity of primates. *Science* **172**, 180–184.

Wandell, B. A. and Pugh, E. N. Jr (1980). Detection of long-duration, long-wavelength incremental flashes by a chromatically coded pathway. *Vision Res.* **20**, 625–636.

Weitzman, D. O. and Kinney, J. S. (1967). Appearance of color for small, brief, spectral stimuli in the central fovea. *J. opt. Soc. Am.* **57**, 665–670.

Wiesel, T. N. and Hubel, D. H. (1966). Spatial and chromatic interactions in the lateral geniculate body of the rhesus monkey. *J. Neurophysiol.* **29**, 1115–1156.

Postreceptoral Adaptation in Suprathreshold Color Perception

STEVEN K. SHEVELL and JANIS P. HANDTE

Introduction

In the last decade, chromatically opponent mechanisms that affect threshold detection have been explored extensively. These postreceptoral mechanisms often are discussed in terms of Hering's opponent colors theory and the classical opponent color studies begun in 1955 by Jameson and Hurvich. However there is little empirical evidence (see Mollon, 1980) that the chromatically opponent mechanisms influencing threshold detection are the opponent color processes affecting suprathreshold color appearance (which is the basis for opponent colors theory).

Recent results have shown that chromatically opponent mechanisms affecting threshold are least polarized when the color appearance of the light is an equilibrium hue. For example, adapting fields that are yellow−blue equilibrium colors result in the least amount of postreceptoral adaptation in the π_1/π_3 pathway (Pugh and Larimer, 1980); and increment threshold sensitivity is lowest at a test wavelength very near the locus of equilibrium yellow for an increment with spatial and temporal characteristics designed to favor detection by a red−green chromatic mechanism (Thornton and Pugh, 1983). These results show that polarization of a postreceptoral opponent mechanism influencing threshold detection is minimum for lights that null an opponent color-appearance response, an important finding but one that shows only that both threshold detection and color appearance are affected by mechanisms that have a *null response* for the same set of physical stimuli. It may be that

COLOUR VISION
ISBN 0 12 000000 0

threshold and suprathreshold mechanisms both are nulled by the same neutral stimuli, but respond differently to nonneutral stimuli (in the same way that many functions $f(x)$ are zero for the same values of x, but are very different for other values of x). Previous results do not bear on whether polarization at a single opponent site due to a light that is *not* an equilibrium color affects both threshold detection and color perception; the present experiments test this hypothesis by investigating opponent-site polarization due to a clearly reddish, long-wavelength adapting field.

The experimental test rests on two empirical facts. First, threshold elevation due to the effect of long-wavelength adaptation on a chromatically opponent mechanism is much smaller when the field is flickered slowly (2 to 5 Hz) rather than flickered rapidly (or presented steadily at the same time-averaged radiance). Transient tritanopia is greatly reduced or eliminated with a slowly flickering adapting field (Loomis, 1980; Reeves, 1981a). Slow-flicker (but not rapid-flicker) adaptation also reduces (relative to a steady light) desensitization of a red−green postreceptoral mechanism affecting extinction thresholds for a 3°, 200-msec long-wavelength test (Reeves, 1981b). Second, equilibrium yellow measurements following adaptation to a steady long-wavelength light reveal an adapting signal that has the effect of adding chromatically opponent greenness to the test field (Shevell, 1982). This signal (the "restoring signal") tends to drive the opponent response from the adapting field back toward equilibrium (cf. Augenstein and Pugh, 1977). The restoring signal is entirely distinct from receptor gain changes that also occur during adaptation.

If a single, chromatically opponent mechanism is affecting threshold sensitivity and color appearance, the opponent restoring signal affecting suprathreshold hue should be much reduced or absent for a long-wavelength adapting field that is flickered slowly, but clearly evident with a field that is flickered rapidly or presented steadily. The present experiments test this prediction.

Methods

Separating the Effect of the Restoring Signal from Sensitivity Reduction

In order to test the single-site hypothesis, the chromatically opponent restoring signal must be evaluated for various adapting conditions. However the restoring signal may not be measured directly because chromatic adaptation can affect receptor sensitivity as well as a postreceptoral opponent mechanism. Both effects of adaptation may alter color appearance, thus in order to evaluate the effect of an opponent mechanism it is necessary to separate the concomitant effect of receptor sensitivity reduction. This can be achieved by measuring mixtures of 540-plus-660 nm lights that appear equilibrium yellow over a 2 log unit radiance range.

This procedure, used in earlier work (Shevell, 1982) and summarized below, assumes the red–green chromatic response is a weighted sum of the three receptor-types' spectral sensitivities (where the weights include the effect of receptor sensitivity reduction due to adaptation) plus a contribution from a restoring signal that tends to counterbalance the opponent-mechanism response due to the adapting field (Jameson and Hurvich, 1972; Shevell, 1978, 1982; Larimer, 1981). For a mixture of 540-nm "green" (ΔG) and 660-nm "red" (ΔR) lights superimposed upon a 660-nm background (R) (inset, lower right of Fig. 1), this implies the retinal illuminance of the 540-nm test light (ΔG) as a function of the retinal illuminances of the 660-nm test (ΔR) and adapting field (R) is given by

$$\Delta G = [\Delta R + R - s(R)]\, g(R), \tag{1}$$

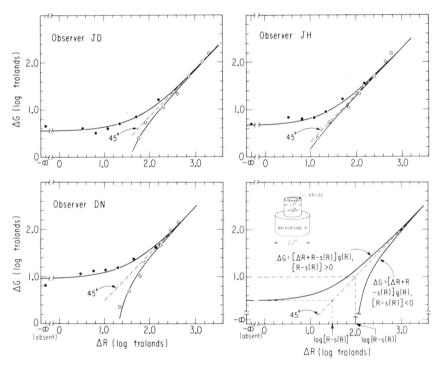

FIG. 1 Equilibrium yellow measurements for three observers. Retinal illuminance of ΔG is plotted as a function of the retinal illuminance of ΔR, for a 2.3 log troland, 660-nm adapting field (a) presented continuously (filled symbols) or (b) briefly extinguished during the test period (open symbols). Lower right: Template curves implied by Equation (1) (see text). Each template curve has a 45° asymptote and either a horizontal or a vertical asymptote; the two asymptotes for a given curve intersect at a point with horizontal coordinate $\log|R - s(R)|$.

where $s(R)$ (the "restoring effect") is due to the chromatically opponent restoring signal and $g(R)$ depends only on receptor relative absorption spectra and gains (after adaptation). For a given adapting field, Equation (1) implies measurements of $\log(\Delta G)$ versus $\log(\Delta R)$ must fall on one of two template curves; the sign of $[R - s(R)]$ determines which one of the templates (Fig. 1, lower right). The templates have been fitted to results from three observers (a) for measurements of equilibrium yellow with the test mixture superimposed upon a steady 2.3 log troland background (filled symbols, Fig. 1) and (b) when the test-field mixture was adjusted for equilibrium yellow during a brief (one second) period with the same steady adapting field momentarily extinguished (open symbols, Fig. 1; prior to these measurements, the observer adapted to the field for at least seven minutes).

Previous work (Shevell, 1982) has shown that the difference between the two conditions at lower test-field levels can be accounted for by different values of $R - s(R)$. When the adapting field is present, $R - s(R)$ is positive (that is, the restoring effect $s(R)$ does not completely counterbalance the effect from the quanta in adapting field R that fall in the test area, so the background contributes some amount of redness to the color appearance of the incremental test). However when the background is extinguished, R is momentarily zero so the quantity $R - s(R)$ is negative. Of course neural signals do not follow the exact time course of physical stimuli, but the open symbols in Fig. 1 reveal that the neural signal due to adapting-field quantum absorption decays sufficiently during the one-second test period to reveal the opponent restoring signal, since the least-squares estimate of $[R - s(R)]$ is negative for each observer (though only marginally so for observer JH, whose results are somewhat different from those of the others both here and in experiments discussed below). A negative value of $[R - s(R)]$, which specifies a template curve that falls below the 45° asymptote at lower test levels (lower right, Fig. 1), indicates that the effect of momentarily extinguishing a long-wavelength adapting field is to add chromatically-opponent greenness to the test field.

Parameter $g(R)$ in Equation (1) locates the 45° asymptote; since receptor gain (but not the restoring signal) influences $g(R)$, the quantity $g(R)$ reflects the effect of adaptation on sensitivity alone. The results in Fig. 1 (and more extensive measurements; Shevell, 1982) show that sensitivity as assessed by $g(R)$ does not depend significantly on whether the adapting field is briefly extinguished.

Procedure

In the experiments of this study, the stimuli were the 0.8–1.3° annular test field and 2.7° circular adapting field described above (inset, lower right of Fig. 1). The experimental sessions were of three types (top, Fig. 2). The adapting field was (1) square-wave flickered at 2 Hz, (2) square-wave flickered at 17 Hz, or (3) presented steadily. At the beginning of each experimental session, the observer adapted to the dark for seven minutes and then to the appropriate 660-nm adapting field for seven minutes. After adaptation, the annular test field was superimposed upon the adapting field and presented steadily for the duration of the experiment; the adapting field then was briefly extinguished once every seven seconds. The observer made his color appearance judgments only while the adapting field was momentarily absent.

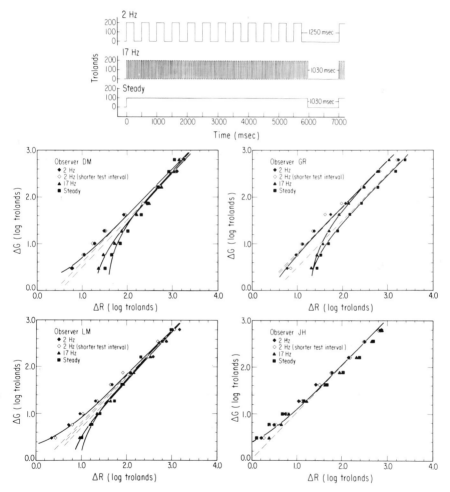

FIG. 2   Above: Schematic representation of the temporal features of the adapting conditions. Below: Equilibrium yellow measurements for four observers made while a 2.0 log troland (time-averaged retinal illuminance) adapting field was extinguished for approximately one second. Axes as in Fig. 1; each symbol represents a different adapting condition (see legend). Solid curves are templates from Fig. 1.

The adapting-field characteristics were designed so the adapting conditions were comparable with respect to (1) the time-averaged retinal illuminance of the adapting light (2.0 log trolands), (2) the time interval between judgment periods (seven seconds), and (3) the duration of each judgment period (1030 msec). For the 2 Hz condition, two different judgment-period durations (1030 msec and 1250 msec) were tested to determine whether observer performance was affected by the relatively long dark-half-cycle time (250 msec) that was included as part of the 1030 msec judgment period.

Within each experimental session, the experimenter fixed the 540 nm test light ΔG at nine levels; for each of these levels, the observer adjusted the radiance of the 660-nm test light ΔR for the equilibrium yellow criterion. Five settings at each level of ΔG were made during each session. Every observer participated in four experimental sessions (run on different days) for each adapting condition. The order of conditions was randomized across experimental sessions.

Results

Results from four observers are shown in the lower portion of Fig. 2. Each point is the average of 20 measurements (five on each of four days). The solid curves are templates from Fig. 1; the dashed lines are the 45° asymptotes for each template curve. Judgment-period duration in the 2 Hz condition did not affect the results, thus the two sets of 2 Hz measurements were averaged (and a single template fit to them); the two sets give an indication of measurement variability.

The results for observers DM, GR, and LM show that flicker frequency (2 versus 17 Hz) had a large effect at low test levels but not at higher levels. For low level tests, with the higher adapting-field flicker frequency equilibrium yellow required more 660-nm light (ΔR) in the test-field mixture for a given amount of 540-nm light (ΔG); this is consistent with the prediction that 17 Hz (but not 2 Hz) flicker results in a chromatically opponent signal that has the effect of adding greenness to a test field presented when the adapting light is briefly extinguished. With 2 Hz flicker, there is no evidence for a restoring signal since at low test levels the best fitting template curves are near or rise slightly above the 45° asymptote. The 2 Hz curves that rise slightly above the asymptotic line suggest a (small) contribution of redness to the test field from the momentarily extinguished adapting light; though the light is extinguished during the brief test period, a small residual neural signal can contribute redness to the test. The important point is that there is no opponent greenness (in contrast to the 17 Hz and steady conditions) that cancels this redness. Thus the chromatically opponent adapting effect is much smaller or absent with a slowly flickered adapting field as compared to a rapidly flickered field, just as is found for threshold detection. At higher test levels the relative effect of any restoring signal is negligible; the convergence of the 2 Hz and 17 Hz measurements indicates that flicker frequency did not affect sensitivity.

For these three observers, steady adaptation was similar to 17 Hz adaptation. For each subject, there was a clear restoring effect similar to that found for the 17 Hz flicker condition. Sensitivity for observers DM and LM was very similar for all adapting conditions; this is indicated by the convergence at high test levels of all three sets of points. Only observer GR showed a sensitivity difference with steady (rather than flicker) adaptation; this result is surprising but does not detract from the conclusion concerning the effect of flicker frequency on postreceptoral adaptation, given his results for 2 Hz and 17 Hz adaptation.

Unlike all other observers, JH showed no effect of adapting condition; a single curve has been fitted to her results. This is not unexpected since JH (unlike two still different observers) in previous experiments revealed a negligible restoring signal following similar steady-field adaptation (Shevell, 1982). Observer JH provides an important test case. Recall Reeves (1981b) found that desensitization of a red – green opponent mechanism produced by a rapidly flickered 15 – 20 Hz (but not 2 Hz) long-wavelength adapting light raises extinction threshold for a 200-msec long-wavelength test. If threshold detection and color appearance are influenced by an adapting effect on a single opponent mechanism, then for observer JH (but not for the other observers) extinction thresholds should be equal following 2 Hz and following 17 Hz adaptation.

This was tested by measuring extinction thresholds for a 200-msec, 660-nm test (annulus ΔR from the equilibrium hue experiments) following adaptation to a 660-nm, 2.0 log troland (time-averaged) field flickered either at 2 Hz or 17 Hz. After seven minutes of adaptation, the adapting field was extinguished for one second once every seven seconds; the test flash was presented 200 msec after the beginning of the one-second period. Since threshold for the 200-msec test is affected by adaptation at a chromatically opponent site (Wandell and Pugh, 1980; Reeves, 1981b), the difference in extinction threshold levels following 17 Hz and 2 Hz adaptation may be interpreted to reflect a difference in opponent-site polarization. As expected for observers DM and LM (GR could not be tested), extinction threshold level following 17 Hz adaptation was significantly higher than following 2 Hz adaptation (0.2 log unit difference for DM, 0.4 log unit difference for LM; $p < 0.02$ for each observer). For JH, the difference was less than 0.1 log unit and not significantly different from zero ($p > 0.1$).

Observer JH has no known visual defect (observers were screened using the Nagel anomaloscope and the Farnsworth Panel D-15 test); moreover, with a continuously presented (rather than a briefly extinguished) steady adapting field, results for JH are undistinguished from measurements for other observers (Shevell, 1982).

Conclusions

The adapting effect of a long-wavelength light on equilibrium hue depends on whether the adapting field is flickered slowly rather than flickered rapidly or presented steadily (at the same time-averaged radiance). A difference between slowly flickered versus steady long-wavelength adaptation previously has been found for measurements of hue (Broekhuijsen, Uilenreef and Veringa, 1979), complementary afterimages (Loomis, 1978), and color discrimination (Loomis and Berger, 1979). The present results demonstrate (at least for equilibrium hue) that the differential adapting effect cannot be accounted for by receptor sensitivity changes.

For most observers, adaptation to a steady or rapidly flickered (17 Hz) long-wavelength field results in a chromatically opponent response that affects suprathreshold color appearance; however there is no observable opponent effect if the same field is flickered slowly (2 Hz). These results parallel the effect of adapting-field flicker frequency on chromatically opponent mechanisms affecting threshold detection. Further, measurements for one observer, which are different from those for the others, reveal no opponent-mechanism effect at either flicker rate, either for color appearance or for threshold detection. These findings are consistent with (but of course do not prove) the view that adaptation at a single opponent site affects both threshold detection and suprathreshold color perception.

Acknowledgement

Supported by National Science Foundation grant BNS-7924024.

References

Augenstein, E. J. and Pugh, E. N. Jr (1977). The dynamics of the π_1 colour mechanism: Further evidence for two sites of adaptation. *J. Physiol., Lond.* **272**, 247–281.

Broekhuijsen, M. L., Uilenreef, P. L. and Veringa, F. (1979). Flicker and chromatic adaptation. *Vision Res.* **19**, 565–567.

Jameson, D. and Hurvich, L. M. (1955). Some quantitative aspects of an opponent-colors theory. I. Chromatic responses and spectral saturation. *J. opt. Soc. Am.* **45**, 546–552.

Jameson, D. and Hurvich, L. M. (1972). Color adaptation: Sensitivity, contrast, and afterimages. In *Handbook of Sensory Physiology, Vol. VII/4* (eds Jameson, D. and Hurvich, L. M.). Berlin, Springer, pp. 568–581.

Larimer, J. (1981). Red/green opponent colors equilibria measured on chromatic adapting fields: Evidence for gain changes and restoring forces. *Vision Res.* **21**, 501–512.

Loomis, J. M. (1978). Complementary afterimages and the unequal adapting effects of steady and flickering lights. *J. opt. Soc. Am.* **68**, 411–416.

Loomis, J. M. (1980). Transient tritanopia: Failure of time-intensity reciprocity in adaptation to longwave light. *Vision Res.* **20**, 837–846.

Loomis, J. M. and Berger, T. (1979). Effects of chromatic adaptation on color discrimination and color appearance. *Vision Res.* **19**, 891–901.

Mollon, J. D. (1980). Post-receptoral processes in colour vision. *Nature* **283**, 623–624.

Pugh, E. N. Jr and Larimer, J. (1980). Test of the identity of the site of blue/yellow hue cancellation and the site of chromatic antagonism in the π_1 pathway. *Vision Res.* **20**, 779–788.

Reeves, A. (1981a). Transient tritanopia after flicker adaptation. *Vision Res.* **21**, 657–664.

Reeves, A. (1981b). Transient desensitization of a red–green opponent site. *Vision Res.* **21**, 1267–1277.

Shevell, S. K. (1978). The dual role of chromatic backgrounds in color perception. *Vision Res.* **18**, 1649–1661.

Shevell, S. K. (1982). Color perception under chromatic adaptation: Equilibrium yellow and long-wavelength adaptation. *Vision Res.* **22**, 279–292.

Thornton, J. and Pugh, E. N. Jr (1983). Red/green color opponency at detection threshold. *Science* **219**, 191–193.

Wandell, B. A. and Pugh, E. N. Jr (1980). Detection of long-duration, long-wavelength incremental flashes by a chromatically coded pathway. *Vision Res.* **20**, 625–636.

Mechanisms of Chromatic Discrimination

ROBERT M. BOYNTON

Introduction

A principal aim of the studies to be reported is to show that conditions which favor a high level of chromatic induction also favor a high level of chromatic discrimination. A second objective is to investigate the levels of visual processing that are responsible for chromatic induction as well as the perception of color differences.

It is generally agreed that the neurophysiological activity underlying the discrimination of color differences begins with differential excitations of the three kinds of cone photoreceptors, and so it is not surprising that trichromatic models are to some degree capable of accounting for the results of chromatic discrimination experiments. In the final analysis, however, because vision does not arise directly from the activity of cones, we may expect that – unlike color matching – color discrimination depends upon much more than signals related only to cone outputs.

The studies to be reported here represent an extension of work previously published by Boynton, Hayhoe and MacLeod (1977), Boynton (1978), Boynton and Kambe (1980), and Boynton, Nagy and Olson (1982). This report should be regarded as preliminary because the data of the six experiments to be presented were obtained from only one subject (the author). Although results from at least one other subject have been obtained for each experiment, some problems with individual differences remain that are not yet fully understood. This additional evidence does not contradict the conclusions to be drawn from the results reported here.

COLOUR VISION
ISBN 0 12 000000 0

Overall Experimental Aims

Imagine an experiment where two vertically-oriented rectangular fields are seen side-by-side with a small separation between them. The left field, which is white and invariant, serves as a reference field. The right field can be continuously varied along a red–green dimension. The left eye is occluded, so that only the right eye views both fields. Starting with a physical match, the amount of change of the right field, as required for a just-discriminable color difference, is determined.

Suppose that the experiment is repeated, but now the left field is delivered instead to the left eye, so that the two fields are seen dichoptically. Consider the following possible outcomes.

(a) When the threshold discrimination steps determined for the monoptic and dichoptic conditions are compared, they might not differ. Such a result would imply, without denying that monocular mechanisms are involved in the transmission of chromatic information to the brain, that there are no strictly monocular mechanisms necessary for color comparisons. Color discrimination would then be a high-level affair, based on visual processing that occurs beyond the level of binocular combination.

(b) Placing the left field – the unchanging reference – in the left eye might be equivalent to removing it from view altogether. The dichoptic experiment would then no longer be a discrimination experiment in the usual sense. What would be judged instead would be the color of the right field with respect to some remembered standard – a comparison between the perception of a physically-present color and a remembered one.

Most of the experimental results that I will report do not support either of these extreme outcomes. Instead, the reference field is usually helpful, even when placed in the other eye, although it is best to have it in the same eye as the test field. (Sometimes, however, judgments based upon the right field alone – that is, made without the reference field – are remarkably acute.) One conclusion that seems to follow from these results is that, not too surprisingly, it is usually better to have a reference field to look at directly than to depend upon a memory of it.

Another benefit of the reference field is that it permits the mechanisms underlying chromatic induction to operate. Consider, for example, two matching white fields seen side by side. As the right field changes physically toward red (by which I mean that the field is altered spectrally so as to increase the excitation of red cones and to decrease that of green cones), greenness is induced into the physically-unchanged left field. The presence of chromatic induction suggests that the patterns of brain activity that underlie the perception of the reference and test fields differ more from one another than they would without induction. With this assist from chromatic induction, which thus serves to exaggerate color differences, less physical change should be required to produce a criterion color-difference step than if chromatic induction did not occur.

Background

Good reviews of work on chromatic induction will be found in Graham and Brown (1965), Walraven (1982), Hurvich (1981), and Kinney (1962). In the work to be reported below, we chose to vary the amount of chromatic induction by varying the separation of fields in time, rather than in space. This seems to have been a neglected topic since some work by Kinney (1967).

One of our experiments (No. 4) requires the use of a dichoptic metacontrast masking stimulus. A review of the metacontrast literature is given by Lefton (1973). The subject is treated in detail by Uttal (1981).

Apparatus

All of the experiments utilized the La Jolla Analytic Colorimeter, a device which is briefly described elsewhere (Boynton and Nagy, 1982). By means of a remotely-controlled stage containing narrow-band red and green interference filters, (visually equivalent to 650 and 561 nm) the fraction of light at constant luminance that is effective upon R and G cones could be varied at will. A detailed technical report by Boynton and Nagy (1981) may be consulted for additional details concerning the apparatus, its calibration, and the methodology of Experiment 1.

Except for Experiment 4, where a bite bar was necessary, the experiments were done with a head rest; free viewing of transilluminated fields was employed throughout. Dichoptic view was provided by placing a septum parallel to the subject's line of sight, running from between the two fields to a point near the subject's eyes.

Experiments

Experiment 1

Viewing Conditions. Color discrimination steps were measured under three conditions of steady viewing.

(a) Dichoptic View. The subject saw a fused array of eight fixation lights (Fig. 1) by reflection from a pair of adjustable glass plates, through which the stimulus fields could be seen. To avoid a strong tendency for horizontally-disparate and vertically-aligned fields to fuse, one eye saw one field just to the left and below the center of the region staked out by the fixation lights, and the other eye saw the other field at the upper right. Each of the fields subtended 0.5 deg on a side, and their corners were separated by approximately 15 min.

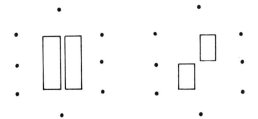

FIG. 1   Stimulus fields. The eight fixation points were seen haploscopically. For viewing of flashed fields, the rectangular fields at the left were used. The reference field (left) and test field (right) could be seen either in monoptic or dichoptic view. To avoid a tendency for steady fields to fuse, it was necessary to reduce the size of the reference and test fields and to displace them vertically as shown at the right.

(b) Monoptic View. Both stimuli were presented to only one eye, where they appeared much the same as in dichoptic view. The other eye continued to view the fixation points as before, but its view of the stimulus fields was occluded by an opaque screen placed just behind the glass plate. Again the effects of chromatic induction were evident. Only one field was presented, and this only to one eye. Both eyes were exposed to the fixation points. Despite the diagonal arrangement of the stimuli, it was quite obvious that a substantial amount of chromatic induction occurred, as predicted from the experiments of Jameson and Hurvich (1961).

(c) Single Stimulus. Only one field was presented, and this only to one eye. Both eyes were exposed to the fixation points.

Procedure.   The positions of the test and comparison fields, and of the viewing eye for monoptic conditions, were varied left and right. For descriptive economy, the procedure is described below only in terms of one of the four combinations. Since there was no significant effect of these variations, the remaining chromatic discrimination experiments were simplified by always presenting the reference stimulus at the left, the variable test at the right, and by using the right eye for monoptic viewing.

In this and other experiments to be described, luminance was held constant at 0.16 cd m^{-2} and stimuli were viewed with natural pupils. When two fields were to be compared, whether monoptically or dichoptically, each experimental trial began with a physical match. Following a warning signal and an unpredictable delay, the right field began to change physically, very slowly, either in the redward or greenward direction. The subject was instructed to respond when the color difference was sufficiently large that he could correctly discriminate the direction of color change. For the single-stimulus condition, the same procedure was followed, except that only the right field was visible. The rate of stimulus change was adjusted on a trial-by-trial basis so that the mean response time fluctuated around 9 sec. For each trial, two values are calculated, each based on the arithmetic mean of 4 measurements, either toward red or toward green. The experiment was designed to minimize order effects.

Results.   The data for one subject were as follows (N is the number of values, $\Delta R/R$ is the mean fractional change in R-cone excitation required for a discrimination step, listed with its standard deviation).

Condition	N	$\Delta R/R$
Monoptic	64	0.0138 ± 0.0032
Dichoptic	32	0.0168 ± 0.0039
No comparison	64	0.0256 ± 0.0060

Conclusions.   The result for the monoptic condition means that, on average, a 1.4% increase in R-cone excitation, combined with a decrease in G-cone excitation sufficient to keep luminance constant, will produce a criterion chromatic difference step. The other results show that the discrimination step is increased by about 22% by placing the steady reference stimulus in the contralateral eye, and that it is nearly doubled when no comparison stimulus is used.

Experiment 2

Aims.   In the first experiment, the fields were steadily viewed, without restrictions on eye movements. Because of a desire to produce data applicable to realistic viewing conditions, such uncontrolled viewing has heretofore been a standard procedure in our program of research. However, the resulting eye movements produce a complex and unmeasured spatio-temporal excitation pattern on the retina, making the analysis of underlying mechanisms difficult. Therefore, in the remainder of the experiments to be described, "long" or "short" flashes of light lasting either 1000 or 100 msec were used. The purpose of this experiment was to study chromatic induction as a function of stimulus-onset asynchrony (SOA) between flash pairs.

Procedures.   Because flashed stimuli display much less of a tendency to fuse, it proved possible to use two rectangular (0.5 × 1 deg) fields, viewed side-by-side. There was an 11 min spatial separation between them. Long flashes were used. The psychophysical method was the same as in Experiment 1, but the stimuli were occluded from view except as flash pairs, presented once every

2.5 sec (when a reference stimulus was used) or as single flashes (when no reference was used). The chromaticity of the test stimulus continuously changed, both between and during the exposure periods, but the rate of change was so slow that no change in color was perceived during the exposure periods. The amount of change was measured according to when the subject responded, whether this was during the stimulus-exposure period, as it usually was, or between exposures.

Results.   Results are shown in Fig. 2. It will be seen that SOA has a powerful effect for the monoptic condition, where discrimination steps are very small when the right field leads the left one by about 200 msec. For SOAs outside

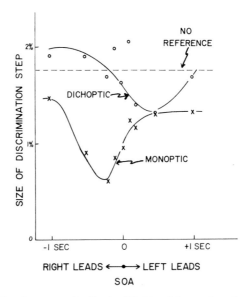

FIG. 2   Discrimination steps for flashed fields of 1-sec duration, as a function of stimulus-onset asynchrony, for monoptic and dichoptic viewing.

the range of roughly plus or minus 500 msec, the steps are about twice as large. The dichoptic data are somewhat ragged, but discrimination is best when the left field leads the right one by about 500 msec, where there is no difference between the monoptic and dichoptic conditions. The dashed line shows the result for the no-reference condition. It can be seen that, throughout the temporal range sampled, the reference is useful for monoptic discriminations. For dichoptic discriminations, on the other hand, the reference is useful only when its onset leads that of the test, especially so when the temporal separation is about 500 msec.

Experiment 3

Aims. This experiment was intended to assess the amount of chromatic induction exhibited for the two SOAs for which the results for monoptic versus dichoptic discrimination differed most in Experiment 2:

(a) reference (left) leads test (right) by 500 msec, and
(b) test (right) leads reference (left) by 200 msec.

The predicted result is an interaction: For condition (a), where there was a large monoptic advantage in the discrimination experiment, there should be more color induction exhibited for monoptic than for dichoptic viewing; this difference should be less for condition (b) and could be zero if the amount of chromatic induction were the only variable affecting differential chromatic discrimination for the two conditions of viewing.

Procedures. Long flashes were used, separated in time by the two values just mentioned, with an inter-trial interval of $10-15$ sec. We developed the following method for measuring chromatic induction. The subject was instructed to judge the hue of the right field and to ignore the left field altogether. Hue was judged along a seven-point scale; strong red (scored $+3$), medium red ($+2$), weak red ($+1$), neutral (0), weak green (-1), medium green (-2) and strong green (-3). On a given trial, either the right or left field was set physically toward red or green by one of three or four amounts. On some trials, both fields might appear at the matching neutral color from which the discriminations had been measured. A change in the appearance of the right field could therefore result either from a physical change in that field, or by chromatic induction from the reference field. It was often difficult for the subject to tell which of these had occurred on a particular trial. Free eye movements were permitted, but fixation tended to be directed toward the test stimulus, which was the focus of attention. Results are based on the summed point values for ten presentations of each experimental condition. Conditions were presented in random order without replacement, in the reverse of that order, and then in a new random order, etc.

Results. Sample data are shown in Fig. 3. The ordinate values represent the summed point values based on ten trials per condition. There are 180 trials represented by the data of the figure. These results are very typical in that the data can be well fitted with linear functions. The induced color, without exception, is the opponent color, but the point values for induced color are multiplied by -1 so that, when plotted, the relative slopes of the two functions can more readily be compared.

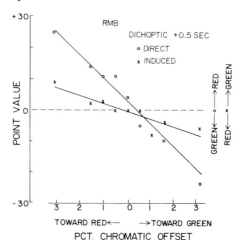

FIG. 3   Sample data (for dichoptic viewing, with reference leading test, SOA = 500 msec, 1 sec flashes) to show analysis of chromatic induction data. Ordinate values are point totals for hue-strength ratings (see text) for the right-hand test field when it was physically varied (direct, ○) or color was induced into it by variation of the left-hand reference field (indirect, ×). The amount of chromatic offset of the stimuli from neutral is shown on the abscissa. Point values for the induced effect have been multiplied by −1 so that the slopes of the two functions can be more easily compared.

An index of chromatic induction.   A suitable index of color induction is the slope of the function for the induced color change divided by that for the direct color change, multiplied by 100 (to express it as a percentage). For example, 50% chromatic induction means that the slope of the function fitting data for trials where the right field did not physically change is half that for trials where it did.

The slopes of regression lines fit to all of the data of the experiment can be compared in the bar graphs of Fig. 4. Chromatic induction (hatched bars) occurs both monoptically and dichoptically and for both temporal delays. Moreover, as predicted, there is little or no monoptic advantage under the condition (+ 500 msec) that yielded no difference between monoptic and dichoptic discrimination in Experiment 2, whereas there is relatively more monoptic color induction for the condition (−200 msec) where monoptic discrimination was superior to dichoptic.

Conclusions.   The results are consistent with predictions based on the hypothesis that the primary basis for the monoptic-dichoptic differences of Experiment 2 lies in the relative amounts of chromatic induction that occur at various SOAs.

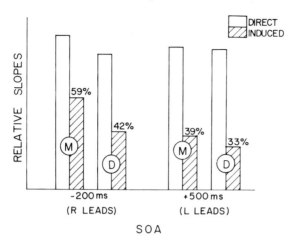

FIG. 4   Results of chromatic induction experiment using 1-sec flashes for an SOA of −200 msec (where the monoptic−dichoptic differences in Fig. 2 are largest) and for + 500 msec (where they are smallest). Open bars show the direct effect; shaded bars, the induced effect, for monoptic (M) and dichoptic (D) viewing. Percent induction (height of shaded bars divided by height of open bars, times 100) is shown below each pair of bars.

Experiment 4

Aims.   The fact that chromatic induction occurs more strongly for monoptic than dichoptic vision suggests, but does not prove, that there is a retinal basis for some part of the effect. If chromatic induction does have a retinal basis, then one would predict that the retinal component of chromatic induction would continue to reveal itself if some means could be found to block the transmission of information about the reference field at a level of visual processing beyond the retina. In considering this prediction, which is made with respect to the type of color induction experiment just described, one should keep in mind that the subject judged only the right field, and was specifically asked not to make a comparison between two fields, but rather to ignore its presence if possible.

Use of dichoptic metacontrast.   To inhibit the transmission of information about the left field at a locus central to the retina, without removing it physically, we have taken advantage of the phenomenon of dichoptically-induced metacontrast. The spatial and temporal conditions were arranged so that the metacontrast masking pattern obliterated the perception of the reference field without having any direct effect upon that of the test. The reference and test fields were presented only to the right eye, the metacontrast mask only to the left. The spatial and temporal conditions of the metacontrast experiment are shown in Fig. 5.

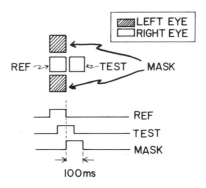

FIG. 5 Conditions for the metacontrast experiment. The reference and test fields, exposed for 100 msec each, are seen by the right eye. The metacontrast mask, which is white, flanks the reference field and is seen in the left eye. The temporal relations among the three stimuli are shown at the bottom.

Because metacontrast does not occur with long flashes, we found it necessary to use short flashes (100 msec) in this experiment. In a subsidiary experiment, using the methodology introduced in Experiment 3, we established that, with the simultaneous presentation of short flashes, 50% monoptic, and 21% dichoptic induction was obtained. On the assumption that monoptic induction occurs as a result of visual processing that takes place both before and following the level of binocular combination, whereas dichoptic induction results only from the latter, the data imply that 30% of the induction occurs in the monocular visual system, with about 20% added beyond the level of binocular combination.

Procedures.   The experiment was run with, and without, the metacontrast mask. For the metacontrast condition, in addition to making the usual chromatic judgment of the right field, the subject was asked to report whether the left field was seen (it very seldom was).

Results.   There was no significant difference in the judgments of the right field, when it was physically varied, that depended upon the presence or absence of the metacontrast mask. The induction results were rather unexpected. Whereas 52% induction was found without metacontrast, in good agreement with the monocular data of the subsidiary experiment, this dropped to only 13% with metacontrast. Even if the mask eliminated the entire 20% induction beyond the level of binocular combination, which is by no means certain, the result implies that it also eliminated more than half of the 30% hue induction that normally would be attributed to the monocular visual system.

Conclusion.   One conclusion that seems safe to draw is that monoptic color induction should not be equated with retinal induction, because there is no reasonable way that the metacontrast mask to the left eye could eliminate so much of a retinally-based effect in the right eye. Instead, it appears that the major locus of the monoptic induction effect is in the brain, in pathways that receive only monocular input so far as chromatic induction is concerned, but which are nevertheless susceptible to the influence of the dichoptic meta-contrast mask. The very small component of chromatic induction that survives metacontrast could be retinally based, or the underlying mechanisms could be located lower in the monocular visual brain, safe from the effects of meta-contrast.

Experiment 5

Aims.   Chromatic induction between temporally coincident fields, usually called simultaneous color contrast, is known to decrease with increasing spatial separation of the fields (Jameson and Hurvich, 1961). Presumably the same thing should happen with increasing temporal separation, and it was one aim of this experiment to show that it does.

Procedures.   The experiment was conducted using the rectangular fields, long flashes, and in the same manner as the chromatic induction experiments already described. On the basis of preliminary observations, SOAs of 0, 0.5, 1, 2, and 4 sec were examined in detail.

Results.   Percent induction was found to be 54%, 48%, 36%, 20% and 11% respectively, showing a monotonic and fairly linear ($r = 0.95$) decrease with SOA, which, if extrapolated, would lead to zero induction at an SOA of about 4.6 sec.

Conclusion.   For the conditions of this experiment, the processes underlying induction apparently persist for three or four seconds, with steadily decreasing effectiveness.

Experiment 6

Aims.   If chromatic induction serves to reduce the size of chromatic discrimination steps as hypothesized, then it should be possible to show a corresponding increase in the size of discrimination steps as a function of the temporal separation of the fields being compared. This is the purpose of the sixth and last experiment, where chromatic discrimination was tested for SOAs of 0 and 4 sec.

Procedures. The method of assessing chromatic discrimination used in Experiments 1 and 2 could not be used in this experiment, where stimuli were to be separated temporally by as much as 4 sec, because too much change would take place between stimulus exposures to permit an accurate assessment of threshold color-difference steps. Therefore we turned to a discrete-trial method designed to generate data for the frequency of seeing the right field as redder than the left one. On each trial, the subject was instructed to judge whether the right field appeared "more red", "the same", or "less red" when compared to the left field. A staircase procedure was adopted, using steps of 0.5% in $\Delta R/R$. Ten per cent "scrambling" (Boynton, Sturr and Ikeda, 1961) was used in an effect to break up the dependency of stimulus level upon the immediately preceding response.

Starting values of $\Delta R/R$ were randomized over nine levels; data collection began with the first reversal. "Same" responses did not result in reversals. Thirty-six trials were used to generate each set of data.

To analyze the data, the number of "same" responses was divided by two and the resulting value was added to the "more red" and "less red" categories. For example, if for some particular level of physical redness of the right field there were 8 "more red", 4 "less red", and 3 "same" responses, the first two categories would be adjusted upward to 9.5 and 5.5 respectively. From this, a per cent "more red" value can be calculated ($9.5/15 \times 100 = 63\%$ in the example). Per cent values were weighted according to the number of trials that entered into their calculation, and the data were fitted by linear regression. The relevant statistic is the slope of the fitted lines: the steeper the slope, the more acute the discrimination.

The experiment was carried out with the same neutral stimulus used in the other experiments, and also with a field calculated to produce 11% more red-cone excitation than the neutral stimulus. This new condition therefore utilized a moderately saturated red reference field; the redness of the test field, which nearly matched it, fluctuated from trial to trial.

Twelve conditions were examined, eight times each, in a randomized-counterbalanced design. SOAs of 0 and 4 sec (test following reference) were examined as follows:

(a) Neutral left field, monoptic view;
(b) Neutral left field, dichoptic view;
(c) No left field, right field judged with respect to remembered neutral left field;
(d) Red left field, monoptic view;
(e) Red left field, dichoptic view;
(f) No left field, right field judged with respect to remembered red left field.

Thirty-six trials were used for each staircase and four staircases were run for each condition.

Results. Results are shown in Fig. 6. For simultaneous presentation of reference and test stimuli (bars labelled 0 sec), monoptic discrimination appears to be slightly better than dichoptic, in agreement with the results of Experiment 1, for both the neutral and red reference conditions. For

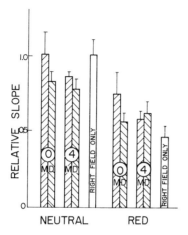

FIG. 6 Slopes of frequency of "more red" responses of Experiment 6. Slopes have been normalized, with the left-most bar set at 1.0. Results for the neutral stimulus condition are shown on the left side of the figure, those for the red stimulus are at the right. For each of these conditions, the bars show the relative slopes for monoptic (M) and dichoptic (D) viewing of simultaneously flashed (0 sec) fields and for a condition where the onset of the reference field led that of the test field by 4 sec. Flash duration was 1 sec. The unshaded bars are for a condition where the subject judged single flashes of the test field on the basis of his memory of the color of the reference field.

SOA = 4 sec, monoptic performance is about equal to that for the simultaneous dichoptic condition. These results are consistent, as far as they go, with the conclusion that the monocular component of chromatic induction can be used to aid discrimination. However, the results are negative and therefore moot with respect to the role of the smaller dichoptic component of chromatic induction: Either, for some reason, it is unable to aid discrimination, or this experiment has not been sensitive enough to demonstrate it.

Conclusions. The results for the single-field conditions suggest that the presence of a red reference field is helpful, but that, a neutral reference is not; in fact, for three out of four conditions it may have a deleterious effect. These results are contrary to those of Experiment 1, where chromatic difference steps for single fields were much larger than when a reference field was present. Because the same subject served in both experiments, methodological differences between the two experiments must lie at the root of an explanation for this discrepancy. In the first experiment, the subject was looking for a change in the appearance of the steady field. In this experiment, he was judging single flashes on an absolute basis, where the remembered reference field was neutral on the red–green dimension. The results suggest that a remembered reference of this kind can provide a remarkably stable criterion against which to judge the test field. Perhaps there may be less variability in the memory of a psychologically unique stimulus than for the percept of an actual field, which in fact can vary in appearance, from trial to trial, from neutral to slightly reddish or slightly greenish. The red reference field, on the other hand, has no quality of psychological uniqueness and is relatively difficult to remember.

The sixth experiment is in the class of experiments where data variance constitutes the dependent measure. To draw firm conclusions from experiments of this sort requires enormous quantities of data. More observations will be required before we can be sure that the results of Fig. 6 are replicable.

General Discussion

From the experiments just reported, certain important conclusions may tentatively be drawn. Most importantly, most of the mechanisms of color discrimination are not retinally based. Theories that assume that there are mechanisms capable of registering differences between receptor outputs in the retina, and that color differences are represented by some mathematical combination of these (Wyszecki and Stiles, 1982, p. 654ff), seem highly suspect, since they do not account for, or even take account of, the effects of chromatic induction; nor can they reasonably explain the good quality of dichoptic discrimination or an ability to make consistent judgments with respect to certain remembered colors. Our results indicate that the monoptic–dichoptic difference in chromatic discrimination may result from an extra enhancement of color difference from chromatic induction, the mechanisms of which lie mainly in the monocular visual pathways, but not to any great extent within the retina.

Acknowledgements

This research has been supported by Grant No. EY-01451 from the National Eye Institute. It is expected that each experiment will be published in more detail, and with more data from additional subjects. Co-authors of these papers will include members of the research team that helped plan, conduct, and analyze these experiments: Melissa L. Monty, Conrad X. Olson, and D. Leo Stefurak. We also wish to thank Dr Allen Nagy for participating in many of our discussions, and for a critical reading of an earlier version of this manuscript.

References

Boynton, R. M. (1978). Discriminations that depend upon blue cones. In *Frontiers of Visual Science* (eds Cool, S. J. and Smith, E. L.), pp. 154–164. New York, Springer-Verlag.

Boynton, R. M., Hayhoe, M. M. and MacLeod, D. I. A. (1977). The gap effect: Chromatic and achromatic visual discrimination as affected by field separation. *Optica Acta* **24**, 159–177.

Boynton, R. M. and Kambe, N. (1980). Chromatic difference steps of moderate size measured along theoretically critical axes. *Color Research and Application* **5**, 13–23.

Boynton, R. M. and Nagy, A. L. (1981). The La Jolla Analytic Colorimeter: Optics, calibrations, procedures, and control experiments. *Report of the Center for Human Information Processing* (CHIP 109). La Jolla CA, University of California at San Diego.

Boynton, R. M. and Nagy, A. L. (1982). La Jolla analytic colorimeter. *J. opt. Soc. Am.* **72**, 666–667.

Boynton, R. M., Nagy, A. L. and Olson, C. X. (1982). A flaw in color difference equations. *Color Research and Application*. In press.

Boynton, R. M., Sturr, J. F. and Ikeda, M. (1961). Study of flicker by increment-threshold technique. *J. opt. Soc. Am.* **51**, 196–201.

Graham, C. H. and Brown, J. L. (1965). Color contrast and color appearances: Brightness constancy and color constancy. In *Vision and Visual Perception* (ed. Graham, C. H.), pp. 452–478. New York, Wiley.

De Valois, R. L. and De Valois, K. K. (1975). Neural coding of color. In *Handbook of Perception*, Vol. 5 (eds Carterette, E. C. and Friedman, M. P.), pp. 117–166. New York, Academic Press.

Hurvich, L. M. (1981). *Color Vision.* Sunderland, MA, Sinauer Associates.

Jameson, D. and Hurvich, L. M. (1961). Opponent chromatic induction: Experimental evaluation and theoretical account. *J. opt. Soc. Am.* **51**, 46–53.

Kinney, J. S. (1962). Factors affecting induced color. *Vision Res.* **2**, 503–525.

Kinney, J. S. (1967). Color induction using asynchronous flashes. *Vision Res.* **7**, 299–318.

Lefton, L. (1973). Metacontrast: A review. *Perception and Psychophysics* **13** (1B), 161–171.

Uttal, W. R. (1981). *A Taxonomy of Visual Processes.* Hillside, NJ, Erlbaum.

Walraven, J. (1982). *Chromatic induction.* Doctoral Dissertation, University of Utrecht, Netherlands.

Wiesel, T. N. and Hubel, D. H. (1966). Spatial and chromatic interactions in the lateral geniculate body of the rhesus monkey. *J. Neurophysiol.* **29**, 1115–1156 (1966).

Wyszecki, G. and Stiles, W. S. (1982). *Color Science* (2nd edn). New York, Wiley.

Sensitivity to Spatiotemporal Colour Contrast

*JOHAN A. VAN ESCH, CEES NOORLANDER and
JAN J. KOENDERINK*

Introduction

Brown and MacAdam (1949) studied the sensitivity to combined chromaticity and luminance contrast at various locations in colour space. They described their data by ellipsoids that can be considered as just-noticeable difference contours (j.n.d.-contours). However, they restricted themselves to a 2° diameter bipartite field. This restricts the applicability of their data in colorimetric techniques because Cavonius and Estévez (1975), van der Horst and Bouman (1969), Kelly and van Norren (1977) and Noorlander, Heuts and Koenderink (1980) have shown that luminance and chromaticity discrimination is very much dependent on the spatiotemporal configuration of the stimulus.

Since Helmholtz (1892) formulated his colour vision theory based on a Riemannian metric, several investigators (e.g. Guth and Lodge, 1973; Ingling and Tsou, 1977; Koenderink, van de Grind and Bouman, 1972; Schrödinger, 1920; Stiles, 1946; Vos and Walraven, 1972) have tried to develop colour vision models describing j.n.d.-contours. Some have compared their models with the experimental data of Brown and MacAdam. Current models can be divided into two types:

1) line elements assuming that the opponent channels are a linear combination of the RGB fundamentals,
2) line elements assuming that nonlinear transformation processing takes place in the opponent channels.

COLOUR VISION
ISBN 0 12 000000 0

In the present study we investigated colour discrimination in colour space first to test the validity of the current colour vision models and second to investigate the sensitivity to spatiotemporal luminance and chromaticity contrast for many modulation directions and several mean colours in colour space. Also colour discrimination as a function of eccentricity was studied.

Experiments and Methods

A computer-controlled sine-wave oscillator generates spatial or temporal sine wave patterns on the screen of a 670-A1 Tektronix RGB monitor. The subject looks at the central part of the screen, which subtends $2° \times 2°$. The frame frequency is 60 Hz and the separate scan lines are not perceptible. The method of limits was used in the experiments. All subjects were males with normal colour vision. For the red (R), green (G) and blue (B) cone systems the Vos–Walraven fundamentals (Walraven, 1974) were used of which the excitation can be derived by means of the relationship between the R, G, B and the retinal illuminances, as defined by the V_λ-curve of Judd (1951), of the red (R_F), green (G_F) and blue (B_F) television phosphors.

$$\begin{pmatrix} R \\ G \\ B \end{pmatrix} = \begin{pmatrix} 0.81860 & 0.60302 & 0.48957 \\ 0.18047 & 0.39525 & 0.42836 \\ 0.00093 & 0.00173 & 0.08207 \end{pmatrix} \begin{pmatrix} R_F \\ G_F \\ B_F \end{pmatrix}$$

Experiments in the Red–Green Plane

We determined discrimination ellipses for five retinal illuminations (3, 10, 30, 100 and 300 td) with a dominant wavelength of 570 nm in the red green plane using 1, 4 and 15 Hz as temporal and 1, 4 and 16 cpd as spatial frequencies. For 30 and 300 td three additional colours were used ($\lambda = 557, 582$ and 602 nm). Results are given for subject CN but were also obtained from two other subjects.

Results. Presentation of the ellipses in a $(G^{1/2}, R^{1/2})$ plane gives us insight into the validity of the de Vries–Rose law (size and shape of the ellipses will be constant along the line $R/G = C$). Discrimination ellipses are given in the Figs 1 to 4 for the above mentioned parameters.

Discussion. In the $(G^{1/2}, R^{1/2})$ plane the 1 and 4 Hz and 1 cpd ellipses exhibit an orientation close to the luminance direction. In this representation the pure luminance and pure chromatic directions are perpendicular. Thus the results indicate that luminance and chromaticity mechanisms are independent. The eccentricities of the ellipses increase with increasing luminance while the minor axes hardly change. This implies that for low spatial and temporal frequencies

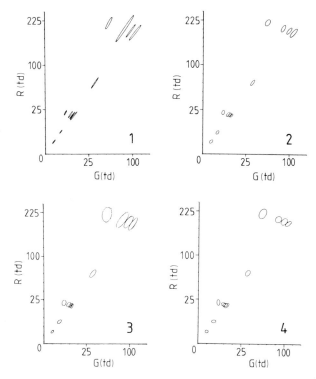

FIGS 1–4   Discrimination ellipses in the $(\sqrt{G}, \sqrt{R})$-plane. Excitation of R and G cone fundamentals are expressed in trolands (td). 1 : 1 Hz ellipses five times enlarged; 2: 4 Hz, five times enlarged; 3: 1 cpd, three times enlarged; 4: 4 cpd, ten times enlarged.

the de Vries–Rose low holds over a larger range of luminance levels for chromaticity discrimination than for luminance discrimination (Fig. 5). This is also supported by other psychophysical experiments (Kelly, 1961; Van der Horst, 1969). For high spatiotemporal frequencies one should be careful when drawing conclusions as a consequence of a possible influence of chromatic aberration.

Let us analyse our results from the theoretical point of view. Suppose the red–green opponent channel can be considered as a linear combination of R and G, namely $R - qG$. For a point in the (R, G)-plane a response in the $R - G$ channel is then proportional to $dR - qdG$. For linearity q must be a constant and may not depend on the mean chromaticity coordinates. The luminance channel has to be proportional to $dR + pdG$ (p being a constant). When we neglect the yellow–blue channel, the ellipses can be described by

$$S_l^2 (dR + pdG)^2 - S_c^2 (dR - qdG)^2 = 1 \qquad (1)$$

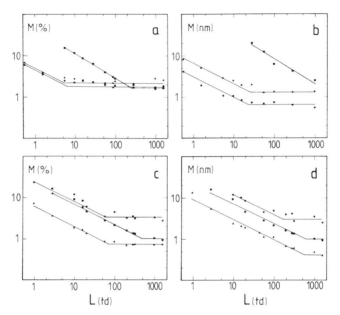

FIG. 5   Threshold modulation M as a function of retinal illuminance L. Panels a and c: luminance modulation in % modulation depth; Panels b and d: chromaticity modulation in nm. Panels a and b: circles 1 Hz; triangles 4 Hz; squares 15 Hz. Panels c and d: circles 0.5 cpd; triangles, 4 cpd; squares, 16 cpd. All lines have slopes of -0.5 (de Vries–Rose behaviour) and 0 (Weber behaviour) except the lines for 15 Hz.

with S_l and S_c being weighting factors which depend on the mean chromaticity coordinates and on the spatiotemporal stimulus configuration. If linearity holds then Equation (1) describes every discrimination ellipse for each spatiotemporal configuration with p and q constant. Our results prove that for low temporal frequencies q is not a constant. From Fig. 1 we may conclude that the ellipses are oriented along the direction $dR = qdG$. If q is a constant they should be oriented along lines $R - qG = C$. These orientations become hyperbolas in the $(G^{1/2}, R^{1/2})$ planes with $R^{1/2} = q^{1/2}G^{1/2}$ as one of the asymptotes. Figure 1 shows clearly that this cannot occur: the ellipses are oriented to the origin of the $(G^{1/2}, R^{1/2})$ plane. This indicates nonlinear processing, namely a term $[(dR/R) - q(dG/G)]$ instead of $dR - qdG$ in Equation (1). The line element

$$S_l^2 (dR + pdG) + S_c^2 \left(\frac{dR}{R} - \frac{dG}{G} \right)^2 = 1 \qquad (2)$$

fits the experimental data well.

Conclusions.

1) For low and medium spatiotemporal frequencies the eccentricity of the discrimination ellipses depends on the average luminance used, because, for these frequencies, the de Vries–Rose/Weber transition point for luminance discrimination is reached at lower luminance levels than it is for chromaticity discrimination.

2) The red–green opponent channel processing is not linear.

3) The line element

$$S_i^2 (dR + p\,dG)^2 + S_c^2 \left(\frac{dR}{R} - \frac{dG}{G}\right)^2 = 1$$

is a useful threshold function for spatiotemporal luminance and chromaticity modulation of various mean luminances and colours in the (R, G)-plane with p a subject dependent constant.

Experiments in Three-Dimensional Colour Space

Discrimination ellipsoids were determined for five points (R, G, B) in colour space and for seven temporal and six spatial frequencies. The mean colour coordinates of the five colours were: white $(22, 100, 2)$, red $(200, 50, 1)$, green $(200, 114, 2)$, yellow $(200, 200, 0.5)$ and blue $(200, 100, 8)$. Temporal frequencies used were $F_t = 0.25, 0.5, 1, 2, 4, 7, 5, 15$ Hz and spatial frequencies $F_s = 0.5,$ 1, 2, 4, 8, 16 cpd.

Results. The ellipses will be presented in the $dR/R, dG/G, dB/B$-space because of the lower sensitivity of the B-cone fundamental (Walraven, 1974). For low spatial and temporal frequencies the principal axes of the different ellipsoids have roughly the same orientation $\phi = 45°, \theta = 37°, \alpha = 90°$ (see Fig. 6). This indicates that luminance and chromaticity discrimination are

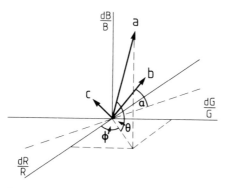

FIG. 6   The orientation angles of the first (a) and second (b) semi-axes of an ellipsoid in colour space. The axis c is perpendicular to a and b.

predominantly orthogonal for low spatial and temporal frequencies. Because we want to compare our discrimination ellipsoids with those given by Brown and MacAdam (1949), we converted some of their ellipsoids to the (dR/R, dG/G, dB/B) space and calculated the mean of the orientation angles ($\bar{\phi} = 50°$, $\bar{\theta} = 57°$ and $\bar{\alpha} = 84°$). These angles are roughly the same as we found for low temporal and spatial frequencies. However as the temporal and spatial frequency is increased the orientations of the ellipsoids change as can be seen in Table 1.

TABLE 1   Parameters of the spatial discrimination ellipsoids of subject CN. F_s is the spatial frequency (in cpd). A, B and C are the lengths (in %) of the principal axes in the (dR/R, dG/G, dB/B) space. ϕ, θ and α are the orientation angles (in degrees);

Colour	F_s	A	B	C	ϕ	θ	α
W	4	6.8	0.73	0.30	10	89	147
R	4	12.0	0.89	0.53	-4	89	174
G	4	7.0	0.67	0.37	79	86	79
Y	4	11.4	0.97	0.39	13	89	146
B	4	8.6	0.73	0.41	63	88	97
W	8	36	1.34	0.37	11	90	147
W	16	40	2.5	1.41	51	90	110

Parameters of the temporal discrimination ellipsoids of subject CN. F_t is the temporal frequency (in Hz).

Colour	F_t	A	B	C	ϕ	θ	α
W	4	4.5	1.83	0.52	47	96	92
R	4	6.3	1.79	0.93	57	85	92
G	4	4.3	1.88	0.63	45	85	96
Y	4	5.7	1.56	0.45	17	88	125
B	4	3.5	1.97	0.51	123	88	17
W	7½	8.4	2.3	1.00	40	89	114
W	15	18.4	4.4	2.7	56	84	118
R	15	41	9.2	5.1	74	84	131
G	15	23	6.4	3.3	49	84	142
B	15	7.5	4.9	3.0	79	45	129

Thus the spatiotemporal frequency domain for which the Brown and MacAdam ellipsoids resemble the present ellipsoids is mainly the low-frequency domain. This comparison also shows that different experimental methods yield approximately the same results, for we used j.n.d. contours whereas the Brown and MacAdam ellipsoids represent standard deviations of colour matching.

Conclusion. Our discrimination data can be considered as an extension of the Brown and MacAdam metric, especially for medium and high spatial and temporal frequencies. When one uses their metric in practice one has to keep in mind that it has been determined for low spatial frequencies. Similar problems arise with any colour difference formula that does not explicitly acknowledge the spatiotemporal structure of the stimulus.

Experiments as a Function of Eccentricity

We determined colour discrimination for red–green modulation of a yellow field and yellow–blue modulation of a white field for a temporal frequency of 1 Hz. The target size was varied from 1/8° to 16° and the eccentricity from 0° to 50°. For a fixed target size we found a decrease in colour sensitivity if the target was moved away from the fovea. The threshold for colour contrast decreases with increasing target size until the size exceeds the integration area. We calculated scaling factors S (the ratio between the foveal and peripheral target sizes for which colour discrimination is the same) that are shown in Fig. 7. Also plotted in this figure is M, the cortical magnification factor calculated by Drasdo (1977). There is good agreement between M and our scaling factor S.

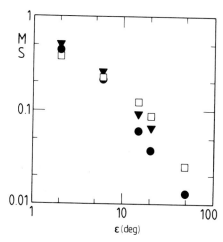

FIG. 7   The ratio S between the foveal and peripheral target size for which temporal colour-discrimination is the same. Circles, red–green contrast, squares, yellow–blue contrast, triangles, scaling factor M (see text).

Conclusion. Colour discrimination in the peripheral visual field is comparable to foveal colour discrimination if the target size is enlarged according to the cortical magnification factor.

432   *J. A. van Esch* et al.

References

Brown, W. R. J. and MacAdam, D. L. (1949). Visual sensitivity to combined chromaticity and luminance contrast. *J. opt. Soc. Am.* **39**, 808–834.

Cavonius, C. R. and Estévez, O. (1975). Sensitivity of human color mechanisms to gratings and flicker. *J. opt. Soc. Am.* **65**, 966–968.

Drasdo, N. (1977). The neural representation of visual space. *Nature* **266**, 554–556.

Guth, S. L. and Lodge, H. R. (1973). Heterochromatic additivity, foveal spectral sensitivity and a new color model. *J. opt. Soc. Am.* **63**, 450–462.

Von Helmholtz, H. (1892). Versuch das psychophysische Gesetz auf die Farbenunterschiede trichromatischer Augen anzuwenden. *Z. Psychol. Physiol. Sinnesorg.* **3**, 1–20.

Van der Horst, G. J. C. (1969). Chromatic flicker. *J. opt. Soc. Am.* **59**, 1213–1217.

Van der Horst, G. J. C. and Bouman, M. A. (1969). Spatiotemporal chromaticity discrimination. *J. opt. Soc. Am.* **59**, 1482–1488.

Ingling, C. J. Jr and Tsou, B. H.-P. (1977). Orthogonal combination of the three visual channels. *Vision Res.* **17**, 1075–1082.

Judd, D. B. (1951). Colorimetry and artificial daylight. Proc. 12th session CIE Stockholm, 1, Techn. Committee 7, Bureau Central de la CIE, Paris, p. 11.

Kelly, D. H. (1961). Visual responses to time-dependent stimuli. I. Amplitude sensitivity measurements. *J. opt. Soc. Am.* **51**, 422–429.

Kelly, D. H. and Van Norren, D. (1977). Two-band model of heterochromatic flicker. *J. opt. Soc. Am.* **67**, 1081–1091.

Koenderink, J. J., Van de Grind, W. A. and Bouman, M. A. (1972). Opponent color coding: A mechanistic model and a new metric for color space. *Kybernetik* **10**, 78–98.

Noorlander, C., Heuts, M. J. G. and Koenderink, J. J. (1981). Sensitivity to spatiotemporal combined luminance and chromaticity contrast. *J. opt. Soc. Am.* **71**, 453–459.

Schrödinger, E. H. (1920). Grundlinien einer Theorie der Farbenmetrik im Tagessehen. *Ann. Physik* **63**, 397–456, 481–520.

Stiles, W. S. (1946). A modified Helmholtz line-element in brightness-colour space. *Proc. Phys. Soc., Lond.* **58**, 41–65.

Vos, J. J. and Walraven, P. L. (1972). An analytical description of the line element in the zone-fluctuation model of colour vision. *Vision Res.* **12**, 1327–1265.

Walraven, P. L. (1974). A closer look at the tritanopic convergence point. *Vision Res.* **14**, 1339–1343.

The Spatiochromatic Signal of the $r-g$ Channel

CARL R. INGLING, Jr and EUGENIO MARTINEZ

Introduction

The $r-g$ Channel

When trying to understand real systems, it may be helpful to first understand simplified or ideal systems. Ideal formulations provide theoretical limits and may suggest a structure for theories of real systems.

It is of interest to discover the ideal or optimal behavior of the principal channel subserving the primate fovea. For this analysis, we will take this channel to be that channel composed of the various classes of tonic, simple-opponent $r-g$ cells, what we will call the $r-g$ X-channel. Primate (and other) visual systems have two parallel channels, X and Y. Although estimates vary, it is clear that the primate fovea is dominated by X-cells, possibly some 90% of foveal cells falling in this category (Lennie, 1980).

The $r-g$ cells are the predominant X-cell type. According to De Monasterio and Gouras (1975), 80% of the cells in their concentric color-opponent category have only R and G cone input. It seems very likely that these are the cells which form the physiological correlate of the $r-g$ channel of opponent color theories. Therefore, because of their predominance as a subtype in the primate central fovea, and because of their likely basis as the psychophysical correlate of one of the three channels in the optic nerve required by the trivariance of color matching, we assume here that the simple-opponent $r-g$ units which predominate in primate fovea can be called a channel. The aim of this paper is to describe the behavior of a channel constituted of such units. Without further

COLOUR VISION
ISBN 0 12 000000 0

experimentation, of course, it cannot be claimed that the theoretical or ideal behavior represents in fact how the real visual system works. Thus the discussion should be understood as hypothesis.

General Considerations and Concepts

The problem is to describe quantitatively a channel that transmits both spatial and spectral information. To avoid confusion, we briefly review some elementary principles and concepts.

In general, the dimensionality of a system is determined by the number of independent variables that must be transmitted. If information about quantum absorptions in 3 kinds of cone must be transmitted, then the system must contain 3 independent channels. For particular reasons, the signals may be transformed but the transformation does not reduce the requirement of three channels. Thus, for example, R, G, B cone signals are transformed into summing (luminance) and differencing (chromatic) signals within the plexiform layers of the retina. This transformation is described quantitatively by the transformation equations of opponent theory, for example:

$$L = a_{11}R + a_{12}G + a_{13}B$$
$$C_1 = a_{21}R + a_{22}G + a_{23}B$$
$$C_2 = a_{31}R + a_{32}G + a_{33}B,$$

in which L is a luminance signal (usually V_λ) and C_1 and C_2 are two opponent or difference channels (e.g., $r-g$, $y-b$). In principle after these signals are transmitted over independent channels, the detector can apply the inverse transform and retrieve the R, G, B cone signals. In this way, for example, color matches which equate quantum absorptions in the three cones on each side of a bipartite field could be made. However, it suffices with no loss of generality to equate the transformed quantities on each side of the field, which is doubtless how real observers make matches. For present purposes, we need to consider only the two-variable case, and note that two channels are required to transmit information about R, G cone signals from the retina to the cortex. These signals may be transmitted directly or transformed to say a sum and a difference: $L = R+G$; $C = R-G$, in which case the two independent channels are L and C rather than R and G. A single channel is color-blind, but with two channels wavelength discrimination is possible if the transformed channels are independent.

The above discussion outlines the dimensionality requirements for transmitting spectral information. The spatial transmission characteristics of a (linear) channel are described by its modulation transfer function. Because such functions are commonplace in vision only a few words will be necessary, the aim being to provide the background for the next section which considers the interaction of the spatial and spectral variables in channel transmission.

The information obtained in the spatial transfer function for a channel can also be represented as a point-spread function; one is the transform of the other. For physiology, which deals with receptive fields, the point-spread function has advantages. Figure 1 shows examples of point-spread functions, or receptive fields, and their transforms. The channel is viewed as a filter which attenuates certain spatial frequencies; the transfer function is simply a plot of the attenuation, or gain, as a function of spatial frequency (ω). The transfer function is the filter characteristic for the receptive field of which it is the transform. It shows which spatial frequencies are maximally transmitted and which are attenuated by the given receptive field. A channel can be tuned, or made to have the shape of a band-pass filter, by adding inhibitory flanks to the receptive field.

Theory

Interaction of Spatial and Spectral Variables

Historically, color vision and spatial vision, by and large, have been studied separately. One aim of this paper is to make it clear that the two cannot be separated. As we will show, it is by means of the interaction of the spatial and spectral variables that the principal channel of the visual system transmits its signals.

Figure 1 shows various possibilities for transmitting both spatial and spectral information over a channel. The spectral variables can be combined with the spatial variables to produce a variety of transfer functions. We factor the receptive fields to separate the spectral from the spatial characteristics, and furthermore, we factor the spectral coefficients not as R and G but as transformed channels $(R + G)$ and $(R - G)$. To factor these fields, we need to represent a spatial and a spectral sensitivity. We represent the spatial sensitivity with unit spread functions: a center, say, as a gate pulse of unit area. For single wavelengths, the R and G spectral sensitivity functions give the coefficient which multiplies the unit spatial spread functions. For non-monochromatic stimuli, these coefficients become integrals. The receptive fields of interest here can be decomposed into two such spread functions (centers and surrounds) modified by either of two classes of cone, R and G. To represent a receptive field, multiply the unit spread function that represents its center by the spectral sensitivity of the appropriate cone (or sum of cones) and add it to the analogous product for the surround; see Fig. 1. In the general case, this form of the receptive field, although widely familiar, is not easily interpretable. Instead of the receptive field form using R and G coefficients, a much more useful form for computational purposes and particularly within the context of opponent theory is obtained by factoring for $(R + G)$ and $(R - G)$ coefficients and transforming the resulting spread functions to the corresponding

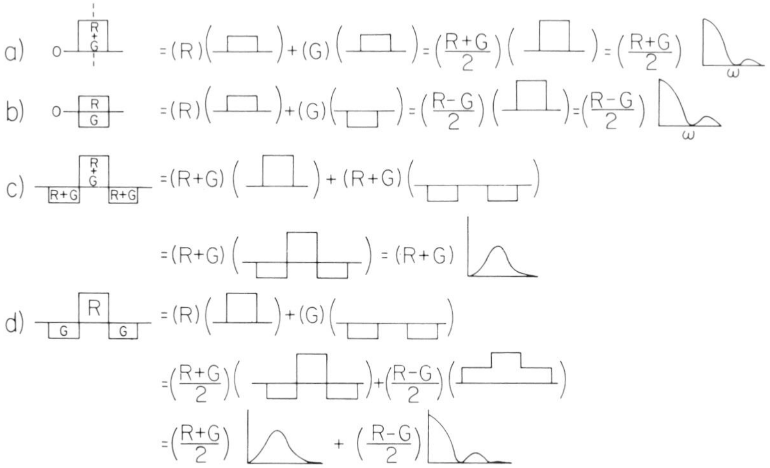

FIG. 1   Factoring of four receptive fields into products of [brightness $(R + G)$ or hue $(R - G)$], and [a low-pass or band-pass filter]. All four receptive fields have R and G cone input. The characteristics of the fields are: (a) no spectral tuning, no spatial tuning; (b) spectral tuning, no spatial tuning; (c) a Y-channel cell with no spectral tuning, but spatially tuned; and (d) an X-channel simple-opponent cell which is a combination of a spectrally tuned cell with no spatial tuning and a spatially tuned cell with no spectral tuning; i.e., it is similar to a combination of (b) and (c) above. The fields were factored by writing them as a sum of products as shown, and substituting into the identity for factoring a sum of products as given in the text.

transfer functions. To factor the sum of products which represents the receptive field, substitute into the identity $Ax + By \equiv \frac{1}{2}(A + B)(x + y) + \frac{1}{2}(A - B)(x - y)$. Figure 1 shows the results of factoring and transforming the resulting spread functions for four receptive fields.

The r−g Simple-Opponent Receptive Field

Figure 1 (d) shows that the response of the simple-opponent $r-g$ cell is identically equal to the sum of two responses. One of these is a band-pass filter with $(R + G)$ or achromatic spectral sensitivity, and the other is a low-pass filter with opponent $(R - G)$ spectral sensitivity. It is thus an inherent property of simple-opponent cells that they produce both summing and differencing signals. The differencing signal is produced at low spatial frequencies and the summing signal at high spatial frequencies. Thus this cell subtracts the signals from quantum absorptions in R and G cones for low spatial frequencies, but adds them for high.

The $r-g$ channel (Fig. 1d) is not a univariant channel. The other channels shown in Fig. 1(a−d) are described by the product of a filter and a spectral sensitivity. The filter shows the spatial frequency spectrum, and the R and G coefficients the chromatic spectrum; the product function completely characterizes the channel. The r−g receptive field (Fig. 1d), however, requires *two* such product functions for its specification. This channel simultaneously carries information about two variables at once; a chromatic transfer function and an achromatic transfer function. This means, for example, that the behavior of this channel cannot be solely determined by experiments which are carried out for equiluminance conditions. Such experiments are said to isolate color channels. In fact, as Fig. 1 shows, the r−g channel is as much a luminance channel as it is a color channel. It requires achromatic or intensity variation as well as wavelength variation in the stimulus to elicit its full response complement.

Although the spectral sensitivities of simple-opponent r−g cells are usually shown as biphasic curves with, say, +R and −G lobes, the factoring shown in Fig. 1 makes it clear that such spectral sensitivity curves are correct only for the special case of $\omega = 0$. For high frequencies, the spectral sensitivity of the simple-opponent r−g cell is the sum $(R + G)$, and resembles V_λ (see also Zrenner, this volume). This transition from subtraction to addition is illustrated in Fig. 2, which shows an additivity index for the mixture of two wavelengths as a function of ω. The index, calculated for a mixture of 520- and 610-nm lights, is obtained by adding half a unit of 520 to half a unit of 610 and plotting the units of the mixture as a function of the spatial frequency. Given the factors shown in the Fig. 1(d) transform for this cell, a qualitative result can be drawn by inspection. Essentially, the terms describing the spectral sensitivity of the cell are modified by spatial-frequency-dependent weights

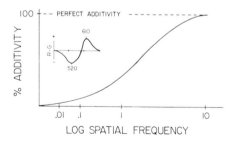

FIG. 2   This curve shows that the r−g cell, generally viewed as a differencing mechanism which computes an r−g opponent spectral sensitivity curve, is photometrically additive (i.e., adds rather than subtracts cone signals) at high spatial frequencies. The additivity curve was calculated for a mixture of 520- and 610-nm lights as shown on the inset curve. At very low frequencies, the 520−610 mixture completely cancels. The inset spectral sensitivity curve is only appropriate for $\omega = $ zero. As ω increases, this curve changes from a difference curve to a luminosity (approximately V_λ) curve.

which change the sensitivity from $(R - G)$ at $\omega = 0$ to $(R + G)$ beyond a certain high frequency; i.e., from that of a color to that of a brightness channel.

Processing of the r−g Channel signals

Signal characteristics.   In summary so far, we have shown that the foveal channel composed of simple-opponent $r-g$ cells sends both summing and differencing signals to the cortex in a *single* channel. This point deserves special emphasis in view of the general proposition, noted above, that R and G cone signals (or their sum and difference transforms) must be transmitted over *two independent channels*.

The problem now is to decode these signals. Because they are both in the same channel, this presents difficulties. To postulate a decoding strategy implies that we know what the signals are used for. We will assume that the aim is to extract from this channel an image (or a transformation of it) of the scene being transmitted. For example, if an algorithm can be devised which estimates the sum and difference signals for each point in the visual field, then the visual system has apparently invented a method for transmitting information about two independent variables over one channel. If this is possible, the brain has substituted computation for band-width by effectively eliminating an entire visual channel.

Is it possible to deduce, from the output of the $r-g$ channel, what the R and G cone signals are at every point in the visual field, or at enough points in the visual field to prevent significant illusion? As noted before, it suffices to determine $(R + G)$ and $(R - G)$, or brightness and hue, for every point in the field. Without computation, this determination cannot be made. The quantities $(R + G)$ and $(R - G)$ are not known for every point in the image. Suppose, for example, that the output of a wire coming from the retina is 8. Is this a sum or a difference? Is it red, white, or bright green? Clearly, more information is needed. By looking at wires nearby the wire with the 8 reading, spatial filtering can be applied. If nearby numbers change rapidly, then the number 8 is likely to be a sum. On the other hand, if nearby number (or their derivatives) are nearly constant, then the number 8 is a difference. In principle, by spatial filtering, the detector can to a certain extent tell whether the number 8 is likely to be a sum. On the other hand, if nearby numbers (or their transmit an image of a scene by transmitting the hue and brightness of every point of the scene. A single channel cannot transmit information about the hue and brightness for every point in a scene. What the $r-g$ channel does is to filter the scene and transmit the brightness for high frequencies within the scene and the hue for low frequencies. Therefore, for a given point within the scene, the central detector has information about only one of these variables, at best. Actually, it has only information about the sum of the brightness and hue signals, although the addends are partially recoverable by filtering.

Therefore, in general, either another channel must be used or the detector must estimate values for hue and brightness at low and high spatial frequencies respectively. The reason for considering the latter alternative without appealing to a second channel is that the detector must at least partially decode the two signals present in the $r-g$ channel in order to preserve any semblance of image fidelity, even with access to a second channel.

To begin with, it is advantageous to know what kind of visual environment the system to be designed must operate in. Here we will assume that the environment contains targets upon backgrounds. Targets tend to be areas defined by a perimeter of high spatial frequencies. Furthermore, they usually differ in both hue and brightness from the background. Within this context, how well can a detector reconstruct the hue and brightness for each point of a visual scene?

Figure 3 (a−c) shows the output of the $r-g$ channel for hypothetical targets. To simplify the specification of the stimulus, we specify the input not in terms of wavelength but as cone outputs. "Real" stimuli could be substituted but would add nothing except another stage of calculation. For R and G cone outputs, these curves show the high- and low-frequency components of the $r-g$ channel response; i.e., the brightness and hue respectively. The total $r-g$ channel signal, also shown, is the sum of these two components.

Detector strategy.   To simplify matters, assume that for very high spatial frequencies the hue signal is not important. It is not resolved for high frequencies by any channel under any circumstances. In other words, we get rid of half of the problem, that of finding out what the low-frequency hue signal is at the high-frequency edge by ignoring it; discrepancies will not be noticed because of blur. However, the opposite problem must be solved; that of finding out what the high frequency $(R + G)$ signal is in those areas of the scene for which we have only the low frequency $(R - G)$ signal. The illustrations in Fig. 3 indicate that it might be possible to base a reconstruction of the scene upon interpolation of the brightness at the edge of objects (or extrapolation in some cases). This assumes that objects can in general be defined by high-frequency contours. The high spatial frequencies at the edges of objects produce an $(R + G)$ signal for the object, but this signal is accurate only at the edge. By extrapolating the value of $(R + G)$ at the edge over the entire figure, $(R + G)$ can be estimated for the figure. This system will be prone to illusions that depend on the failure to transmit correctly low spatial frequency brightness. However, real visual systems are known to suffer from this type of illusion (e.g., Cornsweet, 1970). (Incidentally, Fig. 1 shows that the presumed achromatic channel of the visual system, the Y-cell channel, is a band-pass channel which also attenuates low spatial frequencies.) Apparently illusions present in a system which estimates low frequency brightness from the high frequencies of contours may not be fatal. Although colors can be correctly

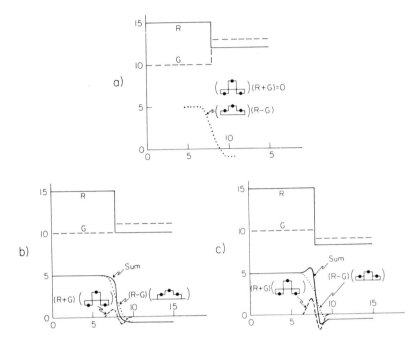

FIG. 3 Output of an *r−g* channel for three different edges. Edge inputs are *R* and *G* cone signals as shown at the top of each graph. (a) shows a field with equal luminance on each side. (*R* + *G*) is the same on both sides so that there is no band-pass signal at the edge. (b) shows the same edge except that an achromatic contrast has been added; the right-hand side has been decreased 15%. This amount of achromatic contrast produces a band-pass or (*R* + *G*) component as shown, but it is insufficient contrast to produce enhancement of the total signal. It does not meet Russell's criterion. (c) Here the right-hand side has been decreased by 30% which adds enough achromatic contrast for the total signal to show enhancement. This edge contains enough contrast to be detected by a Russell filter. If the band-pass component is large enough to be detected, then there are two quantities carried by this single channel which must be made equal on both sides of a colorimetric field for the fields to match; the enhanced or band-pass signal, and the difference or low-pass signal (see text, Discussion).

identified regardless of photopic luminance, absolute luminance levels cannot be. The eye is a poor photometer because no channel transmits d.c. brightness.

Figure 3 shows another way of looking at the results shown in Fig. 1 for the *r−g* cell. As Fig. 3 shows, the *r−g* cell responds in two different ways; it gives a nonenhanced response to hue differences across an edge and an enhanced response to achromatic contrasts. The nonenhanced response is the low-frequency (*R* − *G*) subadditive difference signal. The enhanced response is the additive, high-frequency (*R* + *G*) response to edges. The significance of these two responses is that to the extent that the enhanced response can be recovered from the combined signal, it becomes possible for an ideal processor to estimate the $(R + G)$ signal for low frequency areas from the $(R + G)$ signal at the edge.

Russell's theory.   A theory which proposes a criterion of efficiency for a processor faced with the task of recovering the enhanced component − that is, the $(R + G)$ term − from a signal which contains both $(R + G)$ and $(R − G)$ was developed by Russell (1979) to account for the achromatic contrast required for stereopsis with Julesz patterns. We will now summarize this theory in the context of the problem of detecting the $(R + G)$ signal.

Lu and Fender (1972) discovered that there is no stereopsis for Julesz random-dot patterns when the stereograms are presented at equal luminance − that is, when there is no achromatic contrast between the dots of different hue. They measured the contrast that had to be added to each wavelength to produce stereopsis when presented with a standard wavelength. The amount of achromatic contrast that must be added to each test wavelength to produce depth is not constant (Lu and Fender, 1972). The problem is that stereopsis is not mediated by the color channels, because there is none for a constant luminance, pure hue pattern; on the other hand, were stereopsis mediated by the luminance channel, we would expect to add constant luminance to each wavelength, which is not the case.

Although his hypothesis was presented in less general terms, Russell essentially solved this problem by showing that stereopsis depended upon the band-pass component of the $r−g$ cell response, but that this band-pass reponse could not be used until sufficient achromatic contrast had been added to make the total response band-pass. Figure 3 shows an edge with the same "color" on each side but successively more contrast. For the equal-luminance case, the $(R + G)$ band-pass signal is zero. As more contrast is added, the band-pass signal appears, but the total signal is not enhanced; Russell's criterion is not met. Additional contrast finally produces enough band-pass $(R + G)$ signal to appear on the total. This meets Russell's criterion, and would produce stereopsis in the Lu and Fender experiment.

Russell filtering: r−g channel decoding strategy.   Adopting the enhancement criterion for recognizing the band-pass component of the $r−g$ channel provides a simple method for reconstructing the low-pass $(R − G)$ and band-pass $(R + G)$ signals for all parts of a scene. For any boundary, Russell's filter can be applied to see if there is sufficient contrast present for the boundary to be enhanced. When there is sufficient contrast the enhancement is seen on the total response. Filtering of the enhanced signal provides a measure of the $(R + G)$ band-pass component because a filter can discard the dc $(R − G)$ component. If the $(R + G)$ component is interpolated (or for some figures extrapolated) it is possible within the limits of the enhancement rule to recreate a two-variable specification of a scene from the information in a single channel.

Discussion

Supporting Evidence

Although the aim here is primarily to pursue theoretically the implications of our analysis of the spatial and spectral properties of the $r-g$ receptive field, there are experiments and observations which support our conclusions.

First, the reason for analyzing the spatial and spectral characteristics of the $r-g$ cell arose because of a contradiction between the opponent models of psychophysics and the X,Y parallel channel concept of electrophysiology. According to electrophysiology, the cells most likely to resolve acuity targets are the small, tonic simple-opponent receptive fields of the X-channel. However, it is a well-known result from psychophysical studies that when acuity is used as a criterion for equating lights of different color, mixtures of such lights are photometrically additive. For example, match light A to light S and light B to light S. A criterion is additive if mixtures of A and B in proportions which sum to 1 also match S. Because lights which produce the same acuity are additive, psychophysical studies concluded that acuity must be mediated by the additive luminosity channel of psychophysics, namely the flicker channel. The small receptive fields of the X-channel which predominate in the central fovea are excluded because X-cells are simple-opponent and in the conventional view necessarily subadditive. The opponent channels are used in psychophysics to account for the subadditivity of direct brightness matching and threshold measures; they cannot consistently be used to explain subadditivity and also, somehow, additivity. The analysis shown in Fig. 2 explains how chromatically opponent $r-g$ cells can in fact be subadditive for say threshold, which involves the detection of targets containing low spatial frequencies, and additive for acuity targets such as gratings, Landolt C's, etc. Our analysis of the $r-g$ units makes the psychophysical and electrophysiological pictures congruent, and in so doing supports the theory.

A second piece of evidence: The additive $(R+G)$ signal in the $r-g$ channel does not have exactly the same spectral sensitivity as the $(R+G)$ signal of the V_λ or flicker channel. To be precise, for cone pigments normalized to 1.0 at the wavelength of peak sensitivity, $V_\lambda = k_1(5R + 3G)$, whereas the $r-g$ additive term should be $K_2(2R + 3G)$. While this is not a large difference (amounting only to some 15% in theory) we have confirmed that in fact spectral sensitivity measured with an acuity criterion is more green-sensitive than spectral sensitivity measured with a flicker criterion, in agreement with the prediction (Ingling and Martinez, 1982). This further supports the idea that there are two separate additive channels mediating flicker and acuity.

A possible single-channel experiment. The discovery that a single foveal channel carries information about the two variables, luminance and hue, although at different spatial frequencies, suggests that there is a central processor capable of reconstructing estimates of these two variables for the scene. In a sense, the $r−g$ channel uses a form of spatial-frequency multiplexing by transmitting two different and incompatible signals at the same time, but tuned to different spatial frequencies. This differs from conventional time multiplexing in that signals are mixed; the sum of the signals is always present in the channel. This presents problems for recovering the signals. If the application of Russell's theory is correct for this case, the fact that only the sum is available limits the efficiency of the recovery. However, it is not known how severely this limitation affects the estimation of hue and brightness for all points of a scene. A possible experiment would be to encode by calculation a two-color real scene with a theoretical $r−g$ unit, send it over a single channel, filter the output with a Russell filter, interpolate the $(R + G)$ signal and then visually compare this scene to the original. To the extent that the proposed calculation is correct in mimicking what the real visual system does, the scenes may appear similar.

Color-Matching

Could the $r−g$ channel make two-primary color matches? If the matching fields are constructed so as not to exploit the kind of illusion that the system suffers from, two-color matches can be made using a single channel. Accurate estimation requires that the low-pass and band-pass signals be widely separated in the stimulus. Intermediate spatial frequencies will be carried by both filters and consequently for such frequencies the reconstruction is ambiguous. In this respect colorimeter fields have the right properties. They have high-contrast edges which delimit a uniform area with no misleading gradients. For such fields it is not possible to make both the high-frequency term $(R + G)$ and the low frequency $(R - G)$ equal on both sides of the field unless the cone signals on each side of the field are also equal.

Conclusions

Some portions of this theory are more strongly supported than others. That the $r−g$ channel sends two nominally incompatible signals and interprets them veridically we view as a robust finding. Four pieces of evidence support it: (1) the face validity of the spectral and spatial analysis of the $r−g$ cell; (2) the reconciliation of psychophysical models with experiments which show that an acuity criterion yields a photometrically additive measure for luminance; (3) the greater green sensitivity of luminosity curves measured with an acuity criterion as compared to a flicker criterion; and finally, (4) Russell's theory of the Lu and Fender experiment, which demonstrates the presence of the band-pass component, at least for stereopsis. Taken together, these arguments show that the band-pass component is present and that it is filtered and used to see high spatial frequency test objects and random-dot stereograms. The speculative part of this paper is that the visual system compares the two $r-g$ channel signals to reconstruct or estimate R and G cone signals (or their transforms) across the visual field. That such an estimate might be made is suggested by the large number of illusions in the contrast literature showing that in large measure the perceived brightness of an area depends critically upon the nature of the edge which bounds the area. It may well be to some extent that brightness at low frequencies is a centrally interpolated percept.

If a two-primary scene transmitted over a single channel appears similar to the same scene transmitted in the conventional manner, then the transmission scheme constitutes a theory of environmental redundancy. In effect, the visual system has discovered the nature of the redundancy and eliminated it. The visual system forces figure-ground separations in which contours play a crucial part in separating the figures from the ground. Figures could be separated by a low-frequency brightness signal as well as by a high-frequency contour, or by both. The visual system, in choosing one of these methods, elects not to be redundant. All channels (see Fig. 1) attenuate low spatial frequency brightness. Although the Y-channel has larger receptive fields than the X-channel and is tuned to lower spatial frequencies, it is still bandpass, further supporting the idea that low-frequency brightness is interpolated.

Acknowledgements

This research was partially supported by NEI Grant No. 5 R01 EY 03236 to Carl R. Ingling, Jr.

References

Cornsweet, T. N. (1970). *Visual Perception*, pp. 270ff. New York, Academic Press.
De Monasterio, F. M. and Gouras, P. (1975). Functional properties of ganglion cells of the Rhesus monkey retina. *J. Physiol., Lond.* **251**, 167–196.
Ingling, C. R., Jr and Martinez, E. (1982). The spectral sensitivity of the $r-g$ achromatic channel. *Investigative Ophthalmology and Visual Science (Suppl.)* **22**, 17.
Lennie, P. (1980). Parallel visual pathways: A review. *Vision Res.* **20**, 561–594.
Lu, C. and Fender, D. H. (1972). The interaction of color and luminance in stereoscopic vision. *Invest. Ophthal.* **11**, 482–490.
Russell, P. W. (1979). Chromatic input to stereopsis. *Vision Res.* **19**, 831–834.

Chromatic and Achromatic Border Perception:
A Two-Cone model Accounts for Suprathreshold Border Distinctness Judgements and Cortical Pattern-Evoked Response Amplitudes to the Same Stimuli

B. W. TANSLEY, A. W. ROBERTSON and K. E. MAUGHAN

Introduction

In a series of experimental reports we have shown that photopic human spatial vision is essentially tritanopic. Of the three species of cones believed to constitute the human photopic retina, only the two long-wavelength sensitive ones (the "L" and "M" cones) appear to contribute significantly to the perception of edges (Tansley and Boynton, 1976; Tansley, 1976; Tansley and Valberg, 1979).

Using neural interactions similar to those postulated in zone-type colour vision theories, we have developed a simple model that accounts for the subjective ratings of edge distinctness in chromatic patterns (Valberg and Tansley, 1977). Figure 1 shows a schematic diagram of this model as it applies to both achromatic and chromatic edges. For the achromatic case, the spectrally nonopponent interaction of L and M cones (modelled here by the sum $(L+M)$ over a very small retinal area) is spatially differentiated to give rise to a signal that reflects the contrast of a luminance step imaged upon a patch of retina. In our model a similar signal regarding the magnitude of a spatial discontinuity

COLOUR VISION
ISBN 0 12 000000 0

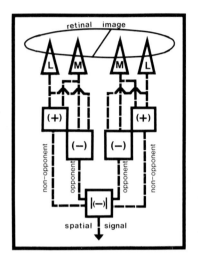

FIG. 1 Schematic of the two-cone spatial model. Two lights, each with a sharp spatial discontinuity juxtaposed with that of the other, produce a simple "pattern" imaged upon the retinal photoreceptor mosaic. Responses from the two long-wavelength sensitive cone classes interact in two ways to produce (L + M) signals and (L – M) signals that are spatially opposed by a higher-order process. The greater the response in this higher order mechanism the more perceptually distinct the border formed by the two lights. The modelled response of this higher-order process is based upon the tritanopic purity difference function described in the text and in Valberg and Tansley (1977). The function derives its name from the similarity of trichromatic spatial vision to the properties of tritanopic colour vision – the tritanope being that rare individual missing the short-wavelength sensitive cones.

imaged upon the retina is also carried in signals from the spectrally-opponent interaction (modelled here by (L – M)) that is spatially opposed in the same way. Though the sum (L + M) may be everywhere the same within the visual mechanisms mediating the response to a given photic pattern, the difference in response between L and M cones will rarely be zero – thus providing a differential signal to higher visual mechanisms. In this condition it is through the spatial analysis of spectrally-opponent responses from small areas of retina that spatial vision remains possible.

In our model the magnitude of the spatial signal is proportional to a constant times the $\log_{10}$ of the difference between either the (L + M) signals or the (L – M) signals arising from either side of the border in the photic array.

Suprathreshold Measures of Chromatic and Achromatic Border Percepts

This model originally derived from the observation that it was possible to equate subjectively the distinctness of a chromatic border to that of an achromatic border using a contrast-matching method. Ward and Boynton (1974) had observers adjust the luminance contrast of an achromatic step until its distinctness was equivalent to that of an equiluminous, chromatic step, which was simultaneously present nearby. Subsequent research demonstrated that observers were capable of rating subjectively the distinctness of achromatic and chromatic borders, and that this method gave results consistent with the contrast matching technique. In agreement with a number of other reports studying the relationship between suprathreshold luminance contrast and subjective border distinctness ratings, Ward and Boynton (1974) and Tansley and Boynton (1978) found a linear relation between the magnitude of subjective border distinctness ratings and the $\log_{10}$ of luminance contrast over a range from contrast threshold to approximately 10 times threshold (3–30%). Tansley and Boynton used the subjective rating method to evaluate the relation between subjective border distinctness judgements and equiluminous chromatic steps and found, similar to the achromatic case, that there was a linear relation between subjective distinctness ratings and the $\log_{10}$ of the difference between the responses of the spectrally-opponent $(L - M)$ process to either side of the edge. This finding was similar, except for the difference in sign between the original photoreceptor interaction, to the achromatic condition. This suggests that a common higher-order process could be involved in spatial information processing from both types of photic differences.

The similarity between subjective border distinctness ratings and the simple interactions between long-wavelength sensitive cone types for both chromatic and achromatic edges led us to consider the relation between subjective border distinctness ratings and cortical pattern-evoked responses to the same stimuli. It has been shown by a number of investigators that the pattern-evoked response amplitude to *achromatic* checkerboards varies linearly with the $\log_{10}$ of the spatial luminance contrast over a range of values similar to that obtained psychophysically at similar adaptation levels (Campbell and Maffei, 1970; Spekreijse, Estévez and Reits, 1977). As our model makes specific predictions regarding the equivalence of achromatic and chromatic spatial contrasts, and, as the linear relation between the pattern-evoked response amplitude and the $\log_{10}$ of luminance contrast is relatively well established, we were led to investigate the relationship between subjective chromatic border distinctness judgements and pattern-evoked potential amplitudes to chromatic patterns.

The basic prediction of the experiment is as follows: if subjective ratings of edge distinctness are based upon the same physiological mechanisms whose activities are believed to correlate with the cortical pattern-evoked response, then our two-cone model should predict the pattern-evoked response amplitudes to both chromatic and achromatic patterns, with only a change in the scaling constant to account for the difference between units. This prediction should hold independently of the size of the colour difference between stimuli to the extent that this difference reflects only the action of the short-wavelength sensitive cones (Tansley and Valberg, 1979). To test this prediction we collected subjective border distinctness ratings and cortical pattern-evoked responses to the same stimuli.

Methods

Apparatus

Stimulus generation and control was carried out through the use of a digital television graphics system, consisting of a host computer (PDP11/03) and a display processor (Norpak VDP) whose output was presented upon a high-resolution video monitor (Hitachi HM2719). We developed a software system that permits the representation and manipulation of chromatic and spatial parameters independent of one another. This system was used to control and specify all stimulus parameters in the study.

The observers' behavioural responses were entered through the keyboard of the host computer control console. Their electrophysiological responses were collected from silver cup scalp electrodes, amplified (1.25×10^6), band-pass filtered (1 to 30 Hz) and fed into a Nicolet (Model 1170) signal averager.

Stimuli

Table 1 shows the chromaticities of all stimuli used in this study. The listed pairs of chromaticities were chosen, on the basis of previous work, to generate chromatic borders of varying distinctness, according to the formula:

$$D_c = K \log_{10} ABS((1.66/R + G)*[dR - dG]/t_0) \tag{1}$$

where K is a scaling constant (usually about 5.3), $R + G$ is equal for both sides of the photometric field; dR is the difference between the responses of the R cones to each chromatic stimulus; dG is the difference between the responses of the G cones to each chromatic stimulus and t_0 is a scaling factor to account for the observation that, typically, no border is seen for equiluminous chromatic steps whose $R - G$ opponent difference (modelled by the term in the square brackets) is less than 0.11.

TABLE 1

Border distinctness rating (D_c)	C.I.E. (1931) $(x_1, y_1; x_2, y_2)$
0	0.387, 0.523; 0.379, 0.474
0	0.340, 0.533; 0.262, 0.624
0	0.365, 0.477; 0.394, 0.524
1	0.421, 0.371; 0.267, 0.343
1	0.587, 0.352; 0.478, 0.296
1	0.481, 0.452; 0.382, 0.532
2	0.291, 0.608; 0.499, 0.438
2	0.423, 0.399; 0.283, 0.608
2	0.458, 0.436; 0.315, 0.501
3	0.249, 0.541; 0.433, 0.272
3	0.172, 0.115; 0.281, 0.240
3	0.415, 0.438; 0.201, 0.148
4	0.172, 0.131; 0.384, 0.238
4	0.552, 0.347; 0.394, 0.511
4	0.172, 0.116; 0.566, 0.384
5	0.173, 0.131; 0.610, 0.351

Procedure

Three male observers, aged 23, 31 and 32, participated in this study. All had normal colour vision, as checked with the Farnsworth-Munsell 100-hue Test and the American Optical Pseudoisochromatic Plates, and were emmetropic at the time of testing. One observer was naive with respect to the aims of the experiment. With the aid of a chin rest each observer viewed the video monitor, with his right eye only, through a precisely aligned achromatizing lens (Wyszecki and Stiles, 1967, p. 212) and a sighting tube. The distance between the subject's eye and the monitor screen was 1.5 metres. The observers were dark-adapted for 10 min before each experimental session.

The experiment consisted of four sections. In the first section the observers were required to equate the luminance of the set of chromaticities, described above, that had previously been chosen to evaluate the two-cone model. Each chromaticity was presented, in turn, with a standard white ($x = 0.33, y = 0.33$; 25 cd m^{-2}) in a circular bipartite photometric field configuration (visual angle = 1 deg). The luminance of each chromaticity was equated with the standard white using the minimally-distinct border method (Boynton and Kaiser, 1968). The results of this section of the experiment were stored as files on magnetic disk.

In the second section the observer was presented with a four-part photometric field. In turn, in the lower two quadrants of this field were automatically presented pairs of chromaticities – each previously equated for luminance with the standard white in part 1 – such that a gamut of chromatic pairs resulted producing borders of varying distinctness. In the upper half of the four-part field, separated from the lower half by a dark line (subtending 10 min of visual angle) was presented the standard white. The observer's task was to change the luminance contrast of the achromatic, upper half field (through the pressing of the suitable key on the response keyboard) such that the border formed by the luminance step across the upper two quadrants appeared to be subjectively equal in distinctness to the border formed by the equiluminous chromaticity step between the lower two quadrants. The average luminance of the upper two quadrants was always equal to the standard luminance. This was achieved by increasing the luminance of the left upper quadrant by the same amount that the right upper quadrant was decreased during the contrast matching procedure. All of these values were then stored in unique data files – each consisting of a given chromatic pair and two achromatic values that produced a luminance step whose border distinctness appeared subjectively equal to the chromatic border.

In the third part of the experiment, subjects were presented with either a chromatic pair or an achromatic pair, from the files established in part 2, and were instructed to rate the subjective distinctness of the border formed between them using an 8-point scale. (On this scale, a "0" corresponds to no visible edge within the test field whereas a "7" corresponds to a Michelson luminance contrast of approximately 30%.) In fact, because of the gamut of chromaticities achievable with the video monitor the range of equivalent luminance contrasts never exceeded about 20% and the subjective distinctness rating never exceeded a value of approximately "5".

Finally, in the fourth part of the experiment these same chromaticity files were recombined into checkerboard patterns and used to generate visually-evoked cortical potentials. In this section of the experiment silver cup electrodes were placed upon the observer's head (Inion $+$, 0_z-, right mastoid common) with collodion and filled with conductive electrode paste. All electrode impedances were less than 1 kΩ. The stimulus pattern subtended a visual angle of 7.5 degrees and consisted of a checkerboard, where the "A" checks alternated with the "B" checks at 1 reversal per sec. Each check subtended a visual angle of 30 minutes. Two sets of pattern-evoked responses were collected from each file established in part 2 (one in response to a checkerboard composed of the chromatic pair and one in response to a checkerboard composed of the achromatic pair in the same file) chosen to yield an equivalent border distinctness rating. Two hundred fifty-six samples of 512 msec of EEG were taken, with the beginning of each sweep triggered by the reversal of the pattern. These samples were averaged in real time and plotted. Pattern evoked response amplitudes were measured by graphical means using calibration pulses obtained under identical conditions, within each experimental session.

Results

Figure 2 shows the average pattern evoked response amplitudes (closed circles) for both sets of chromatic (a) and achromatic (b) spatial contrast stimuli, listed in Table 1. The abscissa is the absolute value of the magnitude of either the spatial difference between $(R - G)$ signals (for chromatic borders) or the spatial difference between $(R + G)$ signals (for achromatic borders) calculated from the model described above.

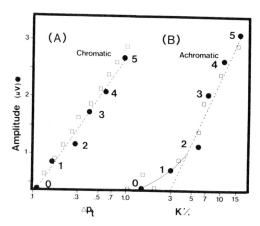

FIG. 2 (A) Correspondence between pattern-evoked cortical potential amplitudes, subjective border distinctness ratings and the two-cone model for chromatic borders. The abscissa units for (A) correspond to the magnitude of the $L - M$ opponent signal difference between lights on either side of a chromatic border Δp_t (described in Valberg and Tansley, 1977). Solid circles show the average pattern-evoked cortical potential amplitudes (for 3 observers) of the major component after 100 msec. These are compared to the dotted line, which represents the predicted two-cone model response. The numbers within the figure show the average subjective border distinctness rating for each data point. Open squares are a replot of the psychophysical results of a similar experiment described in Tansley and Boynton (1978).

(B) Solid circles: average cortical pattern-evoked response amplitude to achromatic checkerboards, as a function of their Michelson contrast:

$$K\% = 100 \, \frac{L_1 - L_2}{L_1 + L_2}, \qquad (2)$$

where L_i is the luminance of check i.

The numbers in the figure are the average border distinctness ratings for three observers, for each data point. Open squares are taken from a similar experiment described by Tansley and Boynton, (1978).

Also plotted in this figure are the average subjective border distinctness ratings of three observers (open squares), taken from an earlier experiment by Tansley and Boynton (1978). There is good agreement between the two sets of data with the correspondence extending to the slope of achromatic and chromatic functions as well as to the idiosyncratic shape of the low-contrast end of the achromatic function. The Pearson Product-Moment correlation coefficients calculated between the amplitudes predicted by Equation (1) and the average pattern evoked response amplitudes obtained in Part 4 are 0.99 for both chromatic and achromatic patterns.

Although the scaled amplitudes of the pattern component of these evoked potentials are predicted accurately by the model, their latencies are not. For sets of waveforms averaged in response to chromatic pairs whose subjective border distinctness was identical – but whose colour difference magnitude was variable – there were significant changes in the waveform latency. This suggests that chromatic information may be at least partly carried in the temporal properties of the electrical response propagating from the retina along the visual pathway.

Discussion

These results suggest that the amplitude of the pattern component of the visually-evoked cortical potential corresponds to rated subjective border distinctness – whether the edge be produced by luminance steps or equiluminous chromaticity steps. The two measures, one subjective and one objective, can be used interchangeably when measuring the suprathreshold magnitude of edges visible to the observer. Technically, however, these methods are far from equivalent. The subjective border distinctness rating method is much preferred because of its simplicity. Under special conditions, however, where human observers are incapable of controlled voluntary responses or when investigating visual function with experimental human analogues, this relationship offers the advantage of a measure that corresponds to what they would likely say if they were able to subjectively rate the visual distinctness of the borders.

Taken together, these results suggest that the coding and transmission of chromatic and spatial information are coupled in at least part of the visual pathway. Psychophysical evidence of this putative coupling is also available from form – colour after-effects (Stromeyer, 1978). To the extent that our model accurately reflects this coupling, then the results of McCollough-type experiments should be predictable from Equation (1). The use of automated digital television display systems, such as the one used in this work, offers the major advantage of being able to combine chromatic, spatial and, to some extent, temporal parameters in more sophisticated ways that enhance the analytic power of visual experimentation.

Acknowledgements

The support of this research through grants from the Natural Sciences and Engineering Research Council of Canada to B. W. Tansley is gratefully acknowledged. A. W. Robertson was supported by a NSERC Postgraduate Scholarship.

References

Boynton, R. M. and Kaiser, P. K. (1968). Vision: the additivity law made to work for heterochromatic photometry with bipartite fields. *Science* **161**, 366–368.

Campbell, F. W. and Maffei, L. (1970). Electrophysiological evidence for the existence of orientation and size detectors in human visual system. *J. Physiol., Lond.* **207**, 635–652.

Spekreijse, H., Estévez, O. and Reits, D. (1977). Visual evoked potentials and the physiological analysis of visual processes in man. In *Visual Evoked Potentials in Man: New Developments* (ed. Desmedt, J. E.). Oxford University Press.

Stromeyer, C. F. (1978). Form-color aftereffects in human vision. In *Handbook of Sensory Physiology*, Vol. VIII *Perception* (eds Held, R., Leibowitz, H. W. and Teuber, H. L.), pp. 97–142. New York, Springer-Verlag.

Tansley, B. W. (1976). *Psychophysical studies of the contribution of chromatic mechanisms to the visual perception of borders.* Unpublished Doctoral Dissertation, University of Rochester, Rochester, New York.

Tansley, B. W. and Boynton, R. M. (1976). A line, not a space, represents visual distinctness of borders formed by different colors. *Science* **191**, 954–957.

Tansley, B. W. and Boynton, R. M. (1978). Chromatic border perception: the role of red- and green-sensitive cones. *Vision Res.* **18**, 683–697.

Tansley, B. W. and Valberg, A. (1979). Chromatic border distinctness: not an index of hue or saturation differences. *J. opt. Soc. Am.* **69**, 113–118.

Valberg, A. and Tansley, B. W. (1977). Tritanopic purity difference function to describe the properties of minimally-distinct borders. *J. opt. Soc. Am.* **67**, 1330–1336.

Ward, F. and Boynton, R. M. (1974). Scaling of large chromatic differences. *Vision Res.* **14**, 943–949.

Wyszecki, G. and Stiles, W. S. (1967). *Color Science: Concepts and Methods, Quantitative Data and Formulas.* New York, John Wiley and Sons.

Sensitivity at the Edge of a Monochromatic Luminance-Step and the Mechanisms of Color Vision

MUNEO MITSUBOSHI

Mach bands, the bright and dark lines that are observed near the boundary of a luminance distribution, are often interpreted as revealing lateral inhibitory interactions in our visual system (Ratliff, 1965). Possibly related to Mach bands is the overshoot in incremental threshold that is found on the brighter side of a boundary: and this threshold phenomenon will be referred to here as the "Mach effect". It is true that the increment threshold does not undershoot on the dimmer side of the boundary (Tachibana, 1977), except in some limited conditions (Mitsuboshi, 1981; Mitsuboshi *et al.*, 1982a); but the overshoot in threshold and the bright Mach band generally go together (Fiorentini, 1972).

In the case of both Mach bands and the Mach effect, one can ask whether the lateral interactions occur independently within individual cone mechanisms. Ercoles-Guzzoni and Fiorentini (1958) showed that neither the width nor the position of Mach bands depended on the color of the field, but these experiments did not isolate cone mechanisms. Under- and over-shoots in hue or saturation – "chromatic Mach bands" – might indicate lateral interactions confined to individual cone mechanisms, but it has proved difficult to obtain such effects with gradients of chromaticity analogous to the gradients of brightness that produce Mach bands (van der Horst and Bouman, 1967; Green and Fast, 1971). In the case of the Mach effect, some relevant findings are those of Matthews (1967), who used Stiles' two-color threshold technique and measured increment thresholds across a monochromatic intensity-step. His results suggested that the Mach effect had different spatial characteristics according to which color mechanism mediated detection, although the main difference was between the short-wave mechanism, on the one hand, and the long- and middle-wave mechanisms on the other. Matthews' observations were confined to heterochromatic combinations of test and edge wavelengths.

The present paper asks directly whether wavelength specificity is found in the Mach effect. In the first experiment, in order to determine whether the overshoot was most marked when target and field were homochromatic, the increment threshold for a monochromatic test slit was obtained across an intensity-step pattern that was also monochromatic. In a second experiment, the target was placed at various positions on the bright side of the edge and "field sensitivity" was obtained by finding the radiance of the step that raised the test threshold by 0.88 log units.

Method

The spatial configuration of the stimuli is shown in Fig.1. All the stimuli were provided by a Maxwellian-view optical system. The subject was presented with a rectangular, monochromatic luminance-step (SP) which had a luminance ratio between its bright and dark sides of 1.64 log units.

Three wavelengths (λ_{SP}) 620, 528, and 440 nm, were used for the step pattern. The luminances of the brighter side, calibrated by flicker photometry, were 226, 218 and 357 cd m^{-2} respectively. This difference in the luminance occurs because the luminance of the step pattern was roughly chosen to make the average threshold levels on the bright and dark sides almost the same for the three conditions. One of the reasons why the second experiment was conducted was to check the effect of these differences in luminance.

A test slit (TS) was briefly presented (20 msec) at nine positions on each of the bright and the dark sides of the border. Each of the three wavelengths (λ_{TS}), 626, 529, and 439 nm, was employed as a test slit for each luminance-step. They were obtained by interference filters with half-bandwidths less than 15 nm. The stimuli were observed with the subject's right eye. Two dim red fixation points between which the test slit was always presented, and a dental impression were used to help secure the subject's fixation.

The increment thresholds for the test slit were measured by the method of adjustment. A total of twelve to thirty wedge setting adjustments obtained in two to five sessions were averaged to give each data point. Two subjects, one of whom was the author, participated throughout the sessions. Both subjects were checked for normal color vision and normal visual acuity.

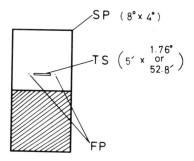

FIG. 1   The spatial configuration of stimuli as seen by the subject. TS: test slit; SP: luminance-step pattern; FP: fixation points. A long (1.76° long) and a short (52.8′ long) test slit were used in the first and second experiments respectively. Three wavelengths, 620, 528 and 440 nm, were employed as SP. Three other wavelengths 626, 529 and 439 nm, were presented as TS.

Results

The results for subject MM are shown in Figs 2 to 4, where the log relative threshold for the test slit is plotted as a function of the angular distance from the border. Positive values on the abscissa indicate positions on the bright side of the step pattern, and negative values indicate positions on the dark side. Zero signifies the position of the border. Figure 2 shows the results for the red (620 nm) step. The three functions in the figure indicate the increment thresholds for the test slits of 439 nm (upper), 529 nm (middle) and 626 nm (bottom) respectively. Each function is displaced arbitrarily for clarity. The results suggest that the Mach effect is wavelength-specific. That is, the increment threshold at the edge on the bright side rises significantly higher for the red test slit than for the test slits of the other wavelengths. This color-selectivity in the threshold suggests, in agreement with Matthews' (1967) result, that at least part of the lateral interaction that underlies the Mach effect takes place within a single color system. Although small, an increase in the threshold for the green and blue-violet test slits can be seen in the figure. This is not unexpected because the red-sensitive mechanism is also sensitive to middle and short wavelengths.

Figure 3 shows results for the green (528 nm) step. A large threshold increase is seen in the function for the green test slit, but not for the red one. These results support the hypothesis that there are lateral interactions that are specific to a particular cone mechanism.

However, such a simple hypothesis does not account for the results obtained for the blue-violet (440 nm) step. In this case, as shown in Fig. 4, a rather large increase in the threshold is observed irrespective of the wavelength of the test slit.

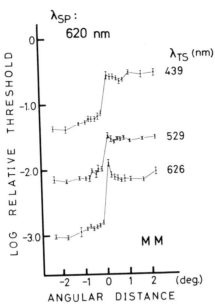

FIG. 2 The results for subject MM, obtained with the red (620 nm) luminance-step. Functions for different test wavelengths are shifted arbitrarily for clarity. The vertical bar at each data point indicates ±1 SD.

Compared with the results for subject MM, the threshold increases for subject TM (not illustrated here) are somewhat larger for all luminance-steps. But the general trends are similar as can be seen from Fig. 5.

In Fig. 5, the magnitude in threshold increase is plotted against test wavelength for subjects MM (upper) and TM (lower). The magnitude of the threshold increase is calculated as the difference between the threshold at the edge and the mean threshold for the three positions most distant from the border. Again, the wavelength-selectivity is strong for the red and green luminance steps. In the case of the blue-violet step MM shows little selectivity; TM shows a maximal effect for the 529 nm target. The large absolute magnitudes for the blue-violet step for both subjects could be explained by the higher luminance of this step (357 cd m^{-2}).

Figure 6 shows the results for the subject MM in the second part of the experiment. Here, the intensity of the step pattern needed to raise the absolute test threshold by 0.88 log unit was obtained at three positions on the bright side of the step: a) at the edge (just above the border), b) at the middle position (52.8′ from the border), and c) at the far position (1.64° from the border). A test slit of half-length 52.8′ was used in this second experiment so that it

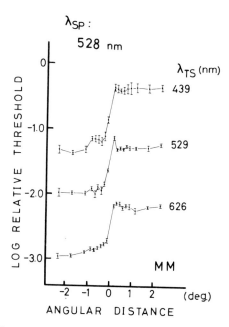

FIG. 3   The results for subject MM, obtained with the green (528 nm) luminance-step.

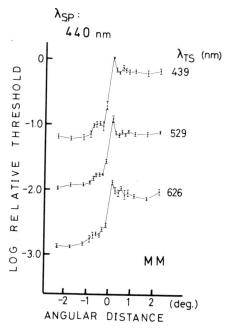

FIG. 4   The results for subject MM, obtained with the blue-violet (440 nm) luminance-step.

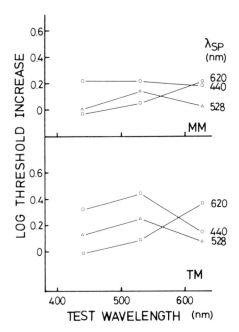

FIG. 5   The magnitude of the threshold increase as a function of the test wave-length for subjects MM (upper) and TM (lower).

would fall completely within the foveola. The average of a total of twenty-four adjustments, obtained in four sessions on different days, was taken as the relative field intensity, and the log reciprocal of this value was taken as the relative field sensitivity.

The three groups of points in Fig. 6 represent the results with the red (upper), green (middle) and blue-violet (bottom) step patterns respectively. In each group, the data points for the three test wavelengths are displaced vertically so that the log field sensitivities at the far position correspond to the value zero (indicated by the open circles). As can be seen, the same trend as in the first part is found for observer MM. The field sensitivities are nearly equal at the middle position independent of the wavelengths of the test and the step stimuli. At the edge position, on the other hand, the field sensitivities are wavelength-dependent as far as the green and the red luminance-steps are concerned. Here again, the wavelength-selectivity is very weak for the blue-violet step. The trends in the results for subject TM are similar to those for MM.

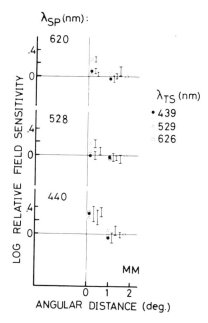

FIG. 6   Field sensitivities for subject MM at the three positions on the bright side of the luminance-step. The top group of data points indicate the results for the red step, the middle and the bottom ones the results for the green and the blue-violet steps respectively. In each group, the results are normalized so that the sensitivity at the farthest position has the value zero for each test wavelength. The vertical bar at each data point indicates ± 1 SD.

Discussion

The Mach effect is often ascribed to the existence of an antagonistic center-surround organization (or receptive field) in the visual system (Ratliff, 1965). The wavelength selectivity found in the present study suggests that such a center-surround antagonism is organized within one and the same cone mechanism, and not between different cones. More or less similar conclusions have been derived from psychophysical studies of various paradigms (Alpern, 1964; Alpern and Rushton, 1965; Alpern, Rushton and Torii, 1970; McKee and Westheimer, 1970; Kerr, 1976; Mitsuboshi and Mitsuboshi, 1980).

There remain, however, some problems. The first problem is the weakness in the wavelength-selectivity for the blue-violet luminance-step. (Mitsuboshi and Mitsuboshi (1980) report an analogous finding in the case of the spatial sensitisation effect.) One possible explanation is that an interaction occurs not only within the blue-sensitive mechanism but also between the blue-sensitive mechanism and the green and red mechanisms, depending on the test wavelength. Foster (1979) reported such interactions in metacontrast masking. Some recent work has shown that the spectral sensitivities for the three mechanisms come rather close at 450 nm (Vos and Walraven, 1971). So, it might be possible that the three mechanisms were nearly equally activated by the 440-nm step. The equal excitation of the different mechanisms would not immediately imply the existence of interactions among them, but such a special situation has been reported to be optimal for the occurrence of interactions (Boynton, Ikeda and Stiles, 1964). A further consideration is that the dimensions of the thin test bar may be such as to induce small-field tritanopia: under at least some of the field conditions the 439-nm target may be detected by the middle-wavelength mechanism.

The second problem is more general. The failure to find chromatic Mach bands has been taken to mean that lateral inhibitory effects, like those underlying the Mach effect, take place only in the brightness-mediating (achromatic) channel. How can this conclusion be reconciled with the wavelength specificity found in the present study? It seems necessary to assume that Mach-type lateral interactions, as suggested by Green and Fast (1971), occur in the brightness-mediating pathway, but before the inputs from the cone mechanisms are combined. The lateral interaction taking place in such a pre-channel brightness pathway is assumed to operate over a small spatial distance (e.g., in the Mach effect, and in the spatial sensitization effect), and it may be different from the one that underlies simultaneous contrast phenomena. It should be noted that simultaneous induction, in both color and brightness, takes place over much larger distances, and that color contrast clearly exists when the test and inducing fields are equal in luminance (Mitsuboshi *et al.*, 1982b).

Acknowledgements

The author is grateful to Professor Shuko Torii of University of Tokyo for facilities, encouragement and advice; and to Professor Satoru Aiba of Hokkaido University for his critical reading of the manuscript and for many important suggestions. The author also would like to express his gratitude to Dr J. D. Mollon and Dr L. T. Sharpe of the University of Cambridge, who suggested revisions of the original manuscript.

References

Alpern, M. (1964). Relation between brightness and color contrast. *J. opt. Soc. Am.* **54**, 1491–1492.

Alpern, M. and Rushton, W. A. H. (1965). The specificity of the cone interaction in the after-flash effect. *J. Physiol., Lond.* **176**, 473–482.

Alpern, M., Rushton, W. A. H. and Torii, S. (1970). Signals from cones. *J. Physiol., Lond.* **207**, 463–475.

Boynton, R. M., Ikeda, M. and Stiles, W. S. (1964). Interactions among chromatic mechanisms as inferred from positive and negative increment thresholds. *Vision Res.* **4**, 87–117.

Ercoles-Guzzoni, A. M. and Fiorentini, A. (1958). Simultaneous contrast effect produced by non-uniform coloured fields. *Atti Della Fond. Giorgio Ronchi* **13**, 136–144.

Fiorentini, A. (1972). Mach band Phenomena. In *Handbook of Sensory Physiology*, Vol. VII/4, Visual Psychophysics (eds Jameson, D. and Hurvich, L. M.), pp. 188–201. Berlin, Springer.

Foster, D. H. (1979). Interactions between blue- and red-sensitive colour mechanisms in metacontrast masking. *Vision Res.* **19**, 921–931.

Green, D. G. and Fast, M. B. (1971). On the appearance of Mach bands in gradients of varying color. *Vision Res.* **11**, 1147–1155.

van der Horst, G. J. C. and Bouman, M. A. (1967). On searching for "Mach band type" phenomena in colour vision. *Vision Res.* **7**, 1027–1029.

Kerr, L. (1976). Effect of chromatic contrast on stimulus brightness. *Vision Res.* **16**, 463–468.

Matthews, M. L. (1967). Mach-band increment threshold and the mechanisms of color vision. *J. opt. Soc. Am.* **57**, 1033–1036.

McKee, S. P. and Westheimer, G. (1970). Specificity of cone mechanisms in lateral interaction. *J. Physiol., Lond.* **206**, 117–128.

Mitsuboshi, M. and Mitsuboshi, T. (1980). The specificity of interactions among the visual photopic mechanisms as revealed by spatial sensitization effects. *Jap. Psychol. Res.* **22**, 4, 197–206.

Mitsuboshi, M. (1981). Mach bands: Its appearance and psychophysical measurements (in Japanese). *Technical report of the Institute of Television Engineers of Japan* **VVI**, 46–2, 29–34.

Mitsuboshi, T., Mitsuboshi, M. and Torii, S. (1982a). The decrease in the threshold at the dark side of the luminance edge in the after-flash effect. *Vision Res.* **22**, 1329–1334.

Mitsuboshi, M., Wake, T., Sagawa, K. and Mitsuboshi, T. (1982b). A quantitative study of color contrast: The effect of the luminance ratio between the test and inducing fields examined by the Cancellation method. In *Psychophysical Judgement and the Process of Perception* (eds Geissler, H.-G., Petzold, P., Buffart, H. F. J. M. and Zabrodin, Yu. M.). Revised and Edited Version of Selected Papers presented at the XXII International Congress on Psychology, Leipzig, 1980, No. 9.

Ratliff, F. (1965). Mach bands: Quantitative studies on neural networks in the retina. New York, Holden-Day.

Tachibana, M. (1977). Threshold change near the light-dark border: A comparison of real and equivalent background light. *Vision Res.* **17**, 117–122.

Vos, J. J. and Walraven, P. L. (1971). On the derivation of the foveal receptor primaries. *Vision Res.* **11**, 799–818.

Luminance and Chromaticity Interactions in Spatial Vision

EUGENE SWITKES and KAREN K. DE VALOIS

Studies of visual sensitivity and visual perception typically use stimuli that vary either in luminance or in chromaticity, but only rarely in both. Yet virtually all naturally occurring visual patterns are composed of both luminance and chromaticity variations. Sometimes they co-vary spatially — as in the case of a bright red pen on a dark grey desk surface — but often they do not. A common example of the latter is shadowing, produced by directional light sources in a three-dimensional world, which leads to pronounced luminance gradients across surfaces of nearly constant chromaticity.

If the responses of the visual system to luminance contrast and to chromatic contrast are completely independent, or if they combine according to some simple rule, then studying each in isolation may be sufficient to predict the response to a compound pattern. If they interact in more complex ways, these interactions must be taken into account when studying spatial vision. This study is a first attempt to elucidate the rules by which responses to luminance and chromaticity variations are combined in the visual system.

Methods

All stimuli were produced by computer (Nova 1220) control of a Tektronix 654 color television monitor. Only the "red" (CIE coordinates x = 0.62, y = 0.35) and "green" (x = 0.30, y = 0.60) phosphors of the monitor were used. The luminance and the chromaticity of each of the 512 lines of the display could be controlled independently. The space-average chromaticity (CIE coordinates x = 0.50, y = 0.44) and luminance (53 cd m^{-2}) were kept constant for all patterns, including the yellow blank field which appeared between stimuli and to which the subjects adapted for 2 min at the beginning of a session. In the stimulus patterns used, either the line-to-line luminance, the line-to-line chromaticity, or both, could vary.

Patterns were viewed monocularly through a 2-mm artificial pupil and a cemented triplet achromatizing lens. The circular field subtended 5.8° at the 172 cm viewing distance used and was set in a white surround of slightly lower luminance. The stimuli were composed of combinations of sinusoidal red luminance gratings and green luminance gratings matched in mean luminance and contrast. When red and green gratings of the same spatial frequency were combined in phase, the result was a sinusoidal isochromatic yellow luminance grating (yellow−black). When they were combined in antiphase, the result was an isoluminant chromatic (i.e. red−green) grating.

A two-alternative, temporal forced-choice masking paradigm was used. The masking grating was present in both intervals; the signal, in only one. The subjects' task was to identify the signal interval. Stimulus intervals lasted 200 msec, and patterns were turned on and off gradually with 60 msec rise and decay times.

The contrast of all mask gratings was 20%. For the chromatic gratings this was defined as the antiphase superposition of two 20% contrast luminance gratings. Spatial frequencies of 1, 2, 4 and 8 c deg^{-1} were used for both mask and test gratings. All combinations of masks and tests were used in a balanced design.

Results

When test and mask gratings were both yellow−black luminance patterns, masking was greatest when mask and test frequencies were identical and decreased as they diverged. The fall-off in masking is sharper when the mask frequency is lower rather than higher than the test. The result is thus an asymmetric V-shaped function of mask/test frequency ratio. Figure 1 (solid line) presents combined data from two naive subjects, averaged across all spatial frequencies. Neither in this nor in any other test was there a strong effect of absolute frequency. Our data on the dependence of masking on the mask/test frequency ratio (for luminance−luminance masking) agree with those of Pantle (1974) and Legge and Foley (1980).

When both mask and test gratings are composed of isoluminant red−green chromatic variations the resulting masking function shows a weaker dependence on mask/test frequency ratio. Although the masking function is usually centered around identical mask-test frequencies, it is typically less peaked than the corresponding luminance masking function. There is often as much masking at mask/test ratios of 0.5 and 2 as when mask and test frequencies are

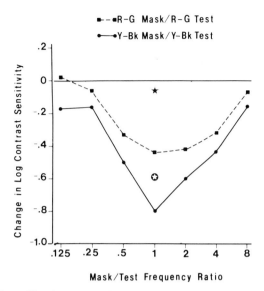

FIG. 1 Masking of luminance by luminance (Y−Bk mask/Y−Bk test) and color by color (R−G mask/R−G test). The data represent an average for two subjects and all mask/test combinations of 1, 2, 4 and 8 c deg⁻¹ gratings. The starred data points are from a deuteranopic subject, using 2 c deg⁻¹ mask and test gratings: square-star, R−G mask/R−G test; circle-star, Y−Bk mask/Y−Bk test.

identical. Figure 1 (dashed line) presents averaged color−color masking data from two naive subjects.

The two additional points represent data from a deuteranopic subject. The task was the detection of a 2 c deg⁻¹ test grating in the presence of a 2 c deg⁻¹ mask. The circle-star represents masking of yellow−black by yellow−black. The square-star shows masking of red−green by red−green. The stimuli were identical to those used with the two normal trichromatic subjects.

When a yellow luminance grating was the mask and an isoluminant red−green grating the test, there was very little reduction in sensitivity to the test grating. Figure 2 presents averaged data from the same two subjects. Masking was significant *only* when mask and test were identical in spatial frequency (although we did not measure masking between nonidentical frequencies less than 1 octave apart). Even then, the amplitude of the sensitivity reduction was quite small. These mixed luminance-chromatic tests were run at relative mask-test phases of 0°, 90° and 180°. There was no significant or reliable effect of mask-test phase.

In distinction to the results described immediately above, the masking of luminance by chromatic gratings was profound. The masking effect was greatest when mask and test frequencies were identical and fell off as they

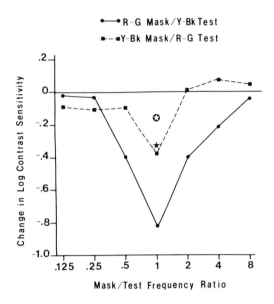

FIG. 2   Masking of color by luminance (Y−Bk mask/R−G test) and of luminance by color (R−G mask/Y−Bk test). The data are averages from two subjects, including all mask/test frequency combinations of 1, 2, 4 and 8 c deg⁻¹ gratings at 0°, 90° and 180° relative phase. (For color and luminance gratings of the same spatial frequencies, the yellow maxima of the Y−Bk luminance grating would coincide with the green, yellow and red regions of the R−G chromatic grating at 0°, 90° and 180°, respectively.) The starred points are data from a deuteranopic subject using 2 c deg⁻¹ mask and test gratings: square-star, Y−Bk mask/R−G test; circle-star, R−G mask/Y−Bk test.

diverged. The function was very similar in form to that found for the masking of luminance by luminance. In fact, in terms of both the amplitude of masking and the shape of the function, the masking of luminance by chromaticity was nearly indiscriminable from the masking of luminance by luminance. The 20% red−green mask we used was more effective in masking a yellow−black grating than in masking a red−green grating. In the masking of luminance by color, as in the converse, no phase dependency was found (De Valois and Switkes, in 1983).

The two additional points represent data from the deuteranopic subject. Test and mask gratings were 2 c deg⁻¹, and their relative phase was 0°. The circle-star represents masking of yellow−black by red−green. The square-star shows masking of red−green by yellow−black.

Discussion

Our data on the masking of luminance by luminance, like those of Pantle (1974) and Legge and Foley (1980), support the suggestion of many fairly narrowly tuned band-pass spatial frequency filters (Campbell and Robson, 1968; Blakemore and Campbell, 1969). Although the bandwidths revealed by suprathreshold masking tend to be somewhat broader than those found by selective adaptation (Blakemore and Campbell, 1969), the shapes of the functions are similar.

The masking of color by color, however, produces a noticeably flatter function. The masking still shows spatial frequency band-pass filtering characteristics and still is roughly centered around a mask-test frequency ratio of 1. Although the bandwidth tends to be somewhat broader than that seen with luminance/luminance masking, the most apparent difference lies in the lack of a sharply defined peak. This may reflect a real and significant difference in the structure and function of the underlying spatial frequency filter mechanisms for color and for luminance.

The most important finding of this study was the impressive asymmetry of the color-luminance interactions in normal trichromats. Color masks luminance (in this experiment) very much more profoundly than luminance masks color. The lack of dependence on relative test-mask phase suggests that these interactions are occurring at some level at which global chromatic and spatial frequency characteristics have been encoded. It is difficult to account for our results by invoking purely local interactions.

The color-luminance asymmetry and the fact that a 20% red–green grating masks yellow–black more than it masks red–green both suggest (though do not imply) that this masking reflects an active one-way inhibitory process. It is difficult to account for these data on the basis of a model which assumes that masking merely reflects the extent to which test and mask stimuli are processed by the same detector, and thus becomes a task of detecting an increment upon a pedestal.

The failure of the deuteranopic subject to show significant masking of yellow–black by red–green implies that the strong asymmetry of masking found with normal trichromats was not due to a luminance artifact. Any unintentional luminance component, whether resulting from a luminance mismatch or from chromatic aberration, should have been at least as great for the deuteranope as for the trichromats. Since the color deficient observer did show significant luminance/luminance masking but did not show significant masking of luminance by color, explanations of the observed masking asymmetry based on luminance artifacts can be ruled out. The profound masking of luminance by color does result from the specifically chromatic properties of the mask.

Acknowledgements

This work was supported by U.S.P.H.S. grant EY00014 and N.S.F. grant BNS 7806177.

References

Blakemore, C. and Campbell, F. W. (1969). On the existence of neurones in the human visual system selectively sensitive to the orientation and size of retinal images. *J. Physiol.* **203**, 237–260.

Campbell, F. W. and Robson, J. G. (1968). Application of Fourier analysis to the visibility of gratings. *J. Physiol.* **197**, 551–566.

De Valois, Karen K. and Switkes, E. (1983). Simultaneous masking interactions between chromatic and luminance gratings. *J. opt. Soc. Am.* **73**, 11–18.

Legge, G. E. and Foley, J. M. (1980). Contrast masking in human vision. *J. opt. Soc. Am.* **70**, 1458–1471.

Pantle, A. (1974). Visual information processing of complex imagery. Report Number AMRL-TR-74-43, Aerospace Medical Research Laboratory, Aerospace Medical Div., Air Force Systems Command, Wright-Patterson Air Force Base, Ohio 45433.

The Interpretation of Metacontrast and Contrast-Flash Spectral Sensitivity Functions

C. R. CAVONIUS and A. J. REEVES

Introduction

When measured with the classic t.v.i. method of W. S. Stiles, the sensitivity of each π mechanism depends only upon the rate at which the receptors of that mechanism absorb photons from the adapting field: it is indifferent to how vigorously other π mechanisms are adapted. Alpern and Rushton (1965) presented compelling evidence that neither this adaptive independence nor adaptation in general is due to pigment depletion alone. Their experimental procedure was to present red, green, or blue test flashes either upon a steady background (i.e., the Stiles paradigm), or within an annular field that surrounded but did not overlap the test flash, and which was presented 50 msec after the test. Although in the latter condition the adapting flash was separated from the test both in time and space, the adaptation that it caused was similar to that of the steady field: red, green, and blue fields that caused the same elevation in the threshold for the detection of, e.g., π_5 flashes when presented as steady backgrounds also caused equal elevations when presented as brief, delayed surrounds.

The generality of these results was cast into doubt by the results of Yellott and Wandell (1976), who equated steady red and green fields for their effectiveness in raising thresholds for the detection of red (Wratten 29) flashes. When the same fields were presented as bars that were flashed adjacent to, and 50 msec after, the test, thresholds were elevated more by the red fields than by the previously equivalent green fields: in fact, the red fields were now 100-fold more effective.

This discrepancy is puzzling, since the methods used in the two studies were similar, other than the geometry of the stimuli: Alpern and Rushton used a 1 deg, centrally fixated, flash that was followed by a 9 deg surround; whereas Yellott and Wandell used a 1 deg wide by 3 deg high rectangular test that was presented about 2 deg parafoveally, and which was followed by flanking bars. Both sets of authors used a stimulus onset asynchrony (SOA) of 50 msec.

To attempt to resolve this discrepancy, we made measurements using the two stimulus configurations, but with the same apparatus and the same observers. We also investigated the effect of varying the stimulus onset asynchrony, since if we are to define a field sensitivity function we must show that there is no interaction between the relative effectiveness of masks of different wavelengths and the SOA: if this is not the case, the results become difficult to interpret, because the field spectral sensitivity of the mask will change if the SOA is changed.

Method

We repeated the main features of the stimuli that were used by Alpern and Rushton, and by Yellott and Wandell. All of the stimuli were presented monocularly in Maxwellian view, in which the exit pupil of the system was always smaller than the observer's natural pupil. For the Alpern and Rushton stimuli we used a $19' \times 27'$ oval test in a 7 deg circular surround; test and masking surround were both presented for 20 msec, with variable SOA. Small points of light above and below the test helped the observer to maintain central fixation. We initially replicated the Yellott and Wandell stimuli by using 1 deg $\times$ 3 deg rectangular test and masking flashes, with 10 msec test and 40 msec mask durations. However, for convenience we later changed to 0.7 deg $\times$ 1.5 deg, 20 msec, tests and masks, which gave qualitatively similar results although the absolute sensitivities were of course different. In both cases, fixation was 2 deg below the center of the test.

To obtain *field sensitivity* data, we deviated from the procedure that is usually followed in metacontrast experiments: rather than varying the test intensity, we kept it constant and adjusted the intensity of the mask so as to obtain a criterion change in the test threshold. The test was typically 0.45 log units above the dark-adapted threshold, and the mask was adjusted so as to return the test to threshold. The 0.45 test proved convenient, since weaker tests were difficult for the observer to detect reliably, whereas more intense tests were difficult to mask, so that the observer soon reached the limit of available masking luminance. (A pilot study showed that the only effect of increasing test luminance was to shift the masking vs. SOA functions, such as those in Figs 1 and 2, down and to the left.) The onset times of test and mask covered the range from SOA −240 (test follows the mask by 240 msec), to SOA +150 (test leads the mask by 150 msec).

Trials were initiated by the observer, with the limitation that the system prevented repetition of trials at intervals shorter than 2 sec. The observer's task was to adjust the luminance of the mask so that the test just disappeared. At SOAs near zero this was not difficult, and a clear threshold could usually be found; but at the extreme values of SOA the observers felt less confident about their settings, and this was reflected in higher variances.

Results

Alpern-Rushton Configuration

Figures 1 and 2 show masking plotted against SOA for two observers, measured with the Alpern and Rushton stimulus, using a 650-nm test and various masking wavelengths. Each data point is the mean of 3 to 5 runs; standard deviations of the data were typically under 0.3 log units except at the rapidly falling ends of the functions, where they increased. The vertical axis

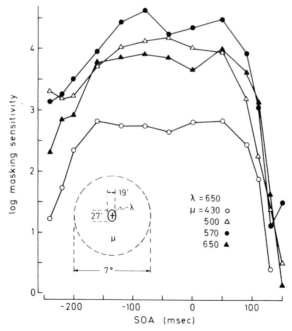

FIG. 1 Relative masking sensitivity (reciprocal of the mask energy needed to raise test threshold by 0.45 $\log_{10}$ units) as a function of SOA, measured with the Alpern-Rushton stimulus (insert): observer DC.

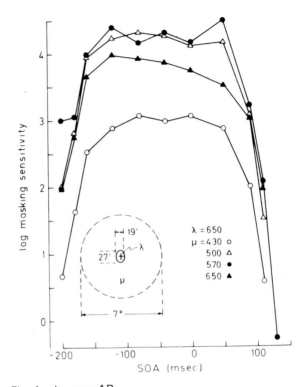

FIG. 2   As Fig. 1, observer AR.

gives the effectiveness of the masks; i.e., the reciprocal of the mask energy that was needed to raise the test threshold by 0.45 log units. The results of a third observer showed the same trends, but all of his functions were more sharply peaked about SOA = 0. In general, the functions resemble an inverted U, and are rather flat, although the data for 570 nm masks tend to show a slight dip about SOA = 0.

The field sensitivity functions shown in Fig. 3 are the means for the two observers from whom we had complete data. Because the masking functions in Figs 1 and 2 are rather flat about SOA = 0, the spectral sensitivity functions from SOA −40 to SOA +50 (open symbols) are similar. The sensitivity functions that are derived from the more extreme values of SOA are depressed uniformly: the values for SOA +120 have been raised by 1.0 log unit to save space. The lines are Stiles' Π_5, expressed in energy and placed arbitrarily on the vertical axis. The shape of the sensitivity function at SOA +50 is quite similar to Π_5, as one would expect from the results of Alpern and Rushton. The functions that were derived from the data at more extreme SOAs tend to be less similar to Π_5, but in view of the variance in the masking data we need

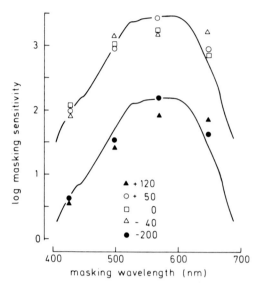

FIG. 3 Means of field-sensitivity functions for observers DC and AR, measured with the Alpern-Rushton stimulus.

not conclude that this reflects any systematic change in the field spectral sensitivity.

Flanking Masks

Masking−vs.−SOA functions that were measured with the Yellott-Wandell stimulus are shown in Figs 4 and 5. The differences among observers are now greater than when the Alpern-Rushton stimulus was used, but certain general trends appeared regularly: one striking feature was that the masking function that was obtained with 430-nm masks peaked to the left of SOA = 0, and declined gradually as more positive SOA values were used, whereas the long-wavelength masking functions tended to be more nearly rectangular, and often had two maxima, one on either side of SOA = 0. The within-observer variance of the data was not remarkably different from that measured with the Alpern-Rushton stimulus; again, the variance increased sharply near both ends of the masking functions.

Since these functions cannot be made similar by translating them vertically, field sensitivity functions derived from them will change in shape as the SOA is varied (Fig. 6). While we never found as large a discrepancy between Π_5 and the measured functions as that reported by Yellott and Wandell, it is clear that none of our functions resembles Π_5. If we disregard the extreme SOA

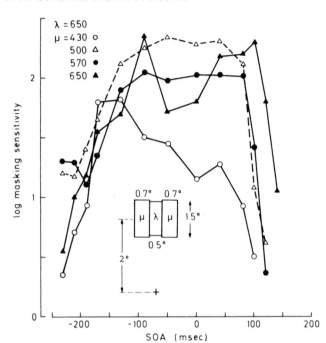

FIG. 4   Relative masking sensitivity as a function of SOA, measured with flanking masks (insert): observer DC.

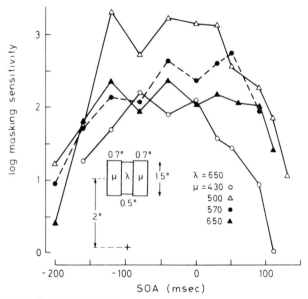

FIG. 5   As Fig. 3, observer AR.

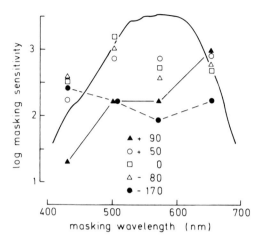

FIG. 6 Means of field-sensitivity functions for observers DC and AR, measured with flanking masks.

values of -170 and $+90$, where the masking sensitivity was changing rapidly with SOA, the most obvious discrepancy is the depression at 570, where Π_5 is near its maximum.

Conclusions

Metacontrast may be defined as a reduction in visual sensitivity, caused by adjacent masks that follow the test in time; this reduction is relative to the sensitivity that is measured when the test and mask are simultaneous. If we adopt this definition, the data that were collected with the Alpern-Rushton stimulus configuration show little evidence for metacontrast, since within the variability of the data, the masks tend to have their greatest effect at SOA $= 0$. In this respect, the data resemble those that are found in conventional masking experiments.

In contrast, the masking functions that were collected with flanking masks and parafoveal fixation are complicated, and show evidence of both metacontrast and paracontrast (a reduction in sensitivity caused by masks that precede the test). Unlike the results from the Alpern-Rushton experiment, spectral sensitivities measured with this paradigm change with SOA, and never resemble Π_5, which suggests that interaction among input mechanisms has taken place. The data obtained with 430 masks are particularly suggestive, since these masks were most effective when they were presented before the test, as if the masking were caused by a sluggish mechanism.

References

Alpern, M. and Rushton, W. A. H. (1965). The specificity of the cone interaction in the after-flash effect. *J. Physiol., Lond.* **176**, 473–482.

Yellott, J. I. Jr and Wandell, B. A. (1976). Color properties of the contrast flash effect: monoptic vs. dichoptic comparisons. *Vision Res.* **16**, 1275–1280.

The Blue Fundamental Primary –
A Revision Based on Dichromatic Alychnes

E. WOLF and H. SCHEIBNER

Introduction

Early detailed investigations on tritanopia were those of Arthur König (1897). He examined some cases of acquired tritanopia resulting from retinal diseases. A convergence point derived from his measurements was reported by Pitt (1944). Its coordinates in the chromaticity diagram based on Wright's (1946) primaries $B(460)$, $G(530)$, $R(650)$ are $g = 0.09$ and $r = 0$ (Fig. 1). However, Pitt preferred a constructed blue convergence point with the chromaticity coordinates $g = -0.055$ and $r = 0.02$.

In 1952, W. D. Wright published tritanopic confusion lines and together with Thomson (1953) he constructed a new tritanopic convergence point. This point was revised by Walraven (1974). The revised point is used by many visual scientists.

All tritanopic convergence points reported, except that of König, imply that the blue fundamental primaries associated with them make a positive contribution to luminance. Such a "blue" contribution to luminance is not consistent with some experimental results. Tansley and Boynton (1978), for example, have shown that the activity of the blue cones does not influence the perception of a border. This implies that the blue cones do not contribute to luminance as measured by the minimal distinct border (MDB) criterion. Furthermore, in 1980, Eisner and MacLeod showed that the suppression of the blue sensitivity by violet backgrounds of high intensities does not influence

COLOUR VISION
ISBN 0 12 000000 0

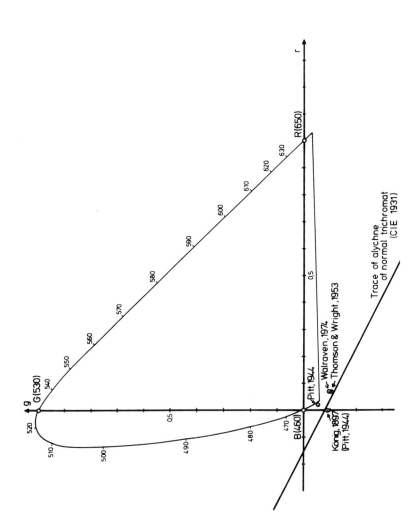

FIG. 1   Tritanopic convergence points published by various authors in the WDW chromaticity chart based on the real primaries **B**(460), **G**(530), **R**(650).

the luminance as defined by flicker photometry. Flicker photometry and photometry according to the MDB criterion are almost equivalent (Wagner and Boynton, 1972).

These and similar results suggest that the blue-sensitive cones do not contribute signals to the luminance channel, as proposed e.g. by the model of Vos and Walraven (1971).

The Blue Fundamental Primary

We should like to advance a new construction of the blue fundamental primary, a construction that is in agreement with the results of luminance measurements mentioned above and is independent of tritanopia.

A first condition for a luminance-free blue fundamental primary is that it should lie in the alychne of the normal trichromat. The alychne is that subspace in a colour space containing the nonzero colour vectors that have zero luminance. Alychnes can be measured by means of heterochromatic brightness matches. In the CIE 1931 colour system, for example, the alychne is represented by the $X - Z$-plane. In addition there is evidence that the blue-sensitive cone mechanisms of protanopes and deuteranopes are essentially the same as those of normal trichromats. Therefore, protanopic and deuteranopic alychnes are additional loci for the blue fundamental primary.

Taking the averaged alychnes of five protanopes (Paulus, 1977, Scheibner and Paulus, 1978) and five deuteranopes (Kröger and Scheibner, 1977; Kröger-Paulus, 1979), we found that the traces of the alychnes of the three types of observers, normal trichromat, protanope and deuteranope, intersect almost exactly in the same point. This is shown in Fig. 2, where the common intersection point is indicated by T.

We suggest that this intersection point describes the location of the blue fundamental primary. The geometric situation may become even clearer when we transform the traces of the alychnes into the CIE 1931 chromaticity chart. The result of such a transformation is shown in Fig. 3. Here, the chromaticity coordinates of the mean intersection point are $x = 0.1506$, $y = 0$, $z = 0.8494$.

A Chromaticity Diagram Based on Fundamental Primaries

Figure 4 shows an equilateral colour triangle based on fundamental primaries **T** (blue), **D** (green), **P** (red). **P** and **D** are the results of measurements performed in our laboratory in recent years; they do not differ substantially from other values reported in the literature. **T** is chosen according to our proposal in the preceding section. The chromaticity locus of the visible spectrum is determined by fixing the fundamental primaries **T, D, P** relative to our instrumental primaries **B, G, R** and by adopting an additional assumption. The latter consists in attributing certain luminous coefficients to the fundamental primaries.

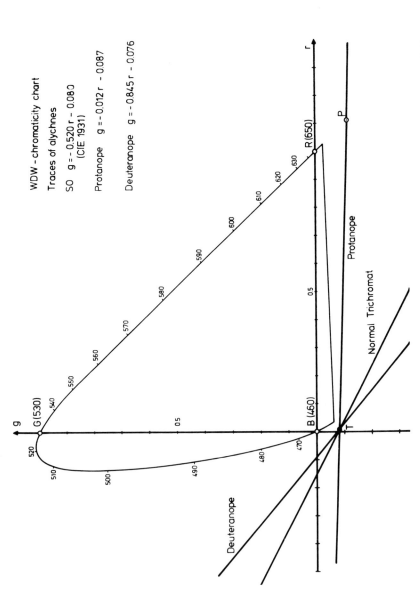

WDW - chromaticity chart

Traces of alychnes

SO   g = - 0.520 r - 0.080
          (CIE 1931)

Protanope   g = - 0.012 r - 0.087

Deuteranope   g = - 0.845 r - 0.076

FIG. 2   Traces of the alychnes of the three types of observers, normal trichromats (CIE 1931 Standard observer SO), protanopes and deuteranopes (average of five observers each). T indicates the proposed tritanopic convergence point defined by the intersection of the three alychnes.

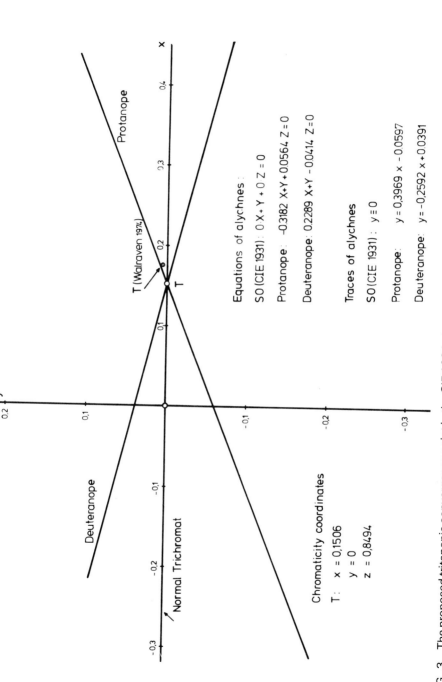

FIG. 3 The proposed tritanopic convergence point in the CIE 1931 chromaticity chart. For comparison the tritanopic convergence point proposed by Walraven (1974). (SO = Standard observer.)

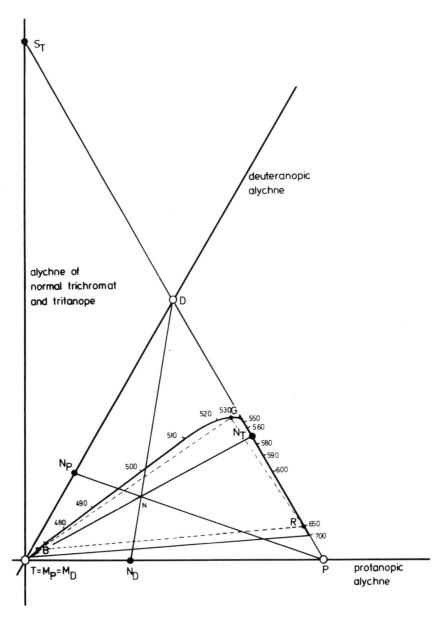

FIG. 4   Chromaticity diagram based on the fundamental primaries **T, D, P**. The points in which the colour vectors penetrate the plane exhibited are indicated − as usual − by symbols without vector notation. Further details see text.

We chose to attribute the values (0, 1, 2) to (**T, D, P**). The first value, zero, follows necessarily from the fact that **T** is located on the alychne, while the green–red ratio is taken from Vos and Walraven (1971).

Some features of this fundamental colour system should be mentioned. The sides of the colour triangle intersecting at the locus of **T** are the traces of the protanopic and deuteranopic alychnes. The traces of the trichromatic and tritanopic alychnes likewise run through the locus of **T** and are otherwise identical if we assume that trichromatic and tritanopic brightness vision are the same (Wright, 1952). If we regard the three types of dichromacy as loss dichromacies, it follows trivially that the sides of the triangle represent the traces of the (two-dimensional) colour spaces of the dichromats, because they contain the remaining fundamental primaries. There exists a one-to-one correspondence between the *points* of a triangle side and the confusion *lines* of the pencil radiating from the convergence point opposite to that side; both kinds of elements form equivalent dichromatic chromaticity diagrams. Therefore, the protanopic alychne trace, being at the same time a protanopic virtual confusion line, corresponds to an alychne point on the protanopic chromaticity line, namely the locus of **T**. The same holds for deuteranopia. In these two cases, **T** is also the chromatic opponent primary, M_P or M_D. It is a chromatic opponent primary by virtue of the fact that chromatic opponent primaries must be located on the alychne, i.e. they must be luminance-free, if colour is to be additively decomposed into chrominance and luminance (Schrödinger, 1925; Klauder and Scheibner, 1980). With respect to tritanopia, the alychne point and therefore the locus of the chromatic opponent primary, S_T, is obtained by the same procedure.

The requirement for the second kind of dichromatic opponent primaries, i.e. achromatic or "neutral" primaries, is that they have no chrominance. This is fulfilled by the neutral zones ("white" confusion lines), which are given by the straight lines connecting the convergence points and the respective neutral points λ_{NZ} in the spectrum. We chose $\lambda_{NZ} = 495$ nm for protanopia, $\lambda_{NZ} = 502$ nm for deuteranopia and $\lambda_{NZ} = 570$ nm for tritanopia. Extrapolation of the white confusion lines to the respective dichromatic chromaticity lines leads to the achromatic opponent primaries of the various dichromats. In summary (Fig. 4) (M_P, N_P), (M_D, N_D) and (S_T, N_T) are pairs of dichromatic opponent primaries, where $M_P = M_D = T$.

References

Eisner, A. and MacLeod, D. I. A. (1980). Blue-sensitive cones do not contribute to luminance. *J. opt. Soc. Am.* **70**, 121–123.

Klauder, A. and Scheibner, H. (1980). Dichromatisches Gegenfarbensehen. *Farbe und Design* **15/16**, 65–70.

König, A. (1897). Über "Blaublindheit". *Sitzungsber. Akad. Wiss. Berlin* (8. Juli 1897), 718–731.

Kröger-Paulus, A. (1979). *Reduktion der Deuteranopie aus der normalen Trichromasie.* Thesis, Universität Düsseldorf; also: *Die Farbe* **28** (1980), 73–116.

Kröger, A. and Scheibner, H. (1977). Reduktion der Deuteranopie aus der Trichromasie. *Ber. dt. ophthalm. Ges.* **75**, 515–517.

Paulus, W. (1977). *Fehlfarben und Alychnen von Protanopen und Protanomalen und ihre Bedeutung für das Farbensehen der normalen Trichromaten.* Thesis, Universität Düsseldorf, also: *Die Farbe* **27** (1978/79), 59–127.

Pitt, F. G. H. (1944). The nature of normal trichromatic and dichromatic vision. *Proc. roy. Soc. Lond.* **B132**, 101–117.

Scheibner, H. and Paulus, W. (1978). An analysis of protanopic colour vision, In: *Colour Vision Deficiencies IV* (ed. Verriest, G.). Basel, Karger.

Schrödinger, E. (1925). Über das Verhältnis der Vierfarben- zur Dreifarbentheorie. *Sitzungsber. Akad. Wiss. Wien IIa* **134**, 471–490.

Tansley, B. W. and Boynton, R. M. (1978). Chromatic border perception: the role of the red- and green-sensitive cones. *Vision Res.* **18**, 683–697.

Thomson, L. C. and Wright, W. D. (1953). The convergence of the tritanopic confusion loci and the derivation of the fundamental response functions. *J. opt. Soc. Am.* **43**, 890–894.

Vos, J. J. and Walraven, P. L. (1971). On the derivation of the foveal receptor primaries. *Vision Res.* **11**, 799–818.

Wagner, G. and Boynton, R. M. (1972). A comparison of four methods of heterochromatic photometry. *J. opt. Soc. Am.* **62**, 1508–1515.

Walraven, P. L. (1974). A closer look at the tritanopic convergence point. *Vision Res.* **14**, 1339–1343.

Wright, W. D. (1946). *Researches on Normal and Defective Colour Vision.* London, Kimpton.

Wright, W. D. (1952). The characteristics of tritanopia. *J. opt. Soc. Am.* **42**, 509–521.

Spatial Resolution of the Short-Wavelength Mechanism

DAVID R. WILLIAMS, ROBERT J. COLLIER and BRIAN J. THOMPSON

At any instant, the retinal image is quantized into an array of discrete samples by the mosaic of photoreceptors, yet this sampling process is perceptually unobtrusive. Theoretical considerations concerning the design of digital information processing systems suggest that this sampling process has inevitable effects on spatial vision. However, in the central fovea, these effects are partly obscured by the fineness of the foveal mosaic relative to the finest detail that can be imaged there. Even interferometric techniques (e.g. Westheimer, 1960; Campbell and Green, 1965) cannot escape the potential contrast-reducing effects of retinal scatter, the light collecting area of individual cones, and the image smear produced by physiological nystagmus. A more convenient system for studying photoreceptor sampling is the short-wavelength sensitive (B) mechanism; the coarse spacing of B cones in the mosaic permits the use of stimuli whose spatial frequencies are much lower and can be rendered at high contrast on the photoreceptor mosaic.

Many lines of evidence from anatomy, physiology, and psychophysics suggest that B cones are sparsely distributed in the primate retinal mosaic. First, the short-wavelength pigment has proven resistant to identification with retinal densitometry (Rushton, 1962). Microspectrophotometric studies of primate cones have either failed to find convincing evidence for cones containing a photolabile short-wavelength pigment (Marks, Dobelle and MacNichol, 1964; Brown and Wald, 1964) or have found that only a few per cent of the total cone population sampled are B cones (Bowmaker, Dartnall and Mollon, 1979).

COLOUR VISION
ISBN 0 12 000000 0

This was confirmed in the baboon by Marc and Sperling (1977), who stained B cones with nitroblue tetrazolium chloride; and by De Monasterio and Gouras (1975), who measured the distribution of ganglion cells with B cone input to receptive field centers. De Monasterio, Schein and McCrane (1981) report that intravitreal injections of Procion yellow in the eyes of macaques stain a small population of cones which they argue are B cones. Williams, MacLeod and Hayhoe (1981b) mapped the sensitivity of the B mechanism in closely spaced foveal areas with a tiny violet test probe on a yellow background, and found discrete sensitive peaks separated by large insensitive gaps, which they argue correspond to individual B cones (or clumps of cones).

The acuity of the B mechanism is correspondingly low, even when the deleterious effects of chromatic aberration are removed (Stiles, 1949; Brindley, 1954; Green, 1968; Kelly, 1973; Daw and Enoch, 1973). Even the most generous estimate of B cone acuity, about 12 cycles deg^{-1} (Stromeyer, Kranda and Sternheim, 1978), is roughly 5 times lower than the resolution limit for luminance gratings seen via middle- and long-wavelength cones. Despite the correspondence between the low acuity of the B mechanism and the low density of B cones in the retinal mosaic, the impact of this sparse mosaic on resolution is by no means clear. This paper argues that the sparse mosaic of B cones can introduce ambiguity into the process of reconstructing high spatial frequency stimuli via aliasing, but that the spacing of receptors does not pose the fundamental limit on resolution.

Measurement of B Cone Resolution

Observers viewed a 10-deg, violet grating in Maxwellian view, superimposed on a 580-nm, 13.3-deg background (11.4 log quanta deg^{-2} sec^{-1}), intended to isolate the B mechanism (Stiles, 1953). The grating was a high contrast, moiré fringe pattern whose spatial frequency could be continuously varied. The fringe pattern was produced by sandwiching together two 113-cycle deg^{-1} Ronchi rulings, which were conjugate with the retina. Rotating one ruling relative to the other provided control of spatial frequency. Most of the higher harmonics in the optical transform of the crossed rulings were removed with a spatial filter conjugate with the pupil, leaving a nearly sinusoidal light intensity distribution on the retina. Since optical quality was critical, refractive errors were corrected. The axial chromatic aberration of the eye was carefully compensated for by adjusting the optical distance of the violet test grating relative to the fixated yellow background field. For one observer (DRW), Mydriacil was used to reduce fluctuations in accommodation. To minimize spatial frequency adaptation, gratings were not steadily viewed; they were presented for 500 msec every third second. Between presentations, a uniform violet field replaced the grating. This substituted field was coextensive with the grating and always had the same average radiance, serving to maintain a constant state of adaptation.

For a series of radiances spanning 2.1 log units, observers adjusted the spatial frequency of the grating to make two kinds of acuity settings, each with a different criterion. First, they adjusted the spatial frequency until they could just detect the presence of bars in the target. Second, they adjusted the frequency until they could just discriminate between the grating and the uniform field that replaced it.

Figures 1A and B show the results for two observers. Unfilled symbols show for each grating radiance the highest spatial frequency at which bars could be detected. Acuity increases with radiance, rising to a maximum of about 10 and 14 cycles deg^{-1} for observers MM and DRW respectively. Filled symbols show the highest spatial frequencies at which the grating could be discriminated from the equiluminous uniform field that alternated with it. At the highest radiance one observer (MM) could distinguish between gratings and uniform fields at a spatial frequency of 23 cycles deg^{-1} and the other observer (DRW) at 35 cycles deg^{-1}, each of these being over an octave higher than the highest frequencies at which they could resolve bars. Similar results, not shown here,

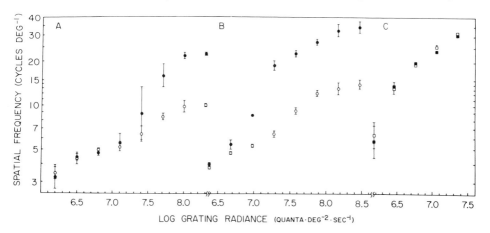

FIG. 1   (A) Unfilled circles represent the highest spatial frequency of a 420-nm grating at which the observer could resolve bars; Filled circles represent the highest spatial frequency at which he could distinguish the grating from a uniform field of equal space-averaged radiance, as a function of the radiance of the grating field. Grating superimposed on an 11.4 log quanta deg^{-2} sec^{-1}, 580-nm background field. Each data point is the mean of 2 sessions, with 2 measurements taken in each session. Error bars represent one standard error of the mean calculated from between-session variability. Observer: MM.

(B) Same as in A except grating field was 440 nm. Mydriacil was used to reduce accommodative changes. Each data point is the mean of 4 sessions. Observer: DRW.

(C) Same as B except grating was superimposed on 10 log quanta deg^{-2} sec^{-1}, 420-nm background instead of yellow background. Each data point is the mean of 2 sessions. Observer: DRW.

were obtained with a third observer, who, at the highest grating radiance (λ = 440 nm) could resolve bars up to 11 cycles deg^{-1} and could discriminate gratings from uniform fields up to 25 cycles deg^{-1}.

As spatial frequency is increased at a given radiance, observers report that the bar pattern begins to break up, finally giving way to a mottled or splotchy appearance similar to two-dimensional noise. This splotchy pattern changes rapidly over time and does not have any predominant orientation. At still higher frequencies, the splotches disappear and the exchange between grating and uniform field cannot be detected.

To guard against observer bias, we confirmed the essential result with a pair of two-interval forced-choice experiments. In the first experiment, each trial consisted of two 500-msec intervals, one of which contained a vertical grating and the other a horizontal grating, randomly determined. The observer's task was to indicate which interval contained the vertical grating. The spatial frequency of the grating was varied to determine threshold for discriminating orientation. This threshold was roughly the same as the threshold for bar detection obtained with method of adjustment. In the second forced-choice experiment, observers were asked to choose which of two 500-msec intervals contained a grating when one interval, randomly chosen, contained a grating and the other contained a uniform field of equal space-averaged radiance. In agreement with the method of adjustment, observers could discriminate gratings from uniform fields at spatial frequencies over an octave higher than those that allowed orientation discrimination. Additional control experiments in which the radiance of the uniform field was varied relative to that of the grating confirmed that observers were not using a brightness mismatch between the grating and uniform field to make these discriminations.

Several arguments suggest that this splotchy pattern originates in the B mechanism and not in the apparatus used in these experiments. First, the essential result was replicated with two separate optical systems, using square-wave stimuli as well as moiré fringes. Second, the splotchy pattern changes over time, yet the only thing moving in the system is the eye itself, suggesting that the origin of the effect lies there. Third, edge artifacts produced by truncating the grating (Kelly, 1970; Campbell, Carpenter, and Levinson, 1969) have been ruled out. Blurring the edge of the grating field and embedding it in an equiluminous violet annulus does not prevent observers from distinguishing gratings from uniform fields at frequencies above those at which bars can be detected.

Fourth, spectral sensitivity measurements show that the splotchy pattern is confined to gratings seen via B cones for spatial frequencies less than 35 cycles deg^{-1}. Figure 2 shows the highest spatial frequency that could be distinguished from an equiluminous uniform field for different wavelengths of the grating field. Data for each grating wavelength are shown with a different symbol. Notice that the abscissa is now plotted in equivalent π_3 units

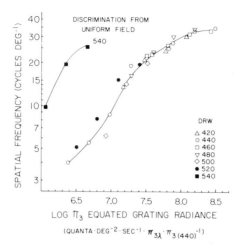

FIG. 2   Highest spatial frequency at which grating could be discriminated from uniform field of equal space-averaged radiance as a function of grating radiance (expressed in units equated for Stiles' π_3 mechanism). Different symbols represent different grating wavelength, all superimposed on the 580-nm background. Each data point is the mean of 4 sessions, with 2 measurements per session. Observer: DRW.

instead of radiance. Data for grating wavelengths of 500 nm and shorter fall along a common template, suggesting that the action spectrum for splotchiness is that of the B mechanism. When π_4 intrudes as it does clearly in the case of the 540-nm grating, the splotchy pattern is not seen near the resolution limit; as spatial frequency increases, the last thing seen are bars not splotches.

But the eye contains other structures that absorb short wavelength light besides the B cones, such as the dense network of retinal blood vessels, and the splotchy pattern could be a moiré pattern produced between the grating and the retinal vasculature. The blood vessels presumably lie in front of both the short- and middle-wavelength cones, so that if they account for the splotches, the pattern should be visible when the middle-wavelength cones detect the stimulus as well. We can shift the detection mechanism from π_3 to π_4 without changing the potential effects of the blood vessels on the grating by keeping the grating wavelength fixed while changing the background from 580 to 420 nm. Figure 1C shows data obtained for the same wavelength grating and the same range of spatial frequencies when π_4 detects the grating rather than π_3. Unfilled symbols show the highest frequencies at which bars are detected and filled symbols show the highest frequencies at which the grating can be distinguished from a uniform field. It is clear that there is no intermediate range of frequencies for which splotchiness but no bars is observed. This tends to exclude hypotheses based on prereceptoral filtering as well as apparatus artifacts. The observation that splotchiness is not observed when the grating is presented in the dark throughout the range of rod vision bolsters the conclusion that prereceptoral filtering is not responsible. Furthermore, splotchiness persists when a fixated, 1-deg grating field is used that falls within the avascular zone of the central fovea (Polyak, 1941) but still excites B cones surrounding the tritanopic area (Williams, MacLeod and Hayhoe, 1981a).

Analysis of the Effects of the B Cone Distribution on Resolution

These experiments argue that the origin of the "spurious resolution" of gratings seen via B cones cannot be accounted for by prereceptoral effects. It is more difficult to distinguish empirically between the hypotheses that the effect originates in the B cone mosaic itself or in some postreceptoral pathway fed by B cones. However, an argument can be made, resting on spatial sampling considerations and what is known about the distribution of B cones in the retinal mosaic, that these effects can be accounted for by the B cone mosaic, with no need to invoke postreceptoral mechanisms.

Digital information processing systems are subject to the problem of aliasing: if a waveform is sampled too coarsely, the sampling process can introduce spurious frequencies into the reconstructed waveform. Consider the simplest case in which the sampling points are equally spaced; the sampling theorem then applies (Whittaker, 1915; Shannon, 1949) which states that un-ambiguous reconstruction of a waveform requires that it contain frequencies no higher than half the fundamental sampling rate, the so-called Nyquist limit. Intuitively, this corresponds to having at least one receptor per bright bar and one per dark bar for the highest spatial frequency in the stimulus. Figure 3A shows a regular lattice of triangularly packed sample points, characteristic of the compound eyes of many insects. Figure 3B shows a vertical sinusoidal grating whose spatial frequency is well above the Nyquist limit given the spacing of columns of receptors in the triangular mosaic. The product of these two patterns is shown in Fig. 3C, and corresponds to the distribution of quantum catches that would result from imaging the grating on the array. The low-frequency, periodic, moiré pattern is characteristic of aliasing by regular mosaics. It is important to distinguish this effect from beating effects that occur when two waveforms of different frequencies are *added* together; in the case of beats, no energy actually appears at the beat frequency, whereas, in the case of aliasing, in which the sampling and stimulus waveforms are *multiplied*, the sampling process introduces energy at the frequency of the moiré pattern. The original high-frequency grating is still physically present in the product of the grating and the mosaic, but a low-frequency grating has been added as well. These two spatial frequencies are members of an equivalence class, both pro-ducing the same distribution of quantal absorptions in the mosaic, in much the same way as appropriate mixtures of two different choices of three primary

Plate 4. Tangential section through inner segment layer of *Macaca nemestrina* near the fovea, stained with Procion yellow. The calibration bar represents 25 microns, uncorrected for shrinkage, or about 9.6 minutes of arc. (It is assumed that the shrinkage factor is 0.78 and that 200 microns corresponds to 1 deg visual angle for this species.)

lights are members of the equivalence class of metameric lights, both producing identical quantum catches in the three wavelength-sampling photopigments of the eye. This kind of aliasing has been observed behaviorally in insects: gratings above the Nyquist limit produce a reversed optomotor response since these moiré fringes move in the direction opposite to that of the actual high-frequency stimulus (Von Gavel, 1939; Hassenstein, 1951).

Unlike the ommatidia of insect eyes, the array of B cones in the primate retina is apparently not a regular lattice. Neither the NBT-stained B cones in the baboon retina (Marc and Sperling, 1977) nor the cones stained with Procion yellow in macaque monkeys (De Monasterio, Schein, and McCrane, 1981; Shapiro, Schein, and De Monasterio, 1982) are regularly arrayed, though neither is their distribution entirely random. This can be seen in Plate 4, which shows a tangential section through inner segments near the foveal center of *Macaca nemestrina*. This specimen, which was prepared in collaboration with William Merigan and Thomas Eskin, has been stained with Procion yellow in accordance with the procedures developed by De Monasterio *et al.* (1981). Roughly 10 per cent of the cones (and an occasional rod) are stained with Procion yellow, and these cones, had they been arranged in a triangular array, would have had a spacing of about 6.3 minutes of arc. Short-range order is evident, in that adjacent cones are never stained, but long-range order is lacking. Nagel (1981) and French, Snyder, and Stavenga (1977) have addressed the impact of irregularity on aliasing analytically and argue irregularity introduces broad-band noise in the detection of high-frequency gratings. Yellott (1982) has modeled the sampling effects of the irregularly arrayed foveal cones optically. A similar analysis of the B cone mosaic has been adopted here, under the assumption that cones stained with Procion yellow are indeed B cones.

From the specimen shown in Plate 4 we constructed a much larger composite mosaic, shown in Fig. 4A. A dot represented each cone stained with Procion yellow. The pattern of cones was replicated in a variety of orientations, and subsections of the original pattern were used to fill in gaps between replications. (The only effect of replicating the original dot pattern was to increase the signal-to-noise ratio in the optical transform described below.) The effects of aliasing by this composite mosaic can be seen in Fig. 4B which shows the product of the mosaic and a 10 cycle deg^{-1} sinusoidal grating (shown in Fig. 3B). The grating period is slightly smaller than the average spacing of Procion yellow-stained cones. Instead of a periodic moiré pattern like that produced by the triangular array, an irregular, mottled pattern is produced that is suggestive of the splotchiness observed psychophysically.

The origin of this mottled pattern can be easily visualized in the frequency domain with the optical transform technique described by Yellott (1982). (See also Harburn, Taylor and Welberry, 1975). A 13.5 mm-square, chrome-on-glass transparency of the composite mosaic was illuminated with collimated light from an Argon laser. The Fraunhofer diffraction pattern formed in the

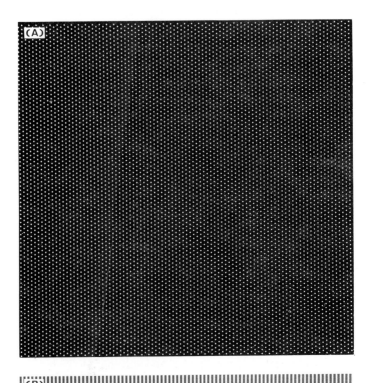

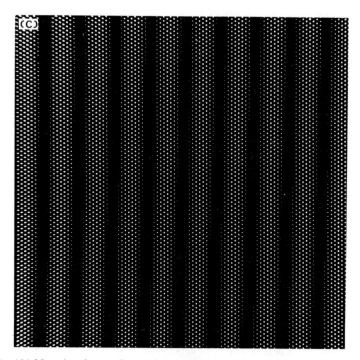

FIG. 3   (A) Mosaic of sampling points with triangular packing.
(B) Vertical sinusoidal grating whose spatial frequency is 0.9 times the sampling rate of the vertical columns of receptors in triangular mosaic displayed in (A).
(C) Product of triangular mosaic and sinusoid showing moiré fringe pattern produced by aliasing.

focal plane of a lens collecting light from the transparency is a display of the spatial frequency spectrum of the transparency; this optical field is mathematically the Fourier transform of the object field and is therefore called the optical transform.

The spatial frequency spectrum of the mosaic of cones stained with Procion yellow, shown in Fig. 5A, consists of a central spike at the origin surrounded by a dark region largely devoid of energy, which in turn is surrounded by a bright ring. The spectrum is characteristic of the spectra of dot patterns with short range order, but lacking long range order (Stark, 1977; Thompson, 1978). The spectrum shown in Fig. 5A is remarkably similar to that obtained from a cynomolgous retina stained with Procion black which Schein, De Monasterio and Caruso (1982) (who kindly provided the specimen) argue stains the same cones as Procion yellow. The spectrum also resembles that of the distribution of human foveal cones described by Yellott (1982). The only pronounced difference between these spectra is the radius of the bright ring which, in all

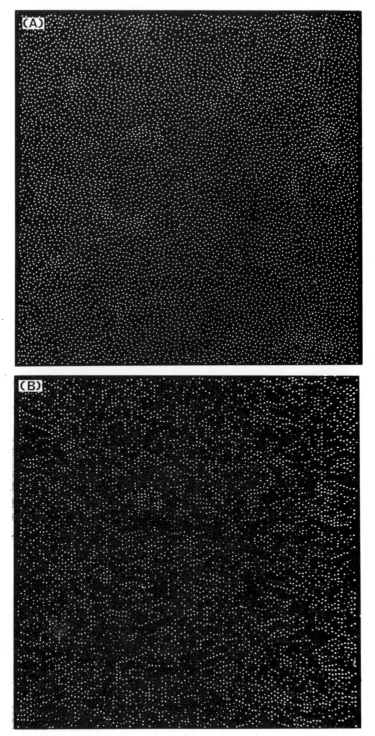

FIG. 4   (A) Composite mosaic of cones stained with Procion yellow. (B) Mosaic of cones stained with Procion yellow multiplied by 10-cycle deg^{-1} grating shown in Fig. 3B.

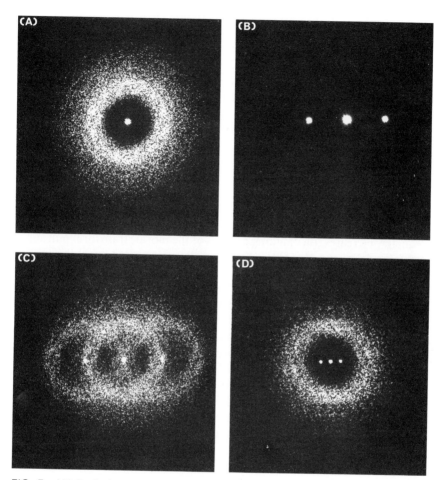

FIG. 5   (A) Optical transform of composite mosaic shown in Fig. 4A. (B) Optical transform of 10-cycle deg^{-1} grating, whose frequency is slightly higher than the reciprocal of average cone spacing, R. (C) Optical transform of product of composite mosaic and grating with frequency, R. (D) Optical transform of composite mosaic and grating with frequency, 0.25 R.

For illustrative purposes, the contrast of these transforms has been enhanced by nonlinear photographic development, so that the reflectance should not be taken as proportional to the energy in the optical transform.

cases studied so far, is roughly equal to the reciprocal of the average spacing of receptors in the mosaic, or twice the nominal Nyquist limit for the array. For the purposes of the following arguments, the assumption will be made that, though cone spacing may vary with species and retinal location, the general pattern of receptors is about the same. Consequently, spatial frequency will be normalized with respect to the radius (R) of the bright ring in the transform of the mosaic.

Figure 5B shows the spectrum of the 10 cycle deg^{-1} grating, whose spatial frequency is slightly higher than R. It consists of a d.c. component flanked by two first orders. Figure 5C shows the spatial frequency spectrum of the product of the grating and the composite mosaic; formed by convolving the Fourier transforms of the grating and the mosaic. It should be noted that Figs 5A, B, C and D show the intensity distributions of the frequency spectra, which are the Fourier transforms times their complex conjugates, not the Fourier spectra themselves, so the phase information associated with the optical field is not displayed. Surrounding the zero-th and each of the first order spectra associated with the grating in Fig. 5C are replicas of the transform of the mosaic. When the spatial frequency of the grating is low, roughly 0.25 R, as shown in Fig. 5D, these three rings largely overlap, but as the grating frequency increases, the flanking replicas of the mosaic transform pull apart, faithfully following the first spectral orders associated with the grating frequency.

Now these frequency spectra show the total distribution of energy produced by the stimulus and the sampling properties of the mosaic, but the sense that the visual system makes out of them depends on the neural filtering that occurs after the sampling operation. (Optical filtering prior to the sampling operation is ignored here since these factors probably do not dramatically affect the effective contrast of the low spatial frequency stimuli used in the psychophysical experiments on B cones.) As Yellott (in press) has pointed out for sampling by foveal cones, the sampling process itself does not remove high frequencies from the representation, even when they are well above the Nyquist limit. For example, the 10 cycle deg^{-1} (R) grating is nearly twice the nominal Nyquist limit (0.5 R) for the Procion yellow-stained mosaic yet its first-order spectra are clearly visible in the optical transform of the product of the grating and the mosaic. With chromatic aberration corrected, postreceptoral factors, not the mosaic itself, must ultimately limit the resolution of the B mechanism. These factors may correspond to the convergence of receptors onto bipolars and ganglion cells, though for the present their physiological embodiment is not critical.

This neural limitation can be incorporated into the optical simulation by adding a low-pass filtering operation following the sampling process. This was done in practice by placing a circular aperture in the plane of the optical transform of the mosaic, centered on the origin, and then reconstructing the image of the mosaic from the filtered transform. An aperture with a radius of about 0.4 R was used, slightly less than half the radius of the bright ring in the transform. The exact radius chosen is not critical. This aperture can be construed as a kind of window in the frequency domain, through which the postreceptoral visual system can peer. Now consider what happens when gratings of various spatial frequencies are sampled by the irregular mosaic, low-pass filtered, and finally reconstructed. Figure 6C shows the reconstruction of a uniform field "viewed" by the optical model of the B mechanism. It is fairly uniform in appearance, though some low-frequency structure is visible, corresponding to local variations in receptor density. Such static inhomogeneities in real retinal mosaics may be disposed of by the same mechanism that renders the retinal blood vessels invisible. Figure 6B shows the reconstruction obtained when the grating spatial frequency is low, 0.25 R as in Fig. 5D, the first-order spectra are passed by the spatial filter and the overlapping three bright rings corresponding to the mosaic transform are occluded, allowing reconstruction of the grating, albeit with some noise. However, when the spatial frequency of the grating is high, as in Fig. 5C, the first-order spectra are occluded by the spatial filter, so that the grating cannot be reconstructed. But the flanking bright rings of the mosaic replicas now pass through the origin, allowing some low-frequency aliased energy to pass the spatial filter. This energy is broadly tuned in both frequency and orientation, and gives rise to the mottled or splotchy reconstruction seen in Fig. 6C. Thus, despite the fact that the grating bars cannot be detected in the optical simulation, the grating field can be distinguished from a uniform field by virtue of this nonoriented, aliased energy; Fig. 6C is much more mottled than Fig. 6A. The optical simulation using the mosaic of primate cones stained with Procion yellow yields just the kind of aliasing required to account for the psychophysical observations. At low spatial frequencies, gratings are resolved, but as spatial frequency increases, the reconstruction of the grating gives way to reconstruction of the grating's alias: broad band noise. The model mimics another aspect of the psychophysical results. If the grating field is shifted relative to the mosaic in the stimulation, the splotchy pattern changes, just as the psychophysically observed pattern changes with movements of the eyes.

The optical simulation of aliasing does not exclude the possibility that the splotchy character of high-frequency gratings seen via B cones has a partly postreceptoral origin. Still, the available anatomical evidence suggests that the B cone mosaic has just the properties required to account for the psychophysical results. Taken together, the most plausible explanation for this spurious resolution seems to be that it is caused by aliasing by the receptor mosaic, and that the human short-wavelength mechanism samples the world through an irregular array of detectors. Indeed, provided high-contrast, high-frequency stimuli can be imaged on such a mosaic, it is hard to see how the visual system could avoid aliasing. Spatial filtering after photoreceptor sampling is ineffective. In the design of digital information processing systems, aliasing is avoided by filtering out frequencies capable of aliasing prior to the sampling process. For the middle- and long-wavelength cones, the optical transfer function of the eye has its cut-off near the nominal Nyquist limit of

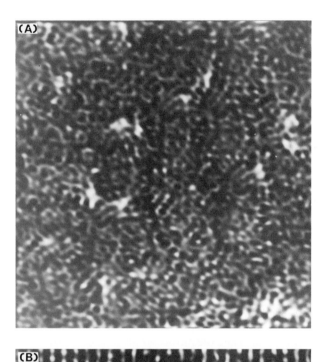

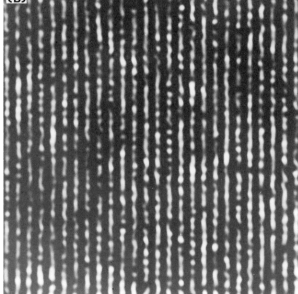

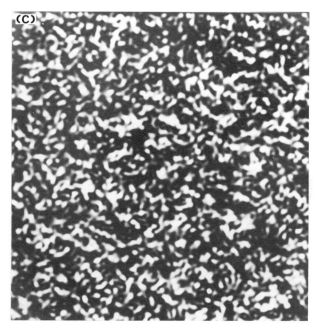

FIG. 6   (A) Spatially filtered composite mosaic, filter cut off: 0.4 R. (B) Spatially filtered product of composite mosaic and grating with frequency, 0.25 R. Filter cut off: 0.4 R. (C) Spatially filtered product of composite mosaic and grating with frequency, R. Filter cut off: 0.4 R.

the foveal mosaic (Green, 1970). This reduces the deleterious effects of aliasing by an irregular mosaic, though there are suggestions that it does not eliminate it entirely. At spatial frequencies near the resolution limit, Helmholtz (1962), Byram (1944), and Campbell and Green (1965) have reported that gratings have a wavy or granular appearance and observations we have made with luminance gratings confirm this. This phenomenon may be equivalent to the splotches observed via B cones. Yellott (1982) has convincingly argued that the spacing of foveal cones does not ultimately limit resolution when the effects of the optics of the eye have been reduced via laser interferometry. The correspondence between the cut-off of the optical transfer function and the nominal Nyquist limit of the foveal mosaic does not reflect a match between optical and mosaic resolution; rather it seems to reveal a clever design to reduce the ambiguity associated with undersampling by the mosaic. Under ordinary viewing conditions, the B cone mosaic, though far coarser than the mosaic of middle- and long-wavelength cones, may similarly be protected from aliasing by axial chromatic aberration of the eye (Cornsweet, Wandell, and Yellott, 1980) which prevents high spatial frequencies of short-wavelength light from reaching the mosaic. Perhaps the spacing of B cones as well as that of foveal cones as a whole is set, not by the demands of resolution, but by spatial ambiguity that would result from a coarser spacing.

Acknowledgements

We thank F. De Monasterio, W. Makous, S. Schein, and J. Yellott for valuable discussions, and William Merigan and Thomas Eskin for preparing the Procion yellow specimens. This research was supported by NEI EY 04367, EY 01319, and an equipment gift from Xerox Corporation.

References

Bowmaker, J. K., Dartnall, H. J. A. and Mollon, J. D. (1979). The violet-sensitive receptors of primate retinae. *J. Physiol., Lond.* **292**, 31P.

Brindley, G. S. (1954). The summation areas of human colour-receptive mechanisms at increment threshold. *J. Physiol., Lond.* **124**, 400–408.

Brown, P. K. and Wald, G. (1964). Visual pigments in single rods and cones of the human retina. *Science* **144**, 45–52.

Byram, G. M. (1944). The physical and photochemical basis of visual resolving power. Part II. Visual acuity and the photochemistry of the retina. *J. opt. Soc. Am.* **34**, 718–738.

Campbell, R. F., Carpenter, R. H. S. and Levinson, J. Z. (1969). Visibility of aperiodic patterns compared with that of sinusoidal gratings. *J. Physiol., Lond.* **204**, 283–298.

Campbell, F. W. and Green, D. G. (1965). Optical and retinal factors affecting visual resolution. *J. Physiol., Lond.* **181**, 576–593.

Cornsweet, T. N., Wandell, B. A. and Yellott, J. I. (1980). The beginnings of visual perception: the retinal image and its initial encoding. University of California, Irvine Social Science Working Paper.

Daw, N. W. and Enoch, J. M. (1973). Contrast sensitivity, Westheimer function and Stiles-Crawford effect in a blue cone monochromat. *Vision Res.* **13**, 1669–1680.

De Monasterio, F. M. and Gouras, P. (1975). Functional properties of ganglion cells of the Rhesus monkey retina. *J. Physiol., Lond.* **251**, 167–195.

De Monasterio, F. M., Schein, S. J. and McCrane, E. P. (1981). Staining of blue-sensitive cones of Macaque retina by a fluorescent dye. *Science* **213**, 1278–1281.

French, A. S., Snyder, A. W. and Stavenga, D. G. (1977). Image degradation by an irregular retinal mosaic. *Biol. Cyber.* **27**, 229–233.

Green, D. G. (1968). The contrast sensitivity of the colour mechanisms of the human eye. *J. Physiol., Lond.* **196**, 415–429.

Green, D. G. (1970). Regional variations in the visual acuity for interference fringes on the retina. *J. Physiol., Lond.* **207**, 351–356.

Harburn, G., Taylor, C. A. and Welberry, T. R. (1975). *Atlas of Optical Transforms.* Ithaca, NY, Cornell University Press.

Hassenstein, B. (1951). Ommatidienraster und afferente Bewegungsintegration. *Zeitschrift für vergleichende Physiologie* **33**, 301–326.

Helmholtz's *Treatise on Physiological Optics* (ed. James P. C. Southall). Dover Publications, Inc., New York, NY (1962), Vol. II, pp. 34–35.

Kelly, D. H. (1970). Effect of sharp edges on the visibility of sinusoidal gratings. *J. opt. Soc. Am.* **60**, 98–103.

Kelly, D. H. (1973). Lateral inhibition in human colour mechanisms. *J. Physiol., Lond.* **228**, 55–72.

Marc, R. E. and Sperling, H. G. (1977). Chromatic organization of primate cones. *Science* **196**, 454–456.

Marks, W. B., Dobelle, W. H. and MacNichol, E. F. (1964). Visual pigments of single primate cones. *Science* **143**, 1181–1183.

Nagel, D. C. (1981). Spatial sampling of the retina. Paper presented at the Association for Research in Vision & Ophthalmology, Sarasota, FL.

Polyak, S. L. (1941). *The Retina.* Chicago, University of Chicago Press.

Rushton, W. A. H. (1962). Visual pigments in man. *Scientific American* **207**, 5: 120–132.

Schein, S. J., De Monasterio, F. M. and Caruso, R. C. (1982). Dye staining of blue-sensitive cones in macaque retina: Mechanism. Paper presented at Association for Research in Vision & Ophthalmology, Sarasota, FL.

Shannon, C. E. (1949). Communication in the presence of noise. *Proceedings of the I.R.E.* **37**, 10–21.

Shapiro, M. B., Schein, S. J. and De Monasterio, F. M. (1982). Dye staining of blue-sensitive cones in macaque retina: Pattern analysis. Paper presented at Association for Research in Vision & Ophthalmology, Sarasota, FL.

Snyder, A. W. and Miller, W. H. (1977). Photoreceptor diameter and spacing for highest resolving power. *J. opt. Soc. Am.* **67**, 5.

Stark, H. (1977). Diffraction patterns of non-overlapping circular grains. *J. opt. Soc. Am.* **67**, 700–703.

Stiles, W. S. (1949). Increment thresholds and the mechanism of colour vision. *Documenta Ophthalmologica* **3**, 138–163.

Stiles, W. S. (1953). Further studies of Visual Mechanisms by the Two-Colour Threshold Technique. In *Mechanisms of Colour Vision.* New York, Academic Press, pp. 183–221.

Stromeyer, C. F., Kranda, K. and Sternheim, C. E. (1978). Selective chromatic adaptation at different spatial frequencies. *Vision Res.* **18**, 427–438.

Thompson, B. J. (1978). A review of Fourier plane signal processing for real-time measurement. Proceedings of the 1978 International Optical Computing Conference, September 5–7, pp. 139–147.

Von Gavel, L. (1939). Die kritische Streifenbreite als Mass der Sehschärfe bei Drosophila Melanogaster. *Z. f. vergl. Physiologie* **27**, 80–135.

Westheimer, G. (1960). Modulation thresholds for sinusoidal light distributions on the retina. *J. Physiol., Lond.* **152**, 67–74.

Whittaker, E. T. (1915). On the functions which are presented by the expansions of the interpolation theory. *Proc. roy. Soc. Edinburgh Sec.* **A35**, 181–194.

Williams, D. R., MacLeod, D. I. A. and Hayhoe, M. (1981a). Punctate sensitivity of the blue-sensitive mechanism. *Vision Res.* **21**, 1357–1375.

Williams, D. R., MacLeod, D. I. A. and Hayhoe, M. (1981b). Foveal Tritanopia. *Vision Res.* **21**, 1341–1356.

Yellott, J. I. (1982). Spectral analysis of spatial sampling by photoreceptors: Topological disorder prevents aliasing. *Vision Res.* **22**, 1205–1210.

Spatial Sensitization Properties of the Blue-Sensitive Cone Pathways

G. HAEGERSTROM-PORTNOY and A. J. ADAMS

Introduction

Antagonism between adjacent retinal areas is most clearly demonstrated in the center and surround properties of retinal ganglion cells. In psychophysical studies, Crawford (1940) showed that increasing the diameter of an adapting field first produced desensitization of the retinal area probed by a small test spot while further increases in diameter caused a relative sensitization. Westheimer (1965, 1967) further investigated the sensitization effect showing that it occurred independently for both rods and cones and also related it to retinal physiology. McKee and Westheimer (1970) suggested that the desensitization/sensitization functions exist within each of Stiles' π_4 and π_5 mechanisms. These results for the medium and long wavelength-sensitive cone mechanisms (G and R cone mechanisms, respectively) suggest that the restriction of desensitization to an individual color system through light adaptation (Stiles, 1978) or bleaching (DuCroz and Rushton, 1966) also exists in the lateral connections across the retina.

The B cone system appears to differ from the G and R cone systems, having quite different spatial and temporal properties and a relatively low density of receptors with a unique distribution across the retina (see Mollon, 1982 for review). There is evidence that signals from B cones have access only to a chromatically opponent post-receptoral channel (Gouras and Zrenner, 1981; Eisner and McLeod, 1980). It has also been clearly demonstrated that signals from G and/or R cones can alter sensitivity to a test flash that is detected by B cones (e.g. Stiles, 1959; Mollon and Polden, 1977).

COLOUR VISION
ISBN 0 12 000000 0

The present experiments were designed to address two questions:

1) Can sensitization functions be demonstrated within the B cone system?
2) Can the function be modulated by signals from G and/or R sensitive cones as well as from B cones?

Methods

The test target and the variable diameter background beam were generated using a two-channel Maxwellian view system. An achromatizing lens corrected for longitudinal chromatic aberration of the eye (Wyszecki and Stiles, 1967, p. 212). The larger surround field was not in Maxwellian view but was seen through the same artificial pupil (4 mm). Radiances were controlled by circular Inconel neutral density wedges mounted on stepper motors. The spectral composition of the three fields was controlled by narrow band interference filters (bandwidth at half-height less than 10 nm). The wedges and shutters were under control of a micro-computer, which also monitored the subject's responses from two pushbuttons.

Radiometric and photometric calibration was performed with the interference filters in place using a Spectra Pritchard Photometer (Model 1980A) and a method described by Westheimer (1966).

All thresholds were measured at 5 degrees eccentricity in the inferior retina using a temporal two-alternative forced-choice staircase technique. The 79% threshold was determined as the average of 8 reversals.

In the first experiment a null method was used to investigate the influence of lateral interactions. The threshold for the 15 min arc test spot (440 nm, 280 msec) was first determined after the subject adapted for 3 minutes to the 4 log troland 20 deg surround (589 nm). The temporal sequence of the stimulus presentation is shown in Fig. 1c. In the null experiment, the radiance of the test spot was set 1 log unit above this threshold. A background (440 nm) was then introduced concentric with the test spot (see Fig. 1a) and the subject then adapted a further 3 min. Threshold background radiance was then determined in the two-alternative forced choice paradigm for each of a series of background sizes. Two experienced subjects (GP, mild protanomal; NC, color-normal) performed each experiment with dilated pupils and bite bar restraint.

Results

Experiment 1: Sensitization within the B Cone System

The B cone system can be isolated using a yellow background which selectively desensitizes R and G cone mechanisms. We first demonstrated this isolation for the test spot (see inset Fig. 2). The spectral sensitivity, on a 4 log td 589 nm

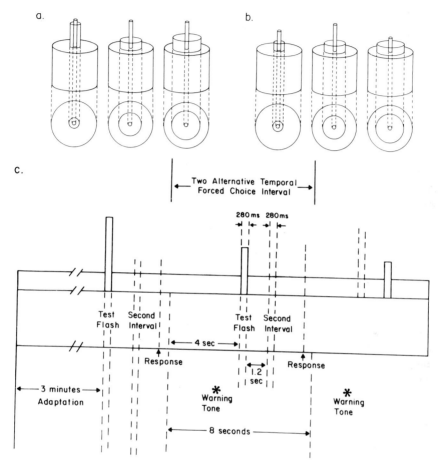

FIG. 1   Stimulus configuration. (a) Test spot (15 min arc, 440 nm) raised 1 log unit above threshold on 4 log td 589 nm 20 deg surround and presented on concentric 440-nm backgrounds of various sizes. (b) Test spot presented on 4 log td 574 nm fixed radiance background, both fields superimposed on 3 log td 589 nm surround. (c) The timing sequence used for both experiments.

surround is well fitted by the Smith and Pokorny B cone function (Boynton, 1979). The radiance of the 440 nm test spot was raised one log unit above threshold on the surround alone. As the background increases up to a diameter of about 60 min arc, its radiance must be reduced to maintain the test flash at threshold (desensitization). For larger diameters, the radiance of the background must be increased (sensitization). Backgrounds larger than 3 degrees produce no further change.

The maximum desensitization occurs for adapting fields of relatively large diameter, similar to results reported for a blue cone monochromat (Daw and

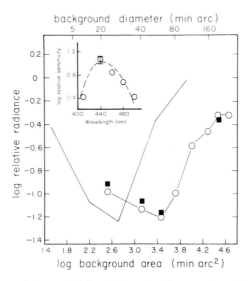

FIG. 2   Radiance of the variable 440-nm background required to reduce the 440-nm test spot to threshold. The inset shows the test sensitivity for 15 min arc, 440 nm, 280 msec test spot alone on the 20 deg, 589 nm, 4 log td surround. The error bars show the *total range* of the means from 5 staircases. The dashed line indicates the spectral sensitivity of blue cones according to Smith and Pokorny (Boynton, 1979). Subject GP: circles; NC: squares. The line without symbols represents the desensitization/sensitization function for "white" light at 5 deg retinal eccentricity (replotted from Enoch and Sunga, 1969). Log relative radiance of 0 on ordinates $= 1.8 \times 10^9$ quanta sec^{-1} deg^{-2}.

Enoch, 1973). At the same retinal eccentricity for "white" light (Fig. 2), the spatial extent of lateral interactions is considerably smaller (Enoch and Sunga, 1969).

To what extent is the function mediated by B cones? To answer this we measured field sensitivities at three background diameters. The results clearly show that B cones produce both the desensitization and the relative sensitization (see insets Fig. 3). This result is consistent with the results reported for G and R cone functions by McKee and Westheimer (1970); they also suggested that the lateral interactions were *restricted* to the cone system under test. Whether or not this is true for the B cone system is addressed in the second experiment.

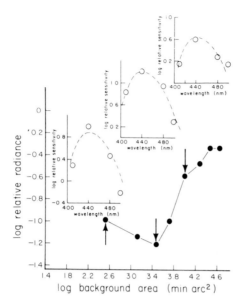

FIG. 3   Desensitization/sensitization function from Fig. 2. Field sensitivities at three different background sizes are shown in the insets for GP. The dashed line shows the spectral sensitivities of B cones of Smith and Pokorny (Boynton, 1979). Log relative radiance of 0 on ordinates = 1.8×10^9 quanta sec^{-1} deg^{-2}.

Experiment 2: Sensitization of the B Cone System Mediated by G and/or R Cones

Large transient changes in B cone sensitivity are known to occur for relatively small changes in a background yellow field (Mollon and Polden, 1977). Consequently, it would be time-consuming to use the null method (Fig. 1a) to attempt to demonstrate sensitization functions with a 574-nm background. Instead, we used a fixed radiance 574-nm background on the 589 nm surround and determined the threshold radiance of the 440-nm test spot for different background diameters (Fig. 1b).

The yellow background produced both desensitization and relative sensitization of the retinal area under the 440-nm test flash with maximal desensitization occurring for a field diameter of 50–60 min of arc (Fig. 4). The spatial dimensions of the function are very similar to those seen in Experiment 1. In order to confirm that the lateral interactions were not produced by direct B cone stimulation by the 574-nm background, we determined field sensitivities at three background diameters. (Threshold versus intensity functions were generated for different background wavelengths and the radiance required to elevate the threshold by the same amount as the 574 nm background was determined.) The spectral sensitivities, thus determined, eliminate B cones as candidates for the lateral interactions (see insets Fig. 4). This finding provides clear evidence that B cone sensitivity can be controlled by lateral antagonistic connections from signals initiated in other receptor types.

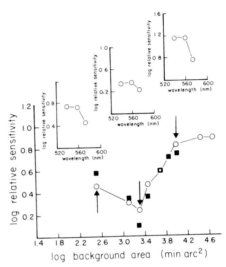

FIG. 4   Log relative sensitivity for 440-nm test spot as a function of log background area (4 log td 574 nm). Test spot and background superimposed on 3 log td 589-nm large surround. The insets show field sensitivities at three different background diameters. Log relative sensitivity of 0 on ordinates $= 5.6 \times 10^9$ quanta sec^{-1} deg^{-2}.

Discussion

Our results clearly demonstrate that the sensitivity of the B cone system can be influenced by lateral antagonistic connections as evidenced by desensitization or relative sensitization depending on adapting field diameter. B cone functions appear to differ from G and R cone functions in two important ways. First, the lateral influences cover a much larger retinal area. While it is difficult to compare the size of this function with those reported by McKee and Westheimer (1970) at the fovea, the functions are nevertheless considerably larger than those reported by Enoch and Sunga (1969) for white light at the same retinal eccentricity used in our experiments. Second, the sensitivity to flashes detected by B cones can be altered by lateral signals initiated in G and/or R cones. This latter result was also recently reported by Schuurmans et al. (1982).

Why are the desensitization/sensitization zones for the B cone pathway much larger than those reported for white light at the same retinal eccentricity? The most obvious explanation may be related to the larger spatial summation areas of B cones (Brindley, 1954). On the other hand, it has been reported that B cones provide signals only to "chromatic" channels (e.g. Eisner and MacLeod, 1980) and it is possible that our results reflect a more general property of responses in "chromatic" channels, rather than a specific property of B cones. We are currently testing this hypothesis.

The desensitization and sensitization functions are probably reflections of receptive field properties and have been interpreted this way by a number of investigators (Westheimer, 1967, Teller *et al.*, 1971, Enoch, 1978). An alternative explanation is in terms of edge effects on thresholds. However, models of edge effects seem inadequate to account for the fact that under cone-mediated conditions sensitization is essentially independent of the number of edges or contours in the background field (Enoch and Johnson, 1976; Ambrose and Hayhoe, 1980). Furthermore, Hayhoe and Smith (1982) have reported that stabilizing the retinal images fails to remove the relative sensitization effect.

The sensitization function seems to be organized early in the visual system. Westheimer (1967), Sturr and Teller (1973) and Johnson and Enoch (1976), have all demonstrated that the function disappears in dichoptic presentations. Werblin (1974) has shown sensitizing interactions at the level of the outer plexiform layer in the mudpuppy retina. On the assumption that the sensitizing functions are organized in the receptive fields of retinal neurons, the results have interesting implications. If one assumes that the results seen in Experiments 1 and 2 are organized within the same cell, the receptive field organization would be quite unlike a conventional double opponent cell, since both yellow and blue surrounds antagonize the blue center. Even without that assumption, the results suggest the existence of blue-center cells antagonized by surrounds also fed by B cones. We are unaware of any reports in primates of such units; B cone inputs appear to produce mostly "on" center cells with inhibitory surrounds fed by some combination of G and R cones (see Gouras and Zrenner, 1981 for review). Why should such blue-sensitive spatially antagonistic cells be difficult to identify in neurophysiological studies? It is possible that such cells do not exist at the retinal level in spite of the fact that sensitizing functions are fairly clearly organized at the retinal level for other cone systems (e.g. Westheimer, 1967). Alternatively, such cell-types may be quite rare, corresponding to the sparse representation of B cones in the retina (Marc and Sperling, 1977; Bowmaker *et al.*, 1980; de Monasterio *et al.*, 1981). We believe another very likely explanation may be that the B cone pathways are very vulnerable to even minor disruptions of retinal integrity; a number of retinal and optic nerve disorders in their early stages have an associated reduction in B cone function (Marré and Marré, 1978; Zisman and King-Smith, 1978; Adams, 1982). We believe it is possible that the methods and the drugs used for the neurophysiological experiments may selectively alter function mediated by B cones.

512   *G. Haegerstrom-Portnoy and A. J. Adams*

Our results could be construed as supporting the model of Pugh and Mollon (1979) in that the gain of the B cones can be altered at the second site by antagonistic signals from the B cones and also from the G and/or R cones. The site of these gain-controlling lateral interactions is probably very early in the retina. Valeton and van Norren (1979) have demonstrated transient tritanopia in the b-wave of the electroretinogram, which is thought to be generated by Mueller cells in the inner nuclear layer. Consequently, this antagonism of midspectral cones on B cones is organized at this level or earlier at the outer plexiform layer.

Our results show sensitization over large spatial dimensions for the B cone system from signals initiated both in B cones and G and/or R cones; the spectral sensitivity of the latter is not yet resolved. This result may not be yet another "oddity" of the B cone system but reflect a general property of "chromatic" as opposed to "achromatic" pathways. The existence of retinal cells having receptive fields with antagonism from B cones is suggested from these experiments although the function of such cells is not clear.

Acknowledgement

Supported by EY02271 to AJA and EY07043 to GHP for post-doctoral fellowship.

References

Adams, A. J. (1982). Chromatic and luminosity processing in retinal disease. *Am. J. Opt. Phys. Opt.* **59**, 954–960.

Ambrose, J. M. and Hayhoe, M. M. (1980). Surround configuration and cone dark adaptation. *Vision Res.* **20**, 883–890.

Boynton, R. M. (1979). *Human Color Vision.* New York, Holt, Rinehart and Winston.

Bowmaker, J. K., Dartnall, H. J. A. and Mollon, J. D. (1980). Microspectrophotometric demonstration of four classes of photoreceptor in an Old World primate, *Macaca fascicularis. J. Physiol.* **298**, 131–143.

Brindley, G. S. (1954). The summation areas of human colour-receptive mechanisms at increment threshold *J. Physiol.* **124**, 400–408.

Crawford, B. H. (1940). The effect of field size and pattern on the change of visual sensitivity with time. *Proc. roy. Soc. (Lond.) Ser. B* **129**, 94–106.

Daw, N. W. and Enoch, J. M. (1973). Contrast sensitivity, Westheimer function and Stiles-Crawford effect in a blue-cone monochromat. *Vision Res.* **13**, 1669–1680.

de Monasterio, F. M., Schein, S. J. and McCrane, E. P. (1981). Staining of blue-sensitive cones of the macaque. *Science* **213**, 1278–1281.

DuCroz, J. J. and Rushton, W. A. H. (1966). The separation of cone mechanisms in dark-adaptation. *J. Physiol.* **183**, 481–496.

Eisner, A. and MacLeod, D. (1980). Blue-sensitive cones do not contribute to luminance. *J. opt. Soc. Am.* **70**, 121–123.

Enoch, J. M. (1978). Quantitative layer-by-layer perimetry. Proctor lecture. *Invest. Ophthal. Visual Sci.* **17**, 208–257.

Enoch, J. M. and Johnson, C. A. (1976). Additivity of effects within sectors of the sensitization zone of the Westheimer function. *Am. J. Optom. Physiol. Opt.* **53**, 350–358.

Enoch, J. M. and Sunga, R. (1969). Development of quantitative perimetric tests. *Docum. Ophthal.* **26**, 215–229.

Gouras, P. and Zrenner, E. (1981). Color vision. In *Progress in Sensory Physiology 1* (ed. Ottoson, D.). Berlin, Springer-Verlag.

Hayhoe, M. M. and Smith, M. V. (1982). The sensitization effect in stabilized vision. In supplement to *Invest. Ophthal. Visual Sci.* **22**, 49 (Abstract).

Johnson, C. and Enoch, J. M. (1976). Human psychophysical analysis of receptive field-like properties—II. Dichoptic properties of the Westheimer function. *Vision Res.* **16**, 1455–1462.

Marré, M. and Marré, E. (1978). Different types of acquired colour vision deficiencies on the base of CVM patterns in dependence upon the fixational mode of the diseased eye. *Mod. Probl. Ophth.* **19**, 248–252 (Karger, Basel).

Marc, R. E. and Sperling, H. (1977). Chromatic organization of primate cones. *Science* **196**, 454–456.

McKee, S. and Westheimer, G. (1970). Specificity of cone mechanisms in lateral interaction. *J. Physiol.* **206**, 117–128.

Mollon, J. D. (1982). Color vision. *Ann. Rev. Psych.* **33**, 41–85.

Mollon, J. D. and Polden, P. G. (1977). An anomaly in the response of the eye to light of short wavelength. *Phil. Trans. roy. Soc.* **B278**, 207–240.

Pugh, E. N. and Mollon, J. D. (1979). A theory of the π_1 and π_3 color mechanisms of Stiles. *Vision Res.* **19**, 293–312.

Schuurmans, R. P., Zrenner, E. and Baier, M. (1982). A spatially induced sensitivity modulation of the blue sensitive cone mechanism mediated by longer wavelength sensitive cones. In supplement to *Invest. Ophthal. Visual Sci.* **22**, 121 (Abstract).

Stiles, W. S. (1959). Color vision: the approach through increment threshold sensitivity. *Proc. natn. Acad. Sci. U.S.A.* **45**, 100–114.

Stiles, W. S. (1978). The directional sensitivity of the retina and the spectral sensitivities of the rods and cones. In *Mechanisms of colour vision*, pp. 54–95, Academic Press, London.

Sturr, J. F. and Teller, D. Y. (1973). Sensitization by annular surrounds: dichoptic properties. *Vision Res.* **13**, 909–918.

Teller, D. Y., Matter, C., Phillips, W. D., Alexander, K. (1971). Sensitization by annular surrounds: sensitization and masking. *Vision Res.* **11**, 1445–1458.

Valeton, J. M. and van Norren, D. (1979). Retinal site of transient tritanopia. *Nature* **280**, 488–490.

Werblin, F. S. (1974). Control of sensitivity. II. Lateral interactions at the outer plexiform layer. *J. Gen. Physiol.* **63**, 62–87.

Westheimer, G. (1965). Spatial interaction in the human retina during scotopic vision. *J. Physiol., Lond.* **181**, 881–894.

Westheimer, G. (1966). The Maxwellian view. *Vision Res.* **6**, 669–682.

Westheimer, G. (1967). Spatial interaction in human cone vision. *J. Physiol., Lond.* **190**, 139–154.

Wyszecki, G. and Stiles, W. S. (1967). *Color Science.* J. Wiley and Sons, N.Y.

Zisman, F. and King-Smith, P. E. (1978). Spectral sensitivities of acquired color defects analyzed in terms of color opponent theory. *Mod. Probl. Ophth.* **19**, 254–257 (Karger, Basel).

Transient and Steady-State Responses of Ganglion Cells Mediating the Signals of Short-Wave Sensitive Cones

PETER GOURAS and *EBERHART ZRENNER*

An excitatory response of the short-wave sensitive cone mechanism can be identified in a subset, about 5 to 10% of the ganglion cells in primate retina (see Gouras and Zrenner, 1981 for a review). These ganglion cells are excited (depolarized) by light stimulation of the short-wave sensitive cones and inhibited (hyperpolarized) by light stimulation of the midspectral or more long wave sensitive cones. There is considerable evidence to indicate that this is the major and possibly the only channel by which the short-wave sensitive cones can influence the rest of the visual system (Gouras, 1968; Zrenner and Gouras, 1981; Gouras and Eggers, 1982a,b and in press).

There are a number of physiological phenomena exhibited by this ganglion cell system which appear to have psychophysical counterparts (Gouras and Zrenner, 1979; Mollon, 1982) and consequently could form valuable linking relationships between single cell physiology and visual perception. This paper focuses on three such phenomena in particular, a saturation of the excitatory response in the steady-state and a transient reduction in this response at both the onset and the offset of a long wave and consequently a hyperpolarizing adapting field. In addition the paper describes a new phenomenon for which there is as yet no corresponding psychophysical counterpart, a more rapid decay of the short-wave sensitive or excitatory response in the presence of a long wave or hyperpolarizing field.

COLOUR VISION
ISBN 0 12 000000 0

Methods

The methods used in these experiments are similar to those we have used before (Gouras and Zrenner, 1979; Gouras and Eggers, in press). Glass micropipette electrodes are introduced into the vitreal cavity of an anesthetized, paralyzed monkey through a small hole a few millimeters behind the limbus and guided back to the retina under direct view using either a fundus camera or an indirect ophthalmoscope. At present we study the same eye in five or more separate experiments of about 6–8 hours duration using the same anesthetic techniques employed on human infants. The monkeys are alert within a few hours after each procedure; the ocular sequelae resulting from the microsurgery are minimal and usually transient. We believe the animals experience as little or no pain as human subjects do recovering from similar or more radical intra-ocular procedures. Monochromatic stimuli obtained from calibrated inter-ference filters are focused on the retinal surface as spots, annuli, slits or edges. An adapting beam obtained from the same light source, either a xenon high pressure arc lamp or a halogen bulb is optically mixed with the test beam. The spectral transmission of the adapting lights is controlled by absorption filters (see figures). The action potentials of each cell are converted into impulse fre-quency histograms by determining the number of impulses occurring within each 33-msec period before and following a light pulse. Usually 5 to 10, but occasionally only one, response to the same stimulus are used to obtain an average response.

The results upon which this paper is based come from 14 ganglion cells in *M. mulatta* which have been detected in different experiments. These cells receive an unequivocal excitatory input from the short-wave-sensitive cone mechanism. This has been established by determining the action spectrum of the excitatory responses which shows its peak sensitivity in the region of 440–450 nm and a ten to a hundredfold loss of sensitivity at 500 nm. This pro-nounced drop in sensitivity remains virtually unchanged in the presence of a strong long-wave adapting field. This latter point is an especially important criterion for distinguishing the short-wave-sensitive cone mechanism from the so called green-sensitive one (Gouras and Zrenner, 1979a; Zrenner and Gouras, 1981).

Results

Figure 1 shows the responses of such a ganglion cell, excited by the short-wave-sensitive cone mechanism and inhibited by the midspectral cones. On a long-wave background (above), the cell is strongly excited by blue (456 nm) but not by orange-red (610 nm) stimuli. With a short-wave background (below), the cell's maintained discharge increases considerably and now light stimuli from the entire spectrum, but most effectively from the midspectral regions, inhibit

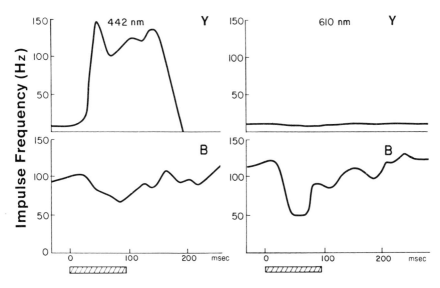

FIG. 1   Responses of a single primate ganglion cell which is excited by the short-wave sensitive cone mechanism and inhibited by the longer wavelength sensitive cone mechanism(s). The upper traces show the responses to a short-wave (442 nm) and a long-wave (610 nm) stimulus on a yellow (Corning glass filter 3482) adapting field of 10^{11} quanta sec^{-1} mm^{-2}. The lower records show the responses to the same stimuli in the presence of a blue (Corning glass filter 5543) adapting field of 10^{11} quanta sec^{-1} mm^{-2} on the retina. Note the change in the maintained discharge frequency produced by the adapting fields. The ordinate indicates the impulse frequency of the cell's discharge and the abscissa the time scale of the responses in milliseconds (msec). The duration of the light stimulus appears as a hatched bar.

the cell. Figure 2 shows how the strength of a short-wave stimulus affects the excitatory response of such a cell in the absence (left) and presence (right) of a long-wave adapting field. Under both conditions the excitatory response increases with stimulus strength up to a maximum. As this maximum is approached the response becomes more prolonged and the maintained discharge rises. These effects are less pronounced in the presence than in the absence of the long-wave field. The long-wave adapting field suppresses the maintained discharge and speeds up the decay of the excitatory response.

Figure 3 illustrates how the peak frequency of the excitatory response depends upon the strength of the short-wave (450 nm) test light in the absence (●) and the presence (▲) of a long wave field. This response increases with stimulus strength up to a saturating level (about 200 impulses sec^{-1}) and then begins to decrease with repetitive supersaturating stimuli. The long-wave field shifts this function horizontally along the intensity axis, making the response less sensitive to the short-wave test light but raising the intensity level at which

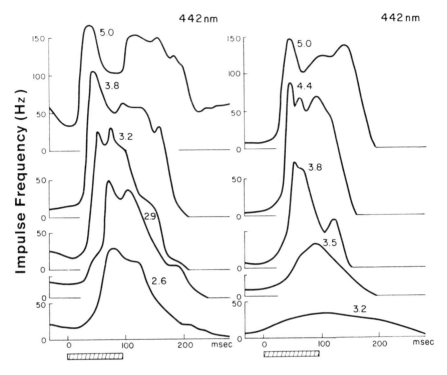

FIG. 2   Responses of the ganglion cell of Fig. 1 to a short-wave stimulus (442 nm) of different intensities, shown above each response as $\log_{10}$ quanta pulse^{-1} μm^{-2} on the retina. The responses on the left are obtained in the absence of an adapting field; those on the right are obtained in the presence of a yellow (Corning filter 3482) adapting field of approximately 10^{11} quanta sec^{-1} mm^{-2} on the retina. The ordinate shows the impulse frequency of the response; the abscissa shows the time scale in milliseconds (msec). The duration of the light pulse is shown as a hatched bar.

the response saturates. A short-wave adapting field ($\blacksquare$) merely raises the maintained discharge frequency and eliminates any excitatory response to any spectral stimulus (Fig. 1). The maintained discharge frequency under supersaturating conditions, i.e. repeated supersaturating stimulation or a maintained short-wave adapting field, is lower than the peak discharge to a subsaturating stimulus.

Figure 4 shows the transient changes that occur when a long-wave field is turned on and then turned off in the presence of a supersaturating short-wave (442 nm) stimulus being presented every second. Before the long-wave field goes on, the peak impulse frequency of the response to the short-wave stimulus rises above a relatively high maintained rate but does not reach the frequency obtainable with a repeated but sub-saturating pulse. When the long-wave

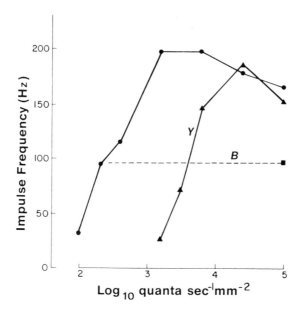

FIG. 3   The relationship between the peak impulse frequency of the cell, the responses of which are illustrated in Figs 2 and 3, to a short-wave (442 nm) test pulse and the strength of the stimulus in the absence (●) and in the presence of a yellow (Corning filter 3482) (▲) and a blue (Corning 5543) (■) adapting field. The strengths of these adapting fields are approximately 10^{11} quanta sec^{-1} mm^{-2} on the retina. The hatched line representing the responses on the blue adapting light reflects the maintained discharge frequency of the cell; under these conditions no excitatory response can be elicited from the cell at any stimulus strength.

adapting field goes on, the maintained discharge frequency of the cell is totally suppressed. The peak discharge frequency of the response to the short-wave stimulus is lower than it is in the absence of the long-wave field but the amplitude of this response remains relatively high because it rises above a low maintained frequency. After about 5 seconds, the maintained discharge frequency begins to increase concomitantly with an increase in the response to the short-wave test pulse. After about 20 seconds in the presence of the long-wave field, the maintained discharge frequency has increased even more and the response to the short-wave test pulse exceeds in amplitude and peak frequency the response elicited in the absence of the long-wave field. The latter condition is essentially the steady-state response of the cell under these conditions.

When the adapting light is turned off, there is a great increase in the maintained discharge frequency, reaching the same level that occurs when the

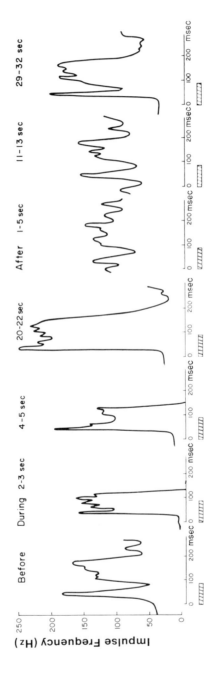

FIG. 4   Responses of the cell illustrated in the previous figures to a supersaturing short-wave (442 nm) test pulse in the absence and then at different times following the onset and offset of a yellow adapting field. The figure illustrates a transient reduction in the peak frequency of the response just as the yellow field has been put on and then just after this field has been removed. The ordinate shows the impulse frequency scale (Hz) and the abscissa the time scale (msec). The duration of the test stimulus is shown as a hatched bar.

excitatory response has been saturated by a strong short-wave adapting field. Concomitantly the excitatory response to the short-wave test light is eliminated just as it is when the response has been saturated by a short-wave field. The maintained discharge frequency recovers in the dark over a period of 10 to 20 seconds concomitantly with the steady-state response to the short-wave test pulse. The long-wave field is able to unsaturate the excitatory rsponse after it has been present for several seconds and then saturate the same response for several seconds immediately as it goes off. Evidently the saturating mechanism must occur at a point which is accessible to the inhibitory mid-spectral cone signal.

These effects of the long-wave adapting field depend upon its strength. Figure 5 shows how increasing strengths of such a field alter the excitatory response to a short-wave test pulse. The weakest (Fig. 5, above) causes an immediate inhibition of the maintained discharge and a reduction in both the amplitude and peak frequency of the excitatory response. Within 5 to 7 seconds the response to the short-wave test pulse has increased in amplitude and peak frequency although the maintained discharge frequency of the cell remains totally inhibited. Within 8 to 12 seconds a low level of maintained activity appears and now the excitatory response to the short-wave test pulse has become maximal. A stronger long-wave adapting field (Fig. 5, middle) causes a similar effect but the maintained discharge frequency of the cell begins to return more rapidly and the excitatory response to the short-wave pulse reaches its maximum sooner. At 8 to 12 seconds, which is representative of the steady-state response, the maintained discharge of the cell has risen to a higher level than it was in the presence of a weaker long-wave field and the excitatory response to the short-wave pulse is reduced. With the strongest long-wave field (Fig. 5, below) the maintained discharge frequency rises even more rapidly and within 8 to 12 seconds reaches saturating levels. Concomitantly, the excitatory response to the short-wave test pulse disappears. Under these conditions there can be no further depression of the excitatory response when the long-wave field is turned off because the excitatory response is already saturated. We interpret these changes to occur because the midspectral cones light-adapt and this decreases the inhibitory input to this cell and the long-wave field begins to activate the short-wave sensitive cones directly as it becomes stronger. It is the latter phenomenon which ultimately drives the cell into saturation in the excitatory state.

Discussion

We would like to suggest a synaptic model that can explain the previously described phenomena (Fig. 6). The critical synapse in this circuit is that between the short-wave sensitive cones and their bipolar cells (Fig. 6a). We assume that the short-wave sensitive cones release a Na^+ conductance decreasing and

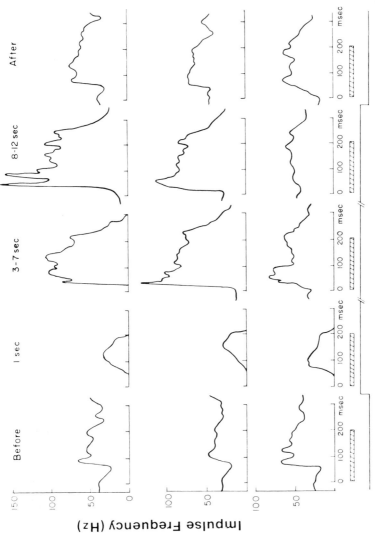

FIG. 5   Responses of a primate retinal ganglion cell which is also excited by the short-wave sensitive cones and inhibited by longer wavelength sensitive cone mechanism(s) to a supersaturating short-wave (450 nm) test pulse before and after strong yellow (Corning filter 3484) adapting field has been turned on over the cell's receptive field and then after it has been turned off. The adapting field is approximately 10^{11}, 5×10^{11} and 10^{12} quanta sec^{-1} mm^{-2} on the retina for the upper, middle and lower sets of responses respectively. The ordinate shows the impulse frequency of the cell's discharge (Hertz) and the abscissa shows the time scale in milliseconds (msec). The lowest shows the time course of the adapting field.

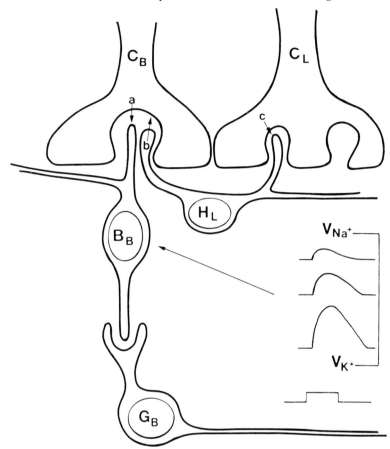

FIG. 6 A hypothetical synaptic circuit for the short-wave sensitive ganglion cell system (G_B) in primate retina. The short-wave sensitive cones (C_B) release a hyperpolarizing (Na^+ conductance decreasing) transmitter on to the bipolar cells (B_B) at synapse (a). A horizontal cell system (H_L) releases a hyperpolarizing trans-mitter (presumably increasing K^+ and/or Cl^- conductance) on to the short-wave sensitive cones (C_B) at synapse (b). The longer wavelength sensitive cones (C_L) release an excitatory transmitter on to horizontal cell (H_L) at synapse (c). The bipolar cell (B_B) releases an excitatory transmitter on to ganglion cells (G_B). The inset on the lower right shows how the response of the bipolar cell is altered by the resting potential of the cell. When this bipolar cell (B_B) is depolarized and con-sequently close to the Na^+ equilibrium potential the response of the ganglion cell (G_B) to light activation of the short-wave cones (C_B) is relatively small; when the bipolar cell (B_B) is hyperpolarized and consequently close to the K^+ equilibrium potential, the response of the ganglion cell (G_B) to light activation of the short-wave sensitive cones (C_B) is relatively large.

consequently a sign-reversing transmitter. This transmitter drives the direct pathway for the excitatory response onto the bipolar cell. A second indirect synaptic pathway is assumed linking the midspectral cones with the short-wave sensitive cones via a horizontal cell interneuron. This circuit is considered to employ two synapses, one excitatory (c) between the midspectral cones and a subset of horizontal cells, the other inhibitory (b) between this subset of horizontal cells and the short-wave sensitive cone pedicles. There is unequivocal evidence for such horizontal cell circuits in other retinas (see Toyoda *et al.*, 1982).

Saturation of the excitatory response occurs whenever all the Na^+ channels on the postsynaptic dendrite of the bipolar cell are opened which occurs whenever the transmitter released by the short-wave sensitive cones is completely stopped. This can be produced whenever the short-wave sensitive cones absorb sufficient light or the midspectral cones are sufficiently darkened. The former hyperpolarizes the short-wave sensitive cones directly; the latter hyperpolarize the short-wave sensitive cones indirectly by depolarizing the horizontal cell which then releases an inhibitory (hyperpolarizing) transmitter on the short-wave sensitive cones. If the amplitude of these inputs is sufficient, all of the transmitter released by the short-wave sensitive cone will stop and consequently any further light stimulation of this cone will become ineffective, i.e. the excitatory response will be saturated. If such saturation were to occur by light stimulation of the short-wave sensitive cones, then this could be counteracted by light stimulation of the midspectral cones because this would depolarize the short-wave cones and release more transmitter.

Strong light stimulation of the midspectral cones would lead to the release of large amounts of transmitter by the short wave cones and this would hyperpolarize the bipolar cell and inhibit the maintained activity of the ganglion cell. Under these conditions the bipolar cell will have a membrane potential close to the K^+ equilibrium potential so that any increase in Na^+ conductance produced by light activation of the short-wave sensitive cones would have a stronger effect on the bipolar cell's membrane potential than it would when the bipolar is depolarized and closer to the Na^+ equilibrium potential. This would tend to enhance the detection of a white (blue and yellow) light in a yellow background.

This synaptic circuit provides a way to explain why there is a transient depression of the amplitude of the short-wave sensitive cone response at both the onset and offset of a long-wave adapting field. At the onset of such a field, the short-wave cones are strongly depolarized, releasing, we assume, more than enough transmitter to block all of the Na^+ channels on the postsynaptic membrane of the bipolar cell. When this occurs any direct hyperpolarization of the short-wave cones by light will only be able to "pull up the slack", i.e. reduce the residual transmitter concentration. In a sense we suggest that the synapse (a) becomes saturated in the hyperpolarized state. As the midspectral cones adapt to the long-wave field, the amount of transmitter released by the short-wave cones is reduced and now light stimulation of the short-wave cone can again begin to modulate the bipolar cell's membrane potential. Since the bipolar is close to the K^+ equilibrium potential each Na^+ channel that is opened will have a relatively strong depolarizing effect on the membrane potential but since there will be a relatively high concentration of transmitter molecules in the subsynaptic environment, this effect will be more short lived and consequently the excitatory response will decay more rapidly.

When the long-wave adapting field is turned off, the previously light-adapted midspectral cones and their corresponding horizontal cell input will be strongly depolarized. This will strongly hyperpolarize the short-wave cones and consequently stop most or all of the transmitter release of these cones. This will saturate the synapse (a) in the depolarizing direction. This saturation will gradually subside as the midspectral cones dark-adapt. The off-depolarizing transients seen in horizontal cells usually occur after a light stimulus has been left on for some time (Gouras, 1960) and consequently after the cones are well light-adapted. A flickering stimulus might not produce such a pronounced depolarizing transient and consequently not produce transient tritanopia (Reeves, personal communication).

The phenomenon that the current model fails to explain is why the maintained discharge frequency at saturation in the excitatory state is less than the peak discharge frequency. This is not a major problem since such an effect could be due to some form of adaptation at either the receptor or bipolar cell. The critical element and perhaps the most iconoclastic aspect of this model is that it puts saturation on the bipolar rather than on the receptor cell of the short-wave sensitive cone system. It is only by doing this that one can allow the horizontal cell interneuron to exert sufficient control on the excitatory response. Putting saturation in the outer segment would greatly reduce the opportunity for a horizontal cell to modulate this response in a way that can easily explain all the observed phenomena. One could also postulate an amacrine cell mediated model but the experiments of Valeton and van Norren (1979) showing that transient tritanopia occurs in the b-wave of the electro-retinogram imply that it occurs at or before the external plexiform layer of the retina, where there is very little amacrine cell involvement.

The synaptic model proposed acts like a "window" discriminator reducing the excitatory response in both the excitatory and inhibitory directions. This is consistent with a formal model of Pugh and Mollon (1979), which postulates that the so called yellow–blue opponent channel produces its maximum signal when it is not polarized greatly in either direction. It must also be understood that the short-wave sensitive ganglion cell system is considered to be an early stage in the formation of such a channel and at this stage signals only the strength of the activation of the short-wave sensitive cones and in this respect is at odds with the Pugh–Mollon idea.

Acknowledgements

This was was supported by the National Institutes of Health Research Grant EY 02591, a Center Grant from the National Retinitis Pigmentosa Foundation, in part by a Professorship Award from Research to Prevent Blindness, Inc. and a PHS International Research Fellowship to E.Z. (1FO5T W 02429) We thank Heinz Rosskothen, Anne M. Leitch, Professor Eberhard Dodt, Drs James Hart and H. M. Eggers for assistance.

References

Gouras, P. (1960). Graded potentials of Bream retina. *J. Physiol., Lond.* **152**, 487–505.

Gouras, P. (1968). Identification of cone mechanisms in monkey ganglion cells. *J. Physiol., Lond.* **199**, 533–547.

Gouras, P. and Zrenner, E. (1979a). Enhancement of luminance flicker by color-opponent mechanisms. *Science* **205**, 587–589.

Gouras, P. and Zrenner, E. (1979b). The blue sensitive cone system. *Excerpt. Med. Int. Congr. Ses.* **450/1**, 379–384.

Gouras, P. and Zrenner, E. (1981). Color Vision: A Review from a neurophysiological perspective. *Progr. Sens. Physiol.* **1**, 139–179.

Gouras, P. and Eggers, H. (1982a). Ganglion cells mediating the signals of blue sensitive cones in primate retina detect white–yellow borders independently of brightness. *Vision Res.* **22**, 675–679.

Gouras, P. and Eggers, H. M. (1982b). Retinal responses to color contrast. ARVO abstract 22, 176.

Gouras, P. and Eggers, H. M. (in press). Responses of primate retinal ganglion cells to moving spectral contrast. *Vision Res.*

Mollon, J. D. (1982). Color Vision. *Ann. Rev. Psychol.* **33**, 41–85.

Pugh, E. N., Mollon, J. D. (1979). A Theory of the π_1 and π_3 color mechanisms of Stiles. *Vision Res.* **19**, 293–312.

Toyoda, J., Kujiraoka, T. and Fujimoto, M. (1982). The role of L type horizontal cells in the opponent-color process. *Color Res. and Application* (2) Part 2: 152–154.

Valeton, J. M. and van Norren, D. (1979). Retinal site of transient tritanopia. *Nature* **280**, 488–490.

Zrenner, E. and Gouras, P. (1981). Characteristics of the blue sensitive cone mechanism in primate retinal ganglion cells. *Vision Res.* **21**, 1605–1609.

Blue and Green Increment-Thresholds on a Sine-Wave Varying Yellow

H. G. SPERLING, T. VIANCOUR, J. MATHENY and L. MEHARG

Introduction and Method

Following the discovery by Stiles (1977) that immediately following adaptation to a large yellow field of high intensity there is a drop in sensitivity to short-wave stimuli and Mollon and Polden's (1977) parametric exploration of the nature of this effect, there have been a number of demonstrations that post-receptoral interactions can be isolated and studied by psychophysical means. It is clear from microspectrophotometric data on cones that the yellow adapting light is very little absorbed by the short-wave receptors themselves and consequently cannot directly affect their sensitivity. Consequently the evident inhibition of short-wave sensitivity must be via an inhibitory pathway from long-wave receptors acting upon the short-wave receptors or upon the pathway from the short-wave receptors to higher orders. This was further established by Mollon and Polden's (1977) silent substitution of a green for a blue adapting field, the two fields being adjusted to have equal effects on short-wave targets in the steady state: the inhibition of short-wave sensitivity still occurred when the blue field was turned off and replaced by the green.

Important to an understanding of this phenomenon is the time course of change in sensitivity. This has been approached by Stiles using repeated square-wave flashes of the background of thirty seconds duration with fifteen-second off periods in which he presented the test flash at 2, 5, 8, 11 and 14 seconds following offset. Mollon and Polden used an 18-second adapting duration interrupted by a three-second dark interval and tested with 18-millisecond flashes at different delay times after offset. Both studies found relatively long effects requiring at least two seconds to return to the sensitivity obtained in the presence of the yellow background and frequently up to 15 seconds. With the exception of a single experiment by Stiles himself (Stiles, 1977), no effort has been made to study the minimum response time of the effect. Since there are many possible retinal pathways, including feedback on the receptors themselves and lateral interactions acting upon bipolar or upon ganglion cells, which might account for the effect, it appears desirable to obtain further information on the temporal characteristics involved, in order to help identify the pathway.

We came to study these questions out of an interest in relating experiments which we had been performing on excised primate retina *in vitro* with different wavelengths of steady and sine-wave modulated stimuli in our attempts to label the color receptors with cytochemical agents. We (Sperling, Harcombe and Johnson, 1982) had found that one of these, tritiated-2-deoxyglucose, heavily labelled cones that had been incubated for 10 minutes in darkness and was largely excluded from pieces of the same retina incubated in the presence of moderately intense white light. Narrow-band 580-nm yellow light produced heavy labelling in widely separated cones spaced approximately the way blue-sensitive cones had been found with another cytochemical technique, the NBT-diformazan reaction (Marc and Sperling, 1977). In an attempt to improve the consistency of our results, we resorted to sine-wave modulated light hoping to reduce the effects of adaptation. We were surprised to find that 2 Hz modulated yellow of the same wavelength and intensity as in our steady light experiments produced even less labelling than had been obtained with comparable flux densities of white light. This raised the possibility that we were seeing a kindred phenomenon to transient tritanopia, acting at the photo-receptor level. Therefore, we decided to vary the frequency of sine-wave stimulation with human subjects, in order to obtain the frequency range over which blue sensitivity was affected, and to then return to the excised monkey retina with temporal frequencies that lay both within and outside the range over which blue sensitivity was affected, providing a quantitative test of the relationship between the cytochemical and psychophysical phenomena. At the time, we also recognized the potential value of a psychophysical technique identical to the increment-threshold procedures, which could introduce time-series analysis of the effects of adapting lights. Very brief test flashes presented at different phases of a sine-wave background might probe the temporal filtering effects of the visual system without disturbing them. We had long wondered why De Lange (1957) and his many followers had never used this simple technique to relate temporal phenomena to threshold sensitivity data.

As shown in Fig. 1, a two-channel Maxwellian view optical system provided a 13 degree diameter circular background which was filtered to 580 ± 6 nm with an interference filter and was sine-wave modulated by fixed and variable speed

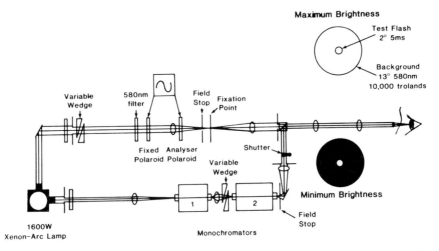

FIG. 1   Diagram of two-channel Maxwellian view optical system used to provide sine-wave varying 13° background and spectral test flashes, as shown.

rotating polarizers. A neutral density wedge provided 10,000 trolands peak retinal illumination. Centered in the background field, a 2 degree test flash of 5 milliseconds duration could be brought to threshold by means of a second variable neutral density wedge. The test flash wavelength was selected by the double monochromator pathway. Two test flash wavelengths, a 445-nm blue of 6-nm bandwidth and a 535-nm green of 6-nm bandwidth were used. Fixation was obtained by an opaque dot positioned in the center of the test flash area.

Thresholds were obtained for either of the two test wavelengths at each of eight equally spaced phases of the sine-wave varying background in each session by the serial method of limits, using both ascending and descending series. Two ascending and two descending thresholds were obtained for each phase angle, for each wavelength in each sitting for a single background frequency. These were averaged to obtain mean threshold values. Background frequency was varied from 0.5 Hz to 16 Hz.

Results

Figure 2 shows mean threshold values for four frequencies of the background, for the blue and green test lights, at different phases of the sine-wave varying background (represented as the solid curves). The mean values, on the log quantum scale, show that the 535-nm green thresholds varied in phase with the background but with decreasing amplitude with increasing background frequency. Also, it is apparent from Fig. 2 that the blue, 445-nm, test light thresholds varied more or less in counter-phase to the background. Data such

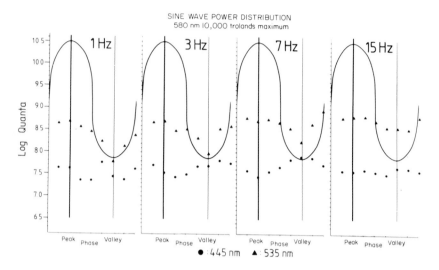

FIG. 2   Threshold variation of green (535-nm: triangles) and blue (445-nm: circles) test stimuli (shown on a $\log_{10}$ quanta scale) at different phases of a sine-wave varying yellow background (580-nm: solid curve).

as these were obtained for one highly trained subject on whom it had been shown that the 10,000 troland 580-nm yellow isolated his π_1 mechanism at threshold. Data were obtained in separate sessions for 18 temporal background frequencies from 0.5 Hz to 16 Hz.

A fast Fourier transform was performed on the two sets of threshold data. Figure 3 shows the harmonic analysis separately for the 535-nm green and 445-nm blue stimuli. Clearly most of the variation in power, as a function of frequency, was found in the first harmonic, with both test wavelengths. The two wavelengths, however, behaved very differently as a function of frequency. The green (535-nm) thresholds showed the greatest effect at the lowest frequency and the amplitude of effect gradually declined as a function of frequency, thus displaying the characteristics of a low-pass filter. The power distribution of the blue (445-nm) thresholds showed high power in the second harmonic at 0.5 and 1 Hz and then the second harmonic rapidly fell to baseline level, meaning that the thresholds followed both on and off parts of the background variation at very low frequencies. In the first harmonic there was little power below 2 Hz, then a roughly rectangular band-pass from 2 to 10 Hz, then beyond 10 Hz there was a return to base-line power. Clearly, the blue thresholds behaved like a 2 to 10 Hz band-pass filter as distinct from the low-pass filter characteristics of the green thresholds.

As seen in Fig. 4, where we analyzed for phase shifts, the thresholds for the two test wavelengths again behave very differently. There is no phase shift

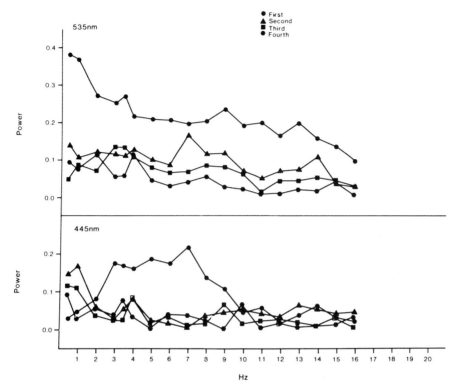

FIG. 3   Fourier harmonics – power as a function of frequency of 535-nm and 445-nm test light thresholds, against a sine-wave varying 580-nm background for frequencies from 0.5 Hz to 16 Hz.

revealed in the data for the green test lights. They simply follow the background with diminished amplitude as frequency is increased. The thresholds for the blue test light, however, show a continuous phase shift over the frequency range of their band-pass. The phase lag plot of Fig. 4 is clearly linear up to about 5 Hz. To the extent that the power spectrum of the first harmonic in Fig. 3 can be interpreted as a rectangular band-pass, the linear shift in phase lag can be interpreted as consistent with a fixed line delay or latency in the yellow to blue inhibitory pathway. The slope of the straight line fitted to the phase lag plot was calculated and yielded a time constant of 60 milliseconds. Although the interpretation of the phase information in these terms is clearly not conclusive, it may be taken as highly suggestive of such a fixed delay or latency. Further data collection is planned on this point. It should be noted that a 60 millisecond latency is long for neural pathways, although horizontal cells in fish have been shown to have latencies nearly this long (Spekreijse and

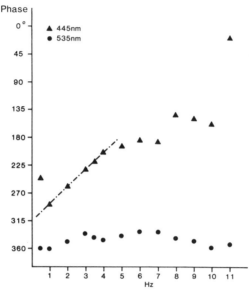

FIG. 4   Phase lag (in degrees) as a function of frequency for the 445-nm (triangles) and 535-nm (circles) test stimulus thresholds, on a sine-wave varying 580-nm background.

Norton, 1970). Another slow mechanism which has been suggested is that release from the inhibitory signal from long- and/or middle-wavelength cones drives the blue receptors or their bipolar cells close to their sodium reversal potential by post-inhibitory rebound. Recovery from this state can be very slow.

In summary: (1) we have shown that a sine-wave analysis of threshold variation may be performed using a brief test flash on a sine-wave varying background in the increment-threshold type of experiment. (2) The variation in thresholds for a blue and green test light on a yellow background are consistently different, in keeping with the fact that the green receptors themselves absorb the yellow energy while the blue ones absorb very little of that energy. They are influenced via an inhibitory pathway from long-wave receptors. The green response varies in phase with the background, with diminishing amplitude as a function of frequency, in a fashion characteristic of a low-pass filter. (3) The blue thresholds reveal a yellow-to-blue inhibitory pathway that responds out of phase with the background and has the characteristics of a band-pass filter with a frequency response which extends from 2 to 10 Hz. (4) A phase analysis shows no phase shift for the green channel but a continuous phase shift for the yellow–blue inhibitory pathway which, given certain reservations, is consistent with a fixed delay or latency in that pathway of 60 milliseconds.

References

De Lange, H. Dzn. (1957). *Attenuation characteristics and phase shift characteristics of the human fovea-cortex systems in relation to flicker fusion phenomena.* Thesis, Delft.

Marc, R. E. and Sperling, H. G. (1977). Chromatic organization of primate cones. *Science* **196**, 454–456.

Mollon, J. D. and Polden, P. G. (1977). An anomaly in the response of the eye to light of short wavelengths. *Phil. Trans. roy. Soc. B.* **278**, 207–240.

Spekreijse, H. and Norton, A. L. (1970). The dynamic characteristics of color-coded s-potentials. *J. gen. Physiol.* **56**, 1–15.

Stiles, W. S. (1977). Early threshold observations of transient tritanopia. *Phil. Trans. roy. Soc. B.* **278**, 233–238.

Sperling, H. G., Harcombe, E. S. and Johnson, C. (1982). Stimulus controlled labelling of cones in macaque retina using ^{3}H-2-D-Deoxyglucose. From: *Structure of the Eye* (ed. Hollyfield, J. B.), pp. 55–60. Elsevier-North Holland Co., Amsterdam.

Color Sensation, Color Perception and Mathematical Models of Color Vision

JOHN J. McCANN and KAREN L. HOUSTON

> By seeing objects of the same colour under these various illuminations, in spite of differences of illumination, we learn to form a correct idea of the colours of bodies, that is, to judge how such a body would look in white light; and since we are interested only in the colour that the body retains permanently, we are not conscious at all of the separate sensations which contribute to form our judgement. H. von Helmholtz (1962 edition)

In "The Science of Color" the Committee on Colorimetry of the Optical Society of America (1953) makes a very important distinction between sensation and perception, following the definitions introduced by the Scottish philosopher Thomas Reid (1822). The Committee defines sensation as the "mode of mental functioning that is directly associated with stimulation of the organism". It defines perception as the "mode of mental functioning that includes the combination of different sensations and the utilization of past experience in recognizing the objects and facts from which the present stimulation arises". The distinction centers on the roles of cognition and recognition in the perception of objects in life-like complex images.

Helmholtz hypothesized that the colors we see are perceptions that involve a number of different sensations. If we consider the visual pathway in more detail, we note that the photopigments in the visual receptors respond to the spectral-energy distribution of the light entering the eye. That spectral-energy distribution is determined both by the spectral energy of the illumination falling on objects and the spectral reflectance of the objects themselves. The Helmholtz hypothesis in effect attributes to the visual system the ability to

COLOUR VISION
ISBN 0 12 000000 0

discriminate between the physical entities of reflectance and illumination. This conclusion is assumed to follow from the fact that observers report constant colors from objects in very different illuminations.

The constant appearance of objects under widely varying conditions has been investigated in both chromatic and achromatic experiments. Examples of chromatic experiments are those of Katz (1935) and of Land (1974). Such experiments show that objects appear very nearly the same, despite large changes in the spectral distribution of the illumination. Achromatic experiments demonstrate a similar constancy despite overall changes in the intensity of illumination. Examples of such experiments are those of Gelb (1929) and Land and McCann (1971).

A shadow creates a situation in which the intensity of the illumination is considerably reduced. In fact, a shadow often creates changes in both the spectral distribution and the intensity of the light coming to the observers' eyes. Such a situation is exemplified by the photograph of a lake scene in New Hampshire shown in Plate 5a. The composition of the illumination on the two visible sides of the swimming float in the center of the image is very different. The right side is lighted directly by the morning sun, while the left side, in the shadow, is illuminated by southern skylight and reflections off the water.

There are three totally different ways of measuring the two sides of the float.

Measure the Physical Stimuli

The physical measurements of the light from the two sides of the float are very different from each other. Measuring the spectra from the original photographic transparency, we calculate the correlated color temperature for the right side to be 3300 K, and for the left side 7000 K.

Conclusion: The two sides are very different.

Measure the Color Sensation

Psychophysical measurements of two sides of the float can determine their color and lightness *sensations*. These measurements could be made, for example, by asking observers to find matches for the left side and the right side from a catalogue of colored papers. An observer would select similar, but clearly distinguishable matches.

Conclusion: The two sides are slightly different.

Measure the Perception

In a third measurement, we might ask the same observer about the material properties of the float. Is the float painted uniformly with the same paint; that is, does it have the same reflectance on both sides? What are the illuminants; what are their spectral characteristics; where are they located with respect to the image? It is easy for the observer to report that the float is painted with white paint and that the sun is low and off to the right. The *perception* of the float is that it is composed of the same material both on the left and the right.

Conclusion: The two sides are the same.

Thus, identical sets of wavelength-energy distributions give rise to three entirely different conclusions. Depending on the level of the question we ask, the sides of the float can be described as very different, slightly different, or the same. In thinking about the visual mechanisms underlying these results, it becomes apparent that *perception* is a much more difficult concept to define and model than *sensation*. Perception requires many things, including the recognition of objects.

Reflectance and Illumination vs. Edges and Gradients

Assuming that the human visual mechanism actually establishes reflectance distinct from illumination implies that any computational model of the visual system must be able to make the same distinction. Calculating reflectance and illumination properties entails solving the equation

$$\text{Energy}(x,y) = \text{Reflectance}(x,y) \times \text{Illumination}(x,y)$$

given only the array of energies for all points in the image (x, y). This approach is discussed, for example, by Marr (1982), Buchsbaum (1980), Horn (1975), and Rubin and Richards (in press).

We make the assumption that the visual system cannot distinguish sensations associated with reflectance from sensations associated with illumination, at each point (x, y). Rather, we assume that the visual system generates sensations that correspond to patterns of luminance. We assume that perceptions of objects are then calculated from arrays of sensations. Such perceptions can recognize objects and illuminants.

A strategy for calculating sensations can be based on experimental observations showing that the visual system responds differently to a given change in luminance depending upon whether that change is abrupt or gradual. Abrupt changes in luminance are associated with large changes in sensation; gradual changes are associated with small changes in sensation. This point was made by Craik (1966) in his experiments with a spinning disk. He made a disk of white paper with a 45-degree black sector. On one edge of the black sector was a saw-tooth shaped projection such that along the radius there was an abrupt increase, and then a gradual decrease of the black portion. When the disk was spun, the observer reported seeing a uniform, light center and a darker surround. Except for the region of the saw-tooth, the inner and outer regions of the spinning disk send the same amount of light to the eye. However, the visual system regards the stimulus as being composed of two nearly uniform, distinct sensations – the central region appears lighter than the outer ring because the abrupt change in luminance creates a larger change in sensation than does the gradual change in luminance. Other experiments by Cornsweet (1970), O'Brien (1958), Land and McCann (1971), and Land (1974) also illustrate this point.

In more complex situations the appearance of a segment of an image need not be simply related to the intensity of the light coming from that segment (Hering, 1964; Katz, 1935; Land and McCann, 1971; Mckee, and Taylor, 1976). Plate 5b is a photograph of a small part of the Black-and-White Mondrian used in an experiment described by Land and McCann (1971). In this experiment a complex array of black-and-white papers is lighted obliquely by a lamp placed below the array so that more light falls on the bottom of the display than on the top. The illumination decreases gradually from bottom to top. In this detail photograph of a part of the image there is a long, white, vertical strip. At point A the paper sends to the eye a certain amount of energy, L. Moving up the strip the amount of light falling on the paper gradually decreases. The intensity measured at B is 1/2 L. There is a small change in the sensation of lightness (range of sensations from white to black) associated with the change of luminance from point A to B. What is of particular interest is that the same change in luminance from L to 1/2 L causes a large change in lightness when presented as an abrupt change at an edge. The point indicated by B' in the lower part of Plate 5b sends to the eye the same amount of light (1/2 L) as does the point B. The sensations associated with B and B' are not the same.

Gradients

The visual system neither responds vigorously to, nor completely ignores, gradients. Gradients are important in the recognition of three-dimensional objects, helping us to distinguish a spherical surface in three dimensions from a planar, circular disk. Gradients provide important information for calculating perceptions (Horn, 1975).

A wide variety of experiments have measured the threshold response to a luminance gradient. These experiments were designed to answer the question, "What is the smallest spatial rate of change on the retina that an observer can detect?" It was found that the gradient threshold is different for different situations, depending on both size and position on the retina. The responses to the two variables are interrelated in such a way as to endow the human visual system with the remarkable property that gradients appear the same over dramatic changes in viewing distance (McCann, Savoy, Hall and Scarpetti,

Plate 5(a).   Photograph of a lake scene in New Hampshire.

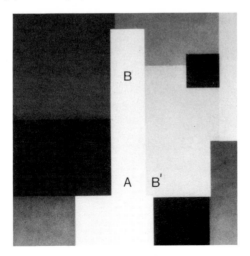

Plate 5(b).   Photograph of a portion of Land and McCann's Black-and-white Mondrian experiment. The ratio of luminance between A and B is equal to that between A and B'. Gradual changes in luminance cause small changes in lightness, whereas abrupt changes in luminance produce large changes in lightness.

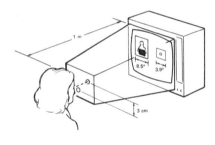

Plate 6.   Images used in the color-matching experiment and Reset Ratio-Product calculations.

1974; Savoy and McCann, 1975; McCann, 1978). This invariance is of considerable advantage because it contributes substantially to the constant appearance of objects at various viewing distances.

Color Matching Experiments

Using the inferences gained from the study of lightness, we return to the general problem of computing color sensations. Land proposed that a particular color sensation is derived from the comparison of three lightness values. Lightnesses are formulated from intercomparisons of sets of independent long-, middle-, and short-wave responsive systems (Land and McCann, 1971; Land, 1964).

In a previous paper (McCann, McKee and Taylor, 1976) the Reset Ratio-Product model for computing lightness was described and used for predicting color sensations in a complex image. The image consisted of a collage of colored matte papers (a "Color Mondrian"). This collage was viewed by an observer under varying conditions of illumination, and color matches were selected for several areas in the image. Calculations were made with the model, using as input only the physical stimulus − the spectral energy distribution coming to the eye from the various patches. The calculation, described more fully later, consists of a sequence of simple arithmetic operations applied to pairs of picture elements in an iterative procedure. The predictions made with the model corresponded very well with the observer matches used to measure color sensations.

More recently, a series of experiments (McCann and Houston, unpublished) in our laboratory have extended the data array from 20×24 to 512×512 pixels and the sampling of the physical stimuli from 18 measurements (one for each paper in the collage) to 262,144 (one for each pixel in the array). The experiments used a set of complex, real-life images (see Plate 6) made under widely differing illumination conditions: tungsten, daylight, and shade. The images were originally recorded on photographic film, then digitized and reproduced on a computer-driven color cathode-ray tube. These images were utilized in two ways: (1) as the stimuli for a series of psychophysical experiments in which observers made color matches to specific areas in the scenes, and (2) as the basis for mathematical computation of the sensations represented by these areas.

In the color-matching experiments, the CRT screen was divided into two parts; on the left was the test image, and on the right, a standard matching display consisting of a central, color-adjustable square in a constant white surround. The observer viewed the two parts of the display through apertures in a black, pyramidal box arranged in such a way that the left eye saw only the test image and the right eye, only the adjustable square. In addition, the eyes were constrained to work alternately; the viewing apertures were separated by 3 cm vertically, so that by raising his head, the observer saw the adjustable square with his right eye and nothing (black) with his left, and by lowering his head he saw the test image with his left eye and nothing with his right.

Each test image included a Macbeth ColorChecker Color Rendition Chart as part of the scene being photographed. The observer's task was to adjust the color appearance of the square in the white surround to obtain the visual match to particular segments in the color chart – these segments were the white square and the six primary hues (blue, green, red, yellow, magenta, and cyan). Because of the markedly different color balance of the illumination in the images, the same test square sends very different spectral energy distributions to the eye in the several cases.

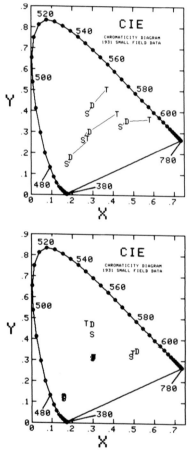

FIG. 1 The top graph shows the physical characteristics, plotted as chromaticities, of the red, green, blue, and white squares in the three test images in Plate 3. Data for tungsten, daylight, and shade are shown as "T", "D", and "S". Observer color matches of the same four squares are shown in the bottom graph. The sensations generated by a particular square in the test images were very similar despite large differences in chromaticities.

Figure 1 (top) shows, as an example, the average chromaticities of the red, green, blue, and white test squares in the three images. The data, plotted on the 1931 CIE diagram, show the large shifts in chromaticities associated with the different illuminants. Observer matches for these stimuli exhibit much smaller variation, as shown in Fig. 1 (bottom), where the average matches made by observer KLH for the same test squares are plotted. These matches were selected under constant illumination conditions using a standard white surround, and so provide quantitative measures of the familiar phenomenon of color constancy.

Mathematical Predictions

Computed sensations for the various test squares are obtained from the Reset Ratio-Product model (McCann, McKee and Taylor, 1976; McCann and Houston, unpublished). The sensations are calculated in the form of lightness values for three overlapping wavelength bands approximating the long-, middle- and short-wave visual pigment absorption curves. In brief summary, the process involves five steps. First the radiant energy coming from the CRT phosphors for each target area is integrated under the pigment curves (Smith and Pokorny, 1975) to produce three input records, analogous to color separations. Each record is then processed separately in accordance with Retinex color mechanism independence (Land, 1974). The second calculation step compares local intensities by taking ratios, and the third step consists in propagating these ratios throughout the entire image by multiplication. Next the image is normalized with respect to white by resetting products greater than unity to 1.00. This normalized product at each image point is averaged with other products computed for the same point and also multiplied by other ratios to form new products at new locations. The final step then averages a large number of such products.

The average product thus computed for each point in the image contains information on the relationship of that point to all other points, and it is this average product that is taken as the predicted lightness for the point in a single waveband. Three such lightness predictions, one for each waveband, constitute the predicted color sensation.

The Reset Ratio-Product algorithm tends to normalize each record independently to its lightest point. This normalization has an effect similar to the application of von Kries coefficients to account for color constancy. The algorithm includes, however, local contrast mechanisms that cause when appropriate the predictions to depart significantly from simple normalization. This is particularly evident in simple displays.

Next we compare the predicted sensations with observer color matches. The calculation for each pixel has a relative value between 0.0 (minimum − black) and 1.0 (maximum − white) for each waveband. We have elected to plot the independent long-, middle-, and short-wave data on three graphs. We now need to scale calculated values so that equal distances on the graphs represent equal increments in lightness. Therefore, the calculated values have been scaled with Glasser's lightness function (Glasser, McKinney, Reilly and Schnelle, 1958). Figure 2 shows a typical set of computer predictions plotted against corresponding experimental matches made by observer KLH. The x-axis values were obtained by averaging the matches for each test square, calculating the long-, middle-, and short-wave integrals of the spectral energy coming from this average matching color patch, normalizing to the corresponding integral for the white surround, and scaling the resulting fraction by Glasser's function.

Figure 2 shows the predicted lightness vs. observed lightness for all the test squares in the image taken in tungsten illumination, daylight illumination and shade. Examination of the graphs reveals good agreement between observed and computed lightness in that the points lie close to the line of unity slope. Similar agreement was found in the older experiments with Mondrian collages (McCann, McKee and Taylor, 1976).

Discussion

The strategy we have adopted for modeling the response of the human visual system to color is based on two observations. The first is philosophical: we consider the distinction between sensation and perception, and elect as a beginning to study sensation only, leaving for a later time the much more difficult task of calculating perception. For purposes of our model, color sensation is defined operationally as the quantity that is measured in observer matching experiments. The second distinction is psychophysical: we believe that the visual system evaluates color by comparing lightnesses in three independent fields (the long-, middle-, and short-wave records), and we observe that lightness is determined by the structure of a scene – its edges and gradients. At the level of sensation, the visual system need not separate reflectance and illumination.

The investigations reported here expand our techniques for studying complex color images. They reconfirm the idea that a normalization-like process is required for predicting color sensations in different illuminations. Various biological mechanisms for normalization have been proposed, such as photopigment bleaching, neural adaptation, and comparison of each image point to an average over the entire image. The computational model used in this paper involves ratios, products, resetting, and averaging of picture elements; there is no analog to photopigment bleaching or neural adaptation. Neither is there a direct comparison of each point to the average of the entire image. No *a priori* information about objects or illuminants is needed. The algorithm provides a procedure for calculating the three independent lightness records required for predicting color sensations. We conclude from the present

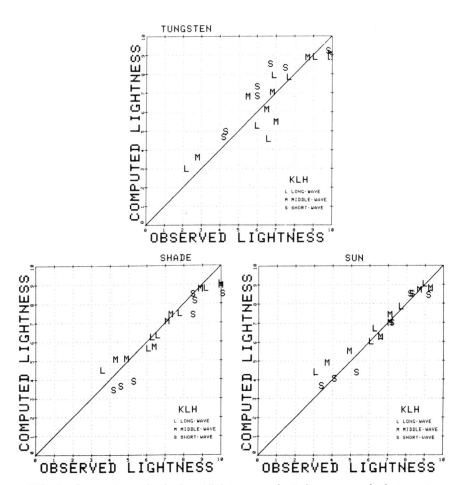

FIG. 2   Comparison of calculated lightness against observer results in tungsten, daylight and shade. The calculated values were obtained from the Reset Ratio-Product model, and the observer results come from binocular matching experiments. The good agreement shows that the model tends to produce accurate predictions of observed color sensation.

experiments that we can calculate a color sensation with reasonable accuracy, given only the array of spectral energy measurements characterizing the original scene.

Acknowledgements

We thank James Burkhardt and W. Alan Stiehl for their assistance with the experiments and calculations.

References

Buchsbaum, G. (1980). *Journal of the Franklin Institute* **310**, 1–26.

Cornsweet, T. N. (1970). *Visual Perception*, pp. 270–279. New York, Academic Press.

Craik, K. J. W. (1966). *The Nature of Psychology*, London, Cambridge University Press.

Gelb, A. (1929). Die "Farbenkonstanz" den Sehdinge. In *Handbuch der normalen und pathologischen Physiologie, Vol. 12* (ed. Bethe, A.). Berlin, Springer.

Glasser, L. G., McKinney, A. H., Reilly, C. D., Schnelle, P. D. (1958). Cube-root color coordinate system. *J. Opt. Soc. Am.* **48**, 736–740.

Helmholtz, H. von (1962). *Physiological Optics* (translated by Southall, J. P. C.). Optical Society of America (reprinted New York, Dover, 1962, Vol. 2, p. 287).

Hering, E. (1964). *Outlines of a Theory of the Light Sense* (translated by Hurvich, L. M. and Jameson, D.). Cambridge, Massachusetts, Harvard University Press.

Horn, B. P. K. (1975). Obtaining shape from shading information. In *The Psychology of Computer Vision* (ed. Winston, P. H.), pp. 115–155. New York, McGraw-Hill.

Katz, D. (1935). *The World of Colour*. London, Kegan Paul, Trench, Trubner and Co.

Land, E. H. (1964). The Retinex. *Am. Scientist* **52**, 247–264.

Land, E. H. (1974). Smitty Stevens' Test of Retinex Theory. In *Sensation and Measurement* (eds Moskowitz, H. R., Scharf, B. and Stevens, J. C.), pp. 363–368. Dordrecht, Holland, Reidel Publishing Co.

Land, E. H. and McCann, J. J. (1971). Lightness and Retinex theory. *J. opt. Soc. Am.* **61**, 1–11.

Land, E. H. (1974). The Retinex theory of color vision. *Proc. roy. Inst. Gt. Britain* **47**, 23–58.

Marr, D. (1982). *Vision*. San Francisco, Freeman.

McCann, J. J. (1978). Visibility of gradients and low spatial frequency sinusoids: evidence for a distance constancy mechanism. *Photogr. Sci. Eng.* **22**, 64–68.

McCann, J. J., McKee, S. P. and Taylor, T. H. (1976). Quantitative studies in Retinex theory. A comparison between theoretical predictions and observer responses to the "Color Mondrian" experiments. *Vision Res.* **16**, 445–458.

McCann, J. J., Savoy, R. L., Hall, J. A., Jr and Scarpetti, J. J. (1974). Visibility of continuous luminance gradients. *Vision Res.* **14**, 917–927.

McCann, J. J., Houston, K. (1983). Calculating Color Sensations from Arrays of Physical Stimulii. IEEE Transactions on Systems, Man, and Cybernetics, Special Issue on Neural and Sensory Information Processing, submitted for publication.

O'Brien, V. (1958). Contour perception, illusion and reality. *J. opt. Soc. Am.* **48**, 112–119.

Optical Society of America, Committee on Colorimetry (1953). *The Science of Color*, pp. 58–59. New York, Crowell.

Reid, T. (1822). *Works of Thomas Reid*. New York, Duyckinck.

Rubin, J. M. and Richards, W. A. *Biological Cybernetics*, in press.

Savoy, R. L. and McCann, J. J. (1975). Visibility of low-spatial-frequency sine-wave targets: Dependence on number of cycles. *J. opt. Soc. Am.* **65**, 343–350.

Smith, V. C., Pokorny, J. (1975). Spectral sensitivity of the foveal cone photopigments between 400 and 500 nm. *Vision Res.* **15**, 161–171.

An Increment-Threshold Evaluation of Mechanisms Underlying Colour Constancy

H. KRASTEL, W. JAEGER and S. BRAUN

Introduction

Most photographers have suffered at least once the disappointment that comes from taking colour photographs with daylight film in artificial illumination. The photographer's error arises because of his experience that colours sub-jectively remain more or less constant in illuminations of different colour temperature (Hering, 1925), a phenomenon generally known as colour constancy.

A second form of colour constancy is seen in the observation that objects do not markedly change their apparent colour as they move about the visual field – a common everyday experience, from which small-field phenomena merely form exceptions (v. Kries, 1897; Willmer, 1950). The classic results of Stiles and Crawford (1933) show considerable differences in spectral increment sensitivity at different retinal loci and at first glance seem to contradict the subjectively experienced colour constancy. But it should be noted that at all locations Stiles and Crawford used small targets of constant size.

In this paper we report two types of experiment. In the first type, we determined whether colour constancy has a correlate in spectral increment thresholds obtained while the subject observed a target and background through different colour conversion filters. In the second type of experiment, spectral increment thresholds were measured at different retinal eccentricities and with stimuli of different diameter.

COLOUR VISION
ISBN 0 12 000000 0

Methods

Stimulus light from a Xenon arc passed through monochromatic interference and neutral density filters. The stimulus was added to the adaptation beam by means of a mixing cube. Both stimulus and adaptation beam were then focussed on the front of a fibre-optics bundle, the exit pupil of which was covered by a frosted glass plate. Stimulus and adapting illumination were presented congruently and were surrounded by a white cardboard screen, which served as a conditioning field. The white adaptation light had a luminance of 630 or 1260 cd m^{-2}. Calibrations were done with an EG&G radiometer and with an SEI photometer. The temporal parameters of the stimulus (300 msec duration, 1 Hz repetition, or 500 msec, 0.5 Hz) were controlled by a square-wave stimulator connected to an electro-optical shutter and were monitored by a photocell and an oscilloscope. Each threshold was determined by a "zero reference" method (such as used by Harris and Kalmus, 1949) and was defined as that lowest intensity of the test spot that could be clearly distinguished from a "zero stimulus", produced by inserting a black shutter in the path of the stimulus light. Intensity was changed in steps of 0.16 log units and the scatter in the threshold data did not exceed one intensity step. Using such a detection criterion, three-peaked spectral increment-threshold curves could be obtained, in accordance with the results of e.g. Sperling and Harwerth (1971), King-Smith and Carden (1976) and Zrenner (1977).

Results

Effects of Colour Conversion Filters

We compared the photopic increment spectral sensitivities of the naked eye to those found during observation through colour-conversion filters. The effects of two filters were investigated:

(1) Schott Bg 34, a bluish colour-conversion filter of −150 mired. The spectral transmission curve of this filter is shown in Fig. 1a.
(2) Schott FG 15, an amber colour-conversion filter of about 120 mired, which converts daylight of approximately 6000 K into light with a colour temperature of about 3200 K (which resembles the light of an incandescent halogen lamp).

FIG. 1 (opposite)   A threshold correlate of colour constancy in illuminations of different colour temperature. (a) Individual spectrophotometric transmission curve of the bluish colour-conversion filter Schott BG 34/2 mm (Uvikon 820 spectrophotometer, slit band-width 2 nm). (b) Comparative examination of spectral increment sensitivity of the naked eye (open symbols) and during observation through the BG 34 filter (dotted symbols).

Only minor deviations of radiant flux at the exit of the stimulus light path are

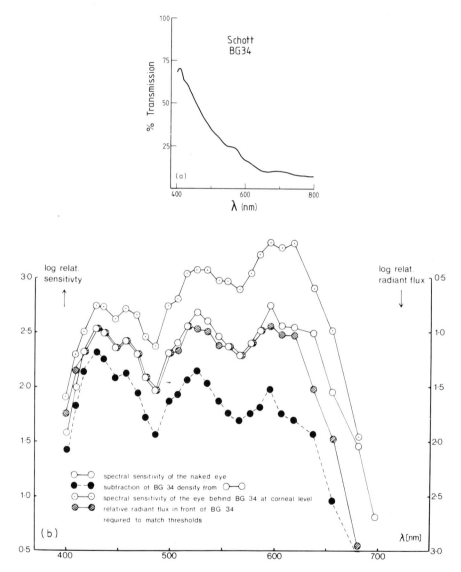

FIG. 1 (contd.) required to match the threshold criterion regardless of whether spectral sensitivity is determined without (open symbols) or with the colour conversion filter mounted in front of the eye (hatched symbols).

Stimuli of 5 deg of subtense, 500 msec duration, 0.5 Hz repetition are presented to the retinal center. They are superimposed on an adaptive field of 5 deg and 630 cd m^{-2} of white Xenon light. A white conditioning surround of 12.6 cd m^{-2} covers a visual angle of 40 deg. Sensory increment thresholds were obtained by means of a zero-reference procedure. The filled symbols represent an arithmetical subtraction of the filter's optical density from the spectral sensitivity of the naked eye.

When the subject observed through the filters, there were only minor deviations from that radiant flux at the exit of the stimulus light path required at threshold when observation was by the naked eye (compare the open and the hatched symbols in Fig. 1).

Adaptational processes almost completely compensated for the attenuating effects of the filter in different spectral regions. In the figure the dotted circles show the actual sensitivity at the cornea when the BG 34 filter has been positioned before the eye. Observing through the FG 15 filter resulted in curves looking like a mirror-image of the curves in Fig. 1: sensitivity throughout the short-wavelength range of the spectrum increases behind the amber FG 15 filter so as to balance its attenuating effects on radiation.

Effects of Stimulus Size and Eccentricity

Under conditions of photopic adaptation (630 or 1260 cd m^{-2}) and central fixation, spectral sensitivities were compared for fields of 4 deg and 69 deg diameter. Though the increase in stimulated area amounted to about 2.5 log units, only small changes in the level and the shape of the three-peaked spectral increment-threshold curve were observed (Fig. 2).

Measurements were made at several eccentricities of spectral increment thresholds for fields of various sizes. It was found that comparable curves could in general be achieved if the stimulus was enlarged towards the periphery. An exception was that short-wavelength sensitivity was depressed in the case of the foveal targets. The difference between foveal and eccentric sensitivities in the range 400–500 nm (Fig. 3) roughly resembles the absorption spectrum for macular pigment (Wald 1964).

Discussion

Our observations with colour-conversion filters demonstrate an adjustment of increment thresholds that parallels the process of colour constancy. Reproducible identification of visual stimuli (e.g. in illuminations of different spectral composition) is, with regard to the teleonomic point of view (Kalmus, 1978), a main concern in visual perception. Why then, does the depression of short-wavelength sensitivity for foveal targets occur? Is there no adaptive mechanism, balancing the filtering effects of the macular pigment? Ruddock's (1972) description of ophthalmoscopically detectable macular pigment at the eye fundus of a subject lacking any detectable influence of macular pigment on psychophysical data strongly argues in favour of balancing adaptational processes in the spectral shadow of the macular pigment. Thus, two explanations for our results may be considered:

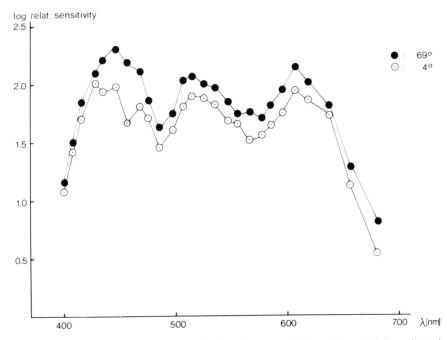

FIG. 2   Spectral increment sensitivity for the centrally fixated small (4 deg, dotted symbols) and large (69 deg, filled symbols) field. Stimuli of 500 msec duration were presented at a repetition rate of 0.5 Hz, congruently with the white adapting field of 1260 cd m^{-2}. Conditioning white surround: 12.6 cd m^{-2}. Enlargement of the stimulated area by about 2.5 log units has little effect on level and shape of the three-peaked sensitivity curve.

1) The filter effects will show up in spectral luminosity only when macular pigment density exceeds that level which can be compensated for by adaptational processes.
2) The foveal reduction of short-wavelength sensitivity is − at least in part and in addition to the first process − due to reduced blue cone density (as shown by Sperling, 1980).

Our findings at different retinal eccentricity confirm those of Johnson and Massof (1982). Provided stimulus area is increased, spectral sensitivity functions of comparable form can be generated as the stimulus becomes more eccentric. For adequate activation of the centre-surround colour antagonism, a test spot of appropriate diameter should stimulate centre and surround of receptive fields simultaneously. Our findings reflect other evidence that receptive fields, estimated psychophysically or electrophysiologically, become larger as eccentricity increases (Ransom-Hogg and Spillmann, 1980; Diehl and

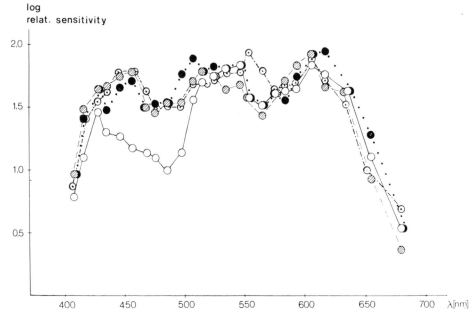

FIG. 3   Spectral increment sensitivity at different retinal eccentricities. Target size was chosen in order to achieve comparable levels of sensitivity at different retinal locations. Stimulus diameter at 0 deg (open symbols): 0.9 deg; at 3.2 deg eccentricity (hatched symbols): 2.6 deg; at 10 deg eccentricity (filled symbols): 4.8 deg; at 33 deg eccentricity (dotted symbols): 16 deg. Stimulus duration 300 msec, 1 Hz repetition. Stimuli are superimposed congruently on the adapting illumination of 630 cd m^{-2} of white Xenon light and surrounded by a conditioning field of 12.6 cd m^{-2}.

Zrenner, 1980). Taken together, Figs 2 and 3 suggest that for large stimuli there will be relatively little change in spectral sensitivity as the stimulus moves from centre to periphery.

The phenomenon of colour constancy doubtlessly is also related to central processing of visual information, e.g. to colour memory (Jaeger, 1982). However some underlying mechanisms can be demonstrated with spectral increment threshold determinations.

Acknowledgements

We are grateful to Dr R. Schläfer, Schott Mainz, for helpful suggestions and for the colour conversion filters. By kind permission of Professor J. Knappe, the spectrophotometric measurements were made at the Institut für biologische Chemie, Heidelberg. We thank Professor H. Kalmus (London), Professor

J. D. Moreland (Bradford), and Drs J. D. Mollon and L. T. Sharpe (Cambridge) for comments on a draft of the text.

References

Diehl, R. and Zrenner, E. (1980). Multispot stimuli reveal spatial organization in the human ERG. *Docum. Ophthal. Proc. Series*, Vol. 23, pp. 209–216. The Hague, Junk.

Harris, H. and Kalmus, H. (1949). The measurement of taste sensitivity to phenyl-thiourea. *Ann. Eugen.* **15**, 24–31.

Hering, E. (1925). Vom Wesen der Farben. Abschnitt I. der Grundzüge der Lehre vom Lichtsinn. In: Graefe-Saemisch, *Handbuch der Augenheilkunde*, Vol. III, 2nd edn, pp. 1–23. Berlin, Springer-Verlag.

Jaeger, W. (1982). Untersuchungen zu Farbkonstanz und Farbgedächtnis. *Sitzungs-berichte der Heidelberger Akademie d. Wissenschaften, Mathematisch-natur-wissenschaftliche Klasse*, Jahrg. 1982, 5. Heidelberg, Springer-Verlag.

Johnson, M. A. and Massof, R. W. (1982). The effect of stimulus size on chromatic thresholds in the peripheral retina. *Proc. VIth Symposium Internat. Research Group for Colour Vision Deficiencies, Berlin 1981, Docum. Ophthal. Proc. Series*, Vol. 33, pp. 15–18. The Hague, Junk.

Kalmus, H. (1978). Teleonomy of normal and defective colour vision. *Mod. Probl. Ophthal.* **19**, 330–332.

King-Smith, P. E. and Carden, D. (1976). Luminance and opponent-colour con-tributions to visual detection and adaptation and to temporal and spatial integration. *J. opt. Soc. Am.* **66**, 709–717.

v. Kries, J. (1897). Über die Farbenblindheit der Netzhautperipherie. *Z. Psychol.* **15**, 297. Quoted from v. Kries, J. (1929). "Zur Theorie des Tages- und Dämmerungs-sehens". In *Handbuch der normalen und pathologischen Physiologie* (eds Bethe, A., v. Bergmann, G., Embden, G. and Ellinger, A.), Vol. XII/1. Berlin, Springer-Verlag.

Ransom-Hogg, A. and Spillmann, L. (1980). Perceptive field size in fovea and periphery of the light- and dark-adapted retina. *Vision Res.* **20**, 221–228.

Ruddock, K. H. (1972). Light transmission through the ocular media and macular pigment. In *Handbook of Sensory Physiology*, VII/4 *Visual Psychophysics* (eds Jameson, D. and Hurvich, L. M.), pp. 455–469. Heidelberg, Springer-Verlag.

Sperling, H. G. (1980). Blue receptor distribution in primates from intense light and histochemical studies. In *Colour Vision Deficiencies* (ed. Verriest, G.), Vol. V, pp. 30–44. Bristol, Adam Hilger.

Sperling, H. G. and Harwerth, R. S. (1971). Red–green cone interactions and the increment threshold spectral sensitivity of primates. *Science* **172**, 180–184.

Stiles, W. S. and Crawford, B. H. (1933). The liminal brightness increment as a function of wavelength for different conditions of the foveal and parafoveal retina. *Proc. roy. Soc. B.* **113**, 496–530.

Wald, G. (1964). The receptors of human color vision. *Science* **145**, 1007–1016.

Willmer, E. N. (1950). The monochromatism of the central fovea in red–green blind subjects. *J. Physiol., Lond.* **110**, 377–385.

Zrenner, E. (1977). Influence of stimulus duration and area on the spectral luminosity function as determined by sensory and VECP measurements. *Docum. Ophthal. Proc. Series* **13**, 21–30.

New Data Concerning the Contribution of Colour Differences to Stereopsis

CHARLES M. M. DE WEERT and KAREL J. SADZA

Julesz (1971) was the first to point out the specific character of the contribution of colour to the process of binocular depth perception. In an informal experiment, equality of colour of the dots in the two monocular random dot stimuli (RDS) led to depth perception even when the brightness contrasts of the dots were reversed in the two eyes. In Lu and Fender's (1972) often quoted experiment no depth was reported under isoluminance conditions in random dot stimuli. For figural stimuli the picture is quite different. Comerford's (1974) study was the first quantitative one to show that stereopsis occurs under isoluminance conditions. He found that performance under isoluminance increased with increasing distinctness of border between figure and ground. The discrepancy between the results for the random dot stereograms and for the figural depth stimuli is clear and has been confirmed by Gregory (1977) and de Weert (1979).

The absence of depth perception under isoluminance for RDS has been interpreted in the light of the presumed roles of colour and luminance in pattern recognition. Absence of stereopsis was taken to confirm the leading role of luminance in fine pattern recognition; and it strengthened the idea that colour coding is an exclusively monocular affair. The assumption of monocularity leans heavily upon the failure to find interocular transfer in a number of colour after-effects, contingent on orientation, velocity or some other attribute. One possible type of explanation fitting the general picture given above was that, for figural stimuli, colour could contribute monocularly to form perception, and monocular forms in turn could be combined centrally to produce form

COLOUR VISION
ISBN 0 12 000000 0

seen in depth; whereas in the random dot stereograms form can occur only after a cooperative process. From the absence of depth in RDS it was concluded: "apparently colour differences alone are not or not sufficiently able to activate the cooperative mechanism which is basic to this process" (de Weert, 1979).

The methodological differences between the figural depth experiments and the RDS experiments performed thus far are considerable. The aim of the present study was to perform a depth detection experiment for random dot stereo stimuli that was comparable, as far as the method was concerned, to the depth detection experiment performed by Comerford for figural stimuli.

Apparatus

It is quite evident that experiments like that of Comerford in which stimuli (wheel form with spokes) were presented very many times with different disparities require a very precise optical arrangement. This type of experiment, i.e. a detection experiment, can hardly be performed for random dot stimuli, because of the rigorous technical requirements.

Our equipment consisted of a R, G, B-colour television monitor, and a system of video memories, controlled by a minicomputer. A more detailed description of the apparatus can be found elsewhere (Wittebrood, Wansink and de Weert, 1981). The two parts of the stereogram were presented on one monitor. A septum was used to mask the right stimulus from the left eye and vice versa. Proper convergence for fusion was made possible by means of a system of 4 mirrors just in front of the subject's eyes. Subjects sat at a distance of 2.5 m from the screen. One unit element in the video memories corresponded to a picture element on the screen of 1.2′ in the horizontal direction, and 0.9′ in the vertical direction.

Experiment 1: Random Dot Stereograms

A two-alternative-forced choice depth detection experiment was conducted.

Stimuli

The stimuli are depicted in Fig. 1a. Block size of the stimuli was 3.6′ horizontally and 2.7′ vertically. The figure to be seen in depth was a rectangle of 57.6′ by 43.2′. The disparity was either +3.6′ or −3.6′ (size of one block). This is about half of the disparity value used in the study of Comerford. We chose this value after a large number of pilot experiments in which block size and disparity were varied from 1.2′ to 14.4′. With this combination of block size and disparity we had a sufficient number of blocks within the depth figure, and an acceptable quality of depth. Crossed and uncrossed disparities were presented at random. The colours of the stimuli were red, green or yellow,

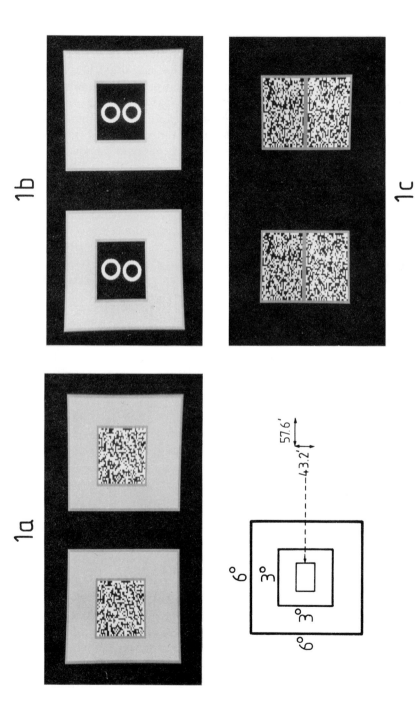

FIG. 1   Stimuli used in the several experiments. The luminance of the surrounding white field was 37 cd m^{-2}.

in each possible combination. Chromaticity coordinates of these colours were: RED: x = 0.654, y = 0.341; GREEN: x = 0.285, y = 0.606; YELLOW: x = 0.436, y = 0.521; and for the whitish surrounding field: x = 0.300, y = 0.246. This white field was continuously present to aid fusion and to keep adaptation as constant as possible.

A flicker-photometric procedure was used to equate the luminance levels of the 3 background colours to a standard whitish stimulus (same as the surround) of 37 cd m^{-2}. A flicker rate of 12.5 Hz was used. This was done for each subject separately. Twenty luminance values around the background level were chosen such that the luminance difference varied from -20% to $+20\%$. Stimuli were presented for 500 msec in series of 496 presentations. Within each series colour and luminance of the background were held constant, while all 20 luminance levels of all 3 colours occurred in the dots.

Between presentations the colour of the background stimulus filled up the whole area within the fusion aid. Time required for one series was about 15 to 20 minutes. For each subject 30 series of measurements were made. A maximum of 3 series were measured in one session.

Procedure

The task of the subject was to report the received direction of the depth plane by pushing one of two response buttons. This procedure is essentially the same as that used by Comerford in the figural depth study. As the figural properties of the part to be seen in depth were completely similar under positive and negative disparity, the subject could not distinguish between the two states on this ground. If the response of the subject was correct a two tone signal was given: after an incorrect response a single tone signal was presented. After each response a 700-msec pause was introduced before the next presentation.

Subjects

Two experienced observers, the authors, served as subjects through all of the experiments to be reported here. Both had normal colour vision.

Results

As one can see from Fig. 2, all heterochromatic curves lie clearly above $p = 0.01$. Thus, we may conclude that all the curves differ significantly from chance level (50%). This result is new, for it places the figural stimuli and the random dot stimuli on one line: if a similar criterion is used for the two types of stimuli the results are similar. From a horizontal cross-section at the minimum of the heterochromatic curves it can be deduced that a pure colour difference has at least an effect similar to that of a homochromatic luminance difference of about 10%.

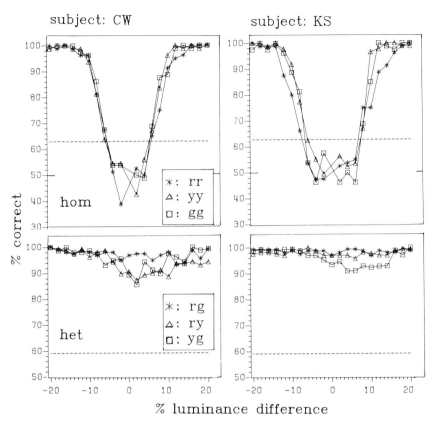

FIG. 2   Results for the two-alternative forced choice experiment. The number of observations was 160 for heterochromatic points and 80 for homochromatic points. Along the abscissa the luminance difference of the variable (second letter) colour with respect to the background (first letter) colour is represented. HOM: homochromatic; HET: heterochromatic; --- is $p = 0.01$ significance level.

Why does depth occur here, and why has it not been reported in the previous RDS studies? There may be very many reasons. It could be that in the present study more favourable spatial and temporal conditions have by chance been used. This is not a likely explanation, because we could replicate the results given above for block sizes varying from 2.4 to 14.4′ (and disparities varying in the same range). The most likely explanation in our view is the difference in criterion in the several studies. In Comerford's study, and in the study presented here, the lowest possible criterion has been used, i.e. detection of the direction of a depth plane. This criterion is much lower than the criterion of identification of a figure in depth. As a matter of fact, in the figural stimuli these criteria are more or less equivalent.

Experiment 2: A Four-Alternative Forced-Choice Form Detection Experiment

To test the effect of a stronger criterion, a series of experiments were performed in which subjects had to identify which part of a square, appearing in depth in front of the background, was left out. Exactly the same figure was used as in Experiment 1, but now one of the quadrants was left out at random in each presentation. All other stimulus conditions were kept the same. The subject was asked to press one of 4 response buttons, indicating which part of the figure was left out. Again 30 series of 496 measurements each were carried out for both subjects.

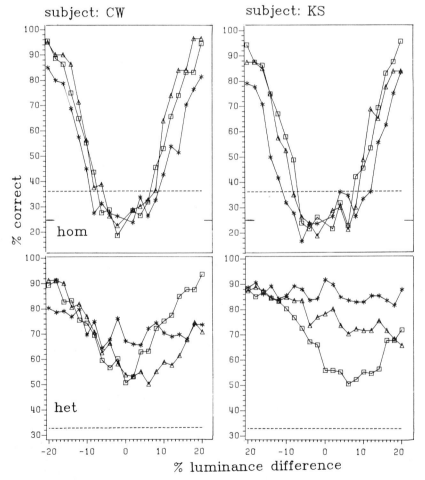

FIG. 3   Results for the Four-alternative forced choice experiment. Chance level: 25%. Number of observations: 160, 80.

Results

It is quite clear that these measurements, presented in Fig. 3, again point to a significant contribution of colour differences to stereopsis at and around isoluminance. All heterochromatic curves remain significantly above the chance level of 25%. It is equally clear that the level of performance in terms of percentage correct is much lower than in the foregoing experiment in which only the direction of a depth plane had to be detected. In order to make the results of our experiment and those of the figural type of Comerford comparable an experiment on monocularly recognizable forms was performed.

Experiment 3: Repetition of Comerford's Experiment on Figural Stimuli

The stimuli are depicted in Fig. 1b. The stimulus conditions are different from those of Comerford. We used two rings in one picture, and we introduced disparity between the rings rather than between one ring and the background as was done by Comerford. In this way a number of irrelevant stereo effects, varying from the binocular effect of colour stereoscopy to monocular brightness-depth effects, were eliminated completely.

One subject took part in this experiment. A presentation time of 500 msec was used, and the subject had to tell which ring was nearer. Disparity was either $+3.6'$ or $-3.6'$. The shift of the figure was randomly divided over left and right pictures. The results presented in Fig. 4 confirm Comerford's results.

In all of the above experiments we have found that colour differences alone can lead to stereopsis. It should be emphasized that the quality of the perceived depth is minimal under isoluminance conditions. Because this experience is only weakly reflected in the data, we felt the need to order the relative quality of the depth sensation in a direct comparison experiment.

Experiment 4: Pairwise Comparison of the Quality of Depth

In Fig. 1c the stimuli used in the pairwise comparison experiment are shown. Each stimulus (6 possible colour combinations, 21 levels of luminance of dots with respect to background (total: 123 stimuli)) is compared with all others. The total number of 7503 stimulus presentations was divided over 17 sub-series, each of about 441 presentations. All further stimulus conditions were as before, except that subjects now could take as much time as they needed to choose the picture with the best depth impression. In Fig. 5 is shown the dominance score, i.e. the number of times (out of a total possible of 122) that a given stimulus was judged to evoke the stronger sensation of depth. As can be seen the order of the results is strongly similar to that found in the earlier experiments.

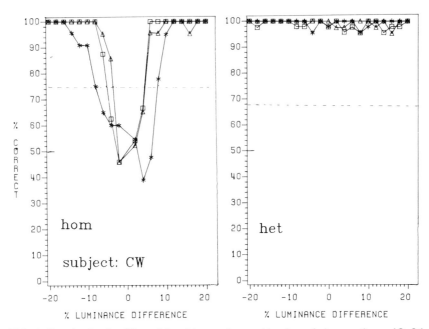

FIG. 4   Results for the 'Figural depth' experiment. Number of observations: 48, 24.

General Discussion

The main conclusion to be drawn from this study is that there is no fundamental difference in the contribution of colour to stereopsis in figural stimuli and in random dot stereograms under isoluminance. It must be emphasized that the decrease in quality of the depth perception at and around equiluminance is considerable. Even after a large number of trials, the two subjects in this study experienced the equiluminance stimulus as a poor depth stimulus, but this decrease in quality of depth perception also occurred for the figural stimuli. This brings us to the still unexplained difference between the reports of no depth in previous studies and the present results. We must assume that the criterion used in the threshold determinations of all the previous studies (Lu and Fender; Gregory; de Weert) is higher than that used in forced choice experiments. Furthermore, learning effects certainly play an important role. The performance of the two subjects had greatly improved in the first few weeks.

Finally, some attention must be given to the possible nature of the contribution of the colour signals to stereopsis. There are two main possibilities:

a) The effect under isoluminance is due to a genuine contribution of the colour signals;

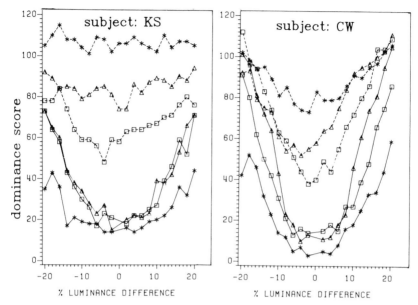

FIG. 5 Results for the 'Paired comparison' experiment. Dominance score (maximum number 122) is the number of times a stimulus was judged to evoke the better depth percept. Symbols: ∗ —: RR; □ —: GG; △ —: YY; △ ⋯: RY; □ ⋯: GY; ∗ ⋯: RG.

b) The contribution is due to "false" luminance signals, introduced by chromatic aberration or by small eye movements which can possibly produce net brightness differences at isoluminance.

It will be very difficult to rule out these possible artefacts completely. Eye movements can be eliminated only by the use of stabilized images. Correction for longitudinal chromatic aberration with achromatizing lenses is not sufficient, and may even degrade contours. We did not use such lenses in the series presented above, but in some pilot sessions in which we used them we did not find differences. For the moment we assume that there is a genuine contribution of colour to stereopsis, even in RDS. More detailed experiments are needed to find out whether the depth detection is based on high-frequency (colour contour) information or on lower-frequency (colour content) information or on both.

References

Comerford, J. P. (1974). Stereopsis with chromatic contours. *Vision Res.* **14**, 975–982.

Gregory, R. L. (1977). Vision with isoluminant colour contrast: 1. A projection technique and observations. *Perception* **6**, 113–119.

Julesz, B. (1971). *Foundations of Cyclopean Perception*. Chicago, The University of Chicago Press.

Lu, C. and Fender, D. H. (1972). The interaction of color and luminance in stereoscopic vision. *Invest. Ophthal.* **11**, 482–490.

De Weert, Ch. M. M. (1979). Colour contours and stereopsis. *Vision Res.* **19**, 555–564.

Wittebrood, J. E. M., Wansink, M. G., De Weert, Ch. M. M. (1981). A versatile colour stimulus generator. *Perception* **10**, 63–69.

The CIE Colour-Coding System

H. TERSTIEGE

Introduction

Colouring in fauna is often for the purpose of protection, when they have to hide themselves in trees, leaves or on the soil against their enemies. They are equipped with nearly the same colour or pattern as their surrounding and their colour serves as a camouflage. On the other hand, male animals often show the most beautiful bright colours to attract their females or to impress possible competitors.

In the history of human.culture, colours have always been used together with symbols to transmit messages. Colours or combinations of colours have been used to identify members of the same clan, military unit or nation. The importance of colour as a code for messages has increased with the increase of transport by sea, land and air; and various forms of international transport would be impossible without an internationally agreed colour-coding system.

Thus in 1982 the Commission Internationale de l'Eclairage (CIE) will publish an official CIE Recommendation "Surface Colours for Visual Signalling" to ensure the proper guidance and control of the various forms of transport so as to increase safety and to facilitate rapid movement. These specifications also apply to warning signs and colour codes in general. The surface colours, with their respective colour limits, have been chosen to ensure maximum probability of recognition of colour and code.

General

Although the human eye can differentiate one million colours it has a very weak ability for absolute identification of colours when they are shown at large time intervals. In colour atlases we realize only 1000 to 2000 of the possible colours, and from colour naming we know that only 8 colours exist without auxiliary names: blue, green, yellow, brown, red, white, grey and black, as violet, orange, rose and purple are named after flowers etc. From the mentioned 8 colours another 3: brown, grey and black can be seen only by contrast with other colours. Thus for a precise colour coding system only five colours are suitable: blue, green, yellow, red and white.

From the physiological point of view the opponent colours blue/yellow, red/green and white/black might be judged the most suitable for colour recognition and colour coding, the first five in a system of light signals and additionally black in a system of surface colours, where black can be detected in contrast to the other colours.

The CIE System

Coding with Light Signals

Coloured light signals have been used for the guidance and control of transport by sea for a long time. The practical experience gained in marine signalling served as a basis for applications in railway and air signalling.

In 1935 the CIE first made recommendations for the colours and tolerances to be used for railway signals, for road traffic lights and for airborne and aviation ground light signals. Other tolerances for marine signals were proposed at the International Lighthouse Conference in 1937.

In this signalling system green and red are the preferred two colours. In a three-colour system of light signals the third colour should be yellow, white or white/yellow. If more than three colours are required for a signal system it is possible to define yellow and white as distinguishable light signal colours. However in some applications it is desirable to define blue as a distinguishable colour. In such cases blue is to be seen only at relatively short ranges. The use of purple or violet as a colour for light signals is not generally recommended by the CIE.

Coding with Surface Colours

In 1978 the CIE published a Technical Report on "Surface Colours for Visual Signalling" which was regarded at the time as a draft for future recommendations. In the same year P. Jainski performed a large-scale investigation in which 565 surface colours were observed by 10 observers with normal colour vision and the percentage of correctly identified colours was determined. The results of the investigation lead to proposals for the colour boundaries of surface colours used in traffic signs. The recommended surface colours have been studied in the meantime in several other countries. On behalf of the British

National Committee the boundary of the green surface colours has been
extended towards yellow for the use of their recently introduced highway green.
This was in agreement with the Jainski results concerning colour recognition
but is disadvantageous for people with dichromatic colour vision (see below).

The CIE recommendation is now based on the practical experience gained
in several countries and is designed to ensure maximum probability of
recognition of colour and code. The recommendation also takes into account
the limitations imposed by manufacturing technology and tolerances of colour
measurements. Therefore different chromaticity coordinates and luminance
factors are recommended for ordinary, retro-reflecting and fluorescent
materials. Figure 1 shows the recommended regions for ordinary colours for
illumination with CIE standard illuminant D65 and for CIE recommended
geometry 45/0 (illumination at 45° and measurement of the reflected light
normally). They are thus defined for an approximation to the conditions of
daytime observation as recommended by the CIE in 1971.

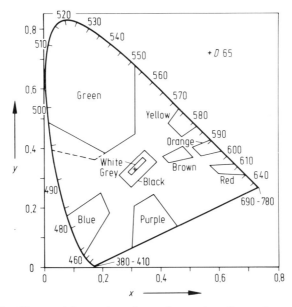

FIG. 1   Chromaticity regions for ordinary signalling colours.

Measurements of surface colours can be done with spectrophotometers and
colorimeters by manufacturers. National governmental institutes supervise the
use of traffic colours and they supply reference colour standards to calibrate
colorimeters. This ensures reliable measurements of the surface colours even
when tristimulus instruments are used.

A significant number of people in the world – about 8% of all males – have defective colour vision, and this fact had to be fully taken into account when the recommendations were set up.

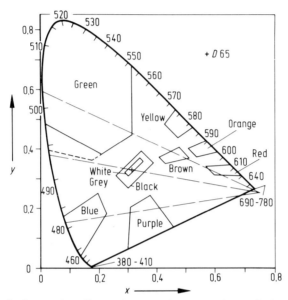

FIG. 2   Ordinary signalling colours and protanopic confusion lines.

Figure 2 shows the recommended ordinary colours and the colour confusion lines for protanopic dichromats, who cannot distinguish between red, orange, yellow and green (after Judd, 1944). Deuteranopic dichromats confuse similar colours as shown in Fig. 3.

Therefore when green is used in a colour-coding system together with yellow and red, a green on the yellow side of the recommended green region should be avoided. Further safeguards against possible confusion can be obtained by suitably adjusting the reflectance factor.

Tritanopic dichromats (who cannot distinguish blue from green, white from yellow, and red from purple) and monochromats (who are completely unable to detect any difference of chromaticity between colours), represent very small proportions of the total population of colour defectives.

As a consequence of the pattern of colour confusion exhibited by the very great majority of people with defective colour vision, the CIE recommends that red, blue, black and white should generally be the preferred colours chosen for a colour-coding system that is not intended solely for the use of people with normal colour vision.

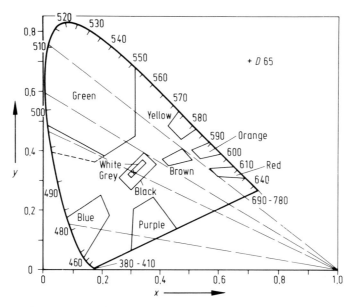

FIG. 3   Ordinary signalling colours and deuteranopic confusion lines.

Conclusion

The CIE has published two documents in which chromaticity coordinates for light signals and surface colours are recommended. These represent a compromise between reliable colour recognition for observers with normal and defective colour vision, existing national practice, and limitations imposed by manufacturing technology and by the uncertainty of colour measurements. For surface colours, different chromaticity coordinates are recommended for ordinary, retro-reflecting and fluorescent materials. Measuring conditions are specified.

References

Commission Internationale de l'Eclairage (1975). Publication No. 2.2: Colours of light signals, Bureau Central de la CIE, Paris.

Commission Internationale de l'Eclairage (1971). Publication No. 15: Colorimetry. Bureau Central de la CIE, Paris.

Commission Internationale de l'Eclairage (1983). Publication No. 39.2: Surface colours for visual signalling. Bureau Central de la CIE, Paris.

Jainski, P. (1980). Wahrnehmung von Aufsichfarben für nicht selbstleuchtende Verkehrszeichen. *Lichttechnik* **28** (No. 10), 410–415; (No. 11), 442–444.

Judd, D. B. (1944). Standard response functions for protanopic and deuteranopic vision, *Bureau of Stand. J. Res.* **33**, 407–457.

Symmetries and Asymmetries in Colour Vision

R. W. G. HUNT

Introduction

Of the three spectrally different types of cone in the human retina, it is well known that the short-wavelength type (B) has many different properties from those of the medium (G) and long (R) wavelength types. This probably arises, at least in part, from the fact that the optics of the eye are not corrected for chromatic aberration. As can be seen from Fig. 1, the R and G cones have spectral sensitivity curves which overlap considerably, whereas the curve for the B cones is well separated (Estévez, 1979); the best overall focus is thus obtained when the middle wavelengths are sharp, leaving the wavelengths affecting the B cones appreciably unsharp.

Luminance

Determination of the overall sensitivity of the eye at photopic levels of adaptation, by the methods of flicker photometry or minimally distinct-border, result in the well-known spectral luminous efficiency curves of the type shown in Fig. 2. Curves of this type can be synthesized satisfactorily by appropriate addition of the outputs of the R and G type cones only; this suggests that the B cones are different in that they do not contribute to the achromatic signal on which the spectral efficiency is based (Eisner and MacLeod, 1980). In Fig. 3 a processing scheme for the signals, R, G, B, from the cones is postulated in which an achromatic signal, A, receives inputs from R and G cones only;

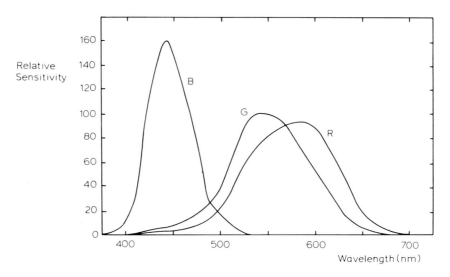

FIG. 1   Cone spectral sensitivities for light incident on the cornea (after Estévez).

however, because it has been estimated that there are about twice as many R cones as G cones, the signal is shown as receiving inputs from two R cones and one G cone. The signals are added together after compression by a power function with an exponent of $\frac{1}{2}$, after Vos (Vos, 1982). Hence the signal, A, equals $2R^{\frac{1}{2}} + G^{\frac{1}{2}}$, and in Fig. 2 a normalized curve of this type is seen to fall near the middle of the range of spectral luminous efficiency curves found in practice for normal observers (Coblentz and Emerson, 1918).

Constant Hue Loci

For photopic levels of illumination, the loci of stimuli that appear to maintain constant hue as their saturation is varied, consist of lines on chromaticity diagrams that are, in general, not straight, but curved; examples of such loci are shown by the broken curves in Fig. 4 (Wilson and Brocklebank, 1955). The curvature of these loci implies that the criterion for constant hue is a nonlinear combination of the cone outputs. The full curves in Fig. 4 are predictions of constant hue from such a nonlinear combination. As shown in Fig. 3, it is postulated that, whereas twice as many R as G cones are used to form the achromatic signal, colour difference signals are formed by taking the differences between the outputs of single cones (Hunt, 1982). Three colour difference signals are postulated:

$$C_1 = R^{\frac{1}{2}} - G^{\frac{1}{2}} \qquad C_2 = G^{\frac{1}{2}} - B^{\frac{1}{2}} \qquad C_3 = B^{\frac{1}{2}} - R^{\frac{1}{2}}$$

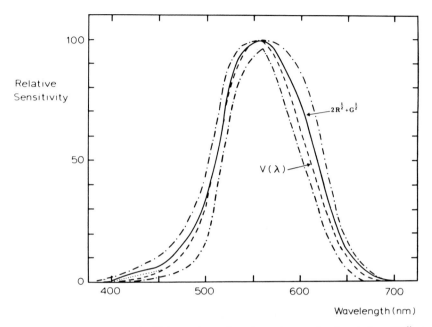

FIG. 2   Full line: spectral efficiency based on the achromatic signal, $A = 2R^{1/2} + G^{1/2}$, plotted as A^2 and normalized to give a maximum of 100; broken line: the CIE relative spectral efficiency function $V(\lambda)$; dotted line: Judd's modification of the CIE $V(\lambda)$ function; dot–dash line: the range of relative spectral efficiency functions for individual observers found by Coblentz and Emerson. (These functions all relate to intensities of stimuli, not of visual signals; hence the need to plot A^2, not A.)

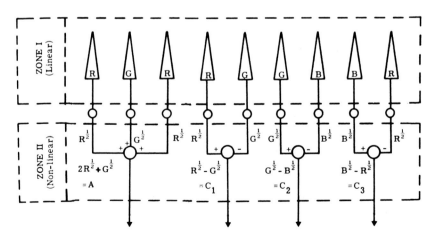

FIG. 3   Schematic diagram showing how R, G, and B cones could be connected in a nonlinear zone.

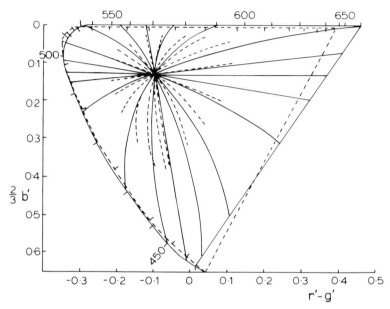

FIG. 4 Comparison of constant hue loci. Full lines: predictions (on a chromaticity diagram in which $\frac{2}{3}b'$ is plotted against $r' - g'$, where r', g', and b' are chromaticities corresponding to $R' = 1.05R$, $G' = 1.35G$, and $B' = 0.6B$); broken lines: experimental results of Wilson and Brocklebank (on the CIE u', v' chromaticity diagram, axes not shown). The u', v' diagram is used because its distribution of chromaticities is visually approximately uniform, and this facilitates estimating goodness of fit; the $\frac{2}{3}b'$, $r' - g'$ diagram is used only as a geometrical approximation to the u', v' diagram, and is not intended to have any physiological significance.

The criterion for achromatic perceptions is postulated as:

$$C_1 = C_2 = C_3 = 0.$$

The criterion for constant hue is postulated as the three colour difference signals being in constant ratio to one another:

$$C_1 : C_2 : C_3 \text{ constant.}$$

Using these criteria in Fig. 4, the predicted (full) curves agree quite closely with the experimental (broken) curves. It is interesting to note that these criteria for achromacy and constant hue are trilaterally symmetrical with respect to the R, G, and B responses. (It should be noted that, because $C_3 = -C_1 - C_2$, the number of degrees of freedom of the system is reduced by the achromatic criterion, not from three to zero, but from three to one, and by the constant-hue criterion, not from three to one, but from three to two.)

Unique Hue Loci

Loci of constant hue can be determined for unique hues: unique reds and greens are those that are neither bluish nor yellowish; unique blues and yellows are those that are neither reddish nor greenish. In Fig. 5 are shown, by the broken curves, loci for unique hues as determined experimentally in the Swedish Natural Colour System (NCS) of surface colours (Tonnquist, 1975). The full curves are those that are predicted by the following postulates for criteria for unique hues:

Red: $C_1 = C_2$ Green: $C_3 = C_1$
Yellow: $C_1' = 0$ Blue: $C_1'' = 0$

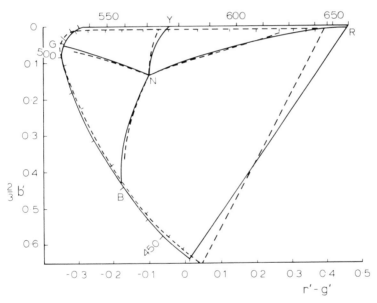

FIG. 5 Comparison of unique hue loci. Full lines: predictions; broken lines: NCS experimental results. (Chromaticity diagrams as in Fig. 4.)

where $C_1' = R^{\frac{1}{2}} - (12G^{\frac{1}{2}}/11 - B^{\frac{1}{2}}/11)$ and $C_1'' = R^{\frac{1}{2}} - (5G^{\frac{1}{2}}/4 - B^{\frac{1}{2}}/4)$ and represent modifications of the C_1 signal as a result of inhibitions of the $G^{\frac{1}{2}}$ signal by the $B^{\frac{1}{2}}$ signal. As can be seen from Fig. 5, these criteria predict the experimental results closely; the criteria are strikingly simple and symmetrical for red and green, but are less simple and are asymmetrical for blue and yellow. An interesting point to note is that, although red and green are opponent (mutually exclusive) perceptual hues, their loci exhibit a discontinuity at the illuminant point: this is also true of the blue and yellow loci. (But constant-hue loci and their associated after-image loci do not exhibit discontinuities at the illuminant point; this suggests that the criteria for the unique hues is established at a stage in the visual pathway subsequent to that at which after-images arise.)

Saturation

It has been known for many years that, for R, G, B signals normalized for a typical reference white, the contribution to saturation from a given change in signal strength in the blue and yellow directions is appreciably less than that from changes in the red and green directions; this is presumably because of the relative paucity of the B cones. One estimate (Vos and Walraven, 1971) of the relative abundances of the R, G, and B cones is that they are in the ratios of 40 : 20 : 1, respectively. On signal-to-noise ratio grounds, this suggests that a factor of $1/20^{1/2}$, or about $1/4.5$, be introduced into a signal indicating blueness–yellowness before combining it with a signal indicating redness–greenness to obtain a saturation signal. The following signals are therefore postulated:

Blueness–Yellowness: $M_{BY} = \frac{1}{2}(C_3 - C_2)e_s/4.5$
Redness–Greenness: $M_{RG} = C_1'e_s$

The term $\frac{1}{2}(C_3 - C_2)$ represents the average of the degree of departure from unique redness, $C_1 - C_2$, and unique greenness, $C_3 - C_1$. The term C_1' represents the degree of departure from unique yellowness (which is not averaged with that from unique blueness because the unique blue locus is less well defined than the unique yellow locus).

The factor e_s is introduced to allow for another interesting asymmetry in the visual system. Analysis of experimental assessments of the saturations of very desaturated colours (Hunt, 1982) shows that there is a basic difference in the contribution to saturation of the redness–greenness signal according to whether it is indicating redness or greenness; and similarly with the blueness–yellowness signal according to whether blueness or yellowness is being indicated. The data show that the values for e_s for the unique hues, relative to 1.0 for green, are 0.8 for red, 0.7 for yellow, and 1.2 for blue; the values of e_s for intermediate hues are interpolated linearly with respect to the angular correlate of hue given by

$$\arctan\{[-\tfrac{1}{2}(C_3 - C_2)/4.5]/[C_1']\}.$$

In Fig. 6 are shown (full curves) saturation contours predicted as

$$(M_{BY}^2 + M_{RG}^2)^{1/2}/(R^{1/2} + G^{1/2} + B^{1/2})$$

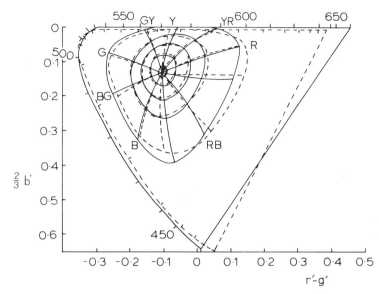

FIG. 6   Comparison of hue and saturation loci. Full lines: predictions; broken lines: NCS experimental results. (Chromaticity diagrams as in Fig. 4).

together with the experimental results (broken curves) of the NCS colours. It is seen that the agreement is quite close (as is also the case for the hue loci, which were predicted in accordance with the criteria for constant and unique hues described above).

References

Coblentz, W. W. and Emerson, W. B. (1918). Relative sensibility of the average eye to light of different colors and some practical applications of radiation problems. *Nat. Bur. Stand. Bull.* **14**, 167.

Eisner, A. and MacLeod, D. I. A. (1980). Blue-sensitive cones do not contribute to luminance. *J. opt. Soc. Am.* **70**, 121–123.

Estévez, O. (1979). On the fundamental data base of normal and dichromatic colour vision. Ph. D. thesis, University of Amsterdam.

Hunt, R. W. G. (1982). A model of colour vision for predicting colour appearance. *Col. Res. Appl.* **7**, 95–112.

Tonnquist, G. (1975). Comparison between CIE and NCS colour spaces. FOA Report No. 30032 – E1, Forsvarets Forkningsamstalt, Stockholm.

Vos, J. J. (1982). On the merits of model making in understanding color vision phenomena. *Col. Res. Appl.* **7**, 69–77.

Vos, J. J. and Walraven, P. L. (1971). On the derivation of the foveal receptor primaries. *Vision Res.* **11**, 799–818.

Wilson, M. H. and Brocklebank, R. W. (1955). Complementary hues of after-images. *J. opt. Soc. Am.* **45**, 293–299.

Linking Propositions in Color Vision

DAVIDA Y. TELLER and E. N. PUGH Jr.

Figure 1A shows the classic hue cancellation data of Jameson and Hurvich (1955), and Fig. 1B shows recent foveal spectral sensitivity measurements of Thornton and Pugh (1983). For more than a century psychophysicists have argued that such data place constraints on models of visual system physiology, and indeed have used subjective reports and psychophysical data to argue for specific physiological models (see for example Boring, 1942). For example, the facts that redness and greenness are subjectively mutually exclusive, and that the two hues cancel each other when lights which produce them are mixed together, have long been taken by some scientists as evidence that redness and greenness are coded by mutually exclusive states of the same neurons. In the same framework, the set of lights that appear in red/green equilibrium is interpreted to be those to which the populations of neurons in question does *not* respond. The short-wavelength hump in spectral sensitivity data such as those of Fig. 1B has been modelled as an action spectrum of the short-wave cones (Sperling and Harwerth, 1971; Thornton and Pugh, 1983 and this volume), while the twin peaks in the middle- and long-wavelength regions can be modelled as action spectra of one (Thornton and Pugh, 1983) or two (Sperling and Harwerth, 1971) homogeneous populations of chromatically coded neurons proximal to the photoreceptors – i.e., neurons having inputs of opposite sign from two different cone classes. In this manuscript we shall re-examine the logic involved in the use of such data as those in Fig. 1 in drawing conclusions about underlying physiological processes.

In 1870, Ewald Hering, lecturing at the Imperial Academy of Sciences in Vienna, said the following:

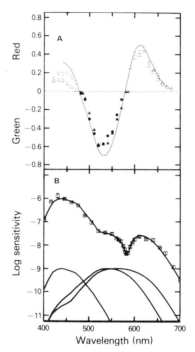

FIG. 1   (A) Opponent-cancellation coefficients for redness (open symbols) and greenness (filled symbols) for observers H (circles) and J (triangles), for an equal-energy spectrum. The solid line is a linear combination of the CIE standard observer's color-matching functions, after Judd. Figure from Krantz (1975b). (B) Two-color increment threshold for Thornton's "low frequency" test; its temporal waveform was one trough-to-trough cycle of a 2-Hz sine wave; its spatial waveform was a radially symmetric Gaussian with a full bandwidth (half-power point) of 3 deg, foveally centered; the adaptation field was a 580-nm, 10-deg foveally centered field of 10^{10} quanta deg^{-2} sec^{-1}. The three lower curves represent estimates of the three human foveal cone action spectra, due to J. J. Vos.

If then, the student of neurophysiology takes his stand between the physicist and the psychologist, and if the first of these rightly makes the unbroken causative continuity of all material processes an axiom of his system of investigation, the prudent psychologist, on the other hand, will investigate the laws of conscious life according to the inductive method, and will hence, as much as the physicist, make the existence of fixed laws his initial assumption. If, again, the most superficial introspection teaches the psychologist that his conscious life is dependent on the mechanical adjustments of his body, and that inversely his body is subjected with certain limitations to his will, then it only remains for him to make one more assumption, viz., that this mutual interdependence between the mental and the material is itself also dependent on law, and he has discovered the bond by which the science of matter and the science of consciousness are united into a single whole ...

This, then, by no means implies the two variables above mentioned – matter and consciousness – stand in the relation of cause and effect ... to one another. For on this subject we know nothing. The materialist regards consciousness as a product or result of matter, while the idealist holds matter to be a result of consciousness, and a third maintains that mind and matter are identical; with all this the physiologist, as such, has nothing whatever to do; his sole concern is with the fact that matter and consciousness are functions one of the other. (Translated and quoted in Butler, 1910, pp. 64–65.)

Hering's remarks contain three themes important to our discussion. The first is that lawful relationships exist between physiological states and perceptual states, and that therefore perceptual and psychophysical data can place constraints on models of visual system physiology. The second is that physical/physiological processes and the phenomenal events of conscious life are from logically separate universes of discourse (Feigl, 1958). The implication of this logical separation is not only that the laws of consciousness can be explored in their own right, but also that the investigation of the ontological relations between physiological processes and phenomenal events requires some explicit assumptions. The early psychophysicists called these assumptions axioms (Boring, 1942). More recently, Brindley (1960) called them *linking hypotheses*. We will call them *linking propositions*.

The third theme is that, in constructing links or bridges between physiological and phenomenal events, the mind–body problem necessarily arises. As Hering argued, the philosophical position that one takes regarding the monistic or dualistic nature of mind and body is probably not critical to the study of the relationship between phenomena and physiology as long as one is willing to assume lawful relationships. We sense, however, that elements of the mind–body problem will arise to challenge our formulations as we attempt to understand the nature of linking propositions in visual science.

The modern history of this topic began with Brindley (1957, 1960). Brindley (1960) addressed the role of a subject's reports of his own sensations in the study of the physiology of vision. He emphasized that phenomenal terms and physiological/physical terms are from logically disjoint universes of discourse, and he coined the term *psychophysical linking hypothesis* to refer to potential bridging relationships between the two levels.

Brindley also divided psychophysical observations and subjective reports into two categories, Class A (embracing complete matching and thresholds) and Class B, which "includes all those (observations) in which the subject must describe the quality or intensity of his sensations, or abstract from two different sensations some aspect in which they are alike". He argued that only one linking hypothesis (the *Identity linking hypothesis* – see below) was required to use Class A observations for testing physiological hypotheses that make predictions of the indistinguishability of sensations; this one hypothesis, he thought, was certainly generally acceptable, and possibly a truism when properly understood. He emphasized the importance and utility of Class B observations in visual science, but argued that the linking hypotheses explicitly used (or implicitly required) to permit valid physiological inferences from Class B observations had little generality or logical rigor. Most psychophysicists feel, perhaps in part because of Brindley's influential analysis, relatively comfortable in using the data of matching and threshold experiments as a basis of physiological inference, and certainly for quasi-physiological modelling.

In this manuscript we reexamine some of the same ideas discussed by Hering and by Brindley. Our purpose is to provide a more formalized and differentiated terminology, so that the logic involved in relating psychophysics to physiology can be examined more explicitly.

The Process of Vision as a Composite Mapping

For the sake of this discussion[1] we shall assume the visual system to consist in a sequence of deterministic maps indexed by k, $k = 0, 1, 2, \ldots n$, which maps the set of physiological states of the neurons at one stage to the set of physiological states of the neurons at the next stage, as follows:

$$\begin{array}{ccccccc} & & & & & \Psi & \\ M_0 & & M_1 & M_2 & & M_n & \uparrow M^* \\ S \rightarrow & \Phi^{(0)} & \rightarrow \Phi^{(1)} & \rightarrow \Phi^{(2)} & \ldots & \rightarrow \Phi^{(n)} & \rightarrow \ldots \end{array}$$

M_0 maps the set S of external stimuli to $\Phi^{(0)}$, the set of quantum catch states of all photoreceptors. M_1, M_2, $\ldots M_n$ map the set of physiological states at one stage to the set of physiological states at the next stage. The symbol Ψ represents the set of all conscious visual perceptions. We explicitly assume the existence of a map M^* that maps the set of physiological states $\Phi^{(n)}$ onto the set of visual perceptual states. Each element $s \in S$ represents a particular physical stimulus; each element $\phi \in \Phi^{(k)}$ specifies the states of all neurons at the kth stage of the visual system; each $\psi \in \Psi$ denotes a particular perceptual state.[2] Sometimes we use a short-hand notation: given a particular $\Phi^{(k)}$−state, ϕ_1, the corresponding phenomenal state may be written ψ_1. By the composition of the maps, we have a map from any stage of the system to any stage of higher index, including in the extreme a map from any externally defined physical state s_i to a corresponding phenomenal state ψ_i: in symbols, $\psi_i = M^* M_n(\ldots M_0(s_i) \ldots))$.

Each of the maps M_k could be one : one or many : one. If a map M_{k+1} is one : one, any two different states of $\Phi^{(k)}$ map to two distinct states of $\Phi^{(k+1)}$. But if the map is many : one, different states of stage k sometimes lead to the same state at stage $(k+1)$ − information is lost by the mapping M_{k+1}. The nature of the map M^* constitutes part of the classical mind−body or brain−perception problem (cf. Feigl, 1958). Of particular interest here is the issue of whether M^* should be thought of as many : one or one : one.

Bridge Locus and Critical Locus

Most visual scientists probably believe that there exists a set of neurons with visual system input, whose activities form the immediate substrate of visual perception. We single out this one particular neural stage, our nth stage, with a name: the *bridge locus*.[3] The occurrence of a particular activity pattern in these bridge locus neurons is necessary for the occurrence of a particular perceptual state; neural activity elsewhere in the visual system is not necessary. The physical location of these neurons in the brain is of course unknown. However, we feel that most visual scientists would agree that they are certainly *not* in the retina. For if one could set up conditions for properly stimulating them in the absence of the retina, the correlated perceptual state presumably would occur.

Most visual scientists also would accept the notion that in a particular experiment the flow of information (e.g., about the spectral content of a stimulus) through the visual system can be importantly blocked, limited or otherwise reorganized at a particular stage (cf. Teller, 1980; Uttal, 1981). If one stage imposes such a critical transformation, this stage will be called the *critical locus*, $\Phi^{(c)}$, for that experiment. In a matching or threshold experiment in which a failure to discriminate two physically distinct states occurs, the principal or dominating locus of information loss is obviously a critical locus. The concept of critical locus for a Class B experiment is difficult to characterize in general terms, but will be discussed further below for the particular case of hue cancellation.

Where do linking propositions fit into this scheme? A linking proposition is a claim that a specific mapping exists between a state ϕ_1 at level $\Phi^{(k)}$ and a state ψ_1 at Ψ. If the physiological level involved were the bridge locus, $\Phi^{(n)}$, the linking proposition would be a claim about the map M^*. If the physiological level is at a level $k < n$, the linking proposition is explicitly or implicitly a claim about the composite map from $\Phi^{(k)}$ to Ψ, always including M^*. Most physiological models in color vision involve models of early stages of physiological processing, and thus involve the postulation of composite maps. These maps could be interesting elements of the models, and it may be useful to examine them explicitly more often than we do (cf. Teller, 1980).

The Identity Family of Linking Propositions

Since matching and threshold experiments are based upon judgments of identity or nonidentity of perceptual states, the linking propositions involved in inferences drawn from these experiments concern the identity or nonidentity of the physiological states underlying the perceptions.[4] The family of propositions which deals with such inferences will be called the *Identity family* of linking propositions (Teller, 1981), and is given immediately below in formal notation:

(1) Identity $\phi_1 = \phi_2 \rightarrow \psi_1 = \psi_2$
(2) Contrapositive Identity $\psi_1 \neq \psi_2 \rightarrow \phi_1 \neq \phi_2$
(3) Converse Identity $\psi_1 = \psi_2 \rightarrow \phi_1 = \phi_2$
(4) Contrapositive Converse Identity $\phi_1 \neq \phi_2 \rightarrow \psi_1 \neq \psi_2$

In initially reading these four logical propositions consider only a specific set of states, $\phi_1, \phi_2 \in \Phi^{(k)}$, $\psi_1, \psi_2 \in \Psi$, and keep in mind that the subscripts are to be interpreted in terms of the composite map i.e., $\psi_i = M^*(M_n(...(M_{k+1}(\phi_i ...))$, as explained above. We now consider the logical interrelations among, and the truth values of, these propositions.

First, since a statement and its contrapositive are logically equivalent (i.e., necessarily have the same truth value), Propositions (1) and (2) are equivalent, and Propositions (3) and (4) are equivalent. Second, in reasoning from psychophysical experiments to physiological conclusions we must necessarily use either (2) or (3). Third, propositions (1)–(2) are logically implied by the existence of a map of $\Phi^{(k)}$-states to Ψ-states. In other words, in a universe of $\Phi^{(k)}$-states and Ψ-states for which there is a map to Ψ-states, Propositions (1)–(2) are true universally, i.e., they hold for all k, and for all $\phi_1, \phi_2, \psi_1, \psi_2$. This analysis captures what Brindley seems to have meant by calling the Identity linking proposition a truism. Fourth, Propositions (3)–(4) are not generally true, i.e., they are not implied by the existence of the composite map. Indeed, in psychophysics we are particularly interested in cases of information loss, i.e., experiments in which physically distinct stimuli give rise to in-distinguishable sensations. For example, consider two threshold stimuli s_1 and s_2 taken from the long-wavelength hump of the spectral sensitivity curve in Fig. 1B, say 600 nm and 670 nm. These stimuli clearly give rise to differential quantum catches in the long- and mid-wave pigments, i.e., different $\Phi^{(0)}$-states. And yet Wandell (1981) has shown under similar conditions that such stimuli generate indistinguishable sensations. That is, we have a case where $\psi_1 = \psi_2$, but $\phi_1 \neq \phi_2$ at level $\Phi^{(0)}$, since the stimuli give rise to differential quantum absorptions. Clearly, then, Propositions (3)–(4) do not hold for arbitrary k. Is there any sense in which they are general, and do not have truth values that must be determined for each experiment?

Interestingly enough, the answer to the question depends on whether or not one is willing to assume that M^* is one : one. If two physically distinct stimuli cause identical percepts, then the information that they are distinct must be lost somewhere in the nervous system, providing it is not lost in the trans-formation of neuronal activity to conscious percepts – i.e., providing M^* is not many : one. By the definition of a map, one guarantees that once the information is lost, it cannot be restored. Of course, the assertion that there exists a particular stage $\Phi^{(c)}$ (the critical locus) at which level and beyond $\phi_1 = \phi_2$, by no means helps one to know at what stage the information loss occurs. The attempt to pinpoint the locus, however, is what drawing physiological inferences from psychophysical data is all about.

We summarize the discussion in this section in the following statements. In drawing physiological conclusions from psychophysical data concerning judgments of the identity or nonidentity of sensations, two linking propositions are involved. Their content and truth-values are as follows:

Given a sequence of maps M_0, M_1, ... M_n, M^* whose composition maps a set of physical states S through a series of sets of physiological states $\Phi^{(k)}$ to a set of perceptual states Ψ, and two stimuli s_1 and $s_2 \in S$ with corresponding states ϕ_1, $\phi_2 \in \Phi^{(k)}$, $k = 0$, ... n, and corresponding perceptual states ψ_1, $\psi_2 \in \Psi$, then the following two propositions hold:

(2′) Contrapositive Identity
$$\psi_1 \neq \psi_2 \rightarrow \forall k,\ 0 \leq k \leq n,\ \phi_1 \neq \phi_2.$$
(3′) Converse Identity
If M^* is one : one, then
$$\psi_1 = \psi_2 \rightarrow \exists \Phi^{(c)},\ 0 \leq c \leq n,\ \text{such that}\ \forall k,\ c \leq k \leq n,\ \phi_1 = \phi_2.$$

Analysis of Chromatic Discriminations and Metameric Matches

If two lights s_1 and s_2 of different spectral composition can be discriminated ($\psi_1 \neq \psi_2$) on the basis of their spectral composition, it follows that $\phi_1 \neq \phi_2$ at every level of the visual system. Assuming in addition only that the nervous system consists of univariate elements, one can deduce that during the discrimination at least two types of elements must be active at every level k. This deduction is a clearcut example of the uses of the Contrapositive identity proposition, (2′).

Two photopic lights of distinct spectral composition that are indiscriminable are called metamers. The trichromacy of metameric matches (see the formulation of Krantz, 1975a) states both (i) that given any four lights a nontrivial match can be made by adjusting the intensity of only three of them, and (ii) that there exist sets of three lights such that no nontrivial match can be formed with them alone. Part (ii) of the law of trichromacy is a statement about discriminability: logically it requires the existence of at least three types of active elements at each level k. This deduction is another example of the use of (2′).

On the other hand, Part (i) of the law of trichromacy is a statement about non-discrimination, or matching. It permits only the conclusion that three classes of elements at each level are sufficient; it does not exclude the possibility of four or more. Most color scientists, however, believe that metamers match because they generate equal quantum catch rates in three classes of cones. This generally held belief about metameric matches is a clear-cut case of the use of Proposition (3′), the Converse, to argue for a specific, early locus of information loss. As such it is not analytically true. In fact it was clear to Brindley in 1957 that this was so, for he took the trouble to publish a paper in which he laid out premises under which metameric matching equality implied equality of the cone quantum catch rates. The assumptions required for the proof are (i) that Grassmann's Laws (including specifically trichromacy of matching) hold; (ii) that color matches are unique; (iii) that the photoreceptors are univariate, and (iv) that there are exactly three types of photoreceptor active in the matching situation. We particularly want to underscore the explicit and essential assumption that the number of photoreceptor types active during matching equals the dimensionality of the matches. If four photoreceptor types were active (and again, the trichromacy of matches does not exclude this), or any of Brindley's other assumptions were invalid, the deduction that the information loss about spectral composition occurs at the level of the quantum catches would be invalid. Indeed, the more usual line of argument is to assume that the information loss occurs at the quantum catch level, and deduce the number of pigments/receptors from trichromacy. In sum, as Brindley (1957, 1960) clearly realized, the argument from a discrimination failure (a match) to a specific locus of information loss necessarily involves the use of a risky linking hypothesis — the Converse — and the argument must always be supplemented by other assumptions and/or laws.

One final note should be added. Brindley's logic did not include the assumption of a one : one map at M^*. If other facts and assumptions are sufficient to imply an early locus of information loss, then the need for the assumption of a one : one M^* map is obviated.

Analysis of Increment Threshold Data

What physiological inference can be drawn rigorously from a measurement of a photopic increment threshold upon a background, using the Identity family? Let b represent the background and t the test flash. On the upper tail of the psychometric function, $\psi_{t+b} \neq \psi_b$ on virtually all trials, and the system preserves the information that s_b is not identical to s_{t+b}. Thus by the Contrapositive identity proposition (2'), it follows analytically that for all stages $\phi_{t+b} \neq \phi_b$. On the other hand, for the lower tail ψ_b and ψ_{t+b} are statistically virtually indiscriminable. And yet clearly, for photopic increment thresholds, the quantum catches from s_b alone and from s_{t+b} are different, and the physical states of at least the photoreceptor neurons in the visual system are not identical for s_b and s_{t+b}. The information must be lost after the level of the quantum catches — possibly at the level of the receptor hyperpolarization, or at some other later noisy or gain control site proximal to the receptors. Thus, as in the case of metamers a valid but limited conclusion can be drawn from the failure to discriminate, by virtue of the Converse identity proposition (3'): assuming M^* is one : one, there is an earliest stage in the visual system at which the information is lost.

In addition, it is important to note that the analysis of threshold just made applies to a single threshold measurement. Usually one has a set of physically distinct stimuli (e.g., differing in wavelength), with associated thresholds T_1, T_2, ... But there is no evidence from the threshold measurements *per se* to argue that the set of equally detectable stimuli of different wavelengths involve loss of information at a common locus (cf. Boynton and Onley, 1962). Putting the point in Brindley's terminology, a single threshold measurement is a Class A experiment; but a set of thresholds is not *per se* a Class A experiment. One must invoke additional evidence to justify attribution of a set of thresholds to a common locus of information loss.

For example, from the data in Fig. 1B one might want to argue that all the thresholds of the short-wave lobe should be attributed to one physiological locus of information loss, and all the thresholds of the middle- and long-wave humps to another. The assignment of a set of thresholds to a common and specific critical locus involves the use of many other kinds of psychophysical data and empirical laws – including, for example Grassmann's laws (Krantz, 1975a), Stiles's displacement laws (Stiles, 1939), test-additivity (Boynton, Ikeda and Stiles, 1964; Guth, 1965; Kranda and King-Smith, 1979; and many others), field additivity (Pugh, 1976), indistinguishable temporal and/or spatial properties (Krauskopf and Mollon, 1971; Friedman, Yim and Pugh, 1981), common shapes of psychometric functions, discriminability or non-discriminability of the test stimuli one from another at or above threshold (Wandell, 1981; Kirk, 1982), and so on. The assignment also involves knowledge of or modelling of the properties of the neurons of the specific locus, such as consistency or inconsistency of the shape of a portion of a spectral sensitivity curve with an acceptable pigment curve, consistency of a double-hump action spectrum with a model of the interaction of two or more receptor types with acceptable spectral sensitivities (e.g., Sperling and Harwerth, 1971), or general similarity of an action spectrum with action spectra of chromatically coded neurons at specific stages of the visual system.

Analysis of Hue Cancellation

The phenomenological foundation of opponent colors theory is the experience that certain pairs of color sensations, viz., red and green, and blue and yellow, are mutually exclusive percepts. In the classic hue cancellation experiment an observer's judgments determine a particular class of stimuli that produce neither sensation of one opponent pair. The judgments are not judgments of the identity or nonidentity of perceptual states, and any given pair of stimuli from one such set (e.g., from the red/green equilibrium set) can be discriminated from each other on other perceptual dimensions. Thus, the Identity propositions cannot be invoked in inferences about physiology from reports of hue quality or from hue equilibrium data. Any physiological conclusion drawn from such experiments involves linking proposition(s) other than the Identity family. One formulation of the linking propositions involved is this: (a) two stimuli that produce respectively two opponent color qualities produce mutually exclusive states in a set of individual neurons (such as driving these neurons in opposite directions from their baseline or "null" state) at at least one stage $\Phi^{(k)}$; (b) stimuli in perceptual equilibrium on one chromatic dimension have the common property of producing the null state of this specific set of neurons.

A deeper analysis of these linking propositions and the general conditions for their truth has eluded us so far, and in any case would take us beyond the scope of this paper. A few points about them, however, bear mention. These propositions are, as Brindley (1960) noted of linking statements for Class B observations, very specialized, and one cannot ascertain at this point if they will be exemplars of a general category of linking propositions (cf. Boring, 1942; Teller, 1981), or if they will simply remain special cases. Both propositions involve implications from percepts to physiology, and so they have direction parallel to the Contrapositive (2) and Converse (3) linking propositions of the Identity family.

One may postulate the existence of chromatically opponent neurons and an earliest stage $\Phi^{(k)}$ at which they occur. One may argue further that this stage is the critical locus $\Phi^{(c)}$ that determines the mutual exclusivity of opponent hue pairs and the form of hue cancellation data. If, however, one wants to argue that the locus that determines data such as hue cancellation is at a site early in the visual system, then one is implicitly making the assumption that there is consistency of coding between that early stage and the bridge locus neurons – that the "sign" of the chromatic code once set, is not altered, and in particular that the null stimuli are not "un-nulled", in the intervening transformations.

Such code-stability seems to imply important constraints on the composite maps from $\Phi^{(c)}$ to Ψ, but it is difficult to formulate exactly what these constraints are. For example, as Jack Nachmias has pointed out to us, logic does not require that the same opponent code be maintained all the way through the system to the bridge locus. At later stages the codes for redness and greenness need not be mutually exclusive: they simply never occur together in normal visual experience, because of the mutual exclusivity of their causal precursors at a critical locus early in the visual system.

This is, of course, where the two sets of data shown in Fig. 1, the Jameson/Hurvich hue equilibria and the Thornton/Pugh threshold data, come together. The extreme depression of sensitivity at 580 nm (the wavelength of the adapting field) in Fig. 1B seems to demand a rather homogeneous population of chromatically coded neurons – presumably at a quite peripheral critical locus. The agreement of the notch with the wavelength of unique yellow measured under these conditions (Thornton and Pugh, 1983) argues that the information about the sign of the chromatic code, once set at the peripheral critical locus, is preserved through the system to the bridge locus neurons. And the mutual exclusivity of redness and greenness implies that, whatever the intervening transformations, nothing in the composite map allows the codes for redness and greenness to occur together at the bridge locus.

Conclusion

Color science employs terms from two logically disjoint universes of discourse – that is, the one set of terms cannot be reduced to the other or vice versa by logical analysis alone. In the one universe of discourse there are subjective reports of the nonidentity or identity of sensations, as well as reports of subjective qualities of sensations, such as redness, greenness, etc. In the other universe of discourse there are the terms of physics, physical optics, photochemistry and cellular physiology. The goals of color research include both the testing of physiological hypotheses about the visual system with psychophysical data, and the development of physiological theories that explain color appearance phenomena.

We think that the ideas developed here – including that of the visual system as a composite map; the link M^* as a mapping of particular physiological states to particular perceptual states; the distinction between critical locus and bridge locus; and the definition of a linking proposition as a composite map always involving M^* – help focus attention on and clarify the issues involved in scientific statements linking visual physiology and visual experience.

Acknowledgements

We thank Drs Jay Thornton, Denise Varner, Jacob Nachmias, and Ken Knoblauch for helpful discussions. Support of the National Science Foundation (grants BNS 81-111927 and BNS 79-24163), National Eye Institute (EY 00102), and sabbatical support to DYT from the James McKeen Cattell Foundation is gratefully acknowledged.

Notes

1. Many complexities, including parallel channels, feedback loops, statistical rather than deterministic mapping, spatial and temporal inhomogeneity, and so on, have been omitted from this scheme for the sake of simplicity. Nontrivial modifications of this framework may be required to bring the analysis into concert with the complex and stochastic nature of neural coding. We believe that the utility of the conceptualizations presented here will survive the inclusion of increasing levels of complexity.
2. The symbol ϕ can be thought of as an N_k-tuple,

$$\phi = (\phi_1, \phi_2, \ldots \phi_{N_k}),$$

where each element in the N_k-tuple specifies the state of one of the neurons of the kth stage.

3. In philosophy of science, the term *bridge law* has come to mean a statement of a definitional or empirical relationship between terms from formerly disjoint universes of discourse. The term *bridge locus* — the location at which the closest associations between Φ and Ψ states occur — is adopted in parallel to this usage.

4. The more behavioristically oriented of us (DYT) has sometimes been heard to argue that when matching (discrimination) and threshold (detection) experiments are performed with forced-choice techniques, the data (% correct) involve only the correlation of the subject's responses with the spatial or temporal location of the test target; hence that no report of sensations is involved, Ψ never enters the argument, and there is no need for the concept of bridge locus. However, we would both argue that even in these cases, the introspections of the experimenter-*qua*-subject enter the theoretical argument. It is the fact that the subject's perceptions are correlated with his or her performance levels that allows one to assume a "sensory" ($c \leq n$) locus of information loss. This point is well illustrated by the question — "How do you know the information loss is sensory?" — frequently asked by visual scientists about experiments on subjects such as infants, from whom introspective reports are not available.

References

Boring, E. G. (1942). *Sensation and Perception in the History of Experimental Psychology*. New York, Appleton-Century-Crofts.

Boynton, R. M., Ikeda, M. and Stiles, W. D. (1964). Interactions among chromatic mechanisms inferred from positive and negative increment thresholds. *Vision Res.* **4**, 87–117.

Boynton, R. M. and Onley, J. W. (1962). A critique of the special status assigned by Brindley to the "Psychophysical linking hypotheses" of "Class A". *Vision Res.* **2**, 383–390.

Brindley, G. S. (1957). Two theorems in colour vision. *Q. J. exp. Psych.* **9**, 101–104.

Brindley, G. S. (1960). *Physiology of the Retina and Visual Pathway* (1st edn). London, Edward Arnold. (1970 – 2nd edition, Baltimore, The Williams and Wilkins Co.).

Butler, S. (1910). *Unconscious Memory*. London, A. C. Fifield.

Feigl, H. (1958). The "mental" and the "physical". In *Concepts, Theories and the Mind–Body Problem* (eds Feigl, H., Scriven, M. and Maxwell, G.). Minnesota Studies in the Philosophy of Science, Vol. II. Minneapolis, University of Minnesota Press.

Friedman, L. J., Yim, P. and Pugh, E. N. Jr (1981). Temporal integration of the π_1 / π_3 pathway. *Invest. Ophth. Vis. Sci.* **20**, 61 (Abstract).

Guth, S. L. (1965). Luminance addition: general considerations and some results at foveal threshold. *J. opt. Soc. Am.* **55**, 718–722.

Jameson, D. and Hurvich, L. M. (1955). Some quantitative aspects of an opponent colors theory. I. Chromatic responses and spectral saturation. *J. opt. Soc. Am.* **45**, 546–552.

Kirk, D. B. (1982). Color discrimination at threshold: the approach through increment threshold sensitivity. *Vision Res.* **22**, 713–720.

Kranda, K. and King-Smith, P. E. (1979). Detection of coloured stimuli by independent linear systems. *Vision Res.* **19**, 733–745.

Krantz, D. H. (1975a). Color measurement and color theory: I. Representation theorem for Grassmann structures. *J. math. Psych.* **12**, 283–303.

Krantz, D. H. (1975b). Color measurement and color theory: II. Opponent colors theory. *J. math. Psych.* **12**, 304–327.

Krauskopf, J. and Mollon, J. D. (1971). The independence of the temporal integration properties of individual chromatic mechanisms in the human eye. *J. Physiol., Lond.* **219**, 611–623.

Pugh, E. N. Jr (1976). The nature of the Π_1 mechanism of W. S. Stiles. *J. Physiol., Lond.* **257**, 713–747.

Sperling, H. G. and Harwerth, R. S. (1971). Red/green cone interactions in the increment threshold spectral sensitivity of primates. *Science* **172**, 180–184.

Stiles, W. S. (1939). The directional sensitivity of the retina and the spectral sensitivities of the rods and cones. *Proc. roy. Soc. B.* **127**, 64–104.

Teller, D. Y. (1980). Locus questions in visual science. Chapter included in *Visual Coding and Adaptability* (ed. Harris, C.), pp. 151–176. Hillsdale, NJ, Lawrence Erlbaum Associates.

Teller, D. Y. (1981). Linking Hypotheses. Paper presented at symposium, "On relating psychophysics and physiology". Center for Visual Science, University of Rochester, Rochester, NY, June, 1981.

Thornton, J. E. and Pugh, E. N. Jr (1983). Red/green color opponency at detection threshold. *Science* **219**, 191–193.

Uttal, W. R. (1981). *A Taxonomy of Visual Processes*. Hillsdale, NJ, Lawrence Erlbaum Associates.

Wandell, B. A. (1981). Red–green opponent-mechanisms have variable sensitivity. *Invest. Ophth. Vis. Sci.* **20**, 62 (Abstract).

FIG. 1 W. A. H. Rushton (1901–1980). William Rushton himself chose this photograph as the one to hang in the collection of the Cambridge Psychological Laboratory. He said of it: "It looks as if I have just said something paradoxical to you — and you can't tell whether or not I'm pulling your leg."

(Photograph by P. Starling.)

Some Rushton Paradoxes Seen from the Other Side of the Atlantic

MATHEW ALPERN

It is natural to speak of William Rushton in Trinity; I never think about the College without thinking of him. I know it has existed for centuries − that it is the College of Newton and Byron, Clerk-Maxwell and Whewell, Lord Rayleigh and the Balfours, Wittgenstein and Keith-Lucas, Bentley, all the others. But the Trinity of my experience is interwoven with recollections of William. I remember the first time he brought me here as vividly as our last evening together two decades later. In the interval between I have been here on occasions when he was not, but on those which quickly come to mind − my last nights in Cambridge, 20 and again 5 years ago − he dominated the conversations even in his absence.

So it is easiest to recall moments we shared here: in Vigani's room, in this Hall, over claret upstairs or walking in the gardens. But the easiest path was never William's way and I avoid it now. Elsewhere, I have shown how his achievements changed our subject beyond recognition, I will not further consider that here, either. Instead I reproduce some vignettes of him obtained from an American perspective:

Paradigmatic of the best in British science, he became (behind his back) "Sir William" to many of us. One American even circulated a petition to the Queen asking it to be made official. Cooler heads prevailed; it was never sent. Were they all that wise? If there were those who might doubt that what William had done was quite enough to be made a knight, no one − certainly not the Queen (once she knew) − could deny that Marjorie is a "Lady". Was it not time she be recognized as Lady Rushton? Knighted or not, the nobility of Marjorie's way of living and the originality of William's way of thinking left immutable impressions on the lives of many Americans.

William took time, plenty of time, to think; just to think; only to think. The results, more often than not, were superb thoughts. He took time to study musical composition with a famous composer. He took time, a whole undergraduate year, "to work out" number theory, not by reference to standard texts, but on his own. Always there was a highly curious and original mind at play.

But it did not relent to frustration in search of truth. There was single minded concentration on the current stumbling block in his research wherever he was, at his desk on the roof, digging in the garden or on the beach at Alligator Point. The final resource when all else failed was a hot bath tub. He approached it confident that an insight would at last come. He was seldom disappointed. Once he found the way, the experimental and theoretical implications were exhaustively examined, equations filling one page after the next. He caressed and nurtured the idea with the devotion and loving care of a father for his favorite child, ignoring everything which did not fit (even occasional experimental points which fell conspicuously off the predicted curve) as the minor misbehavior of youth. But should experiment prove the idea wrong, he disowned it immediately and forgot it.

He had a remarkable ability to fire ambition in American minds. After William's lectures at a small Oregon college a man I never met wrote to me to inquire about further study in Ann Arbor. His letter concludes:

> Dr Rushton's lectures here were more than an inspiration: they showed the necessity for working as hard and as decently as one can.

Characteristically, he was a bit different for each of us. John Bean, an Ann Arbor physiologist with hair whiter than mine, still recalls the chronaxie Rushton with wonder. Another, Horace Davenport, remembers being taught as an Oxford undergraduate the theory of the yawn which William allegedly discovered during the long rests assigned to the bassoon in many orchestral compositions. Professor Davenport referred me to the following:

> One further theory concerning the yawn has come to my attention. It has been suggested that as the nuchal muscles are recruited in the stretch they squeeze upon the thyroid gland, express thyroxine into the blood stream and thereby accelerate metabolism. The literature has been searched in vain for the origin and subsequent reference to this idea (Heusner, 1946).

With hindsight provided by more recent physiology, my daughter reminds me that the thyroid scarcely needs *muscles* to do what is managed well by the release of TRH by a few nerve endings in the hypothalmus, but William never denied paternity of this brain child conceived 50 years ago. He liked the idea of the yawn as an expression of interest and of the effort to understand what one is being told, not a manifestation of boredom with it. The imaginatively different view of the commonplace was idiosyncratic. He had a story about how he knocked himself unconscious in an experiment with the Benedict–Roth apparatus trying to disprove his hypothesis. Unfortunately I took no notes and the physiological details are no longer reproducible.

He had an irritating habit of posing extraordinarily difficult (mainly geometrical) problems to us. Nothing delighted him quite as much as discovering their solutions. This was like road-work for a boxer, or continuous practice at the keyboard for a concert pianist, mental push-ups keeping ganglion cells in trim for their role in his research.

Ed Pugh wrote up part of his thesis for the *Journal of Physiology* under the title *Rushton's Paradox*. The difficulty is that future generations, never having known him, may come to believe there is only one paradox, when in fact they are innumerable. In his delightful reminiscences, for example, Sir Alan Hodgkin (1982) points out that Rushton approached research "... somewhat emotionally with the temperament of an actor or an artist. Yet in spite of his love of the dramatic William's treatment of science was basically logical and mathematical."

One of his paradoxes struck home driving back to Tallahassee from Sarasota. There was a flat and no spare. After a series of frustrating false starts we found help in the backwoods from a superb specialist working effortlessly under the trees with no shirt and a minimum of modern tools. Matters were set right in record time; William's respect and admiration for the man and his achievement were profound. What is to be admired most was the first-class way a job is done regardless of the significance of the job. Experiencing the event it was hard to disagree; it is a characteristic British view. But Americans are bred with the illusion one can do almost anything if one tries hard enough. Does one take up only that task, however trivial, one is certain to complete in a first-class way, or attempt a more ambitious problem that just might be solved if given all one has, even if mistakes inevitable in the process deprive that solution of the elegance characteristic of the first-class? William became FRS for work on nerves. He took up vision because he saw the competition in our subject easier to dominate. Indeed he reigned supreme over it for the rest of his life. Whether he might have done the same in nerves is unimportant; the point is, he judged he would not. Rushton's paradox is that he inspired many of us to follow not his *example*, but his *subject*; to try, in the American pattern, to be better than we are, to make the results of our work as close to what he might have done, as best we can with whatever ability we have. He remained throughout his life English to the core, but his years on our side of the Atlantic were not without a peculiarly American effect on color science. Whether or not this troubled him I do not know.

Part of Rushton's American legend was built 20 years ago by that love of the dramatic of which Sir Alan speaks. For an invited lecture to the annual meeting of the Optical Society of America, he took on the task of setting Hecht's theory of adaptation to rest. The misleading simplicity of Hecht's idea perpetuated it long beyond its time as William's results made abundantly clear. He wanted, he said, to nail down only three points. Point one was neatly printed on a card in large letters. THE PHOTOCHEMICAL EQUILIBRIUM EXPLANATION OF THRESHOLD IS UNTENABLE. As he summarized the evidence making this inference unequivocal he took out hammer and nails from behind the rostrum and soundly nailed the card to a board beside him. The second point was also on a card and was similarly nailed down. And so the lecture went, as the hammer drove the nails to fix his final point to the board, the lid to the coffin of the photochemical theory of brightness discrimination was sealed forever.

He was ruthless in attack at the first sign of loose, glib or wrong thinking. Here are a few examples provoked over the years by drafts of papers I sent for his criticisms. (It is easy to enjoy the sharpness of the criticisms but we must not forget the remarkable kindness and patience of the critic taking time from more important work to deal with such matters at all.)

> I don't think your recent typescript would be very good as a letter to *JOSA* or *Science* but since I have a grudge to pay against both those I should not be sorry to see them saddled with a rather bad letter.

> ... I judge you are overworking with a desperate but quite unnecessary urge to publish before you have quietly thought through what you intend to say.

Now this:

> Granit said to Merton "People don't respect you if they can understand you." Are you bidding for their respect?

Or this:

> I am under the weather with a heavy cold or something and stream at nose and eyes. I suggest to you that the higher flights of intellect are achieved by resonance in the frontal sinuses of the skull. When those are filled with inflammatory exudate it entirely changes the resonance properties (see Helmholtz's *Tonempfindungen*) and one becomes a numbskull. So it is with me.
>
> Though you say your draft is based upon that treatment I gave you in Ann Arbor in October, I find it so hard to follow that in two careful readings I can't make it out. Now, even with sinuses awash, if I can't understand this topic not many others will be able to.
>
> ... I will therefore give a few assorted difficulties. You may find them trivial, but I find them difficulties.

In discussion at a meeting he could be even more devastating. Witness this remark, evidence, if you need it, that I was by no means the only beneficiary of his critical faculties: "If the thesis of the last speaker could not be demolished in a single sentence, it would be unworthy of demolition. Fortunately only one is required. It is this ..." Carefully counting the number of sentences necessary to demolish what one said, in the event he judged it worthy, was, I suppose, a way to keep his mind active as a member of the audience.

Yet he was a man of great charm who could also exhibit a delicate sensitivity to feelings of those around him. "You must call me William", he insisted at the beginning, "and become accustomed to the practice by so referring to me in conversations with others."

He was embarrassed at a meeting to scrutinize the name tag of a familiar face with a forgotten name, silently confessing thereby his memory lapse to the very person whose feelings were most sensitive to it. So he tried to revolutionize conventional practice by pinning his own name tag on his *back*. However logically sound the scheme, it was a political failure. No one needed *William*'s tag to find out who *he* was, so relief from embarrassment never provided the reinforcement the practice required to become general. Those who never asked, misinterpreted it as ostentation and no one was sufficiently innovative to dare to imitate the practice.

I have spoken of mathematical problems which so entertained him. When I failed to deal with these, he took to examining my familiarity with the Book, in which he was extremely well versed; unusually (if not paradoxically) so for an exemplary man of science. The stream of geometrical problems was replaced by an endless series of Old Testament stories none of them familiar, all of them precisely accurate (as subsequent search invariably showed) and nearly all revealing my ancestors in less than ideal light. Almost-but not quite-all, for there is one particularly Rushtonian hero:

In Gideon's time Midianites had overrun the land; their camels, cattle and tents were numerous beyond counting. From an angel, Gideon learns he must lead the struggle against Midian. Protesting he was from the poorest of families, and the least among it, he requests evidence of the angel's authority. Gideon sets a kid and some meal on a rock; when touched with the angel's staff they are consumed by a roaring inferno emerging from the rock. This produces fear and respect but does not dispell skepticism. For additional proof Gideon scatters fleece of wool on the grass suggesting, as the multitude assemble for the battle, the following experiment: "If You will save Israel by my hand, please make the fleece wet but leave the earth around it dry". In the morning he squeezed a bowlful of dew from the fleece though the ground was dry. But Gideon was not home yet; he then prays: "... Let not Your anger be hot against me, and I will speak but this once: let me make trial, I pray You but this once with the fleece; let it now be dry only upon the fleece and upon all the ground let there be dew". And so it was (Judges 6, 20–38).

I introduce this digression not only because I would never have come across this remarkable story but for William, but because I find it symbolic of his legacy. The study of color is difficult and the moments of discovery when the meal is consumed in the roaring inferno so rare, there is always that great temptation to share it with you immediately without bothering to do the next experiment i.e. documenting wet fleece superimposed on the dry earth. When even that has been done it is useful to think again of William and of what he learned from Keith-Lucas who, perhaps, learned it from Gideon. *You are not home yet*, the *Journal of Physiology* expects you also to show dry fleece on the wet ground!

Acknowledgements

I thank Professor H. W. Davenport and F. Zwas for assistance.

References

Heusner, A. P. (1946). Yawning and associated phenomena. *Physiological Reviews* **26**, 164–165.

Hodgkin, A. L. (1982). Some recollections of William Rushton and his contributions to Neurophysiology (1925–52). *Vision Research* **22**, 623–625.

Index